THE AIR DEVILS

AIRMEN & AIRCRAFT
Martin Caidin, General Editor

Also:

THE
AIR
DEVILS

The Story of Balloonists,
Barnstormers, and Stunt Pilots

by DON DWIGGINS

J. B. LIPPINCOTT COMPANY
Philadelphia and New York

To my own Air Devils—*Donl* and *Toni*

Frontispiece—*Cole Brothers Air Show photo*

Acknowledgments

MUCH OF THIS BOOK is based on personal recollections of airmen I have known or flown with in the past twenty years, both as a pilot and as an aviation editor for the *Los Angeles Daily News* and *Los Angeles Mirror*. To name a few, living or dead, my special thanks go to Skeet Sliter, Gene Carney, Spider Ross, Hank Coffin, Alvin Algee, Pancho Barnes, Ivan Unger, Art Goebel, Dave Burt, Bobby Rose, Bon MacDougall, Ken ("Fronty") Nichols, Sam Greenwald, Roy Knabenshue, Bob Fowler, Charlie Willard, Fish Salmon, Tony Le Vier, Snake Reaves, Hal Grimes, Jerry Phillips, Carl Squier, Frank Tomick, Jimmy Angel, Jimmie Mattern, Dick Grace, Paul Franklin, Lloyd Geraldson, Frank Clarke, Jim Barton, Frank Tallman, Paul Mantz, Cliff Henderson, Walt Hunter, Matty Laird, Jimmy Haizlip, Jimmy Doolittle, Myra Slovak, Herb White, Mort Bach, Duane and Judy Cole, Capt. Chuck Hamm, Col. Chuck Yeager, Mike Murphy, Cliff Winters and Dutch Rutgers.

To get the stories of those *air devils* who went West before my time, I found exciting adventure in such volumes as *Astra Castra*, by Hatton Turnor (London, 1865); *A History of Donaldson's Balloon Ascensions*, by Dr. M. L. Amick (Chicago, 1875); *My Balloons in Peace and War*, by Prof. T. S. C. Lowe (unpublished manuscript); *Through the Air: A Narrative of Forty Years as an Aeronaut. Comprising a History of the Various Attempts in the Art of Flying by Artificial Means From the Earliest Period Down to the Present Time. With an Account of the Author's Most Important Air-Voyages and His Many Thrilling Adventures and Hairbreadth Escapes, also, an Appendix in Which Are Given Full Instructions for the Manufacture and Management of Balloons*, by John Wise (Philadelphia, 1873); *The Influence of Aerial Demonstrations on Airpower*, by Capt. Robert D. Janca, USAF (Air University, Maxwell AFB, June, 1965).

Contents

"We have lived long enough when we have added some-thing to humanity . . . ."

—Pilâtre de Rozier, 1785.

1

Gone with the Wind

HE WAS the world's first stunt pilot.

Young, vital, imaginative, Jean-François Pilâtre de Rozier at twenty-eight already had been widely acclaimed in Paris as a brilliant lecturer on physics and chemistry.

He was a sort of eighteenth-century astronaut, the hero of his countrymen, competent to venture where no man had ever gone, into a void where unknown dangers lurked.

Blond, blue-eyed, handsome, de Rozier was a witty conversationalist, a favorite with the ladies of the court of Louis XVI and his seductive queen, Marie Antoinette. He was also the envy of those cavaliers above whom he soared with the freedom of an eagle, although coughing and choking in a billowing cloud of smoke that marked the rise of a *montgolfière*.

Within the span of two centuries, thousands of other sky adventurers would follow de Rozier's lead to penetrate deeper into the atmosphere, and eventually into space. Many would pay for fame with their lives, a gamble the French pioneer balloonist dismissed with a shrug. By cutting the shackles of gravity that had bound mankind to earth since the beginning, he was achieving a glorious thing—he was freeing humanity to ride the winds in search of new horizons and to change the course of human events in unpredictable ways.

Oddly, history has kept alive the glory of the brothers Joseph and Etienne Montgolfier, who invented the hot-air balloon; but who remembers Jean-François Pilâtre de Rozier as the first aeronaut?

No better choice could have been made to first probe the sky's mysteries in a smoking *montgolfière* on November 21, 1783, just one year after the Montgolfiers successfully launched their first hot-air balloon. On September 19, two months before his pioneer flight, de Rozier had galloped off to recover a 74-foot *montgolfière* that had lifted a sheep, a rooster, and a duck from the garden at Versailles in a command performance, to see whether the sky could sustain life or if it was a seething ocean of poisonous ozone.

Finding the animals unharmed, de Rozier pleaded with King Louis to bring honor to France by allowing him to become the first human sky voyager; but his majesty considered it too risky. Instead, he ordered a condemned wife-killer brought to Versailles; if he survived, he would go free.

This was too much for de Rozier; he objected strenuously, but not until a bit of court intrigue was employed did the weak-willed monarch finally give in and agree to let de Rozier risk his fool neck. The person who interceded for him was the beautiful Comtesse Louise-Marie-Joséphine of Savoy, the wife of the King's brother, Louis le Désiré, Comte de Provence, a leading patron of the arts and sciences.

De Rozier, who was a favorite of the comtesse, had often amused her with laboratory stunts. Filling soap bubbles with hydrogen and letting them rise shimmering into the air was one that always delighted her.

"François," she once asked, "could you make a bubble big enough to carry me into the sky?"

"I'm afraid not," he replied. "Unless . . ." He was suddenly thoughtful. "But of course!" he exclaimed. "I must go to the Academy!"

The directors of the austere Academy of Science listened to de Rozier with reserved enthusiasm. He was brilliant, they agreed, but foolhardy.

Born in Metz in March, 1757, he was a youth of barely seventeen years when he arrived in Paris and found employment as a laboratory assistant to a chemist whose dream was to convert lead into gold. Forming a close friendship with the Marquis de Maisonfort, de Rozier was introduced to the centers of learning in Paris. De Maisonfort recalled: "He attended all the courses, heard all the lecturers, read with avidity all the books. Intelligent, tractable, studious, he marched with the strides of a giant in this newly-discovered career. Nature had bestowed on Pilâtre de Rozier all the gifts that form the natural philosopher and the chemist. Laborious, daring; who possessed more than he the love of that glory which makes us undertake; the patience which makes us execute; and that courage which makes us succeed?"

At twenty-three de Rozier was chosen to fill a professorship of chemistry at Rheims, but his insatiable thirst for knowledge brought him back to Paris, where the Comte and Comtesse de Provence became his sponsors.

Thus, when Louis XVI proposed to send a murderer up in a balloon, de Rozier asked the comtesse to intercede. "For the honor of France," he cried, "the first aeronaut should be a man of science, not a murderer! And for the honor of Your Majesty, the first venture into the sky should do so with courage and with God-given knowledge of the physical laws that make this great feat possible!"

Permission granted, de Rozier and the Montgolfiers fabricated a giant aerostat 74 feet high and 48 feet in diameter. Around the bottom opening, 15 feet across, was a doughnut-shaped wicker catwalk 3 feet wide. Beneath the balloon hung a brazier for making smoke, a substance which the Montgolfiers firmly believed contained the mysterious power of neutralizing gravity.

In October, de Rozier tested the *montgolfière* at the end of a rope tether, anchored in the garden of La Muette, the royal château in the suburb of Passy. After a successful 200-foot ascent he hauled it down and climbed aboard. Gingerly he tossed a handful of straw onto the coals. The smoke poured into the bag, swelling its sides until, with a soft lurch, he felt himself lifted from the ground.

For a thrilling moment he looked down on the rooftop of the château; then, gasping for breath, he cried through the cloud of smoke to be hauled down. Confident now, he made plans for history's first free flight, on November 21, with a passenger. The Marquis d'Arlandes, an infantry major, had the foresight to see the balloon as a novel military weapon.

At 1:54 P.M. de Rozier and d'Arlandes boarded the *montgolfière*'s catwalk; the rope was cut. They rose slowly into a gray overcast, where a gentle northwest breeze drifted the smoking bag toward the Ecole Militaire. Higher it rose, becoming a mere dot in the sky, 3,000 feet above the city of Paris, floating gently across the Seine.

De Rozier was spellbound. Never before had human eyes looked down upon a city from such a glorious height! The sound of barking dogs and men talking could be heard plainly, and now the breathtaking panorama seemed to be growing closer. Suddenly aware that they were dropping toward the rooftops of Faubourg St. Germain, de Rozier cried: "Throw on more straw!"

So energetically did the Marquis d'Arlandes comply that soon a shower of sparks was flying upward.

"Enough!" de Rozier cried. "You're setting us afire!"

He quickly worked his way around the catwalk sponging out the hot spots while the Marquis, moving around opposite him, kept the fire going. The balloon rose once more and the crisis passed. Again they could enjoy the view, gazing down on a scene too beautiful to describe.

Watching the snaking Seine slip by beneath them, de Rozier picked out familiar districts: Poissy . . . St. Germain . . . St. Denis . . . Sève. . . . In the distance lay the heart of the city, the cathedral of Notre Dame. D'Arlandes threw on more straw, causing the balloon to lift gracefully over the towers of St. Sulpice and on past the woods of Luxembourg.

Then suddenly the flight was over. Back on the ground twenty-five minutes after soaring skyward from Passy, the two adventurers settled back to earth at Butte aux Cailles. The gas bag collapsed. They stepped to the ground on wobbly legs and hugged each other. History had been made. They had safely ventured into the great sea of the atmosphere, navigated after a fashion for five miles, and landed without mishap.

A thoughtful witness to history's first manned flight was Dr. Benjamin Franklin, United States Minister Plenipotentiary to France, who lived near La Muette in Passy. Franklin hurried to his study, clipped on his homemade bifocals, and penned a note to a close friend, Sir Joseph Banks, a member of the Royal Society of London. Like d'Arlandes, Franklin was not unaware of the balloon's potential as a war machine:

"This experiment is by no means a trifling one," he scrawled with his quill. "It may be attended with important consequences that no one can foresee. . . . This method of filling the balloon with hot air is cheap and expeditious, and it is supposed may be sufficient for certain purposes, such as elevating an engineer to take a view of an enemy's army, works, etc., conveying intelligence into or out of a besieged town, giving signals to distant places, or the like."

Already Franklin had witnessed that first public ascension of a hydrogen balloon, on the damp afternoon of August 27, 1783, when the French physician and friend of Pilâtre de Rozier, Jacques Alexandre César Charles, poured oil of vitriol over a keg of iron filings for four days, slowly generating gas to inflate a 13-foot globe of silk. When the balloon finally went up, a skeptic asked: "What good can a balloon possibly be?"

Franklin's retort was the bon mot of the day: *"Eh, à quoi bon l'enfant qui vient de naître?* [What good is a newborn babe?]"

The manned balloon flights of 1783 served to relieve world tensions in a manner curiously similar to the hoopla of a Cape Kennedy spacecraft launching; the French capital at the moment was anxiously awaiting settlement of the war she had gotten into with England on behalf of upstart America. One week after watching the Charles balloon—or *charlière*—ascend, Franklin ramrodded a peace treaty with England, and on the same day France and England settled their differences.

Franklin reported to Sir Joseph one more remarkable stunt flight on December 1, when a *charlière* carried up its inventor and its manufacturer, M. N. Robert, to the dizzy height of 2,000 feet. They landed near Nesle, 27 miles away, where Charles reascended alone, shooting up to 9,000 feet in the lightened balloon. The experience so unnerved him that he gave up active ballooning for good.

The balloon craze began wearing off and for a while the soirées in Franklin's Passy home turned their attention to a new fad; Friedrich Anton Mesmer, whose theories on animal magnetism were rejected in Vienna and Berlin, had suddenly gained favor with Marie Antoinette. De Rozier momentarily forgot about ballooning himself and joined the controversy at Franklin's salons, where eminent scientists were viewing the vogue with alarm as possibly leading to some sort of mass hysteria.

According to Mesmer's principles, animal magnetism was a universal fluid by which all ills could be cured. Patients formed a ring around a boiling cauldron, and male healers, applying pressure with their hands, directed the flow of animal magnetism to affected parts of their bodies. Many susceptible ladies wrongly interpreted an erotic excitement as the mysterious "magnetism" at work, leading to scandalous gossip over what was really taking place under Marie Antoinette's gay leadership. The basic idea of hypnotism had been strangely overlooked.

At one of these soirées de Rozier took Franklin aside and asked his opinion of whether or not a balloon could be made to navigate the atmosphere with the ease of a sailboat on water. The elderly scholar, who had earned a reputation as a roué as well as a wit, chuckled and showed de Rozier a love letter from the wife of Jean-Baptiste Le Roy, the director of the King's laboratory at La Muette. Madame Le Roy, whom Franklin called "La Femme de Poche" (the pocket-wife), had written to tell him she had made a balloon ascension, but wished that it might have carried her to his arms.

"These machines," he told de Rozier more seriously, "must always be subject to the winds. But perhaps mechanic art may find easy means to give them progressive motion in a calm, and to slant them a little in the wind. . . ."

De Rozier's next wild scheme was to construct a monster hot-air balloon towering 140 feet high, with royal funds secured by his benefactress, the Comtesse de Savoy. On January 19, 1784, de Rozier, Joseph Montgolfier, and five friends climbed onto the catwalk and had the ride of their lives as the smoking, puffing giant lurched its way to an altitude of 3,500 feet. Then came an unexpected thrill: With the sound of a gunshot a seam split wide open from top to bottom. Like a huge exploded puffball the *montgolfière* hissed and writhed in dying convulsions as it shot earthward, carrying its seven passengers to their apparent doom. But at the last moment it formed a crude parachute, stabilized, and dropped to earth without further damage.

It was well and good to go up and down in balloons, but de Rozier realized their ultimate utility lay in getting from one place to another with them. An English Channel crossing, de Rozier decided, would dramatically demonstrate the potential of aerial navigation, but before he could put the scheme into effect another balloonist, the French aeronaut Jean-Pierre Blanchard, beat him to it.

On the afternoon of January 7, 1785, Blanchard and an American physician, Dr. John Jeffries, who had returned to England from the Colonies as a turncoat, sailed off from Dover Castle, bound for France. Dr. Jeffries, a former Bostonian, had once served as one of American patriot Samuel Adams' Sons of Liberty, but in 1776 he defected to General Howe's army as a field surgeon, traveling with them to Nova Scotia. In 1779 he went on to England to work with the noted Dr. John Hunter, winning fame for himself both as a surgeon and as a meteorologist.

Although he had personally financed the proposed Channel flight with the idea of joining Blanchard as a passenger, Dr. Jeffries arrived at Dover Castle just in time to see the aeronaut hurrying to get off alone. Indignant, Dr. Jeffries climbed into the basket, glared at the Frenchman, and ordered him to cut the rope.

By mid-channel they were speaking to each other—in alarm. The balloon seemed drawn to the water, even after all their sand ballast had been jettisoned. Overboard went a pair of silken oars that Blanchard had dreamed up, their food, and finally their topcoats, shirts, and pants.

About three fourths of the way across, Dr. Jeffries would recall later, "We were fallen so low as to be beneath the plane of the French cliffs. We were then preparing to get up into our slings when I found the mercury in the barometer again falling, and looking around, soon observed that we were rising, and that the pleasing view of France was enlarging and opening to us every moment, as we ascended, so as to overlook the high grounds. . . . We now ascended to a much greater height and exactly at three o'clock we passed over the high grounds between Capes Blanez and Blackness; thus forming in our ascending entrée a most magnificent arch; at which time, nothing can exceed the beautiful appearance of the villages, fields, roads, villas, etc., under us, after having been just two hours over the sea."

The crossing ended safely in the forest of Guines when Jeffries stopped the balloon's progress by grabbing a treetop, but not before, as he wrote, they were "forced to adopt one last and curious expedient to lighten the balloon."

In his pocket, Dr. Jeffries carried the world's first air-mail letter, posted with him by Dr. Franklin's son, William, to the elder statesman's grandson, William T. Franklin. Jeffries personally delivered it at Passy five days later.

On hand to greet the balloonists from across the Channel was Pilâtre de Rozier, who had been waiting impatiently for favorable winds for more than a month for his own projected Channel crossing, Boulogne to Dover.

There would follow more months of tedious waiting for the winds to stand fair for England, months in which his friend the Marquis de Maisonfort stayed with him at Boulogne as an assistant. The tedium was broken, however, by a love affair de Rozier enjoyed with Susan Dyer, the seventeen-year-old daughter of an English shipping merchant. Plans were made for their marriage, but the father insisted they wait until after Pilâtre completed his crazy balloon ride.

The aerostat de Rozier had designed for the journey was unlike any ever seen before. To settle an argument with Academy of Science sponsors over whether it should be a hydrogen-filled *charlière* or a hot-air *montgolfière,* de Rozier combined both types into a highly dangerous double aerostat 40 feet in diameter, which he called the *charlo-montgolfière.* Directly below the main hydrogen gas bag hung a 10-foot fire balloon, with which he intended to regulate its rise and fall.

Since the Montgolfiers' first balloons opened the skyroad to mankind, more than forty ascensions had been made with no fatal or even serious accident; and although the audacity of hanging a fire balloon directly beneath a bag of inflammable hydrogen was apparent, de Rozier must have decided that the possibility of sparks reaching the upper bag was remote. And then, de Rozier was losing patience.

De Maisonfort recalled: "I will tell you that, during six months, he passed his time in the most frightful uncertainty! The days in getting ready his machine—the nights in consulting the winds! Thrice he filled it; three times he was seated in the gallery, where I have seen him lying down broken-hearted; and three times the inconstant winds rejected his vows and destroyed his hopes!"

Finally, on the night of June 14, 1785, the wind veered around and de Rozier got ready to depart for the fourth time. "I saw him restless, melancholy," his friend remembered, "the whole night consulting the winds. I pressed him to take some sleep; he refused. He said, pointing to England, 'My fortune, my glory, and my life are all on that side!' "

By dusk the following evening, the hydrogen bag was inflated; the hot-air balloon filled with smoke, and de Rozier kissed Susan Dyer goodbye and climbed into the wicker gallery, followed by the balloon's manufacturer, Pierre Romaine. De Maisonfort started to climb in next, but de Rozier stopped him.

"No, it is not a certain wind," he pleaded. "It is not a sure experiment!"

De Maisonfort shrugged; he saw the gnawing uncertainty in his friend's face. "He clasped me in his arms," he recalled. "Trying to shake my constancy, he attempted to frighten me with the danger he foresaw and feared for me whilst he dared it himself. I yielded.

"At last the final moment approaches; the fire is lighted; my hands alone still keep my friends to the earth. They escape me! They fly upwards! They ascend with majesty! My eyes follow them, and I breathe with difficulty. All my senses are suspended; I, most fortunate, still envy them!

"Already thirty minutes are elapsed in this violent agitation. I hear shrieks all around me; horror environs me; a rapid motion accelerates and brings back the machine to earth!"

Other eyewitnesses, not so emotionally involved as de Maisonfort, reported seeing the *charlo-montgolfière* rise steadily to 3,000 feet over the coastline, where red flames suddenly appeared, licking upward from the burning hot-air bag. A brilliant ball of flame engulfed the aerostat, a muffled explosion was heard, and the whole thing plunged to earth. As it fell, the two luckless aeronauts dove away from the searing flames, tumbling out of sight below the cliff.

Leaping astride his horse, de Maisonfort raced off to the scene. He found de Rozier's body broken on the rocks, near the surf line at Wimereux. Romaine was still alive, but unconscious, nearby. He died moments later.

The tragedy marked the beginning of the end of the hot-air balloon for aerial exploration, although a century later, carnival parachutists would still use them to reach high altitudes for thrilling free falls; and in the 1960's, they would again be revived, greatly refined, in a resurgence of sport ballooning. Even that sport would take its toll of human life as men sought newer ways to tempt fate in the sky. De Rozier, the first stunt pilot to die, certainly would not be the last.

2

The Balloonatics

THE UNTIMELY DEATH of Jean-François Pilâtre de Rozier, history's first astronaut, left his rival, Jean-Pierre Blanchard, as France's number-one sky adventurer at the close of the eighteenth century, in a swiftly changing decade in which dueling gave way to ballooning as a demonstration of manhood.

Hundreds of thousands of Europeans were thrilling to the sight of Blanchard's gaily decorated aerostats surging skyward from Brussels, Hamburg, Liège, Valenciennes, Nancy, Strasbourg, Nuremberg, Basle, Metz, and Warsaw. Other adventurers were conceiving newer ways to utilize the balloon for probing the atmosphere and exploring remote regions of the earth itself. On August 6, 1786, Jacques Balmet and Jacques Paccard landed their balloon atop the snowy summit of Mont Blanc and planted the French flag in the snow pack. Others drifted over hidden valleys of the Alps to gaze down on their awesome beauty.

The rise of stunt ballooning was cut short by the bloody revolution that removed Louis XVI and Marie Antoinette and installed the First Republic; but from the turmoil of this social upheaval comes the amazing story of André-Jacques Garnerin, the first man to entrust his life to a parachute.

Garnerin, in 1793, had been sent as a special commissioner of the Republicans to the Army of the North, on the Austrian frontier. A wild-haired young soldier of fortune, Garnerin hoped to find glory on the field of battle, not in the sky. But at Marchiennes on October 31, he got himself involved in a military action that ended with his capture by the Duke of York. He was imprisoned for thirty-one tedious months in the fortress of Buda, high on a cliff across the Danube from Pest.

Garnerin had a lot of free time to think. He later wrote in his memoirs: "The love of liberty, so natural to a prisoner, gave rise to many projects to release myself from the rigors of detention. To surprise the vigilance of the sentries, pierce walls ten feet thick, throw myself from the rampart without being injured, were schemes that afforded recreation."

A parachute, he mused, might allow him to leap off the cliff into the Danube without killing himself. He recalled that Blanchard had thrown a dog overboard from a balloon basket, tied to a canvas parachute, in 1785. The animal had landed safely, although too frightened to bark.

"Blanchard's idea," he went on, "appeared only to require a careful mathematical comparison; I applied myself to the problem. After deciding on the size of the parachute for descending from a rampart or precipice, I devised the size and form of a parachute for descending several thousand feet from a balloon."

Released from Buda prison before he got the chance to try out his parachute idea there, Garnerin won the financial backing of the French government of the Republican Year VI (1797) to construct a balloon and make a descent in a parachute not unlike those of today in design.

Made up of thirty-two gores of white canvas, formed into a 23-foot hemisphere, Garnerin's chute had a 10-inch wooden disc at the top. Through a center hole ran short pieces of tape, fastened to the gores. A wooden hoop, 8 feet in diameter, hung 5 feet below the disc. To this were tied riser cords from each seam of the canopy, so that when the balloon arose it hung draped like a curtain. A basket dangled below the hoop, and in this rode Garnerin on the afternoon of October 22, ascending from the park of Monceau, Paris.

Thousands of people jammed the park and swarmed over the rooftops nearby to watch Garnerin kill himself; they were certain he would meet the same fate as Pilâtre de Rozier. It was the same lust that would attract other morbid crowds to watch aerial stunt exhibitions in later years, hopeful of seeing a violent death take place before their very eyes, not to applaud the adventurers for their pioneering efforts to conquer the sky.

Garnerin fooled them.

At 5 P.M., an eyewitness recorded, "Garnerin slashed the restraining cord with a knife and his balloon shot skyward. There were no cheers; a hush fell over the crowd. Excitement and uneasiness were depicted in every countenance. When he had reached an altitude of more than 6,000 feet, he cut the cord that attached him to the aerostat, which ascended until it exploded, whilst the parachute holding Citizen Garnerin descended rapidly. The oscillations it underwent at last drew forth a cry from the spectators, and many women fainted. . . ."

Garnerin was having the time of his life, until the wild swinging of the basket, during its 10-minute descent, brought on nausea. In vain he tugged at the riser cords to dampen the oscillation. The last thing he remembered was smacking the ground hard on the downswing. When he regained consciousness, the Duke of York, his old nemesis, was looking down at him from horseback, shaking his head.

"You'll never learn," the Duke said sourly, riding off. Garnerin got up and brushed himself off, quite happy to be alive. Then he keeled over, out cold from the aftershock of his parachute ride.

As a government balloonist, Citizen Garnerin in 1801 was paid 15,000 francs by Minister of the Interior Lucien Bonaparte to stage an aerial extravaganza at the Fête of the 1st Vendémiaire. Bonaparte specified that it would include:

"1. Two pilot balloons, to show the direction of the wind.

"2. A gilt balloon to reflect the rays of the sun, and which will appear like a large star.

"3. Your ascent and descent in a parachute."

All these acts would have modern counterparts, incidentally; weather balloons are in use today, the passive satellite Echo I made a fine space reflector, and sky diving is commonplace. But

Garnerin's fine showmanship would prove his undoing. Early in December, 1804, at the coronation of Emperor Napoleon at Notre Dame Cathedral, where the amazing little revolutionary soldier made history by rudely snatching his crown from the Pope and placing it on his own head, and where Josephine, the Creole beauty, became Empress, the balloon Garnerin provided tugged at its moorings, waiting to send news of Napoleon's glory across the world.

At eleven o'clock, thousands of tipsy celebrants cheered hoarsely as Garnerin cut loose the balloon, which bore a startling sign proclaiming Napoleon as Emperor of France. It was the first aerial billboard, illuminated grandly by 3,000 blazing lanterns.

"One sees it rise slowly and majestically," wrote a spectator. "It is, indeed, a fine sight; but who could then guess the direction it would take, or the sensation it would cause?"

A sensation it indeed caused; the next morning, startled Romans saw the giant *charlière* bouncing over St. Peter's Cathedral and the Vatican, finally sweeping beyond the city to fall into Lake Bracciano.

Word came back to Emperor Napoleon that the balloon had ignominiously snagged on the tomb of another emperor—Nero —tearing a large hole that brought it down. The incident naturally caused much amusement in court, but not to Garnerin. Napoleon, red-faced with anger, dismissed him as his royal balloonist and henceforth would have nothing to do with aerostation. Plans to invade England by war balloon were abandoned, and France's busy aerostatic school at Meudon was closed.

That pioneer aerial establishment had existed for ten interesting years since its formation on April 2, 1794, under the direction of a civilian chemist, Guyton Morveau, and Captain of Aérostiers Colonel Jean-Marie-Joseph Coutelle, who was responsible for the training of fifty young officers. At one time the French Aerostatic Corps included four 17,000-cubic-foot war balloons, the *Entreprenant, Céleste, Hercule,* and *Intrépide.*

Colonel Coutelle and two other officers made a daring reconnaissance ascension in June, 1794, in the *Entreprenant,* to observe maneuvers of Austrian troops on the plains of Fleurus. Cannon shells whizzed uncomfortably close to the frightened balloonists, who hurriedly rose above the line of fire. There they signaled back information that helped France win a decisive victory.

Garnerin's last sky voyage of record was a hairy night flight from Paris, on September 21, 1807, in which he rode out a storm for nearly ten hours. Illuminated like a Japanese lantern with ten lamps, his balloon rose directly into the teeth of a boiling frontal system that swept him 300 miles across the landscape of France, to crash-land on the white summit of Mont Tonnerre.

During this wild journey his relief valve jammed; and trying to get down, he risked his life by tearing a 2-foot hole in the side of the balloon, allowing gas to escape dangerously close to the lanterns. It was a miracle that Garnerin did not end up as de Rozier and Romaine had.

Joseph Louis Gay-Lussac, the noted French scientist, was a different sort of aerial adventurer who, like his father, Antoine Gay, could not let well enough alone. Not wishing the son to be confused with other Gay boys, Antoine had added "Lussac" to the family name, after a piece of real estate he owned near St. Lemand. The younger Gay-Lussac, whose name would be associated with the study of gases in future physics classes, went up in a balloon one day to see what the sky was made of.

The morning was hot and humid on August 23, 1804, when M. Gay-Lussac and another ardent French philosopher, M. Biot, ascended from Paris' Conservatory of Arts into a deep stratus cloud layer. There, in an experiment to see whether the earth's magnetic field extended into the sky, they crouched over a magnetic compass needle at an altitude of 6,500 feet and held their breaths.

"*Mon dieu!*" cried Gay-Lussac. "It spins 'round and 'round!"

M. Biot looked closer. Sure enough, the needle was sweeping through all points of the compass. They were puzzled. This had not been expected. There must be an explanation! M. Biot looked over the rim of the basket at the balloon's shadow on a cloud below them.

"Ah, but of course!" he laughed. "We are spinning, not the needle!"

The airborne scientists' next experiment was one for the birds; at an altitude of 11,000 feet, they uncaged a little green linnet.

"It flew away directly," Gay-Lussac noted in the log. "But, soon feeling itself abandoned, in the midst of an unknown ocean, it returned and settled down on the stays of the balloon. Then, mustering fresh courage, it took a second flight, and dashed downwards to earth, describing a tortuous yet almost perpendicular plunge."

A month later Gay-Lussac went up alone, armed with a new magnetic compass, a thermometer, two hygrometers, a barometer, and a couple of wine bottles from which all air had been exhausted. At 23,000 feet over Paris, he fumbled at the instruments with numbed fingers. It was 15 degrees below zero, the humidity low. The barometer had fallen to 12.95 inches; Gay-Lussac breathed with difficulty in air less than half sea-level density. He uncorked the bottles; with a whistle, they filled with the thin air of the high sky. He corked them tight.

Back on the ground, Gay-Lussac rushed the bottles to his laboratory. He opened them under water. They only half filled. On analyzing the air in them, he found that it was made of the same stuff 4 miles up as it was at the surface—basically 215 parts oxygen per 1,000 parts air. From this he wrote up "Gay-Lussac's Law," which, as any high-school student will tell you, is, "The volume of any gaseous product bears a simple ratio to that of its constituents."

By going up in a balloon, Gay-Lussac had won immortality as the adventurous father of meteorology, and for his discovery that the magnetic field extends upward through the atmosphere where future ships of the air could use it to navigate by, and where future spacemen would find it a hazard—in a higher region called the Van Allen Belt.

His fame did more for him, in a practical sense—he would make a small fortune as technical adviser to the French wine industry, while earning a nice government pension as its expert on saltpeter and chief assayer to the mint. He died at seventy-two in 1850.

Nearly half a century elapsed from the pioneering sky explorations of Gay-Lussac to the historic ascension, on September 5, 1862, of another scientific balloonist, Henry Tracey Coxwell, and a member of the austere British Association, James Glaisher, extending knowledge of the sky upward to an altitude of 7 miles. Theirs was a scientific stunt, pure and simple. They were the first to probe the stratosphere; with no oxygen supply, they risked their lives by exposing themselves to the potentially fatal hazards of hypoxia. A scientist as eminently qualified as Glaisher knew that oxygen deprivation was physically harmful; and from Gay-Lussac's tables he must have known there would be only a trace of the vital gas at the balloon's ceiling, 39,000 feet.

Nevertheless, at 1:03 P.M. on September 5, 1862, Coxwell cast off the anchor rope and the scientific balloon, built at his own expense for the British Association project, ascended from a field at Wolverhampton, England; at 6,700 feet it broke into bright sunlight above the clouds. There Glaisher fumbled with a dry-plate camera loaned him by a Dr. Hill Norris, but the balloon was rotating too fast to make an exposure.

Near the end of the second hour aloft, Coxwell found the valve rope tightly twisted. Already breathing hard from the rarefied air and the cold, he climbed into the rigging and stood tiptoe on the ring. The rope dangled just beyond reach. His right foot slipped. He half fell from his precarious perch.

"Henry!" Glaisher cried. "I cannot see!"

Coxwell looked dumbly at him. A blackness was cobwebbing his own consciousness. Glaisher gasped for breath. He could barely make out the column of mercury in the barometer by squinting his eyes. They were passing 29,000 feet—higher than man had ever gone before! A voice sounded very far away . . .

Coxwell, slumped in the rigging above him, whispered, "I cannot reach the rope!" Glaisher did not hear this—he was unconscious.

In the bitter cold at the top of the troposphere, the stillness of death fell over the silent balloon as it rose higher and higher, lifting its human cargo toward eternity. Coxwell's eyes fluttered; he forced himself back to consciousness. Hoarfrost covered his clothing, his face and hands. By a miracle, the valve rope dangled before his blurred eyes. He tried to rise, fell back, muscular coordination gone. He laughed hysterically. Hypoxia was at work. In a moment, Coxwell reasoned tiredly, they would drift beyond the limit of human endurance, and the balloon would go on its ghostly way carrying two corpses.

Straining, he brought his eyes into focus on the rope. Then he leaned out as far as he dared, hanging from the rigging, finely balanced, dangerously close to tumbling into space. He opened his mouth and tipped forward. With relief he felt hemp rope slide between his teeth; he clamped his jaws on it with all his strength. Tugging hard, he heard a slight soft hissing above him and knew he had succeeded; the valve was open. Then he collapsed.

Some time later, Coxwell and Glaisher opened their eyes. Both had throbbing headaches. Glaisher struggled up and looked at the barometer. They were dropping rapidly. He studied the minimum thermometer, a delicate instrument on which was recorded the lowest temperature they had reached. It read —12 degrees; that meant they had risen to the astounding altitude of 39,000 feet—unconscious!

The *London Times* paid high honor to the aeronauts, commenting that "the courage of a man of science deserves to have a chapter of history devoted to it. . . . His feats give you a better guarantee for real courage because they are solitary, deliberate, calm and passive. . . . He has to fight alone against the faintness of nature, without men shouting or flags flying, or trumpets clanging around him. He faces the invisible forces of nature, the gas that explodes or the poison that penetrates, and is at the disadvantage of having to be fully conscious and self-

possessed. . . . The aerial voyage just performed by Mr. Coxwell and Mr. Glaisher deserves to rank with the greatest feats
of experimenters, discoverers and travelers. . . ."

It was the humidity, not the heat, that made the growing
crowd irritable July 17, 1784, a typically sultry summer day for
Philadelphia. It seemed that the city's entire 25,000 population
was gripped with a suffocating sense of something unusual
about to happen. The low rumble of a welcome, advancing
thunderstorm gave promise of a drenching; the air might clear
by nightfall.

In Centre Square, a rudely constructed gallows was the
center of a small fever of activity as John Downie and John
Martin, convicted street robbers, were led toward it from Walnut Street Prison at Sixth and Walnut. Mounting the steps to
the gallows, they were delivered to the hangman, who effi-
ciently and quickly sent them on their way without ceremony.

Such a show ordinarily would have drawn a good crowd in
the quiet Quaker City, but now even the hangman was anxious
to cut down the corpses and leave.

Back inside the prison yard, things were contrastingly different; the high brick walls echoed the hum of hundreds of excited
voices. Beyond the walls the streets were filled with an even
larger crowd.

Center of attention was a young Baltimore man, Peter
Carnes, who was sweating over a smoking fire pit. Above it,
suspended from what looked like another gallows tree, hung a
35-foot balloon, seeming to breathe as its sides puffed and
shrank with gusts of a rising zephyr. Finally it blossomed like
a giant puffball, tugging at its ropes. Carnes climbed gingerly
into the basket and signaled his helpers to let the ropes go.

A cheer went up from the crowd inside the prison yard as
America's first man-carrying balloon lifted into the hot sky. And
from behind barred windows, yells and catcalls from the prison-
ers added to the tumult as they enviously watched Carnes rising above the walls. Their calls were cut short, turning to a
unified cry of alarm; some 20 feet above the yard a gust from

the advancing storm viciously slapped the aerostat. Carnes
hung on tight. The basket swung in an arc and smashed back
into the brick wall, tumbling him roughly to the ground. The
balloon, thus lightened, shot skyward and headed rapidly
southward in the teeth of the wind. In a moment, spectators
outside the wall, unaware of what had happened, raced after
the balloon, yelling and shouting encouragement to Carnes,
who they thought was still aboard. Sailing high over the rooftops it dwindled in size "to the appearance of a whiskey keg,"
one spectator reported afterward.

The balloon suddenly turned a bright crimson as sparks set
the bag afire, and quickly it was dropping earthward like a
blazing meteor. The shocked crowd ran full speed to where it
came down beyond the city limits, drawn by the expectation of
seeing freshly spilled blood. They were disappointed. Carnes
had escaped a horrible fate, although he lost the distinction of
perhaps becoming the New World's first aerial stunt man.

New York City in 1789 was the scene of numerous celebrations held in observance of three concurrent events—the inaug-
uration of General George Washington as first constitutional
President of the United States, the first assembly of the new
Congress, and the birth of the Federal judiciary under John
Jay. Fireworks, parades, and state balls held the interest of the
Manhattanites. Joseph Deeker, a British showman who claimed
to have been an aeronaut back home, was raising money by
subscription to repeat Carnes' effort to become America's first
balloonist.

On August 10, Thomas Greenleaf's *New York Journal and
Weekly Register* reported that Deeker had sent aloft a trial hot-
air balloon 24 feet in circumference; it had dropped in Harlem.

Deeker himself summoned courage on September 23 to attempt an ascension in a larger balloon. The event created intense
excitement; Congress, meeting that day in Federal Hall to de-
bate the critical issue of deciding on a permanent residence for
the footloose Federal government, voted to adjourn so that its
members could "see the balloon let off."

On the following day, the *Journal* reported: "The day arrives —crowds of spectators fly to the theater of action—our hero partly inflates his aerial vehicle—the upper retainer is loosed— and alas! the gas fails!—the balloon fails!—the fire communicates!—and the expectations of thousands ascend in fumo!"

To say nothing of Deeker's.

America's first stunt pilot turned out to be not a citizen of the United States but the French aeronaut Jean-Pierre Blanchard, now a veteran of more than forty European ascensions. Blanchard, like Carnes, decided on Philadelphia, America's center of culture and scientific interest, as the best launch site.

At 9 A.M. on January 9, 1793, President Washington himself appeared at the Walnut Street Prison yard, stepping from his carriage to the thunder of a fifteen-gun salute by Captain Fisher's Company of Artillery. Another two cannon shots barked every fifteen minutes during the next hour's countdown, to keep the crowd from drifting off.

Blanchard's balloon was a *charlière* of brilliant blue and gold; a spangled blue car hung from strong rope netting. The aeronaut was even more resplendent in a tight blue suit; a cocked hat set off with white feathers sat jauntily on his head. His pet dog, Charles, wagged his tail happily inside the basket, barking at the crowd.

At ten o'clock sharp, reported the *Federal Gazette*, "the balloon began to ascend perpendicularly, slowly, while Mr. Blanchard waved the colors of the United States and those of the French Republic, and flourished his hat to the thousands of citizens from every part of the country who stood gratified and astonished at his intrepidity. . . ."

During a 15-mile drift, Blanchard performed some scientific experiments at the request of the American scientists who were sponsoring the flight; he measured his pulse rate (it was normal) and weighed a stone at altitude (Blanchard claimed that it weighed less than it did on earth). He came down gently near Woodbury, New Jersey, where awed natives stood back cautiously until the Frenchman tossed them a bottle of wine and displayed a "passport" signed by President Washington, requesting that citizens not molest him.

Blanchard that evening paid Washington a visit at the Executive Mansion, presenting him with the small American flag from his balloon. In return, Washington accorded him the first official accolade by a President to a returning sky explorer, a custom revived in the twentieth century for returning astronauts.

For Blanchard, the glory was fine; but as a business proposition, the first American manned ascent was a flop. His expenses totaled more than $3,000; he had taken in only $405. On June 5, to recoup, Blanchard advertised a cut-rate ascension (fifty cents admission) from a board enclosure in the front yard of Governor Thomas Mifflin's mansion on Chestnut Street.

Mifflin was a man of stature—as the first President of the United States in Congress Assembled he had received General Washington's resignation as Commander of the Continental Army, and had once led an obscure movement to replace Washington as commander-in-chief with General Horatio Gates.

Again—trouble.

A gang of young hoodlums, unable to resist the sight of the gas bag bobbing around inside the enclosure, made short work of it with sticks and stones. Disgusted, Blanchard returned to France after issuing a statement to the press that he was "through with ballooning in America."

Such unruly mobs had deterred other foreign balloonists from coming to the United States; and for more than two decades after Blanchard's unhappy experience, there was no further progress toward aerial exploration at home. Nevertheless, two other French aeronauts, Messieurs Michel and Stanislaus, finally decided to try and make a fast Yankee buck from the "savages" of Philadelphia, announcing on September 8, 1819, a "glorious ascension" to be made from Vauxhall Gardens, a showplace resort Philadelphians were proud of.

Nervously keeping an eye on the growing crowd, they began inflating their balloon, in which they had promised to perform aerial acrobatics, capped with a 2,000-foot parachute descent and a spot landing.

By noon, rising winds brought the inflation to a halt. The crowd grew ugly. Paling, the Frenchmen pleaded with them to have patience. The crowd responded with jeers. Then an inflammatory incident occurred that set off rioting. An attendant caught a small boy climbing the fence; the boy was badly hurt in a fall. A rumor spread like wildfire that he had been killed.

Inflamed now, the crowd began throwing rocks at the balloon, finally attacking it with knives and ripping it to shreds as the Frenchmen ran for their lives.

Outside, the mob of freeloaders, who had hoped to see the balloon go up without paying admission, rushed the fence, toppling it over. Someone made off with the cash box, containing about $800. The acid barrels, used to make hydrogen gas, were smashed; many rioters were badly burned.

Next the crowd turned its fury against the main building, raiding the bars, theater, and pavilion. The stage scenery was set afire and soon the whole structure was ablaze. The city fire and hose companies rushed to the scene, too late. By nightfall, beautiful Vauxhall Gardens was a smoldering ruin.

The *United States Gazette* reported the riot as an affront to the Quaker City's reputation: "A mobbing spirit has not been characteristic of Philadelphia, and it is with regret that we publish that such a disgraceful riot has taken place."

3

The Yankee Doodle Dandy

"THE QUEEN DESIRES TO CONGRATULATE THE PRESIDENT UPON THE SUCCESSFUL COMPLETION OF THE GREAT INTERNATIONAL WORK, IN WHICH THE QUEEN HAS TAKEN THE GREATEST INTEREST. . . ."

The first transatlantic cable message, twenty-five words at a dollar a word, from Victoria in England to Buchanan in the United States, flashed and crackled over Cyrus Field's wonderful submarine line on August 17, 1858, marking the culmination of years of effort to join up the Old and New Worlds.

The cable faltered and died within a month, but it gave fresh stimulus to four balloonatics who would attempt to cross the Atlantic by air. Three of these were already experienced aeronauts—John Wise, John Steiner, and John La Mountain. The fourth was about to make his first ascent over Ottawa in an exhibition flight to celebrate the completion of the cable.

Thaddeus Sobieski Constantine Lowe, a dashing, handsome traveling magician who couldn't resist the lure of the sky, was born on August 20, 1832, at Jefferson Mills, Coos County, New Hampshire, and was immediately saddled with his tongue-twisting name by his mother, who hoped to endow him with the courage of the hero of a book that had deeply impressed her—*Thaddeus of Warsaw.*

As a boy, Thaddeus had attended a lecture given by a showman who demonstrated the wonders of chemistry to the delight of his rural audiences. During the evening, he volunteered to act as his assistant; and when the lecturer left town, Lowe went along.

The next spring, Lowe, eighteen years old and big for his age, set out on a lecture tour of his own as "Professor Carlincourt." One of his demonstrations was the same that the world's first aeronaut, Pilâtre de Rozier, had used to amuse his sponsor, the Comtesse Louise-Marie-Joséphine of Savoy; he filled soap bubbles with hydrogen gas and sent them soaring over the heads of his delighted audiences.

One pretty girl stayed late after the lecture to meet the handsome speaker—Leontine Augustine Gachon, a French refugee whose father had been a member of deposed King Louis Philippe's Royal Guard. They fell in love and married.

With his young bride as his assistant, Lowe added a marionette show to his repertoire and toured the South as Professor Carlincourt and His Yankee Doodles. By 1858, he had saved enough money to buy a balloon and go into the big time. Following his first ascent at Ottawa, Lowe went up over Portland, Maine, on July 4, 1859, and released forty-eight small hydrogen balloons to check the upper wind currents that he believed could carry him to Paris. One was recovered 600 miles at sea.

Convinced he could make it, Lowe began construction of a giant gas bag, 130 feet tall, at Hoboken, New Jersey, much to the irritation of two of his rivals, John Wise and John La Mountain, who attacked him in the press as an "unscrupulous plagiarist and magician by profession." On November 15, 1859, a letter from Professor Wise to the *New York Tribune* appeared under the heading, THE BIG BALLOON A HUMBUG! A Southern newspaper suggested that Lowe intended bombing Charleston from the air, with the idea of rescuing John Brown from prison and carrying him to England.

Lowe's balloon, the *City of New York,* was built to hold 725,-000 cubic feet of coal gas, which he estimated could lift 11 tons, including a 20-foot basket and a lifeboat, from which dangled a drag rope with floats.

Freely admitting that Professor Wise had discovered the "river of air" flowing from west to east, Lowe disregarded the charges of plagiarism and went ahead with his plans. "It is time that someone should make a bold push," he said. "If nothing is done but talk and theorize, or make an occasional excursion, the aeronautic art will remain where it is."

The transatlantic scheme was viewed with proper alarm by many. *Harper's Weekly* warned that "there are many parts of the eastern coast of Africa which are entirely desert," in case the west wind should blow Lowe that way, but observed that "Mr. Lowe [they refused to call him Professor] has laid in a store of Roman candles and rockets" for signal flares, and one hundred parachutes to drop messages to passing ships.

Finally completed, the great balloon was taken to the Crystal Palace grounds in New York, where Lowe ran into a problem he had overlooked; the Manhattan Gas Works refused to sell him the coal gas he needed.

"We would black out Manhattan!" an official cried.

At this point a crafty Philadelphian came to Lowe's rescue. Dr. John C. Cresson, president of the Franklin Institute, invited him to bring the balloon to the Quaker City for inflation. Dr. Cresson just happened to be president of the Point Breeze Gas Works there and knew good business when he saw it.

Renamed the *Great Western* at the suggestion of Horace Greeley, publisher of the *New York Tribune,* the transatlantic balloon made its first test flight from the Point Breeze Gas Works on a bright June day in 1860. Lowe took along five passengers, including Garrick Mallery, associate editor of the *Philadelphia Inquirer,* who later reported: "When Mr. Lowe was over the city, managing his great creature like a charm, he burst out from the hoop above into the involuntary exclamation: 'Here at last is the *Great Western* afloat, after all prophecies against her, and half a million witnesses to the fact!' "

Lowe postponed his projected ocean voyage until the following spring when the gas bag was torn on landing; and during the winter months, he formed a friendship with Professor Joseph Henry, of the Smithsonian Institution, a leading authority on meteorology. Professor Henry, while enthusiastic over Lowe's scheme, advised him to test the upper winds on a flight over the continental United States before attempting the ocean trip.

Lowe agreed, moving his base to Cincinnati, but already storm clouds were gathering on the horizon—a new kind of storm. On April 12, 1861, civil war came to America when Brigadier General P.G.T. Beauregard directed the shelling of Fort Sumter, South Carolina. Three days later, President Lincoln was calling on the northern states to raise 75,000 volunteers to quell the uprising. And by week's end, Lowe was blithely ready for his test hop, to check the winds from Cincinnati to the eastern seaboard.

Attending a banquet in his honor given by Murat Halstead, editor of the *Cincinnati Commercial,* Lowe was interrupted by a messenger with word that the west wind was rising. Excusing himself, Lowe swept a pile of cookies into his napkin and left at once for the balloon station, still dressed in top hat and tails. At 3:30 A.M. on April 20, he ascended alone, carrying a bundle of Halstead's newspapers, which featured a story on his forthcoming adventure. It would turn out to be much more of an adventure than either man had anticipated.

Lowe felt the icy cold of the winter night cutting through his dinner clothes like a knife. At an altitude of one mile, the sudden drop of temperature froze droplets of moisture suspended inside the balloon and formed, Lowe reported, "a fine, glassy, beadlike hail, which in the absolute stillness I could distinctly hear falling upon the silk and rolling down the neck of the balloon. . . . A bushel or more of this fine hail was discharged."

The sunrise was like the promise of a new world, as Lowe watched the dawn from an altitude of 18,000 feet. "The streaks of light running around the horizon resembled bands of molten gold," he wrote later. "And when the sun itself appeared I was never more astonished and surprised. There was a total absence of its usual dazzling appearance. It resembled a disc of burnished copper. . . . The sky, too, was inexpressibly beautiful, resembling a rich, dark-blue velvet, and the sun, moon and some of the stars were all visible at the same time. . . ."

Crossing the Alleghenies, Lowe ascended to a height of 4½ miles. "Though racing through space with such extreme rapidity," he recalled, "everything around me was perfectly quiet and still—so still that I could have carried a lighted candle without any protection. . . ."

With the Blue Ridge Mountains looming ahead, Lowe dropped down to make a flying inquiry of his position, but a crosscurrent suddenly swept him toward the south. Floating along only a few hundred feet up, he was puzzled by the sound of gunfire. Finally, in the backwoods of South Carolina, the balloon came down near the settlement of Pea Ridge. An ugly crowd quickly gathered.

"You from the North?" he was asked.

Lowe stepped from the basket and tossed over the bundle of Cincinnati papers; it was a bad mistake. "Better come along with us," a lanky farmer snapped, prodding him with a long rifle. At Unionville, Lowe learned to his astonishment that he had landed in Confederate territory and was, in fact, the first Yankee captured in the Civil War!

After spending the day in prison, Lowe was finally released when faculty members of South Carolina College interceded on his behalf. Issued a pass through the lines, he returned to Cincinnati by rail, a four-day trip that made a great impression on the balloonist. Crowds milled at every station; bands played *The Girl I Left Behind Me;* men in gray uniforms were hurrying up into Virginia; refugees like himself were anxiously fleeing before the gathering storm.

The transatlantic scheme was now forgotten; Lowe hurried to Washington to offer his services to President Lincoln as head of a Balloon Corps. With Professor Henry's help, Lowe staged a demonstration ascent from the Columbian Armory, taking up a telegrapher who sent history's first telegram from the air, directly to President Lincoln and to the War Department.

"From this point of observation," Lowe dictated, "we command an extent of country nearly 50 miles in diameter. . . ."

Lincoln invited the aeronaut to spend the night at the White House, where they talked until the small hours of morning about Lowe's proposed Aeronautic Corps. Lincoln finally smiled and sent Lowe over to see General Winfield Scott, the Union Army commander-in-chief.

The rat-race began for Lowe, who complained bitterly that "the general's mind was centered on the makeup of an army as he had always known it; he did not care for innovations. It was evident that the General of the Army had no interest in an Aeronautic Corps."

Besides, another rival balloonist, James Allen, who had joined the First Rhode Island Regiment, was already making experimental reconnaissance ascensions, and John Wise was pulling strings to sell the government a war balloon.

A comic-opera battle ensued, with Lowe and Wise fighting like boys over who got to use the city gas main to fill his balloon. Wise finally got his balloon up at the Battle of Bull Run; but when it suddenly broke loose, he ordered his ground crew to shoot it down. He retired from military service there and then.

Lowe, still a civilian, met with incessant opposition from the military until he found a friend in General George B. McClellan, commander of the forces defending Washington. Little Mac, trying desperately to prevent the rebels from sweeping into the capital, sent Lowe up on a reconnaissance flight from Fort Corcoran on July 24.

The flight ended disastrously; both Union and Confederate troops began firing on the balloon as it started down.

"Show your colors!" someone shouted from below. Lowe had no flag. He did the next best thing and tossed overboard his remaining ballast. He landed on Mason's Plantation, more than two miles outside the Union picket lines. When he failed to return, his pretty French wife, Leontine, took things in her own hands. When night fell, she disguised herself as a farm woman and drove a wagon through the lines to the farm where scouts informed her her husband was concealed.

In the darkness, Lowe and his wife loaded the balloon into

the bottom of the wagon and covered it with straw. He burrowed down beside it; and Mrs. Lowe nonchalantly drove back to Washington.

By the time snow fell, in November, 1861, Professor Lowe had forged a highly efficient Aeronautic Corps to operate with McClellan's Army of the Potomac. Largest of his war balloons were the *Union* and the *Intrepid,* twin-sized pongee aerostats of 32,000 cubic feet each, and three smaller ones, the *Constitution,* the *United States,* and the *Washington.* In December, Lowe had added two more, the *Eagle* and the *Excelsior,* for solo flights.

Less dramatic but highly significant was Lowe's patented field gas generator, a mobile unit with which he could manufacture hydrogen and inflate a balloon in less than three hours.

To man this pioneer United States Air Corps, Lowe hired a number of professional balloonists, who forgot their old rivalries to help crush the rebellion by operating as a civilian observation wing. William Paullin, who joined on October 11, was quickly dismissed by Lowe; Paullin was using the war balloon to take photographs of the battles, which he sold by the dozen as a sideline.

James Allen joined Lowe's outfit in March, 1862, actively participating in the Peninsular Campaign against Richmond and eventually replacing Lowe, who left the Corps in 1863. Allen's brother, Ezra, joined him later.

In December, 1861, John Steiner joined Lowe, operating the *Intrepid* along the upper Potomac until February, 1862, when he shifted his base to the Western Department of the Army for service along the Mississippi. There the German balloonist found conditions deplorable and wrote angrily to Lowe:

"I can not git eny ascistence here. Thay say thay know nothing about my balloon business thay even laugh ad me . . . let me hear from you as soon as possible and give me a paper from headquarters to show theas blockheads hoo I am."

He added a postscript: "All the officers hear are as dum as a set of *asses.*"

Later, he complained about not receiving payment for his

services, something that already had distressed Lowe himself: "I am here like a dog wisout a tail and I dond know ware I will be abel to draw my pay for no one seams to know eny thing. . . ."

Another of Lowe's aeronauts, John B. Starkweather, used the *Washington* to spy on Charleston in a tethered ascent from the deck of the river steamer *Mayflower,* until an accident grounded the balloon and he retired.

Ebenezer Seaver joined the Corps in November, 1861, and later replaced Paullin at Budd's Ferry; but he was finally fired by Lowe for staging a sit-down strike for back pay. But the one balloonist who gave Lowe the biggest headache was Jacob C. Freno, a Philadelphian, who joined the Yankee aeronaut in January, 1862.

After a year's service, Lowe dismissed Freno "for repeated absence without leave, for expressing disloyal sentiments, opening a faro bank for the purpose of gambling, and for the demoralizing effect which he had upon the subordinates of this department."

In revenge, Freno ripped a large hole in the *Constitution.*

Full justification for Professor Lowe's Aeronautic Corps came on May 31, 1862, when McClellan's mighty Army of the Potomac was bogged down in the swamps created by spring flooding of the Chickahominy River near Richmond. The Confederate defenders of the Rebel capital were swiftly taking up positions around Fair Oaks, threatening to divide and conquer the Union forces.

Ascending near Mechanicsville at noon, Lowe scanned the battle lines with his field glass and was shocked to see the Rebel troops moving into position to attack the Union Army's exposed flank. A major battle was shaping up, he realized; he must get closer!

Back on the ground, Lowe sent a rider off to McClellan with the bad news, then leaped on his horse and raced to his main balloon station six miles away to ascend with a telegrapher in the larger *Intrepid.* It was only half filled. Nearby was tethered the solo balloon *Constitution.* Lowe thought fast; if he could get the gas from the *Constitution* into the *Intrepid,* he could save two hours' time.

"I spied a ten-inch camp kettle lying on the ground," Lowe recalled years later. "Instantly I seized it and had one of my mechanics cut out the bottom. The *Intrepid* was disconnected from the inflating apparatus and by means of the camp kettle was attached to the *Constitution,* and in a very short time the gas filled the larger balloon. An hour saved! Immediately the *Intrepid* apparatus was placed in the car of the balloon and, accompanied by Mr. Park Spring, the Chief Telegrapher, I ascended to a height of one thousand feet and there witnessed the titanic struggle. The whole scene of action was plainly visible and reports of the progress of the battle were constantly sent till darkness fell upon the grand but terrifying struggle."

Lowe's quick thinking, reported Major General A. W. Greely, Chief Signal Officer, U.S.A., was the horseshoe nail that saved an army. "It may be safely claimed," he wrote, "that the Union Army was saved from destruction at the Battle of Fair Oaks by the frequent and accurate reports of Lowe, which clearly discovered to McClellan the determined intentions of Johnston to overwhelm an army divided by the practically impassable rivers and swamps. . . ."

If Lowe had saved the North and preserved the Union in an almost singlehanded act of heroism, few officers regarded him as anything but an interfering, meddlesome civilian. A bout with swamp fever and constant opposition from jealousy-motivated army officers drained his energies; and then came an even worse blow. In March, 1863, he was called before a Congressional committee investigating charges of misconduct among key officers. McClellan had been replaced by General Ambrose Burnside, and control of the Aeronautic Corps switched to the Corps of Engineers. Lowe told Congress all he knew of the ball of snakes and on May 7 resigned.

Recuperating from the swamp fever he'd contracted along the Chickahominy, Lowe cast about for some way to support his wife and their four children. Settling down in Norristown, Pennsylvania, he applied for and was granted patents on an

Jean-François Pilâtre de Rozier, world's first aerial stunt artist, was renowned scientist before he took up ballooning in 1783. He was killed two years later when balloon caught fire.

(Author's collection)

On Dec. 1, 1783, balloonmaker M. N. Robert and physicist Jacques Alexandre César Charles, inventor of the hydrogen aerostat, soared to 2,000 feet above Paris, landed 27 miles away. Inflammable hydrogen gas was severe fire hazard, but it gave more lift than hot air used by Montgolfier balloonists. (Author's collection)

André-Jacques Garnerin, French soldier held a prisoner of war in Buda tower, conceived idea for parachute as way to escape jail. He later tried it out (October 22, 1797) in drop from balloon 6,000 feet over Paris. It worked.
(Author's collection)

British balloonist Henry Tracey Coxwell (top) and physicist James Glashier made amazing ascension to 39,000 feet on September 5, 1862, and became first victims of deadly anoxia—lack of oxygen. Close to death, both managed to get down alive.
(Author's collection)

Frenchman Jean-Pierre Blanchard made New World's first human ascension over Philadelphia on January 8, 1793. President George Washington arrived early to witness ascent. (Author's collection)

*Balloonist John La Mountain tried to reach New York by air from
St. Louis, landed in tree in upstate New York.* Frank Leslie's Illus-
trated Newspaper, *July 16, 1859, published this action woodcut of
the incident.* (Author's collection)

Professor Thaddeus S. C. Lowe built giant airship City of New York *to cross Atlantic in 1859, but the Manhattan Gas Works wouldn't sell him the necessary 725,000 cubic feet of gas—they feared it would black out the town!*   (Author's collection)

Professor Lowe planned to cross Atlantic Ocean in balloon City of New York *(later named* Great Western*), beneath which hung giant basket and lifeboat (named* Leontine *for his wife). Vertical propeller at rear was designed for rising and for lowering balloon to find best air current. Passengers unidentified.*

(Photos from Lowe papers, courtesy Augustine M. L. Brownback, Norristown, Pa.)

Professor Lowe's Great Western *being inflated for test hop from Philadelphia in 1860. Lowe hoped to reach Paris by jet stream discovered by rival balloonist John Wise, but Civil War interrupted oceanic attempt. Professor Lowe stands in front center in top hat.*

History's first aerial photo, taken October 13, 1860, shows Boston, Mass. (Note masts of clipper ships in background.) Photographer James Wallace Black made wet-plate negative in time exposure from balloon piloted by aeronaut Samuel A. King, called "Nestor of American Aeronauts." King later taught ballooning to James Allen, who became America's first military aeronaut in Civil War.

(Photo courtesy W. N. Jennings)

As a Civil War balloonist, Prof. Thaddeus S. C. Lowe starts ascension from field station near Richmond. Ground crew lets up rope so aeronaut can observe battle action from 1,000 feet. One such observation, Lowe claimed, saved entire Union Army at Battle of Fair Oaks.
(U. S. Army Signal Corps)

Last photo taken of professor T. S. C. Lowe, Pasadena, Calif., before he died on January 16, 1913. Lowe bought a mountain near Pasadena, named it for himself and set up weather bureau to forecast winds for balloon airline he planned to inaugurate. During Civil War Lowe was Lincoln's chief aeronaut. (Author's collection)

Inventor Charles Richtel paddled his own dirigible through the skies in the 1870's.
(Author's collection)

John Wise, veteran U. S. balloonist, faced death when his balloon exploded high in the sky. It turned inside out, formed a parachute that gently lowered him to earth. (Author's collection)

Washington Harrison Donaldson fooled 'em again—when his stunt balloon burst, he rode it to earth as a parachute, escaped death.
(Author's collection)

History's first aerial wedding was performed over Pittsburgh, Pa., in 1870's. Balloon was piloted by Washington Harrison Donaldson (top); bride was Elizabeth Walsh, a bareback rider, and groom was Charley Colton, an acrobat. All were members of P. T. Barnum's traveling Hippodrome road show. (Author's collection)

Dear God, what do I do now? Frightened lady aeronaut, Miss Lucretia Bradley, faced this predicament when her balloon exploded. It formed parachute and let her down gently. Balloon had been purchased by her from Washington Harrison Donaldson.

(Author's collection)

artificial gas generator, adapted from his military balloon-gas field equipment, and on a gas refrigeration unit. He had gotten the idea for the latter by observing frost that formed on a cooling unit of his field generator, in which the temperature of the hot gas from an acid vat was cooled by expansion.

Lowe found the skipper of a small freighter—the *William Tabor*—who was willing to gamble with him on turning the vessel into the world's first artificially refrigerated cargo ship. Lowe's idea was to load the ship with freshly slaughtered beef at Galveston, Texas, and ship it frozen directly to New York City, instead of driving the cattle over the long, dusty Chisholm Trail into Kansas for shipment east by rail.

The *William Tabor* was a success, but the idea was not; both the vessel and its cargo vanished after running aground off the Florida coast. Years later, Lowe bumped into the skipper in a Los Angeles hotel lobby. The seaman admitted selling the whole shebang to a San Francisco man, who founded an industrial empire manufacturing gas refrigerators based on Lowe's patents, which had expired.

But his love of ballooning was strongest; and after the Civil War, Lowe picked up one of his military field generators and the balloon *United States* on the war-surplus market. With these, he opened a grand "Aeronautic Amphitheater" in New York City, at the corner of 59th Street and Sixth Avenue.

Although this was pretty far uptown, crowds came daily to buy rides in captive aerostats at Lowe's balloon park and to watch a daring stunt man, Frank Leslie, perform breathtaking feats at the end of a rope suspended from the *United States*, while Lowe piloted it over the city to advertise his showplace.

On one such trip, Lowe and Leslie drifted 20 miles north to Bramille Station, where the aeronaut threw out the anchor to land. It hooked under an eave of a house whose occupant, Peter Archer, proceeded to serve a writ of trespass on the flying professor. A contemporary journal commented: "Mr. Archer is one of the cowboys of the revolution and does not know how to read or write. For twenty years he has not been to New York and for seventeen not to Yonkers, not two miles distant." The irresistible march of progress, however, had stepped upon his roof.

Lowe received a novel request in October, 1865, from a friend, Dr. John F. Boynton, who wanted to get married in the sky. Lowe fixed up the car prettily with curtains and flowers and invited the hellfire preacher Henry Ward Beecher to officiate. Theodore Tilton, editor of the *New York Independent,* wrote a letter of introduction to Beecher, urging him to make the trip. He commented: "It will carry you nearer to heaven than most ministers are likely to get!"

Beecher declined, a snub Tilton never forgot. Tilton later hauled Beecher into court on a charge of committing adultery with his wife.

An old man in his seventies in 1910, Professor Lowe was comfortably retired on a fortune amassed by selling his artificial-gas plants to communities that had no natural gas supply. One of these was Pasadena, California, where he found the climate to his liking and settled down to await death.

The call of the high sky was still a dissonant note he could not ignore, and when the world's first international aviation meet was held, at nearby Dominguez Field, Lowe, full of his old enthusiasm, designed a revolutionary passenger balloon resembling his old *City of New York,* but which was far more luxurious in its trim. Powered with a gasoline engine, the *Lowe Planet Airship* featured a gondola with a dining salon, observation deck, and—prophetically—an in-flight magic lantern show.

On April 6, 1910, he applied for a patent on the *Planet Airship;* but when the Mexican government offered to purchase one for $50,000, Lowe declined. He'd had enough of war balloons.

In sun-drenched Southern California, Lowe saw a great future for aeronautical manufacturing and pilot training; he even bought a mountain—Mount Lowe—behind Pasadena and established an efficient weather observatory at its summit, as a preliminary to organizing the Planet Airship Line, coast to coast.

Death cut short Lowe's ambitions on January 16, 1913, following a bad fall in which he suffered a broken hip. Four months later, his Planet Airship patent—his eighteenth—was granted, but the grand scheme never got off the ground; there was no one to carry on.

Lowe was one of the last of the individual giants of aeronautics; and his fiery blood would flow in the veins of an individualistic granddaughter, Florence Lowe ("Pancho") Barnes, woman speed flier. Pancho won a highly publicized legal victory over the United States Air Force in a land condemnation suit in the 1950's, when the government forced her to abandon her ranch home on the Mojave Desert, to make way for a giant military runway at Edwards AFB.

The USAF finally got the property away from her, in an action which even she was quick to admit was vitally necessary for space-age expansion, but at her price—close to half a million dollars.

"What the hell," Pancho rebuked her critics, "my granddaddy *invented* the Air Force!"

4

The Confederate Air Force

CAPTAIN JOHN RANDOLPH BRYAN fought back a stinging bitterness and tried to accept the logic that he would not be in the
mess he was in if he had not volunteered, without even knowing what he was volunteering for. He was a cavalryman, not a
damned circus stunt balloonist!

He spurred his bay mare and hurried forward, riding lightly
in the saddle, with the natural grace of a Southern aristocrat.
They were waiting for him in the clearing ahead, laughing. . . .

It was a late afternoon in mid-April, 1862. The enemy was
dangerously near. General George B. McClellan's mighty Army
of the Potomac, after months of idleness around Washington,
was on the march, gathering irresistible momentum.

With the deadly monotony of a drumbeat, giant supply
wagons rumbled forward along the rain-soaked Yorktown Road,
westward from Fortress Monroe, following an invincible horde
of 112,000 men slogging toward Richmond, heart of the Confederacy. The end of the Great Rebellion seemed near at hand.

In the distance, beyond the thinly spread Rebel lines, a cloud
of dense, black smoke suddenly billowed skyward. McClellan's
advance pickets reined their horses, puzzled. The great army
ground to a halt while McClellan, the scientific tactician,
studied the smoke through his telescope. The Union general
could not see that it came from a huge bonfire of turpentine
knots, blazing in the middle of a clearing deep within the piney

woods bordering the south shore of the York River, near Yorktown.

Hidden from his view was a giant, pear-shaped monstrosity,
tugging at a half-inch manila rope. Sweating, cursing Rebel
soldiers struggled to hold it against the afternoon breeze from
the sea. At this moment, the young Southern officer rode up,
dismounted, and hurried toward them.

Captain Bryan hid his excitement as he stepped gingerly into
the frail wicker basket swinging below the huge cotton bag
that now was gorged with smoke. He spoke curtly:

"Watch what you're doing, there! Steady now. . . . Let her
go!"

With a lurch, the balloon started off, spinning upward and
sending him sprawling half out of the basket. He recovered his
balance and clung desperately to the ropes, coughing violently
as the smoke struck his face, stinging his eyes. Fighting back
nausea, he watched the ground drop away from him, far below.
The Confederacy's one and only war balloon, her secret
weapon, was going into action for the first time.

Bryan made out the white tents where Confederate General
Joseph Johnston and Major General John Bankhead Magruder
were encamped, on the high knoll beyond Lee's Mill. A blood-
red sun hung low over Yorktown's shingled rooftops farther
back.

Orienting himself, Bryan turned about and gazed down the
peninsula toward the east and, with a shock, saw the giant
steamroller Yankee army drawn up beyond the marshes of the
Warwick River. By comparison, Magruder's tiny Army of the
Peninsula, spread out below him, seemed laughable. Less than
12,000 men, dug in, arrogantly awaiting the Northern colossus.

The fear that had knotted Bryan's stomach was gone. All the
bitterness, the anxiety, was swept away by sudden anger at
the great invasion army.

A bright flash drew Bryan's attention to the left. A field bat-
tery was opening up. With volcanic fury, other siege guns
erupted to life along the Union lines. Shots whistled through
the air, too close for comfort.

Bryan waved his felt campaign hat and pierced the sky with a blood-curdling Rebel yell. The balloon trembled as a shroud line was severed by a Minié ball. He clutched the suspension ropes and glanced upward. Smoke was hissing from a hole in the cotton bag.

He would have to work fast now. Adjusting a small folding telescope, he meticulously studied the enemy positions and drew sketches of them on a pad.

Bryan could see that big siege guns were being rolled up behind hastily dug breastworks. Enormous one- and two-hundred-pounder rifled Parrott guns, batteries of seacoast mortars, and nasty-looking howitzers glinted in the late sun. And everywhere troops, supply wagons, and cavalry units were pressing forward.

The Warwick River could stop them momentarily, he saw. It was a good thing Magruder had ordered it dammed up, so that the heavy spring rains would turn the whole peninsula into a morass, from the York to the James.

Suddenly Bryan paused, grinning. There, in the distance, a balloon hung low above the horizon, like a rising moon. That would be the daring Yankee aeronaut, Professor Thaddeus Lowe, chief of the Federal Balloon Corps, who had had the whole sky to himself for more than a year now.

Bryan wondered what Lowe would think when he spotted the Confederate war balloon. For the first time in military history, two enemy airmen were fighting for control of the skies! It mattered little to him that Lowe had a taut, hydrogen-filled aerostat, complete with air-to-ground telegraph and signal flags. The Southern balloon, a stinking, smoking cotton globe, ready to burst her seams, had gotten him into the sky for a reconnaissance flight that could prevent disaster—if he could get word to Magruder in time!

He pulled a Colt .44 revolver from his new riding boot and fired two shots, the signal to pull him down. Eager hands began winding the anchor rope in with a crude windlass. Musket fire followed him as the balloon dropped from the darkening sky.

Leaping unhurt from the basket, Bryan saluted the man

who was riding up on a black stallion. General Joe Johnston's ramrod West Point bearing was tempered by smiling eyes and the sideburns, goatee, and mustache of a Virginian.

"At ease, Captain," he said. "What did you see?"

The two men went to the blazing campfire and sat on a log. Bryan pulled his map from under his field jacket. "It doesn't look good, sir," he said quickly. "McClellan must have more than a hundred thousand troops out there, with more coming. There's a loaded siege train over here, and the Cockletown Road is alive with wagons."

Johnston frowned. "Magruder must know this immediately. How do the earthworks look to you?"

Bryan felt impressed; at twenty-one, here he was, sitting beside Fighting Joe Johnston, commander of the mighty Army of Northern Virginia, discussing man to man the fate of the South.

"There's about fifteen works out there. I'd say they're getting ready for a long siege. The Warwick's stopped them, and they appear to be concentrating on Lee's Mill. I think they'll strike there, sir."

The elderly commander smiled grimly. "Good work, Captain. I'll never know why Little Mac doesn't try to smash right on through to Richmond, as Lincoln told him to! There'd be no stopping him now."

"We'd give him a hot reception!" Bryan cried.

Joe Johnston stood up. "There are other ways to win wars than with a strong frontal attack, Captain. A well-organized drive may seem invincible, but never underestimate the element of surprise."

"Thank you, General," Bryan smiled, jumping to his feet. He knew what Johnston meant. With his aerial reconnaissance, Johnston and Magruder might still be able to throw the Union commander off balance.

Johnston mounted, then turned to Bryan once more before riding off. "I want you to move your balloon camp closer to Yorktown, Captain. I have a feeling we'll be needing you in a hurry. Don't forget—you're the only experienced aeronaut in the South now!"

As Johnston spurred his horse Bryan turned to his men, eyes blazing. "We'll show those damned Yankees how to fight on Virginia soil! You heard the General, didn't you?"

Bryan could not sleep. Rolled up in his blanket before the campfire, he kept seeing the vast Union Army spread out across the peninsula. The immensity of the shaping conflict was almost overwhelming to his imagination. And here he was, playing a key roll in one of the war's strangest dramas, one that would call for unknown, untried aerobatic skills on his part.

He thought back to just before Johnston's arrival at Yorktown with 50,000 tough Confederate troops, when, as aide-de-camp to Magruder, Bryan had intercepted a note from Johnston. The paper work had been killing him. He wanted action. He took a chance, opened the note, and started reading it.

"Dear General," Johnston had scrawled, "I think it would be a good thing for you to pick someone well acquainted with the countryside to observe the enemy's movements and see if we can't anticipate his moves. . . ."

Bryan folded the letter hurriedly and delivered it to Magruder. "From General Johnston's headquarters, sir," he said.

Magruder nodded and read the letter, frowning. "Bryan," he said, "gather some volunteers for a special mission. Men who know the peninsula well."

"Sir," Bryan blurted, "I can handle that! I'm a good horseman and I know this country like the back of my hand!"

A faint smile passed over Magruder's face as he studied the sincere young aide standing before him. Bryan was young, handsome, lean, an ardent Southerner. "I'm not certain you qualify, Bryan," he said.

Bryan persisted. "What I may lack in experience, sir, I make up in my loyalty to the cause!"

Magruder laughed. "Then I guess the job is yours. Here!" He handed over the letter.

Grinning boyishly, Bryan almost blurted out the truth, that he had already scanned it. The first part, anyway. He took the note and reread it, then stopped and went back. Johnston was proposing to spy on the Union Army *from a balloon!*

"I've never even seen a balloon, sir," he said weakly.

Magruder's eyes narrowed. "I understood you to volunteer, Captain."

"Yes sir, I did." Bryan saluted.

"Good luck then, Bryan," Magruder smiled. "Report to General Johnston in the morning."

Bryan sat on the edge of his bunk and thoughtfully began working tallow into his brand-new riding boots, an elegant pair of elkhide Wellingtons he had bought in Yorktown for sixteen dollars. His mind was on Nancy Andrews, pretty daughter of the sutler who had sold them to him, and how he had made her eyes light up with wild tales of daring exploits he had never made.

An hour later, Bryan was sitting on the porch of the Andrews' home, his arm around Nancy's waist.

"I'm going up in a balloon," he whispered importantly. "Imagine, a mile up there in the sky, looking down on the whole battlefield!"

Nancy trembled. "Do be careful, John," she said, touching his lips gently with her fingertips. The handsome young officer pulled her to him and kissed her.

"Wait for me," he told her. Then he mounted his horse and rode off into the night, his mind on what lay ahead. He suddenly laughed; it doesn't pay to volunteer—every army private knows that. It only gets you into trouble. He wondered how he would go about getting a balloon into the air. . . .

He had seen the Yankee balloons many times. Under the skillful supervision of Professor Lowe they had been making daily ascensions along the York and James Rivers ever since Lowe had come up from Fortress Monroe with General Fitz-John Porter's advance guard.

General Porter himself had gone up once to have a look around at the Confederate positions, a flight that nearly ended in disaster when the rope broke. The balloon had drifted over enemy lines and drawn heavy artillery fire until a crosscurrent wafted it back. In his excitement, Porter opened the gas valve wide while still a mile high. Falling rapidly, the bag turned inside out, forming a parachute that lowered him to the ground, a thoroughly frightened general.

Annoyed by the Northern aerial snoopers, Magruder had sent out a detachment of 35 sharpshooters to bring down Lowe's balloon. A Yankee patrol captured all but six. It was then that the Confederacy decided it needed its own air force.

General Johnston, charged by Jeff Davis with the defense of Richmond, called on an old West Point schoolmate, General Thomas Fenwick Drayton, to organize the South's aeronautic unit. It was easier ordered than executed. There was not a yard of balloon cloth to be had in Richmond. Drayton decided on a cotton balloon instead, to be filled with hot air, like a carnival performer's aerostat.

While this was being assembled, a quantity of silk was located by Captain Langdon Cheves, Jr., a member of a prominent family of Savannah, Georgia. On April 18, 1862, Captain Cheves received authorization to construct a silken balloon in Savannah's Chatham Armory, from material supplied by a Charleston, South Carolina, importer, E. L. Kerrison.

Historians have garbled the story of that balloon, which they supposed was made from dresses donated by loyal ladies of Richmond. Nevertheless, it served valiantly later on as the only other operational Confederate aerostat in the Civil War, making timely observations during the bloody battle at Gaines' Mill under the direction of General E. Porter Alexander, ordnance chief of Johnston's Army of Northern Virginia.

By that time, young John Randolph Bryan had already risked his life as the Confederacy's original one-man air force, performing an heroic service with sufficient skill and daring to change the course of the war.

Bryan had not even known where to begin when Johnston showed him the pile of fabric and ropes that arrived at the Yorktown armory by supply train and wagon from Richmond. But then, neither had anyone else. By improvising, he had assembled a makeshift ground crew organization and figured out a way to inflate the cotton sphere without setting it afire.

His first ascent a success, Bryan felt better when he prepared to go up into the sky for the second time, on the night of May 1, 1862. This time he had a span of horses to haul him down more quickly in the event the Yankee sharpshooters found his range.

Bryan's ground crew chief, a lanky Carolinian named Lafe Wilkins, shook his head and spat. "Cap'n," he said, "I don't know what in hell this war's comin' to, fightin' up in the sky!"

A volunteer from the First Georgia Infantry, John Jacobson, shifted his tobacco plug and swallowed. "No sense to it," he observed. "I'm gettin' all-fired sick of sittin' around here day after day, waitin' for them Yanks to hit us. I say let's go out and kill 'em now."

Bryan kicked the fire to life. "You won't have long to wait, soldier. Little Mac's about ready now. I'll know soon as I go up for another look. You'll see plenty of action then."

Billowing smoke curled up from the burning pitch knots and into a wooden flue that led across the clearing to where the balloon bag hung from a tree branch.

"Hold her neck over the flue!" he yelled to the group of men standing beneath the dirty cotton bag. Slowly its folds began to swell as the smoke poured inside through the appendix. It was already night. A bright moon threw a silvery light and black shadows across the scene. A few night birds chirped nearby; a hoot owl called mournfully from the swamp. Sporadic gunfire sounded, far away.

In half an hour the balloon had blossomed into a firm, rounded globe, straining to be off. The horses whinnied in fright, alarmed by the giant spectre. Bryan checked the ropes, then stepped once more into the basket. A Rebel flag fluttered above him.

"Up she goes!" Bryan yelled. "Don't let the line foul!"

Slowly the Confederate balloon rose into the night sky, turning round and round. Bryan, crouched inside the basket, felt a wave of vertigo and held tight to keep from falling. Gradually the spinning slowed. He breathed easier.

His eyes grew accustomed to the blackness of the night sky, and he looked away from the bonfire below him to stare off toward the east. Moonlight turned the York River into a silver ribbon, and night sounds flooded up from the earth; barking dogs . . . the creak of a distant wagon wheel . . . voices of men singing in camp . . . scattered sniper fire.

At a height of nearly 1,000 feet, the balloon stopped. A light wind from the southwest gently moved it over the swamp thickets along the Warwick River. Bryan could hear his heart beat. He was practically over the Union lines!

Leaning out over the edge of the basket, he looked down on a breathtaking scene. Enemy campfires blazed brightly for miles. This could mean only one thing: they were cooking their meat, getting ready for a forced march!

Suddenly he saw the silhouette of Professor Lowe's gas balloon, startlingly close by. He waved his hat and let go with a high-pitched Rebel yell.

"Hyaaa, Professor! You tell Little Mac we're ready for him!"

A burst of musket fire from below greeted his sally. Bryan laughed. "Yippee! Missed me a mile!"

A rocket shell exploded to his left. Bryan ducked, then looked down. For an instant, the enemy's positions were etched indelibly in his mind. He noted each detail with photographic clarity. Then it was dark once more.

Bryan pulled out his Colt and fired twice.

Below, he heard John Jacobson holler, "Giddap, goddam you! Gotta get ol' Balloon Bryan out'n the sky!"

Thus was born a nickname John Randolph Bryan would never live down. Henceforth the South's one-man air force would be called Balloon Bryan.

The basket struck the ground with a thud. Bryan tumbled out, then jumped up grinning and brushed himself off.

"How'd the horses like being tied to a balloon?" he asked.

"Horse on one end, jackass on t'other," Lafe Wilkins spat. "You're gonna bust your neck yet, Cap'n."

Bryan laughed and rode off to Johnston's headquarters.

"The enemy's strength has increased all along the river road," he reported. "Campfires burning everywhere. This looks like it, sir."

Johnston sat listening thoughtfully. When Bryan had finished, he said, "Captain, I know you're tired out. But I must ask you to go back up again immediately."

Bryan looked puzzled. Johnston continued: "I think they've been waiting for your last ascent. I think they'll move before dawn, now that you're down."

"You want me to sneak back up there and find out?"

"Not sneak, Bryan. This will be a very dangerous ascent on your part. If what I suspect is true, it will be the most important balloon flight ever made."

"Dangerous in what way, sir?" Bryan asked curiously. He had already been shot at, with cannon and Minié balls, and had risked his life dangling beneath a bag of hot air.

"I want you to go up, make sure the Yankees are on the move, and get down in record time; the outcome of this entire battle may hinge on what you find out."

"I'll be back by two o'clock, sir," Bryan replied. He saluted and hurried off.

Jacobson grumbled with purple profanity, in true army style, when Bryan shook him and told him to roll out.

"Gather your crew," he told Jacobson. "We're making another ascent right away!"

Bryan threw a can of kerosene on the fire. The blaze leaped high, forcing him back. Soon the cotton bag was inflating once more. He carefully checked the lines, then swung up into the basket.

"All right, ease off!" he called.

Sleepily, the men began paying out the line, through the pulley. The balloon moved silently skyward into the star-studded night. Bryan watched the black outline of the pine tops drop away. The moon was bright and high.

Suddenly the balloon jerked to a stop. There was a noisy commotion below. Bryan looked down. He could see men running.

Lafe Wilkins' voice cried: "Leggo my damn foot!" By the light of the fire, Bryan saw what was wrong. A coil of rope had fouled around Lafe's foot and yanked him to the ground. He was bouncing across the clearing, dragged toward the squeaking pulley, as the balloon tugged on the rope.

"Look out there!" Jacobson cried out. He grabbed an ax and strode toward the rope.

"Don't, for God's sake!" Bryan shouted down. He was too late. With a flashing stroke, Jacobson severed the rope. The balloon shot skyward, unfettered.

Afraid to cry out, Bryan hurtled upward, spinning around and around so that the whole world seemed to be on a turntable. More than a mile high, he became hopelessly confused as to which was north, south, east, or west.

Higher still he rose, the balloon swelling until smoke began pouring out of the appendix and through the seams. Then, slowly, it began to level off.

Bryan looked down and gasped. The world was a flat panorama of silvery rivers, black forests, and patterns of lights. Gradually things became identifiable to him; he was looking down on the world's mightiest army, drawn up for a terrible, final blow at Richmond, glowing in the distance.

The cold of the high sky cut through Bryan's clothing like a knife. He shuddered. Looking directly below him, he saw that McClellan's army was massing for a dawn attack. He had to get down fast and brief General Johnston. But there was no way to come down. Not until the smoke cooled.

For long minutes, he floated over the Virginia countryside, a virtual prisoner of the sky. He reached for the balloon neck and tugged at it, hoping to rip a seam open. It held. Then, helpless as a baby, he crouched in the wicker basket and watched the world drifting by below him.

It came as a shock that he was now floating out over the York River, nearly four miles wide. He could not swim. In desperation, he drew his Bowie knife and slit the leather of his fine elkhide boots, then kicked them off.

The balloon was dropping now, slowly, toward the river. Hurriedly he unbuttoned his jacket and slipped it off, then loosened his belt and kicked off his pants. He shivered in the cold, but at least, he felt, he might not drown now.

Less than 500 feet from the water a crosscurrent of wind wafted the balloon back toward shore, behind the Union lines. He prayed that, since it was well past midnight, no one would spot him. In the silvery moonlight he saw the shoreline approaching, now only fifty feet below. The anchor rope was trailing across the glassy water.

As the rope touched shore, Bryan threw out his clothing, then clambered naked over the side and began to slide down the rope. He struck the ground just as the balloon crashed into a tall tree. He wound the rope around a branch and hurried back for his clothes.

Barefooted, he trotted across the fields until he came to a road, which he followed for nearly two miles without being discovered. A horse whinnied nearby; he climbed a fence and ran to the animal. Climbing on bareback, he coaxed the animal forward. Even bareback he felt more at home on a horse than he had in the balloon. He cut across the fields through the moonlight, back toward his own lines.

Near the Warwick River, a Union picket stepped suddenly from a thicket and challenged him. "Who goes there?" the husky voice cried.

Bryan did not wait to answer. He raised his revolver and fired. He heard the man groan and saw him fall; then he slid from the horse and took off on foot. He ran lightly along the back road toward Lee's Mill and cut through the swamp. Wading waist-deep through the water, he made his way to the piney woods. There he began to run once more.

Nearing exhaustion, his feet cut and bleeding, Bryan grimly pushed on; time was important now. It was past two o'clock, and General Johnston would be impatiently waiting.

Stumbling at last into the headquarters area, the bedraggled captain rushed toward Johnston's tent and called for the guard.

Stepping inside, he stood before the general, shoeless, wet, and covered with mud. "You were right, General!" he gasped.

"Sit down, Captain," Johnston said. Then, turning his head, "Bring this man some whiskey!"

Balloon Bryan knew, by this gesture, that he had won a promotion.

Johnston smiled, looking at him with pride. "Start at the very beginning, Captain, and leave out nothing."

Bryan related all that had happened, from the moment the rope had hastily been cut, sending him out over the enemy lines, where he could see the great Northern army massing behind the piney woods. He swallowed the whiskey and felt good inside.

"We'll meet their attack here, sir?" he finally asked.

The general smiled. "No, Captain. I have a surprise for Little Mac. We won't be anywhere near here when he strikes at dawn."

Bryan remembered what Johnston had said—the element of surprise. He threw back his head and laughed.

The Union Army, as Johnston predicted, hit at the first gray streak of day. Big siege guns opened first, hammering their deadly barrage across the Warwick. Then came the First Vermonters, leading a great wave of blue-coated infantry, sweeping across the swamp with fixed bayonets.

McClellan was elated. The rebels were offering no resistance to this steamroller attack that had ended the siege of Yorktown. But his elation quickly turned to dismay; Johnston's element of surprise, so carefully planned with Balloon Bryan's help, turned Little Mac's face red with anger. The Confederate guns they had valiantly charged were dummies—wooden logs set on top of the breastworks. There was no enemy!

The Army of Northern Virginia had already pulled back in a masterful strategic withdrawal that has since become a model for military tacticians. Now it was safely dug in on Richmond's perimeter, ready to annihilate the invaders should they choose to press on.

McClellan knew he had been outfoxed. His one big chance to crush the Rebels and bring the bloody conflict to a close was gone. Richmond was safe, and the terrible Civil War would rage on.

The skillful airmanship of Balloon Bryan, the one-man Confederate Air Force, had scored an historic victory with well-timed aerial reconnaissance. The cost: one pair of ruined elk-hide boots.

5

The Daring Young Man
on the Flying Trapeze

PROFESSOR WASHINGTON HARRISON DONALDSON's aneroid barometer hanging on the side of the balloon basket read 5,280 feet, mean sea level.

He sucked in deep draughts of cool, moist air, swept the Massachusetts landscape with a quick gaze, and then got down to the business at hand.

"We are exactly one mile high, Miss Taylor," he said in a voice that betrayed tension. "And you are about to make history!"

Clinging in fright to the rim of the basket beside him, an attractive young woman, attired in a daring costume, gasped and held her hand to her mouth.

"Oh, Professor Donaldson!" she exclaimed, "I'm . . . I'm afraid!"

Donaldson patted her hand. "Don't be alarmed, my dear. Do as I say and I'll get you down in one piece!"

Maggie Taylor, a voluptuous circus bareback rider who had made the mistake of not keeping her feet on the ground, took one look over the side of the balloon basket and lunged into her companion's strong arms, sobbing uncontrollably.

There was nothing like a lady in distress—real or imagined—to give Donaldson's masculine ego a supercharged inflation. His eyes blazed with an inner fire as he drew the girl to him and gently lifted her face to his. Brushing quickly at his mustache, he kissed her.

On that sensuous afternoon, April 19, 1875, Miss Taylor found out that heaven was what you made of it. Whether it was the altitude or her attitude, she found an excitement she'd never experienced bouncing around the circus ring on a Percheron's crupper, while waving gaily to her audience. Up in a balloon, alone with the handsome professor, was heady stuff.

The occasion for this ascension was the centennial of the firing of the "shot heard 'round the world" at Concord Bridge, Massachusetts, where the whole idea of American liberty had exploded in 1775, exactly one mile below where their balloon floated in the sky. With Professor Donaldson, however, the distinction between liberty and liberties was indeed thin.

Lest the frolicsome balloonist be remembered as a gold-spangled cad in an aerialist's tights, it is officially recorded that Donaldson eventually did propose marriage to his lovely companion. That he never lived for the marriage to take place is one of those tragedies of the lusty youth of American stunt piloting.

Not that Donaldson let the grass grow under the drifting shadow of his free balloons, with which he exuberantly rode the wild winds from New York to Chicago on more than 100 exciting ascensions. More often than not he was accompanied by a lass who would discover too late there was no way to walk home.

Not until Donaldson met Maggie Taylor, the prima donna of the equestriennes of old P. T. Barnum's Traveling Hippodrome, was he goaded to delay the tantalizing conquest until he had passed the first milestone in the sky. With others he never reached such heights of ecstasy; a mere 500 feet or so did nicely.

Professor Donaldson's romantic affair with Miss Taylor began four years after he had given up circus life as a tightrope walker to take to the clouds on the afternoon of September 4, 1871, when he had shot skyward from the town square at Reading, Pennsylvania, dangling from a slender trapeze swinging a dozen feet below the suspension ring of a tiny, 26-foot balloon, the *Comet*.

With no safety net below him, Donaldson rode 3,000 feet above the green countryside, thrilling at the sight. The idea had been a challenge, and now he felt a clammy fear for the first time in his life.

He shut his eyes and wiped away beads of cold sweat. Then, as hundreds of townspeople watched from the square down below, he gritted his teeth and toppled over backward.

A horrified scream rose up as the watchers saw the tiny figure tumble, but it ended in a sigh of relief as Donaldson expertly spread his legs and hooked his feet on the ropes. He hung upside down, blowing kisses to the crowd below him. He knew he was in his element at last.

Climbing back onto the trapeze bar, Donaldson had an inspiration; why not string a tightrope between two balloons drifting a mile apart and walk from one to the other? He dismissed the thought; it could wait.

Already Donaldson considered himself to be the world's greatest tightrope walker, possessing a skill exceeding the ability of Jean-François Gravelet Blondin, the French stunt man who crossed the thundering Niagara Falls on a 1,300-foot rope in 1859.

On September 20, 1864, Donaldson actually did surpass Blondin's feat by traversing the Genesee Falls, near Rochester, New York, on a rope 1,800 feet long and 200 feet high, without a misstep. When Blondin retaliated, to save his honor, by cooking an egg while balancing on a tightrope, Donaldson publicly offered to cook, eat, and sleep for a whole week on a tightrope stretched across the Schuylkill River—for a fee, of course.

Such stunts palled for Donaldson eventually, after fourteen years on the tightrope; and when he read about the balloon adventures of a lady aeronaut named Leona Dare, the "Queen of the Antilles," in 1871, he decided to become the original "Man on the Flying Trapeze."

Finishing his high act over Reading, Donaldson now valved a little gas from the *Comet* and began a slow descent. He was still more than 2,000 feet up when something occurred that almost caused a mass heart attack below; as the *Comet* sank slowly in the west, the crowd was shocked to see a figure tumble earthward.

The falling object was a dummy; at the end of a 100-foot cord it jerked to a quick stop. It split apart, showering down thousands of copies of a small bulletin entitled *Balloon Gazette* —the world's first aerial newspaper—in which he had sold $300 worth of advertising space to pay for his ascension.

There was still more excitement for the crowd on that historic venture; Donaldson's gas valve jammed open, and the *Comet* began a wild plunge earthward. The uprush of air turned the gas bag inside out, forming a rude parachute canopy that lowered Donaldson gently into the top branches of a large oak on the edge of town.

Where a saner man would have given up the foolhardy notion of stunting in cloudland after such narrow escapes, Donaldson decided to make a career of performing daring feats higher than any acrobat had ever performed before.

On January 15, 1872, dressed in flesh-colored tights, a purple satin bodice, and blue kid boots, he began a grand tour of the eastern seaboard with a new balloon twice the size of the *Comet*.

Called the *Magenta*, Donaldson's new aerostat made her maiden ascent from Norfolk, Virginia, when he hung by one knee from the trapeze bar and slashed the anchor rope with a sharp knife. Waving gaily, the bareheaded, mustachioed aerobat soared aloft, high above the heads of the crowd.

All went well for a while, until a new danger suddenly shook Donaldson's icy nerve; drifting into a cold front, he found the *Magenta* being swept irresistibly toward the Atlantic Ocean. Added to this terror, the valve rope was immobile; ice had frozen the valve stiff.

Buffeting winds hurled the *Magenta* faster and faster toward the shoreline. Donaldson was aware that he must act swiftly or face drowning, for he could not swim. Holding his knife between his teeth, he clambered up the netting of the swaying balloon and with one stroke slashed it open. There was a rush of hissing gas escaping, and the *Magenta* settled to earth not 100 yards from the surf.

Donaldson's fame spread as, with each crazy new stunt, he courted death time after time but somehow lived; the press called him "that crazy balloonatic."

Death came uncomfortably close on July 4, 1872, when thousands of horrified spectators saw the *Magenta* driven across Chicago and out over the wild waves of Lake Michigan by winds of hurricane force. The balloon dropped lower and lower and, in the distance, was seen to bounce along over the raging whitecaps and collapse. Half drowned, Donaldson made shore somehow and was rescued by passengers pouring from an express train that had ground to a stop when the alert engineer saw the near disaster.

The irrepressible aeronaut was working on a new stunt—riding into the high sky standing on top of his balloon instead of swinging beneath it—when he learned of an even crazier idea. John Wise, a rival balloonist, was planning to cross the Atlantic from New York to Paris by air!

Wise, chief meteorologist at Philadelphia's Franklin Institute, readily agreed to let Donaldson join in the project, on one condition—that he raise enough funds to finance the trip.

As a starter, Donaldson manufactured a paper balloon from 225 yards of wrapping paper and promised to ascend over Reading, Pennsylvania, set the paper bag afire, and descend in a parachute. Sparks set fire to the balloon prematurely, and Donaldson barely got down alive in an emergency jump.

In the summer of 1873, Donaldson and Wise found backers in James H. and Charles Goodsell, publishers of the *New York Daily Graphic,* who realized the tremendous promotional possibilities in a transatlantic balloon crossing.

Donaldson's razzle-dazzle showmanship was too much for Wise, the careful, scientific balloonist. The trapeze artist meant to travel in comfort, regardless of weight. He loaded a lifeboat with an air mattress, table, camp stools, lime stove, a liquid phosphorescent light, thirty days' provisions, guns, fishing tackle, rope and a harmonica. When the inflated balloon, a giant of 600,000 cubic feet capacity, tried to lift the cargo she split her seams. Two days later a second launch attempt aborted for the same reason.

In disgust Wise ended his partnership and gave the whole bag of problems to Donaldson, who by October 6 had cut down the pay load and reduced the balloon's size by half. This time the balloon held.

After the two false starts, the aeronaut, accompanied by two reporters, Alfred Ford and George Ashton Lunt, shoved off from a vacant lot in Brooklyn—destination Paris. Waving champagne bottles and blowing kisses to the ladies in the crowd, the three voyagers headed skyward.

Instead of finding the "river of air" which Wise had promised would be waiting to whisk them to France, the adventurers floated headlong into a black squall line. Helpless as a soap bubble in a maelstrom, the transatlantic balloon bobbled and spun crazily inside a massive thunderhead that pelted it with big hailstones and finally spewed it out to crash-land at New Canaan, Connecticut.

As a newspaper promotion the flight was a fizzle, but one shrewd reader saw tremendous possibilities in what the handsome young balloonist had to offer. He was Phineas T. Barnum, the veteran showman, who was putting together his "Greatest Show on Earth" at Madison Square in New York.

To house his "Great Roman Hippodrome and Politechnic Institute," Barnum rebuilt the old Harlem and New Haven Railroad Depot into a glamorous showplace, which he called Madison Square Garden.

When Barnum's Hippodrome opened to a packed house on April 27, 1874, Donaldson stood in the crowd, mouth agape, watching the Roman chariot races with gorgeous ladies driving teams of two, four, and six horses. But he snorted in disgust at the French trapeze artiste, Henri Joignerey; this man was a mere exhibitionist, performing indoors in the light of 2,000 gas jets.

Leaping from his seat, Donaldson dashed across the sawdust-covered stage and confronted Barnum. "You, sir, have the greatest show on earth!" he cried, "but I have the greatest show above it!"

The interruption amused Barnum; he already knew about Donaldson, and in fact meant to look him up. His eyes twinkling, Barnum grabbed Donaldson's hand and pumped it.

"Welcome to the Hippodrome!" he boomed. From then on, Donaldson would perform his thrilling aerial feats in the sky above the Garden, to lure the suckers, one of whom, Barnum maintained, was born every minute.

When Barnum's Hippodrome hit the road on seventy flatcars and in half a dozen Pullman coaches, Donaldson and his balloon went along as its featured attraction. And it was then that he discovered that Barnum's immortal line about suckers applied to the ladies as well. Once he got them up in his balloon for a look around, they did not come down until he had decided they were ready.

Playing Pittsburgh, Donaldson made headlines by taking aloft a wedding party of six persons, including Mary Elizabeth Walsh, an equestrienne, the bride; Charley Colton, an acrobat, the groom; the Reverend Howard B. Jeffries; and three nervous witnesses. It was history's first airborne wedding, and the whole thing gave Maggie Taylor an idea.

For months, Donaldson had been giving the lovely bareback rider the big rush act—both in the sky and on the ground—but her suggestions of marriage were brushed off. Now she confronted him with the success of the Colton-Walsh nuptials; he finally agreed to a June wedding, but in the meantime meant to sow his wild oats.

Thus began Donaldson's second effort to prove himself a man, a motivation that has driven a sizable number of otherwise contented individuals to tempt fate by taking up aerial stunting. Faced with the imminence of marriage, not death, Donaldson's balloon brinksmanship continued in an amorous vein at Allentown, Pennsylvania, early in 1874, upon meeting a pretty, brown-eyed young school teacher who told him of a remarkable dream she had had the night before.

"I saw myself up in your balloon, high above the world," she related excitedly at a Town Hall meeting. "You and I were alone together, and I was throwing down bags of ballast. But I awoke and found myself sitting on the headboard, throwing pillows to the floor!"

They both laughed and Donaldson patted her hand. "My dear," he said gallantly, "why not let me make that dream come true?"

Soon he and the school teacher were soaring high over the rooftops, and the townspeople heard the girl's laughter floating down from above. Shortly they were startled to see her bonnet come sailing earthward, and then a shoe. The shocked Quakers of the countryside slammed their doors and bolted their shutters. Donaldson's balloon landed after dark in a distant wood, and by dawn Allentown's gossips had the poor girl running home through the streets without a stitch on.

Donaldson, in fact, was too much the gentleman to let such a thing happen; he had loaned her his topcoat.

One of Donaldson's wildest rides with female passengers took place on Friday, October 23, 1874, according to his biographer, a Chicago dentist named Dr. M. L. Amick, who in 1875 posthumously published the amazing balloonist's diary. Celebrating his 100th ascension, Donaldson took aloft not one beauty but four, Dr. Amick blushingly reported. They were Agnes Pitman, Eva Ludwig, Laura Leaman, and Ella Jenifer, all from Cincinnati, Ohio.

After a pleasant afternoon of drifting over the green countryside in the company of his charmers, Donaldson suddenly frowned; a giant cumulo-nimbus storm cloud was building up over the western horizon and moving rapidly toward them.

Lightning stabbed the sky and peals of thunder shook the balloon's gas bag ominously. Before Donaldson could valve off sufficient gas to descend, the rain squall struck; sheets of water drenched the party to the skin, and large hailstones pelted Donaldson, as if the gods were angry at his effrontery in turning the grandeur of the heavens into a place of revelry.

The following summer, Donaldson moved his base of operations to the Hippodrome grounds in a Chicago suburb, where he made his last ascent with the lovely Maggie Taylor. High over the Windy City he held his betrothed close and kissed her passionately while the balloon slowly turned about.

There in the high sky, feeling the exhilaration of the rarefied air, Donaldson's blood coursed hotly, and, according to Dr. Amick, Maggie must have responded eagerly. By nightfall, flushed and laughing, she stepped from the balloon looking for all the world as if she had been in heaven.

Maggie Taylor's initiation into the Mile High Club of Washington Harrison Donaldson came none too soon; on July 15, 1875, the balloonist made his last ascension from Chicago, one destined to end in disaster.

Less than a fortnight before their wedding date, Miss Taylor gave Donaldson a worried kiss and watched him soar off toward the north, accompanied by a reporter, Newton D. Grimwood of the *Chicago Evening Journal*. Grimwood had drawn straws for the ride with a rival reporter, James Maitland of the *Chicago Post & Mail*; he was anxious to write a colorful feature story on ballooning with the popular showman. It would be Grimwood's last—and greatest—story.

In the late afternoon, Maggie Taylor watched the small dot in the sky that was her fiancé's balloon, the *P.T. Barnum V*, drifting languidly toward Lake Michigan. A rising wind began to accelerate it, and by six-thirty rain started falling. Thunder and lightning turned the sky into a sudden battleground of the elements, as cold Canadian air churned with moist, hot tropical winds from the Gulf of Mexico.

Soon the balloon disappeared, but Maggie refused to leave her post. Alone in the black of night, she knelt and prayed for her lover's safe return. At seven o'clock, far to the north, some 30 miles off Grosse Point, the skipper of the lake steamer *Little Guide* was startled to see a balloon bouncing across the wild waves. He changed course to pursue it, but it soon vanished behind a veil of rain and scud. He logged the incident, the last time the *P.T. Barnum V* was ever seen. Newton Grimwood's bloated body washed ashore one month later, near Stony Creek.

In a pocket was found his notebook, in which he had written his epitaph:

"Professor Donaldson seems to be a very pleasant gentleman, although a philosopher and an aeronaut. . . . I cannot help reflecting that if we fall, we fall like Lucifer, out of the heavens, and that upon our arrival on earth, or rather upon the water—for we are over the middle of Lake Michigan—we would literally be dead. . . ."

Donaldson's body was never recovered.

For Maggie Taylor there was only despair, although she found some solace, singing softly under the stars at night, from the words of her lover's favorite ballad:

> . . . *His movements were graceful, all girls he did please,*
> *And my love he's purloined away . . .*

6

Taking Lessons from the Birds

OH, SHE WAS LOVELY, the *Santa Clara,* as she sat in the morning sunshine, her graceful wings of oiled muslin spread like a dragonfly's as it rested on a honeysuckle vine.

Daniel Maloney walked around her, reverently—for the Reverend Father Robert E. Kenna, S.J., had just blessed this wonderful flying machine of Professor John J. Montgomery, whose brilliant mind had conceived her lines, and whose hands had fashioned her from hickory sticks, cloth, and wire.

Jauntily, Maloney leaped into the saddle, as if he were mounting a fine stallion. Ahead and behind him spread her 24-foot tandem wings; behind the wings hung her X-shaped tail.

Nearby, a hot-air balloon tugged at her moorings; a line ran to the *Santa Clara.*

Professor Montgomery fussed with the rigging like an old maid with a kitten.

"Remember, Daniel," he cautioned, "you'll be going like sixty! Be very careful you don't tip over!"

Maloney laughed, swinging his feet gaily and waving to the crowd of 15,000 spectators jamming the Santa Clara Fair Grounds. He, too, was a splendid sight in his bright scarlet tights, blue sash, and soft, blue satin slippers. Across his back were embroidered the letters, PROFESSOR LASCALLES.

"I just may not come down, Professor, if she's all you say she is!"

"No tricks, now, Daniel," Montgomery repeated, as he stepped back and signaled the ground crew to release the balloon.

Gently the *Santa Clara* lifted from the ground, a 42-pound masterpiece of engineering the world had scoffed at, but one which Daniel Maloney was about to demonstrate as history's pioneer heavier-than-air stunt pilot.

Soaring higher and higher beneath the smoking aerostat, Maloney was completely at home. A veteran hot-air balloonist and parachute jumper, he loved the freedom of the sky, where he was king. He was, as the colorful posters advertised, "Taking Lessons From the Birds."

A devout Catholic, Montgomery kneeled, hat in hand, to lead the crowd in a prayer for God's blessing, as the *Santa Clara* grew smaller and smaller on its journey into the bright morning sky.

Sunlight glinting on its wings, the frail craft suddenly spun around, then dropped away from the balloon. Astride the glider's saddle, Maloney had cut the rope; and now he was plunging earthward in a steep dive. Below him, the Santa Clara Valley spun dizzily as he spiraled down from an altitude of 4,000 feet, the highest man had yet gone in a heavier-than-air machine.

The wind tore at his hair and tears streamed back from his eyes; and Daniel Maloney howled with excitement, leaning from side to side to lead the *Santa Clara* through corkscrew turns to the right and left. Montgomery had given strict instructions on how he thought the ship should be flown. But he, Daniel Maloney, was the pilot, not Montgomery! The sky was his! He was achieving what he had always dreamed of—flying like a bird!

Three quarters of a mile away from the Santa Clara Fair Grounds lay an open field; Maloney could see the tiny specks of men rushing toward it. By prearrangement, he was to land there, safely away from the crowds. He bent the craft around in a steep turn, then dropped its nose in another steep dive that made the wires scream. He leaned back and felt the nose come up above the horizon. Then he settled down into a gentle spiral and volplaned easily over a row of eucalyptus trees.

Professor Montgomery ran into the middle of the field, waving his arms. Maloney headed for him in a flat glide, pulled up at the last second, and stalled in over the inventor's head. He landed lightly on his feet, running.

Stepping from the *Santa Clara*, Maloney ran to Montgomery and embraced him, tears in his eyes.

"Beautiful, Professor!" he sobbed. "It was just beautiful!"

A new science was born that happy day, April 29, 1905—the science of aerobatics. Or was it an art? Man had suddenly grown wings, and what Daniel Maloney had done was prove that man had the inherent skill, the artistry, to soar with a newfound freedom, defying gravity with irresponsible disdain for hidden dangers, for violent death that lay waiting in the shadows of his artificial wings.

Death beckoned always, with its shrieking siren call, to those pilots sailing high above the Loreleis who would lure them down, back into the clay. Maloney heard the call in the singing wires of the *Santa Clara*, and tragically was seduced by it. Montgomery, too, listened, and followed. . . .

Who was the first? The Wright brothers in 1903? Lilienthal in 1890? Montgomery in 1884? Go back through time, into history, into legend, to Daedalus and Icarus . . . to the Wizard Osmene . . . to Kai Kaios, King of Persia . . . to Da Vinci, the Great One.

Or to Melville M. Murrell, a farm kid tinkering with his father's tools in a big barn near Panther Springs, on the Knoxville-Bristol coach road, deep in the hills of Tennessee.

Birds can fly; why not Melville Murrell? Hell, gimme some scrap iron and canvas, Dad! I got me somethin' in my head I got to build! Dad, oh Dad, I think I can fly!

It was in 1877—August 14—that the United States Patent Office granted the twenty-two-year-old lad official recognition for his brainstorm, "Improvement in Aerial Navigators." You sit in this seat, see? And push your feet against this crossbar here; and that makes the wings go up and down, like a bird's!

Would it fly?

"Sure it flew!" says Melville's son, William. "Pappy flew it three times, right over the apple orchard!"

What he flew was not exactly what he patented; a photo in the family album shows that it looked more like a canard-type monoplane glider with a jazzed-up tail, and a rope in front to launch it. The fact is, Melville never claimed he beat the Wrights; he turned to God, and for forty-five years he rode circuit through the mountains where the blue grass and the smoky hills blended with towering clouds that he loved to watch—clouds where the birds soared. . . . If God had meant man to have wings, he would have given him wings.

Let the other damn fools kill themselves!

Five-year-old John J. Montgomery loved to lie on his back in the tall grass behind a fence at the rear of his grandmother's farm in Oakland, California, counting chicken flaps—how many times a chicken flapped its wings as it struggled squawking over the fence, chased by John's laughing sisters.

The chickens went into the stew pot, and John turned to kites. Kites are tied to earth by a string; he was searching for freedom, escape from earth. He found it when he was twenty-five, in a blacksmith shop on his father's ranch at Otay, California, near the Mexican border. He built his first man-carrying glider there, in 1883.

Of course, the neighbors laughed at the crazy Montgomery kid; so he and Jim, his younger brother, tried it out one morning at 3 o'clock, when a damp sea breeze rustled up a slope to where they stood facing the wind, the sky, and God. Jim held a rope; and when John got up his nerve, they ran down the slope together, into the wind, and suddenly, beautifully, he was airborne! Breathlessly he soared over Jim's upturned face, wobbling down the slope to land 200 yards away.

They wrecked the glider, finally, because John did not really know how to fly. So he started all over, at the beginning, with studies of birds' wings, their construction, their curves, their flexibility. It became compulsive, this dream of learning from the birds. When he accepted the chair of physics at Santa Clara University, he began putting his notes in order.

By 1905, Professor Montgomery knew he had all the aerodynamics worked out. All he needed now was money to build a powered version of the *Santa Clara* tandem glider, which Daniel Maloney had demonstrated so beautifully with the April 29 flight; the noted engineer Octave Chanute had enthusiastically called that "the most daring feat ever attempted!"

Up and down the state, Montgomery put on an amazing series of demonstrations to raise funds for his continued experiments. In his entourage were five hot-air balloons and one gas aerostat, half a dozen tandem gliders, and three "graduate" stunt pilots: Maloney, David Wilkie, and another balloonist named Defalco.

Carefully, scientifically, Montgomery trained these pioneer stunt men in history's first aerobatic school at Santa Clara. He would write: "In some of these first flights, the aeroplane did little more than settle in the air. But as the rider gained experience in each successive flight, I changed the adjustments, giving him more liberty of action, so he could obtain longer flights and more varied movements. But in none of them did I have the adjustments so that the rider had full liberty, as I did not consider that they had the requisite knowledge and experience necessary for their safety. . . ."

Maloney, Wilkie, and Defalco did not like this restraint. On each flight they forced Montgomery's nimble acrobatic gliders to the limit of their controls.

"The reckless parachute jumpers were ready to try anything," the professor admitted. "On one occasion, Maloney pressed very hard upon the stirrup which gives a screw shape to the wings and made a side somersault. The course of the machine was very much like one turn of a corkscrew. After this movement, the machine continued on its regular course.

"Wilkie, not to be outdone, told his friends he would do the same in a subsequent flight and made two somersaults, one in one direction and one in the other; then he made a steep dive and a long glide and, when about 300 feet in the air, brought the aeroplane to a sudden stop and settled to earth. . . ."

In the modern sense, these breath-catching gyrations of Daniel Maloney and David Wilkie were history's first true aerobatic maneuvers, displaying a reckless daring in execution by forcing their frail craft to the limits of their endurance. Unlike modern precision aerobatics, Maloney's corkscrew somersaults and Wilkie's death dive, as it came to be known, were not preplanned. They were, rather, the result of trial-and-error control movements made deliberately "to see what would happen."

Unfortunately for Maloney, who wore no parachute on his stunt flights, there was no precedent on which to set a limit. Montgomery, watching him perform on his aerial stage with chilling disregard for his own safety, finally decided to re-rig the *Santa Clara* "so as to allow only straight sailing or only long curves in turning."

Despite the chances they took, the band of daredevil glider pilots cheated death for long months until, late in 1905, tragedy overtook them. Determined to demonstrate his skill before a group of friends, Maloney declared he would show them "the most sensational flight they ever heard of."

Wrote Montgomery: "As the balloon was rising with the aeroplane, a guy rope dropped, switching around the right wing and breaking the tower that braced the two rear wings and which·also gave control over the tail.

"We shouted to Maloney that the machine was broken but he probably did not hear us as he was at the time saying: 'Hurrah for Montgomery's airship!' and as the break was behind him he may not have detected it.

"When the machine started on its flight, the rear wings commenced to flap, thus indicating that they were loose, and the machine turned on its back. . . ."

Cries of horror reached Maloney's ears as the broken wings of the *Santa Clara* fluttered helplessly toward earth. He struggled to right the craft, but now it was beyond control. Montgomery and his assistants ran to where Maloney struck the ground with a sickening thud. He died thirty minutes later.

"The only mark on his body was a scratch from a wire on the side of his neck," the anguished professor recalled. "The six attending physicians were puzzled at the cause of his death. This is remarkable for a vertical descent of more than two thousand feet."

Montgomery's bad luck continued the next year, when he prepared to launch a glider from a rope sling 4,000 feet up the side of Mount Hamilton, near Lick Observatory; on April 18, 1906, while the professor was adjusting the wire stays of his new machine, the mountain suddenly rumbled and shook with a frightful swaying motion that brought his workshop crashing down on the flying machine, destroying both. It was the great earthquake that also destroyed San Francisco.

In 1911, Montgomery returned to his gliding experiments, determined to do the piloting himself. On October 31, he took off from a wooden track atop a 600-foot hill near Evergreen, California. Two assistants, Cornelius Reinhardt and J. C. Vierra, shoved the glider downhill on wheels, then watched the professor sail skyward. When he was at an altitude of 30 feet, they saw him suddenly release the controls and slump to one side, apparently ill. The craft nosed up, hung motionless, and then fell off into a tight spiral dive, crashing headlong to the ground. Montgomery stepped out, pale but smiling; twenty minutes later he died.

7

The California Flying Fool

A SMOKING, struggling wood-and-wire biplane clawed its way up into the cold, windy sky on the crisp fall afternoon of October 7, 1913, high above the crowd gathered at Curtiss Field near Hammondsport, New York.

Balanced precariously on the lower front wing spar, like a monkey on a stick, squatted the undersized figure of an intense young man, shivering from exposure in the icy wind blast. At 2,000 feet above the shore of Lake Keuka, the great Lincoln Beachey was on stage again after a six-month retirement; he had sworn he would never fly again when the press blamed him for the shocking rise in airplane fatalities among amateur birdmen who tried to imitate his amazing aerobatic feats. They called him—derisively—the California Flying Fool, but everyone knew that Linc Beachey was the greatest of them all, the world's nonpareil stunt pilot.

Staring down between his boots, pressed firmly on the nose-wheel axle, Beachey studied the row of hangars below; people were clambering over the roofs. He knew why they were there —why they stood craning their necks at his awkward Curtiss pusher. He swung savagely into a steep turn, forcing the world and the crowd to spin about.

Beachey was going to loop the loop—something that no pilot in America had ever attempted—or break his neck trying. And for the first time in his career, America's greatest aviator was as jittery as a jay bird.

He set his jaw angrily, adjusted his goggles tighter, and tested his harness straps. If the Frenchman Adolphe Pegoud could fly through a loop, by God, so could he! It did not matter to Beachey that Pegoud had used a specially built aerobatic ship, powered with a Gnome rotary engine that could run upside down as well as right side up. He would loop a barn door if he had enough power!

Beachey closed his eyes and nosed over into a stomach-tightening steep dive, picking up speed. The rushing wind sang a high-pitched wail through the wires and tore at his face, forcing his lips open. He grabbed futilely for his backward-turned checkered flying cap; it flew off and disappeared in the blur of the propeller directly behind him.

He was about to haul back on the controls when a sudden premonition of disaster flashed through his mind. He could still call it off; but down there, he knew, the crowd would be yelling hysterically, pointing at him and betting he would not make it. Beachey hated crowds even more than he feared death. These were conflicting emotions, but he resolved them with an impulsive tug on the wheel.

He felt the wings strain and bend. His arms were heavy as the biplane zoomed upward, standing on its tail, the propeller fighting desperately against gravity. The horizon flashed past Beachey's vision, and then he was staring at a fleecy cloud that would not go away.

Linc held the wheel back in his lap, against the biplane's wild shuddering, until his arms ached. He simply hung suspended in the sky, coasting to a stop. The shuddering became a terrifying shaking; a flying wire snapped with the sound of a gunshot. He was poised on the brink of a vicious whipstall. He knew from experience that if he didn't get over the top of the loop the ship would slip backward in a killing tail slide and come apart in mid-air. A dozen pilots already had died that way.

It was now or never; Beachey, at the last second before disaster, spun the rudder wheel and leaned against the shoulder yoke; he half-rolled over into a breathtaking stall turn, once more in full command of his ship, diving back toward the field and hurling cusswords into the screaming wind. Once again Lincoln Beachey's incredible flying skill had saved his life.

Until Beachey began doing the impossible with a flying machine, birdmen had been satisfied to stagger about the sky, mechanically yanking levers to go up, down, or sideways. It was Beachey who invented flying with a powered aircraft as an art. He seemed to have been born with a sensitive coordination that might have helped him to become a violinist, or a sculptor, or a poet. He chose flying instead.

Linc Beachey was an artist in the sky, and more; he was America's greatest stunt pilot, an aerial toreador who battled in daily combat with an unpredictable enemy—the invisible, ever-restless atmosphere. Airport crowds, like those who attended bullfights, came to see blood and death. Yet, if he hated the crowds, he needed them as well—the 20 million shrieking spectators, who hailed him as their favorite hero, back in an age before the Eddie Rickenbackers and Billy Bishops and Manfred von Richthofens. The crowds fed Beachey's enormous ego, and at the same time sharpened what aviation psychologists today call the compulsive death wish.

As a schoolboy, Lincoln Beachey had been inordinately fat, the butt of jokes, laughed at by the other boys and teased by the girls. He simply *had* to become a hero. But to hold on to that dizzy pinnacle of success without falling, he was in perpetual conflict with three negative forces—the sky, the crowds, and lastly, himself. With uncanny skill, he mastered the sky; but the struggle that went on between the crowds and his ego continued through his life, an unrelenting tug of war. He was swept up in a fatalistic pursuit of death, sure to come on fabric wings, sooner or later. . . .

On this day, high over Hammondsport, he had cheated death by his own quick thinking; but the crowd was still there, crying for blood. For the first time, Beachey let his emotions get the best of reason. Eyes narrowed, he bit his lip, shoved the controls forward, and plunged vertically toward the airport in his much publicized Dive of Death—a screaming drop from the sky, like an eagle's attack on a paralyzed hare. Many times he had sent the crowds tumbling pell-mell from the bleachers as he roared down on them, only to zoom upward scant inches from catastrophe. This time, with the failure of his loop stinging his ego, he would really show them—he would roll the wheels over the hangar's tin roof!

Four tiny figures loomed larger in his watery eyes, as he dove closer and closer. They were waving him to go away. The Curtiss biplane whined on down, until Beachey recognized them— two student Army pilots, Lieutenants Bellinger and Richardson, and the pretty Hildreth sisters, Ruth and Dorothy.

Linc's lips pulled back in a bloodless grin; although he had not flown for months, he would show them why the press called him the Flying Fool! Closing in now at nearly a mile a minute, Beachey felt elated to see the four figures turn and try to escape by jumping off the roof, in panic. . . . Now it was time to pull out. He eased back—too late! The hangar roof rushed up at him; he struck it with a splintering crash.

His right wing tip snagged something; Beachey glanced at it and saw with a shock a sight he would never forget; Ruth Hildreth's torn body flying crazily through the air. In the next instant, he crashed to the ground.

Beachey felt agonizing pain; his legs twisted beneath his body, but miraculously the biplane cartwheeled away and left him lying dazed, staring at the crowd. They ignored him; they were rushing to see the lifeless body of Ruth Hildreth.

Staggering to his feet, Beachey pushed through the crowd, his face ashen. His mechanic, Arthur H. Nix, was bending over the girl. He touched Nix's shoulder.

"Is she all right?" Linc breathed, almost pleading.

Nix silently shook his head. He stood up and turned to face Beachey, his eyes moist. "She's dead, Linc. You killed her!"

Beachey turned away, feeling sick. He went behind the hangar and vomited. There was no guilt feeling inside him, only a loathing, a hatred of the sea of upturned faces that had lured him to go too far.

Death had hovered around Lincoln Beachey from the very start of his career; he first saw a man die in a crack-up when he was standing on the dirt track at Dominguez Field, Los Angeles. It had been the closing day of the world's first International Aviation Meet, December 31, 1910. Beachey, a stocky, twenty-three-year-old dirigible aeronaut, was concerned over a gusty Santa Ana wind that had sprung up; any pilot who would fly in such a wind was crazy, he was thinking.

The only birdman crazy enough to be up at that moment was the incomparable Arch Hoxsey, whom Beachey watched with admiration and a touch of envy. Hoxsey, a Wright Exhibition Team flyer, had just established an unofficial world altitude record by climbing more than 2 miles—to 11,474 feet. The feat was considered nothing more than a "stunt"; for, after all, what sense was there in going that high? Commented the conservative *Los Angeles Times* the next day, "The altitude record is high enough for any practical purpose. In fact, it is *too* high, experts say."

As Beachey looked on, Hoxsey buzzed low over the field, preparing to land. A sudden gust of wind uptilted a wing; trying to level the ship, Hoxsey stalled at 500 feet above the ground. The Wright biplane plunged uncontrollably earthward and piled up in a heap of twisted wood and wire, almost at Beachey's feet.

The crash tore from Hoxsey the honor of having officially flown higher than any other human in a heavier-than-air machine, for it demolished the barograph before the Aero Club of America's observer, Professor Harry La Verne Twining, could check its calibration.

Professor Twining was deeply shocked at Hoxsey's death, for he had helped organize the aviation meet at Dominguez Field. A controversial figure, he had once made headlines by killing mice to discover whether they possessed a soul—he claimed they must have, because "they appear to lose weight immediately upon expiring."

An engineering instructor at Polytechnic High School, in Los Angeles, Professor Twining was a sort of black sheep among the faculty because of his interest in flying machines—he once built an ornithopter that beat its wings fifty-two times a minute when he pumped a lever, but it never got off the ground, except for a short leap or two. With another Aero Club of California member, W. S. Eaton, he later built a Blériot-type monoplane that did fly, but that crashed ignominiously on its first landing. Eaton later designed and built a special racer for Beachey, who stood beside Twining, stunned, when Hoxsey crashed.

The crowd had killed Hoxsey, Beachey thought angrily; they had yelled for him to fly against his better judgment, and he had paid for it with his life. Beachey heard a thundering roar, like a crashing surf. He looked up in disbelief to see the crowd surging onto the field, moaning, crying, fighting to get to the wreckage. He and Al Hazzard, Hoxsey's mechanic, grabbed pieces of splintered struts and flailed into the crowd, clubbing down a dozen men before mounted police galloped in.

He was sickened to see a panting woman pull a bloody splinter from Hoxsey's body and retreat with the grisly thing clutched above her head, shrieking: "Look—blood!"

Beachey knew then there was a fortune in flying machines; dirigibles were passé. The spectators wanted speed . . . action . . . sudden death! If that was what they wanted, he would become the world's greatest aviator and clip the crowds for all they were worth. But to cheat death, he had to invent a brand-new system of flying. He meant never to get caught short as had Hoxsey, whose death, the thirty-fifth in the seven short years of the mechanical Air Age, was pointless and preventable.

Beachey went to see Glenn Curtiss, after Wilbur Wright had refused to accept the headstrong young California dirigible pilot as an exhibition flyer. It was there he won his wings, as a protégé of the Curtiss Thirteen Troupe of death-defying cloud-slicers, who included some of the nation's topflight aerobatic men—men like Eugene Ely, Charley Hamilton, Al Shriver,

Hugh Robinson, and Jack McCurdy. By the time he had made the team, Linc had busted up only three of Curtiss' ships.

Robinson claimed that Beachey really was an inept pupil. Perhaps he was trying too hard, or maybe his early years as a rubber-cow jockey had given him wrong ideas about flying. At San Francisco, early in 1911, Beachey did his level best to emulate the aerial contortions of his mentors, who were thrilling the crowds with such maneuvers as Dutch rolls, zooms, and death dips. He did fairly well, but landing was something else; airplanes did not behave like dirigibles. His landings were spectacular controlled crashes.

In desperation, Robinson took Linc aside one day for a fatherly talk. "Linc," he said gently, "you're trying too hard! Don't let the ship fly you; you've got to fly it! Be part of it!"

Beachey recalled what Robinson had said when he staggered off the ground the next day to practice ocean rolls, buzzing low over the field, dipping his wings left and right. Suddenly, at 500 feet over the far end of the field, his engine quit. Beachey instinctively grabbed the wheel tightly and yanked back. The ship stalled and began to fall.

Beachey remembered what had happened to Hoxsey; the afterimage of the falling Wright pusher was a living scar on his mind. He acted on instinct, doing the opposite of what Hoxsey had done; he shoved the wheel full forward, diving toward what looked like certain disaster!

The crowd gasped, but Beachey did not hear this time; his whole body was straining for the solid feel of the wind on the controls to return with his experimental stall recovery. Close to the ground he found it, the viselike grip of fast air, the controls solid in his hands, responsive to the singing airflow!

With a tingle of excitement along his stiffened back, Beachey swung the ship around into the freshening Pacific breeze; he was soaring now, a great canvas gull, swooping and darting over the grandstand, wires whistling in the wind. Grinning broadly, he shoved the nose down and dove toward the crowd, watching them scurry for cover. He drove the biplane along inches above their heads, then banked around, cut the throttle, and set her down lightly as a feather in front of the judge's box. The crowd thundered approval; Beachey, the California Flying Fool, was on his way to stardom.

From that moment, Linc began to discover new things about airplanes that others had overlooked. When the popular Eugene Ely dropped from the sky to his death in a flat spin, Beachey wanted to know why. He climbed deliberately above the clouds and forced his ship into a flat spin to see what happened.

At first, the biplane began its dizzy dive toward the cloud layer, which became a sickening blur before his eyes. Linc raised the nose and leaned back; the ship spun faster and faster, seeming to drop like a rock. He was in the flat spin. He had a brief moment of fear that he might not get out. Then he began experimenting with the controls. At first, nothing happened; the spin seemed to become even wilder. Then, shifting his weight and slamming the controls against the turn with full force, he felt the spin slow and finally blend into a shallow dive. He tried it once more, and knew he had conquered it.

If Beachey heard of another birdman performing a new maneuver, he not only duplicated it, he improved upon it. By the time the Curtiss Thirteen was ready for the 1911 spring road show season at San Diego, Los Angeles, Miami, and Havana, Beachey had overnight become a headliner.

Bill Pickens, a shrewd exploitation man who had himself graduated from the balloon school of acronautics, saw a golden future ahead for the San Francisco stunt flyer.

"There's a million dollars waiting for you, Linc!" Pickens cried enthusiastically when they first met. He lit up a Havana cigar and winked. "The woman doesn't live, son, who wouldn't fall for you!"

Perhaps it was the promise of sudden wealth that made Beachey decide to team with Pickens, or maybe it was the memory of the schoolgirls who had made life so miserable for him. Whatever it was, Pickens and Beachey became the nation's greatest combination in the mushrooming barnstorming business. Beachey was to accumulate such wealth that today no one can guess what his actual earnings amounted to; Pickens wisely handled the books, to keep the free-spending Beachey from throwing it all away.

And if Linc had known how to handle women with the same finesse with which he flew, his life would have been far happier. He married in haste, overcome by the charms of a nineteen-year-old beauty who lured the flyboy into a new realm of adventure. The marriage failed, and Beachey was careful not to make the same mistake again.

With Pickens' urging, Beachey cached his growing fortune in safety deposit boxes across the country; the trouble was that he kept no accurate records of where all the boxes were. Today a sizable estate is probably gathering dust somewhere between Bangor and Balboa.

Earning up to $5,000 a flight, Beachey came to have little regard for money. It was a way to have a whale of a good time, if he felt like relaxing from the strain of his stunt work; but for him there was no substitute for the excitement of flying. At least, the way he did it. Cigar-chewing Bill Pickens might dream up new stunts for Linc to perform, but it was Beachey who figured out how to execute them.

On May 5, 1911, Beachey startled the world by carrying out a promise to go over Niagara Falls in a flying machine. Away with barrels; Linc was going to fly smack into the awesome mist-shrouded gorge, defying reports that it was a "death trap loaded with air pockets, vortexes and down trends," waiting to dash him to pieces.

While thousands of spectators watched from the bridge and along the rim of the falls, Linc came streaking down the river and shot over the edge of American Falls, then plunged down into the blinding spray, to the horror of shrieking honeymooners. Seconds later he emerged, wings glistening in the sun, to continue on down the gorge, dipping his nose wheel into the whirlpool rapids and buzzing beneath the great suspension bridge.

From coast to coast, Beachey thrilled more thousands who paid to watch the Flying Fool dive under power lines, bounce his wheels over rooftops, flutter earthward in a falling leaf, or plunge suicidally in his famed vertical Dive of Death.

Then, one windy day in Chicago, Beachey got a rude shock. He was tired of leaving his tire marks from one end of Michigan Boulevard to the other, forcing frightened automobilists onto the sidewalks, and scattering wagons and dogs and children before his wild onslaughts; he wanted to do something different, like setting a new altitude record.

Pickens called a press conference to announce the attempt, but he was interrupted by Dan MacGregor of the *News*.

"Linc, I've got some news for you," MacGregor said.

"Talk to me later," Beachey snapped irritably. He had little interest in what others were doing.

"You'd better read this," MacGregor said grimly. He shoved a sheet of yellow teletype paper at him. Linc read it and paled. The report was brief:

"Twenty-two aviators have lost their lives attempting to imitate the feats of Lincoln Beachey, the self-styled California Flying Fool. Latest victim is Rutherford Page, the well-known sportsman and Yale graduate, who yesterday crashed to his death in Los Angeles after boasting that he would 'show Beachey a thing or two he has never heard of.' "

MacGregor grabbed the sheet back. "What about this, Beachey? Don't you think you've gone far enough?"

When Beachey flushed and turned angrily to leave, the reporter grabbed his arm. "Look, son; my city editor said to be sure to ask that before you go up today, so we'll have a good story in case you kill yourself!"

"I'll answer your question when I get back!" Linc retorted.

The wind felt cool on his face as Beachey climbed into the cold sky above Chicago; he was bitter toward the world. Now they were blaming him for every damn fool birdman who had risked his life and lost because he had not figured things out the way Beachey had.

At 11,575 feet, Beachey's engine finally sputtered and quit, out of gas. He had beaten the late Arch Hoxsey's record by a good 1,500 feet. He nosed down in a screaming dead-stick vertical dive, bottomed out in a zoom and a wingover, and dropped in for a spot landing, where the reporters were waiting.

"All right, you wanted a story!" Beachey cried. "Go tell your damned editors I'm through with flying! I just set a world altitude record and there's not a man alive I can't outfly, but I'll not take the blame for the carelessness of others!"

Pickens ran after Beachey, yelling over his shoulder: "He doesn't mean it! You just got him stirred up, that's all!" He was too late; Linc had made his mind up, and the reporters already were running for the telephones. It was a banner story—the incomparable Lincoln Beachey was quitting.

Pickens tried to smooth it over, as he trotted along beside Beachey, leaving the field. "You can't stop now, Linc! It's in your blood! You belong up there! You're gonna keep right on flying until you die!"

Pickens wished he had not said that; he knew it was the truth, and he loved Linc like a son. The roar of the crowds, the song of the wind, and the ever-present lure of female companionship were too much for Beachey. The flyer finally grinned and said, "All right, you fat so-and-so! Now get me out of this mess!" He would go on flying just to please Pickens, but he would not forget what MacGregor had said—that twenty-two men were dead because they had tried to emulate him. Secretly he made up his mind to something else; he began studying the reports of those twenty-two fatal accidents to discover what had gone wrong. That way, he felt, maybe he could make it up to them; they would not have died in vain.

It became startlingly clear to Lincoln Beachey what was happening, why one birdman after another was crashing to his death attempting even mild aerobatic maneuvers. Excitedly, he got Pickens out of bed one night in a Los Angeles hotel and showed him a sheet of paper with sketches of falling airplanes all over it.

"I've got it, Bill! Look here!" he cried. Pickens rubbed the sleep from his eyes and tried to understand, but it was all too much for the publicity man. "If you say so, Linc, it's so! I believe you! Now will you go back to bed and let me get some sleep?"

The next day, Beachey was climbing his ship to 5,000 feet,

high above a stratus layer lying along the Malibu coastline, where nothing could happen to anyone on the ground if things went wrong. He was thinking back to San Francisco, to the first time his engine had quit in the sky, and to what he had done to stay alive.

Fighting back his inner excitement, Linc reached behind and switched off the engine. The air was suddenly quiet, only the wail of the wind in the wires. He gripped the wheel and hauled back—the way the others must have done when their engines stopped in flight. The plane shuddered and dropped off into a sickening spiral, diving swiftly toward the cloud layer.

The accident reports had each told the same story—"the pilot lost control in a dip or a roll when the engine quit, and the ship spiraled to earth, crashing and killing the pilot." The wording varied, but not the facts.

Beachey watched the world spinning upward and felt his body pressed against the seat as the spiral tightened. The instinctive reaction, when falling, would be to simply pull the nose up. This, Beachey discovered, was where the trouble lay.

He shoved forward on the wheel and spun it hard against the turn, at the same time shoving the rudder into the wind. Beachey reasoned that the ship had been falling in a wild spinning maneuver because one wing was stalled and the other was not. Ergo: unstall the stalled wing by diving even more steeply, then roll the wings level!

It worked.

Singing happily, Linc shoved the nose down once more, the force of the wind restarting his engine, and plunged through the billowy softness of the clouds, then raced back to the airport to land. He had beaten the mysterious stall-spin maneuver, and he would give the knowledge to the world. He had cheated death, but death would get even for the affront.

An ironic thing to Beachey was the Federal government's attitude toward aviation—it did not exist. Early in 1912, when European skies were filling rapidly with war planes, Uncle Sam owned six flying machines. One already was gathering dust among the relics in the Smithsonian Institution; another was on a slow boat for Manila.

Thus, when Congress finally blew the moths from its wallet and bought five brand-new airplanes for the fledgling Army Signal Corps, Linc was eager to show the brass—patriotically, of course—how they ought to be flown. The military, notoriously cold toward civilian crackpots, slammed the door in Bill Pickens' face, almost snipping off the end of his cigar, when he tried to get Beachey a soft berth as a flying instructor consultant. They slammed the door on the wrong man; you did not say No to Bill Pickens.

One of the five new government ships was a single-seater Curtiss Speed Scout, with which the Army hoped to dazzle the world. It was a dream ship, faster than anything ever seen in American skies; Captain Charles de Forest Chandler, commandant of the Army field at College Park, Maryland, let his deputy, Lieutenant Harold H. ("Hap") Arnold, in on a top-level secret. "She'll do sixty-five miles an hour straight and level!" the Captain confided.

"No!" Arnold replied with disbelief.

"She'll have a hundred-mile range, and she'll climb up to eighteen hundred feet in three minutes flat!" Chandler smugly lit a cigarette, with a how-do-you-like-that flip of the match.

Arnold frowned. "How do we know she will?" he asked, with a familiar curiosity that would get him to the top one day as a five-star air general.

"Because the specifications specifically specified it!" Chandler stuttered.

"Oh," Arnold grinned. "Then maybe we'd better send for Lincoln Beachey to show us how to do it!"

The snows had melted and the cherry blossoms were in bloom along the Potomac, when Chandler backed down, in May, 1912, and wired Glenn Curtiss to send down Beachey, his chief test pilot. The boys were having their troubles with the Speed Scout.

Beachey arrived the next day and looked it over. Then he parked his car, climbed in the plane, and took off. Three minutes later, he waggled his wings—at 3,000 feet! He chopped the engine, shoved the nose down, and screamed earthward in a flashing Dive of Death. This, he decided, was something like it!

Later, Chandler called him into his office.

"Beachey," he said, slamming his fist down hard, "this is an Army airfield, not a carnival! I'm here to train pilots, not kill them! When you fly government planes, you fly them my way, understand?"

Linc chewed on a stick of gum and grinned. "How do you get out of a tailspin, Captain?"

Chandler reddened. "You know as well as I do that a spin is nearly always fatal! That's why we teach our cadets to avoid them!"

"Suppose one happens accidentally. Then what?"

Chandler stood up angrily. "When we want to rewrite the curriculum at this school, we'll send for you!"

"You can always reach me through Curtiss," Linc smiled. "See you later."

On October 21, Beachey was back at College Park, on another delivery flight. Thirty-five hundred feet below, the Maryland countryside was a riotous carpet of brilliant fall colors. In the center was a brown patch, College Park Airfield. Beachey shuddered at the thought that America's military pilots were being taught all wrong.

He had personally instructed one officer, Lieutenant L. H. Brereton, that the rudder is not there to turn the airplane, like a sailboat, a fallacy the Army was beating into cadet skulls. You turn an airplane the way a bird turns, leaning into it, so that the shoulder yoke warps your ailerons into a smooth bank. He leaned to the left and felt the Curtiss Scout respond, rolling into a graceful sweeping turn with the ease of a buzzard; he barely touched the rudder, enough for it to serve its purpose—to equalize the drag of the low aileron.

Suddenly, Linc tightened the turn, hauled the nose high, chopped the throttle, and booted the Scout into a wild spin right over the airfield.

Captain Chandler, staring up at the gyrating plane coming straight down at him, turned pale. "Good God!" he cried. "He's going to kill himself!"

Beachey's eyes narrowed, studying the blur of the ground rushing at him with express-train speed. He snapped his head around on each turn, watching a road flash past, counting. Faster he spun, the wires shrieking a dirge. The Scout disappeared from Chandler's view, behind a hangar. Chandler held his breath, waiting for the awful crash. . . .

Suddenly, the Scout zoomed up and over the roof of the hangar, played leapfrog over a line of parked ships, and then banked around to streak across the field, the propeller clipping a swath through the grass. Beachey stuck a wingtip inside the hangar, then hauled up in a beautiful wing over and arced around for a perfect three-point landing.

Jumping out, Beachey turned his cap around beak-front and stuck a fresh stick of gum into his mouth. "That's how you get out of a spin, Captain," he said thinly. "Think you can do it, now?"

Chandler, beet-red, counted slowly to ten and let fly. "I could court-martial you for that exhibition of recklessness, Beachey, if you were an Army pilot, which, thank God, you are not! Fortunately for you, all I can do is restrict you from ever flying a government ship again. Do I make myself clear?"

Beachey shrugged. "Sure, Captain. And say, can I borrow your car this afternoon, then?"

Chandler looked as if he could cry.

If Beachey could not convince the Army it did not know how to fly, he could not convince his own civilian rivals either. By May, 1913, the fatality list of his would-be imitators was growing at such an alarming rate that Beachey made good his threat to retire, as a protest against reckless flying.

For months, Linc sat on the sidelines, restless and irritable. He belonged in the sky, where amateur aviators were turning stunt flying into a Roman circus of splintering crashes. One day in September, Linc's brother, Hillary, tossed him a newspaper.

"I see where that Frenchman Adolphe Pegoud looped the loop yesterday, Linc."

Beachey grabbed the paper and studied it, then slammed it to the floor angrily. He picked up the telephone and called the telegraph office. "I want to send a wire to Glenn Curtiss, at Hammondsport, New York," he snapped. "And make that collect!"

Beachey's new exhibition ship was something special; Curtiss had it ready and waiting, knowing Linc would be back. Double-stressed, it had a modified control system and a specially modified carburetor.

"She flies upside down real easy," Curtiss told him.

At 3 o'clock on the afternoon of October 7, 1913, Beachey took off to try and duplicate Pegoud's success in flying through a loop. His mechanic, Arthur Nix, had spun the prop and yelled to him just before takeoff: "How does she feel, Linc?"

Beachey had been silent for a moment, getting familiar with the cockpit. He had not flown since May; he knew he was rusty. He had snapped an irritable "Contact!" and gone up for a flight that would end in death—not his, but Ruth Hildreth's. And he failed to complete the loop.

The girl's death left Beachey numbed inside, not with the chill of fear; that was gone. There was something else, a sense of futility, inevitability, a feeling that edged his flying technique with an almost morbid desire to see how far he could go, the way he had once touched a hot stove as a boy, quickly, to see if he could do it without getting burned. He had found he could not.

The feeling was still with him a month later when, on November 12, he arrived at North Island, San Diego, with the Curtiss Exhibition Team, for the winter season. The fun had gone out of flying; it was a deadly business now.

"I'm going to fly her upside down today, Art," he told his mechanic. "Check her over good."

Back in the air, Beachey climbed for altitude, forced his ship into a screaming dive, and then executed a half corkscrew roll. He shoved the wheel forward, holding the nose up, with the

earth and sky in changed places. He was flying inverted, hanging by his belt strap, a feat never before accomplished in America.

Death struck again the following week; Beachey had just
arrived at the Curtiss school for a morning flight, when two
student Army pilots collided and fell before his eyes. It did not
affect him; the scars of Ruth Hildreth's accident had not healed.

That same afternoon, November 19, Beachey took the new
machine up to 3,000 feet, dove for speed, and then pulled
gracefully up and over through the first loop ever performed
outside Europe. Day after day, he drove himself to perfect his
skill, until he felt there was no more room for improvement.

Tirelessly working out new maneuvers with a cold-blooded
precision that left his audiences gasping, he shot under bridges,
through hangars, between tall buildings and trees; over Fresno
he looped the loop six times in a row—with his hands out-
stretched like a bird.

All this was so much mishmash to Bill Pickens; how could he
sell tickets for an air show that people could watch from their
own backyards? He had a sudden idea.

"You're going to race Barney Oldfield tomorrow," he told
Beachey. "Think you can beat him?"

Beachey laughed. It was a great idea—get the suckers inside
a board fence to see an air show on the ground! "Sure I can
beat him, but I'll make it look as if I can't!"

The act was a sensation. While the crowd roared, Lincoln
Beachey, Demon of the Sky, roared around the race track with
his wingtip glued to Oldfield's steaming radiator cap. Again
death came close at Fresno, when Linc rolled out on the back
turn to streak down the straightaway, virtually on top of the
cigar-chomping automobile daredevil.

Heading into a blinding sun, Beachey failed to see the finish
wire stretched taut above Oldfield's head.

"He'll be cut in two!" a woman screamed.

Beachey saw it too late; he pulled up, thereby saving himself
from being bisected, but the nose wheel struck the wire. The

ship seemed to stop in mid-air, then lunged forward as the wire snapped.

Fearlessly, the two rivals battled each other through the grand circuit. At Emeryville, California, on January 10, 1914, Beachey narrowly missed killing Oldfield when Barney's car shot under him while he was landing. Linc swerved and crashed, but walked away from the wreckage.

Three weeks later, at the Los Angeles Ascot Speedway, Beachey's plane struck a tree on a wide turn in a cross wind. The ship shuddered and cartwheeled to the ground, a complete washout. Linc disappointed the crowd by getting scornfully to his feet and walking away.

Women left their husbands to follow the ruggedly handsome little flyer from town to town; the golden trickle became a flood of blood-money that filled Linc's safe deposit boxes to overflowing. At the rate he was going, Beachey could retire as the world's wealthiest birdman; he and Pickens were raking in more than half a million dollars a season. There were never any no-show refunds; Beachey never canceled a flight.

Beachey's hatred of crowds was becoming obsessive. At Sacramento, California, even Governor Hiram Johnson was not immune to his scathing dislike of grandstand thrill-seekers.

"We thought for sure you were going to be killed!" the governor remarked at the completion of a breathtaking stunt routine. Flushing, Beachey turned without a word and strode back to his flying machine.

For ten terrifying minutes, he pulled every stunt he knew, rolling, looping, and diving at the grandstand, forcing the governor to duck for his life. He chased a dozen cars off the road, ran a cow through a fence, and then came barreling back across the field, standing up, look Governor, no hands! He zoomed back, stripping off his coat and tossing it to the ground. Then down came his vest, shirt, pants, shoes, and socks. He landed in front of the governor's box, stepped out, and strode off to the hangar in his long underwear.

"I wonder how he liked that?" he grinned to Nix.

From coast to coast, the press and the public hailed Lincoln

Beachey as the greatest stunt flyer of all time; he had, it appeared, done everything that could be done with an airplane. But in September, 1914, with the guns of war booming overseas in Europe, Linc could not forget how pitiful the Army's Air Corps had looked, flubbing around the sky back at College Park.

"They need our help, Bill," he told Pickens seriously.

Pickens raised an eyebrow. "I thought you were mad with the military." He lit a cigar and blew smoke thoughtfully upward. "You're not going to enlist?"

"How can we make the government understand that America is unprepared to fight a war in the air?" Beachey pressed.

Pickens knocked ashes off the end of his cigar. "I may have a gimmick, Linc. Leave it to me. That preparedness bit is not bad."

On the hot afternoon of September 28, 1914, President Woodrow Wilson glanced up from his pile of work, startled to see an angry hornet of a biplane buzzing down from the sky above the White House. He ran to the window, adjusted his pince-nez glasses, and stepped back. A wood-and-wire contraption was rushing straight for him, threatening to crash smack into the East Wing. At the last second, it pulled up and over the roof. Wilson peered up from beneath his desk and read the big block letters on the bottom wing: B E A C H E Y.

For the next ten minutes, President Wilson forgot the war; he witnessed the zaniest air show Washington had ever seen, or ever would see.

Congress adjourned to watch.

The Secret Service trained guns on the flying daredevil.

Pump wagons rushed toward the Executive Mansion.

At last Beachey landed—on the Capitol lawn; he sat calmly awaiting the rush of angry officials that swarmed toward him.

Beachey stood up to his full five feet and raised his hand. "Just a minute! This is what can happen here—if you continue to weaken America with an ineffective air corps! Airplanes have made isolationism a myth! We need more planes!"

A handsome, dignified man pushed through the crowd and

gripped Beachey's hand. He was Secretary of War Lindley
Miller Garrison, who already had launched a preparedness campaign by establishing summer training camps to turn out a reserve of commissioned army officers.

"He's right, gentlemen!" The Secretary's words hushed the
startled group. "I think it's time that we gave more considera-
tion to building up an adequate air arm. That is why I invited
Mr. Beachey to put on this demonstration."

In the background, Bill Pickens was beaming. He had certainly picked the right man; the strings he had pulled to get
Garrison to invite Beachey to Washington had worked. This
was the greatest publicity stunt he had ever rigged; and besides, it gave him a warm glow of patriotic pride. But there was
no use resting on his laurels; the Panama Pacific Exposition
was already in full swing in San Francisco. Tens of thousands
of tourists with money in their pockets were flocking there to
join California's salute to the opening of the Panama Canal, on
August 15th.

Back where he had first learned to fly, Beachey seemed to
perform with a greater recklessness than ever before. "It's a
front page story every day that Lincoln Beachey remains alive,"
commented the *Indianapolis Star*.

Over a glass of orange juice in a fair booth, Beachey lost his
heart for the second time, to a pretty twenty-two-year-old
dancing teacher named Ethel Shoemaker. "Be careful, Linc,"
she told him one evening as they strolled through the midway,
hand in hand. "Aren't you taking unnecessary chances?"

Beachey patted her arm. "Don't worry. I've got a charmed
life!"

As if to prove it to Ethel, he set a world record the next day
by looping the loop eighty times. Then, on New Year's Eve, he
announced that he would fly through one of the exhibition
buildings—Machinery Hall—in one door and out the other. A
nervous crowd gathered as Beachey circled the fair grounds
and then swept in low and fast from off the Bay. Under perfect
control, he dove in through the big doors. The crowd, like spectators at a tennis match, swung their heads to the left, waiting

for Beachey to come out. They waited and waited. He finally emerged—on foot.

"Hooked the wing tip on the back door," he grinned sheepishly when Ethel ran up to him. His clothes were ripped and torn and he was a mass of bruises; but he seemed unconcerned.

"Linc!" Miss Shoemaker cried, "how can you go on this way? You've made almost half a million dollars. Why not quit while you're ahead?"

In answer, Beachey reached in his pocket and pulled out a piece of paper. "Look here!" he said enthusiastically.

It was a blueprint of the new Lincoln Beachey Special, a graceful monoplane of his own design. It was being built at that moment in a San Francisco barn by W. S. Eaton, of the Aero Club of California. Poised on a tricycle undercarriage, her slender silver fuselage and lovely yellow wings, sweeping out from her midsection, spelled speed. A snug cockpit sat behind the trim cowling of her 80-horsepower Monosauppe Gnome Rotary engine.

"She'll do better than a hundred," Beachey said. "She'll be the fastest ship in the world!"

While the Beachey Special was nearing completion, Linc was flying harder than ever to keep up with his press agent. Pickens knew the crowds were getting tired of loops, death dives, and ocean rolls. They demanded spectaculars. On January 1, 1915, the day after his crack-up inside Machinery Hall, Linc gave them one.

For days, San Francisco had been plastered with gaudy twenty-four sheet billboards showing Lincoln Beachey sinking the mighty battleship U.S.S. *Oregon*. More than seven years before General Billy Mitchell's bombers sank the former German dreadnaught *Ostfriesland* in twenty-one and a half minutes off the Virginia capes, to demonstrate the potency of airpower, Bill Pickens had the same idea. He had artfully created the posters from photos of the actual warship and an oil-well fire; after all, real warships were hard to come by.

Nevertheless, thousands of eager Exposition visitors were glad to pay a dollar each to watch Pickens' "national preparedness spectacle" from a special grandstand. Half a mile offshore, he had anchored a make-believe battleship, the "U.S.S. *Gorgonzola*," a 200-foot model made of wood and painted canvas, riding on two barges. Masts and funnels added a touch of realism that prompted a detachment of 100 sailors from Goat Island Naval Training Station to board her and wave their hats gaily from her flimsy deck.

Promptly at one o'clock, Beachey appeared over the grandstand, waved at the crowd, and swung out to sea. He circled the *Gorgonzola*, then dipped down for the attack. A puff of black smoke appeared under his wing, and a second later an explosion rocked the *Gorgonzola*.

"The sailors . . . they'll be killed!" an hysterical woman cried. Pickens wondered if he had gone too far.

Beachey flew like a madman, diving on the pasteboard battleship from every angle. Each time, a thundering blast occurred, toppling a smokestack or blowing a big hole in her side, until a cloud of smoke engulfed her. Unseen by the awed spectators, a tug moved in behind and took off the sailors. Beachey swept in for the *coup de grâce*, and a gigantic explosion shook the *Gorgonzola* from stem to stern. She settled beneath the waves as Linc flew back, waggling his wings in a victory salute.

In a manner of speaking, he had become the world's first airman to sink a battleship—with fifty direct hits. They actually were touched off by a sailor on the tugboat who slammed down a plunger to set off a dynamite blast each time Beachey dove on his target. The crowd did not mind that it was all make-believe; they loved Beachey and were happy to line his pockets —and Pickens'—with $8,218.80 for the day's work.

Early in March, the Beachey Special was ready to fly, and Linc climbed eagerly into the cockpit for a shakedown. She behaved beautifully. By March 14, she was ready for her public debut. Parked before the Palace of Mines building on the Exposition grounds, she was as graceful as a dragonfly, streamlined from her bright spinner to her yellow tail, an aircraft far ahead of her time.

A roar went up from the crowd as Beachey strutted to his

Forgotten by history is this intricate glider, patented August 14, 1877, by Melville M. Murrell of Panther Springs, Tenn. Relatives claim Murrell made successful flights over the family apple orchard, then turned to religion, giving up flying.

(Photo courtesy William H. Murrell)

Professor John J. Montgomery's glider (half circle at right of balloon is a rudder) is attached by ropes to hot-air balloon before ascension at Santa Clara, Calif., on April 29, 1905. Dan Maloney, a parachutist, rode glider back to earth to become history's first heavier-than-air stunt man. Jesuit fathers watch crew chief Ed Unger and his men inflating balloon with hot air.

(California State Library photo)

Professor Montgomery and stunt-man Dan Maloney standing beside the beautiful glider which Montgomery designed and built.

(California State Library photo)

Dan Maloney, stunt pilot, ascends on his fatal flight to 4,000 feet beneath hot-air balloon in Montgomery glider, over San Jose, Calif., in 1905. Crowds cheered and prayed for safety. Maloney spiraled to earth repeatedly in amazing corkscrew rolls, finally was killed when a wing broke. (California State Library photos)

Charles F. Willard, early-bird performer at aviation meets, had this fancy leather flying suit designed especially for him. Photo taken at Dominguez Field, Los Angeles, in January of 1910.

(Security First National
Bank collection)

Professor Harry La Verne Twining's first airplane flew like a bird, but didn't land like one. Here is result of first flight (1910) that ended nose down. Twining built ship with W. S. Eaton, also of Aero Club of California. (Author's collection)

Heroic birdmen of 1910. Posing before grandstands at Dominguez Field, in January of 1910, are (left to right) *Hillary Beachey, Col. F. K. Johnson, Glenn Curtiss, Louis Paulhan, Charles F. Willard, Didier Masson, Lincoln Beachey, Roy Knabenshue, Charles K. Hamilton.* (Security First National Bank collection)

The incomparable Lincoln Beachey at the controls of famed Curtiss pusher. In this ship, rudder controls were linked to the wheel, which also operated elevators when pulled back, as in modern control system. Aileron flaps (between wings) were controlled by pressing shoulder against lever—pilot "leaned into the turn." Note Beachey's flying garb—checkered cap turned around, celluloid collar, pin-stripe suit; also note foot brake beside right foot, passenger seat (without safety belt!) and accelerator under left foot!

Lincoln Beachey, the boy wonder dirigible pilot, scrambles monkeylike along catwalk of dirigible No. 2 in race at Los Angeles' Dominguez Field, January 1910. Later he gave up dirigibles for faster (40 mph!) Curtiss pushers. (Security First National Bank collection)

William Randolph Hearst became first publisher to fly. Shown here (in right-hand seat) beside Louis Paulhan, in a Farman biplane at Dominguez Field, January 1910.
(Security First National Bank collection)

The great dirigible race! Lincoln Beachey (foreground) defeats Roy Knabenshue, in rear airship, in race at Dominguez Field, Los Angeles, January 1910. Beachey later switched to stunt flying.
(Security First National Bank collection)

Arch Hoxsey, one of the great early stunt pilots, who crashed to his death at Dominguez Field on December 31, 1910. (Security First National Bank collection)

Professor Harry La Verne Twining, member of Aero Club of California and Aero Club of America, built this ornithopter, dubbed the "Flip-Flop" by newsmen. Wings beat 52 times a minute when inventor pumped handle. The ornithopter weighed 240 pounds and had a 27-foot wing span. It hopped off the ground ... once. Twining claimed that the "upbeat" was the important part of bird flight, and sought to duplicate it. (Author's collection)

Professor Twining, as official observer of the Aero Club of America at Dominguez Field Air Meet, December 31, 1910, denied Arch Hoxsey's altitude record of 11,474 feet when barograph was found demolished in wreck that killed him. Twining once claimed a mouse has a soul, because it was found to lose weight at death.

(Author's collection)

At Dominguez Field, Los Angeles, 1912, Lincoln Beachey, famous
"California Flying Fool," played trick on rival Blanche Stuart Scott
by dressing as a woman and buzzing field in Curtiss pusher.
(Author's collection)

Lincoln Beachey, flying a Curtiss pusher, practiced low-level turns
so he could race Barney Oldfield around auto speedways to lure
suckers inside fence. This picture was taken at Los Angeles' Dominguez Field in 1913. (Author's collection)

With his cap spun around backwards, the great Lincoln Beachey performs 40-mph speed run across Dominguez Field, Los Angeles, in 1913 air meet. (Author's collection)

The Lincoln Beachey Special, fastest ship in the world when Beachey flew it to his death at San Francisco on March 14, 1915, was powered with a Gnome rotary engine that had high torque. Unused to such forces and such speed, Beachey exceeded limits in a power dive, broke a wing, and crashed into San Francisco Bay. In an era when open-air cockpits and wood-and-wire biplanes were being flown, Beachey's enclosed cockpit, cowled engine, and tricycle gear were far ahead of their time. (Security First National Bank collection)

new ship, dressed in a new silk and rubber flying costume, knitted helmet, and goggles. He checked over the ship with care, testing the guy wires, wing bolts, cowling, control surfaces. Satisfied, he climbed into the cockpit and settled down behind its racy windshield. Nix, his mechanic, waved from in front of the ship.

"Contact!" Beachey called.

Nix grabbed the propeller and spun it. The Gnome rotary barked to life. The Beachey Special trembled, straining to be going. Nix pulled the chocks and the sleek aerobatic ship rolled forward, gathering speed, and seemed to leap off the ground, less than a hundred feet away.

Climbing in a steep chandelle, the tiny monoplane glistened in the afternoon sun. The crowd watched it dwindle to a mere speck in the sky, and then turn back.

"Here he comes!" they yelled. Beachey was streaking down the sky like a meteor, gathering speed. He pulled up and zoomed through a graceful low-level loop, then another, and another. Ethel Shoemaker watched fearfully for the next ten minutes as Linc put his dream ship through a breathtaking display of aerobatic maneuvers—loops, rolls, spins, the works. He dropped so low to the Bay a crash seemed inevitable, then at the last moment bottomed out and dashed toward the shore, landing lightly where he had started.

"She's a homesick angel, Art!" he told his mechanic happily. "Gas her up; I'm going back up again!" He climbed out, wiping castor oil from his goggles and waving to Ethel.

Nix hesitated, then said, "Linc, take it easy for me, huh? This baby is a lot faster than anything you've ever flown."

"Don't worry," Beachey grinned. "But keep your eyes open! I'll wring her out this time!"

Beachey felt a freedom he had never known; crouched inside the cramped cockpit, out of the wind blast, he sensed power throbbing heavily in rhythm with the barking exhaust of the Gnome rotary. The slightest finger pressure brought controlled response. He was at 6,000 feet over the Bay; he had completed his full repertoire of maneuvers. It was the moment of truth, time to prove that he, not the ship, was the master. He snapped inverted and, by crossing controls, left joystick, right rudder, smoothly banked and turned to bring the ship over the grandstand. Then he pulled down into a screaming dive.

The Beachey Special gathered speed quickly, more so than he had anticipated. Her streamlined fuselage was a plunging hawk; rigging wires sang a shrill protest. Beachey watched the world rushing up, his world, a world of shouting, yelling people, calling him down, down, 3,000, 2,000, 1,000 feet from death. It was there—it always was—waiting for him to make a mistake.

Faster than any human had ever flown, Beachey streaked down from the sky, until reflexes acted to begin the pullout. He did not have to think. His eyes saw the milling crowd become individual, terrified humans; his nerves flashed the message; his hand tightened on the joystick. But his eyes deceived him. Unused to such speed, they tricked him. Diving at twice the velocity he had ever dived before, he could not know it would take four times the distance to recover.

He sucked the stick back harder and harder, watching the world rush up to strike him dead. The Beachey Special shuddered, and something broke. Linc looked left; the wing had torn away.

"Oh, God!" the crowd screamed. The Beachey Special, its wing gone, dropped like a rock into San Francisco Bay, directly in front of the grandstand. The crowd rushed forward, across the grass field, to the water's edge, and there it stopped. The waves had subsided; beneath them, the world's greatest stunt flyer was dead, trapped in the tangled wreckage of his lovely silver and yellow ship.

Joseph Maerz, a Navy diver, lowered himself over the side of a rescue launch and groped down through the murky water. At 60 feet, he found the Beachey Special, half buried in the mud. He attached a line and signaled for the winch crew to haul up.

They found Linc's body still trapped in the cockpit, his hands cut to ribbons from trying to claw his way out. Dr. David E.

Stafford, the autopsy surgeon, shook his head sadly when Ethel Shoemaker asked whether he had died instantly. Linc had drowned.

The tragedy that robbed America of her first great aviation hero at the peak of his popularity left the nation in grief. The story was headlined, along with a black-boxed tribute from the popular author Elbert Hubbard: "Each art has its master worker, its Paderewski, its Saint-Gaudens, its Milton. There is music and most inspiring grace and prettiest poetry in flight by man in the heavens, and posterity will write the name of Lincoln Beachey as the greatest artist on the airplane. In his flying was the same delicacy of touch, the same inspirational finesse of movement, the same developed genius of Paderewski and Milton. . . ."

It was the end of an era, the first wild, impulsive era of barnstorming and stunting by aviation's first daring young men and their flying machines. But then, two months later, Elbert Hubbard himself would go down on the *Lusitania*. Both he and Lincoln Beachey would soon be forgotten in a world at war.

A few did not forget. Even taciturn old Orville Wright was later moved to admit: "He was the most wonderful flier I ever saw—the greatest aviator of them all."

8

What Did *You* Do in the Great War, Daddy? *(U. S. Army World War I recruiting poster)*

HE WAS ABSOLUTELY GLORIOUS in his oval goggles, tight leather helmet, white scarf fluttering in the slipstream, and a red garter snapped on his arm. . . . He was the *enfant perdu* of the sky, the World War I fighter pilot, a hard-drinking, hard-loving, hard-flying fellow—but wait a minute! Just how hot a pilot was this brave, colorful character?

Chances are, if he was up carousing all night, he was not in top form on the dawn patrol; but if he lived to fly again, he was still a hero, for he was up there alone getting shot at, wasn't he? And if he was shot down in flames, well, he was still magnificent! Their stories get better as the years go by, and maybe they are better for the retelling. To recall a few:

Jean Navarre, a French ace who wore a woman's silk stocking in place of a helmet, once roared off into the sky clutching a long-bladed butcher knife in one hand. He intended using the knife to "disembowel" a Zeppelin reported flying over Paris. The Zeppelin turned out to be a lenticular cloud.

Jean Chaput, another Frenchman, was admittedly a lousy shot. Chaput invented a suicidal stunt to compensate for his bad marksmanship; he simply flew into the tail of an enemy ship and chewed it off with his propeller. Later, Chaput's aim improved; he downed four balloons and a Fokker, shooting the pilot with a burst of only four bullets.

Albert Ball, a frail, consumptive British pilot, was shot down not once but seven times, yet still scored forty-four victories before disappearing in a cloud, never to be seen again. Ball's trademark was a head-on "chicken run" attack; he gambled that the enemy pilot would turn away at the last split second, giving him a fleeting shot at the vulnerable underbelly of the enemy plane.

Ball was imaginative, resourceful, and inventive, all qualities of a first-rate stunt pilot. Once when outnumbered five-to-one, out of ammunition and alone, Ball pulled off a stunt that became legendary in the Royal Flying Corps; he booted his ship into a wild spin all the way to the ground, but recovered in a wild leap over a fence to land in a small field. Three of the Germans who had "downed" Ball buzzed the field and raced home with the news that England's ace was a prisoner. The other two landed to grab him. But Ball, who was hanging out of the cockpit playing dead, suddenly gunned the engine and roared off, thumbing his nose at his would-be captors.

The great French hero Major Raoul Lufbery was assigned originally to a bombardment squadron, when his flight instructors found him too heavy-footed to fly as a *pilote de chasse*. He learned fast, becoming one of the most skilled pilots of the Lafayette Escadrille and the mentor of such other American heroes as Captain Eddie Rickenbacker and Lieutenant Douglas Campbell.

As good a pilot as he was, Major Lufbery died the hard way, on May 19, 1918, hurling his little Nieuport fighter against an incredible new German secret weapon that appeared lumbering over the American sector north of Toul in the late afternoon.

It was a heavily armored Albatros bomber, whose pilot and two gunners, armed with six bristling machine guns, rode in cockpits plated with quarter-inch steel sheeting. Half a dozen fighters went up to shoot it down, but their bullets bounced off the plating like hailstones. "The scene looked like a lot of swallows pecking at a giant bird of prey," wrote one eyewitness. Lufberry dived at the monster "flying tank" time after time without success, and finally his Nieuport was seen to trail smoke. He dived away, trying desperately to reach the earth, for he was afire and wore no parachute. It was too late. At 1,500 meters, he stepped over the side and plunged to the ground, rather than burn to death. Lufbery was buried with full military honors in a field of buttercups, while six squadron mates flew low overhead, scattering roses.

Most colorful of America's World War I aces was Frank Luke, top-gun westerner from Arizona, who shot his way into first place as the United States' leading ace, scoring eighteen kills in seventeen days of contemptuous flying. A graduate of the Curtiss School at North Island, San Diego, Luke wore the brand of the late, great wood-and-wire daredevils Lincoln Beachey and Eugene Ely, who had pioneered military aerobatics long before the war began. It was Beachey who had sunk the cardboard battleship U.S.S. *Gorgonzola* in a farcical demonstration of "air power" at San Francisco, and Ely who, in 1910, had made headlines by landing an airplane on one cruiser deck and, later, taking off from another.

Both Beachey and Ely were scornful of military pilots, preferring to risk their lives barnstorming the nation for big money. And both died in action, Beachey at San Francisco and Ely at New Orleans. "The grewsome feature of the tragedy," commented a reporter who saw Ely die in a Death Plunge, "was the fight by spectators to get souvenirs. . . . The field was cleared of every bit of wreckage. Ely's tie, collar, gloves and cap disappeared. The collar was taken from his neck."

The legacy of the early birdmen was not pleasant; by the spring of 1913, the rising death toll of professional stunt pilots and barnstormers had reached an alarming 462. Major J. Robinson Hall, a soldier of fortune back from two years on the Eastern Front with the Royal Imperial Flying Corps, warned: "The very few expert aviators now in America are too valuable to their country to sacrifice their lives in foolish, criminal stunt flying. We may need their services badly one of these days."

The qualities that made Lincoln Beachey and Eugene Ely great were the same requisites of the combat pilot, men who could think and act with lightning-fast reflexes, skill, and valor. And they had to be inventive, if they were to function in the sky with an automatic response that allowed them to concentrate on killing. Such a pilot was Frank Luke.

Although he is remembered as a "Balloon Buster" who waged a quixotic one-man war against enemy rubber cows, Luke actually was a natural dogfight specialist who flew hard, viciously weaving through massive German formations and then escaping with his famed split-S reversement that put him on the tails of his pursuers.

The day Luke died lives in legend. Grounded for refusal to obey orders, Luke strode to the airfield late in the evening, climbed into his Spad, and headed for the front lines, dropping a note to an advance American outpost to "Watch three Hun balloons on the Meuse." Trapped by a top cover flight of Fokkers, Luke flew like a madman, sending two spinning to earth in flames, then polished off the hydrogen bags in flaming explosions, one-two-three. He escaped his attackers by tumbling earthward, apparently out of control, in one of Beachey's old crowd-thrillers—a falling leaf.

Troops on the ground, watching in stunned silence, were sure he had crashed. And when he failed to return, Luke was written off as "Missing in Action." Not until after the war—on January 3, 1919—did Luke's squadron buddies learn what had happened. On that date, an officer of the newly formed American Graves Registration Service reported he had exhumed the body of an aviator killed at Murveaux and had identified it from a wrist watch as that of Luke.

Witnesses told how Luke had landed, leaped out gun in hand, and fired blindly at advancing German troops, who killed him. He won the Congressional Medal of Honor posthumously.

Luckier was one of Luke's enemies, a remarkable German aviator born Anton John Rutgers von Rosenberg in Elberfeld-Barmen in 1899. "Dutch" Rutgers remembers wistfully that he was *not* the hottest pilot ever to stagger over No Man's Land; and besides, he did not *really* want to kill anybody. . . .

On his first dawn patrol, Dutch wandered off from his formation to go hunting Spads by himself, leaving his buddies unprotected. "Three of them were shot down," he sighs. "I was grounded for ten days."

On July 16, 1916, Dutch was out on patrol again in his Junkers and somehow got himself lost. He turned up over enemy territory and saw down below a big fat target of opportunity— a convoy of three French trucks.

"When I came buzzing back, the men leaped out and crawled under them. I had three bombs, and it would have been simple to blow those trucks up. But it was my father's birthday. I just *couldn't* bomb them; in my heart I didn't hate anybody. So I flew out over a river and dropped the bombs there."

On his way home, Dutch was jumped by a British pilot flying a Sopwith Camel, who could not know that his adversary was just a softhearted Hun. The Limey opened fire, but Dutch was not able to return it—his machine gun jammed.

"I went into a falling leaf, stalling for time," he tells friends today. "I'd heard about this chivalry, where the other guy doesn't shoot you if your guns jam, but he kept right on. I banged my head, biting my tongue so badly my mouth got full of blood. He flew past, giving me the victory signal. I guess he thought he'd killed me. I was so disappointed in him I shot him down."

Rutgers' faith in the enemy was restored a few days later. He had had a great day, shooting down three sausage balloons —there were no observers in them—and was thinking about a little *Fräulein* he had a date with that night. Then, out of the sun, of course, dove a Sopwith Camel, guns spitting tracers at him.

"We milled around and I got a few shots in, but he'd shot one of my wing struts in two and the wings were wobbling something awful. I saw a little field and set her down, alongside of some shell holes and barbed wire. I saw the Camel come sailing in from the other direction and land a hundred yards away. I thought to myself, well, here's the end. I pulled out my Luger to defend myself. But here came this big, tall, blond American boy, waving a white handkerchief.

"I felt like a damn fool."

The two enemy pilots grinned and shook hands and tried to communicate, but neither spoke the other's tongue. They looked over each other's fighter plane, and then sat down for a smoke.

"Finally this fellow got up and walked over to his ship," Dutch said. "He came back with a package and opened it. There were ham sandwiches. Well, I had a couple of bottles of wine in my crate, so we sat there for a couple of hours and enjoyed ourselves.

"When we were ready to go, he helped me fix my broken strut with a piece of barbed wire, and then he told me his name was Gerald Kline, from Philadelphia, and with sign language invited me to look him up after the war. We both took off and put on a sham battle to make it look good in case anybody saw us. I never saw him again."

The following year, Dutch Rutgers became something of a legend as the "Black Devil" of the German Air Force.

"I flew a Pfalz; I was wearing a black uniform and a black mask, as I had a bad cold. Two Englishmen got in front of me on my way home and I shot them down. I needed an aspirin bad."

His notoriety won the attention of the great German ace, Baron Manfred von Richthofen; and soon, Rutgers recalls, he was flying with the dreaded von Richthofen Circus.

"It was awful," he sighs. "The Baron sat up there in the sun where the enemy couldn't see him, while we went to work disabling the enemy ships. Then the *Schnapp* would come diving down out of the sun, guns blazing like hell, and finish them off to grab the credit. I got seventeen kills, but who ever heard of me?"

After crashing nine German ships during the course of the war, Rutgers figured he had done more for the Allies than for the Kaiser. On Armistice Day, he decided to go to America and look up Gerald Kline.

"I never found him, but I did contact Alfred Schmook, the nephew of a squadron mate, in Warsaw, Illinois. I'd had enough flying, and so I went into real estate. . . ."

Better known on that side of the war was Lieutenant Franz Max Immelmann, an arrogant, intellectual airman with an unpleasant personality, who became Germany's first ace by inventing a "chicken" maneuver that today bears his name—the Immelmann turn.

In order to stay alive, Immelmann decided he needed the finest equipment and something new in the way of escape and evasion. Assigned the second Fokker Eindecker fighter, equipped with Tony Fokker's new interrupter gear machine gun, which fired through the propeller, Immelmann shot himself down twice and, naturally, blamed it on the gun mechanism.

When he figured out how to shoot the thing properly, Immelmann ran up an impressive string of fifteen victories by employing the Immelmann turn. He was one of the first airmen to discover the surprise factor of hiding in the sun and waiting for an enemy ship to appear below him. Streaking down from the blind spot with his fancy new gun blazing away, he flashed past his victim and pulled up through a tight loop. At the top, he executed a half roll and took off for home in the opposite direction. On July 18, 1916, Immelmann died in a bloody crash behind his own lines, an accident the army blamed on structural failure. Fokker indignantly insisted that the cause was pilot trouble. Regardless, Max had left his mark in the sky.

It was a Frenchman—Armand Deperdussin—not a German who first suggested using a machine gun on an airplane; and another Frenchman, Roland Garros, was the first to try it out in combat, accounting for five straight kills to become the first Allied ace of the war. A talented designer but a poor risk with a franc, Deperdussin produced a new French fighter that hopelessly outclassed the Fokker Eindecker. This was the famed Spad, whose letters stood for *Société pour la Production des Appareils Deperdussins*. It was Deperdussin's misfortune, however, to draw a five-year prison sentence in 1917 for forgery, swindling, and embezzlement, in plunging his aircraft factory $5,600,000 into debt.

Short, stocky, square-shouldered Ernst Udet was as skilled a stunt flyer as ever lived, and as icy-veined. They called him the

Ace with Nine Lives because of his incredible, hairbreadth escapes. Emerging from World War I with a string of sixty-two victories—second only to von Richthofen's eighty—Udet, the war hero, became even more famous as a precision stunt flyer and a roué. A baroness in a leopard-skin coat followed Udet across Europe, and finally shot him. He recovered to run up a score of boudoir victories surpassing the number of enemy planes he had shot down. It was said he had learned chivalry from the French; Georges Guynemer, the great Gallic airman, once spared Udet's life, when he saw the German ace's guns had jammed.

At the Cleveland Air Races in 1931 and in 1933, hero Udet chilled American crowds with demonstrations of his superb aerobatic flying skill inches from the ground. His favorite stunt was to slam across the field inverted, then right himself and adroitly scoop up a lady's handkerchief with a flick of the wingtip, a feat requiring perfect coordination and timing.

Udet also took the opportunity, while a guest in America, to study the latest U.S. Navy dive bombers, even wangling a ride in one under the pretext of wanting to buy it for use in air shows. It became the prototype for the Luftwaffe's deadly Stuka.

Accident-prone, Ernst Udet seemed to have no regard for human life; few friends would fly with him, fearing his phenomenal luck would surely run out. In July, 1934, Udet pulled the wings off an American dive bomber in a dive test over Templehof Airport. He parachuted safely. Two years later, while Charles Lindbergh was visiting Germany on a wide-eyed inspection tour of Germany's incredible air arm, Udet, who by then was chief of the Technical Department of the German Air Ministry, again tore a new ship apart, on a demonstration run high above the Heinkel Works at Warnemünde.

Udet's closest brush with death came at Zurich, in 1937, during an air race, when he flew a low-wing Messerschmitt ME-109 smack into a 30,000-volt trolley wire. The impact jerked the cable car violently uphill but slowed the ship down like an aircraft carrier arresting cable. Udet stepped from the wreckage without a scratch.

A jovial *bon vivant* and practical joker who liked to draw cartoons buffooning Nazi and Luftwaffe leaders, Udet never took Hitler seriously, but *der Führer* knew talent when he saw it. There was no question that Udet was one of the world's greatest living airmen. Against his better judgment, Udet accepted the post of head of aircraft production and materiel for Germany's gargantuan war machine. In June, 1941, he was certain he had made a serious mistake, when Hitler launched his senseless invasion of Russia—on advice of his astrologers.

Only a drastic step could save Germany from disaster, Udet was certain. As Germany's leading fighter pilot, he shared with General Adolf Galland the view that superior aircraft must go immediately into production or the air war would be lost by 1943. At Augsburg, Udet and Willi Messerschmitt met with Field Marshal Erhard Milch and proposed a radical move—start immediate production of jet aircraft!

Had Milch listened to Udet and Messerschmitt, and had the deadly ME-262 reached operational squadrons a year earlier, who knows what might have happened? But Udet knew that you cannot win a war with *ifs*, and Hitler's panzer divisions and Luftwaffe squadrons were already committed to a struggle Udet knew must fail.

On November 18, Udet, seemingly in high spirits, threw a wild party in his Berlin apartment. There were girls, laughter, champagne, music, all the things he loved best. At the height of the party, he excused himself and stepped into his private room, carefully locking the door. He was alone.

Udet picked up his favorite revolver, filled the chamber, and calmly fired five shots into a target at the far end of the study. Each hit the bull's-eye. Then he turned the muzzle to his forehead and squeezed off the last shot.

9

Come, Josephine

THE SKY WAS THEIR TENT and the whole countryside was their audience. They were the barnstormers—aviation's madmen, who brought the Air Age to the country villages, scaring hell out of the rubes who paid a dollar a ride to peer over the side of a tired old Jenny or Standard biplane and wave at the Old Man down there on the farm.

And when passenger-hopping fell off, there was always a way to stimulate business—with a limitless repertoire of blood-chilling stunts that, put together, became known as the Flying Circus.

Their stunts had to be good; if they were not, there was the chance of being run out of town, as happened to Art Smith down at Bay City, Texas, back in 1912. Smith, known as the Smashup Kid for the way he used up airplanes, had to cancel a show at Bay City when torrential rains turned the ball park, where he was operating, into a sea of mud. Smith crated up his Wright pusher, nicknamed the *Honeybug* for the girl Art later married, and had it drawn to the railroad station in a wagon, to move on to the next town. At the station, a crowd of more than a hundred angry citizens was waiting for him.

"You ain't leavin' town until we see you fly that thing!" a tall, square-jawed Texan drawled ominously, resting his hand on his gun butt. "We don't hold to swindlers here!"

"Swindlers?" Smith cried. "You can see I was rained out!"

"Then what's that sign doin' on the crate—*Humbug*?" the other snapped.

Smith sighed in relief and put his arm around the pretty girl beside him. "Honeybug," he said, "tell 'em they made a mistake, will you?"

Barnstormer Slats Rodgers, who operated out of Love Field, Texas, once flew off another field just in time to escape an angry crowd, led by a bunch of angrier cops blowing whistles and firing their revolvers over his head. Slats had just fooled a crowd of 16,000 spectators who had come to watch his wing-walker, Gene Brewer, get himself killed. He had taken up a dummy and tossed it out at the top of a loop; and when it landed, in full view of the horrified crowd, he had an ambulance driver rush in and remove it before the deception was discovered. The driver raced all the way to the hospital with red light and siren —with the cops clearing the way. But at the emergency ward, yanking the ambulance doors open, the cops took one look at the busted dummy and raced back to the field to throw Slats in jail. Rodgers took off, flew around for a while, and then decided to land and face the music.

"What do you want me for?" he asked innocently.

"You endangered the lives of hundreds of people," one of the cops roared.

"Well, go get the sheriff," Slats retorted. "This is county territory!"

The sheriff laughed. "Hell, I don't want him! Give him a pat on the back! That was a great show he put on!"

The dollar-a-ride gimmick was a specialty of the famed Gates Flying Circus, which in 1927 had thirteen stunt ships on the parking apron at Teterboro Airport in New Jersey and was credited with introducing more than one million passengers to aviation before the circus broke up. In one single day in 1928, at Steubenville, Ohio, a Gates pilot named Bill Brooks smashed all passenger-hopping records by roaring on and off the field 490 times, from dawn to dusk. Carrying two passengers on each hop, Brooks finished the tiring day with $980 in his tin box.

To keep a barnstorming pilot that busy, there had to be a

queue of eager rubes waiting with dollar bills clutched in their nervous hands. Ivan R. Gates, a former San Francisco used car dealer, who knew that a fool and his money could be soon parted if he thought he was getting something for nothing, was a past master at this kind of persuasion. He worked a deal with the Texas Oil Company to supply free gas and oil for displaying the Texas Star trademark emblazoned on the lower wings of the Circus' Hispano-Suiza-powered Standards; then he bolted steel ladders on their sides for faster loading and enlarged the cockpit so four customers could crowd in at once—without safety belts, of course.

Gates got into the flying business back in 1911—at the time Bill Pickens was making a fortune for Lincoln Beachey—by booking exhibition flights for three pre-war birdmen, Didier Masson, Fred Hoover, and Art Smith. Masson, a clean-cut young American who affected a bow tie and a carnation boutonniere, was the first to leave Gates; in the fall of 1911, he shipped his biplane, *Pegasus II*, to the Orient to clean up a fortune putting on flying exhibitions in Japan. Smith, the Smashup Kid, won brief fame as the Human Comet by simulating a night air raid with dazzling pyrotechnics fired from his airplane, to help the war effort.

After the war, Gates started up again with two ex-army pilots, Clyde Pangborn, the first of the war-surplus gypsy pilots, and Captain Lowell Yerrex, who later on moved to Central America and won an air mail contract by dive-bombing an uprising that threatened to oust the president of Honduras. It was the beginning of TACA Airline.

Constantly on the move, the Gates Flying Circus in 1919 worked its way West, playing to enthusiastic audiences in Salt Lake City, Denver, Reno, and San Francisco. One member of the gypsy troupe, Lloyd Geraldson, remembers flying low across Colorado with Pangborn when a full storm appeared dead ahead. "We kept flying lower and lower to stay under it," he recalls. "Finally Pang dove down into a deep canyon and began following that. We could see a railroad track below us and figured it had to go some place. It was the Royal Gorge, and at places it was so narrow our wingtips were scraping the walls. It was like flying through a tunnel!"

Parachute jumps worked fine as crowd-pleasers for a while, but eventually Gates saw the necessity for coming up with newer and more exasperating stunts to hold an audience. At Venice Field, near Hollywood, he found his man in Wesley May, a wing-walker who was working for another barnstormer, named Earl Dougherty.

Dougherty had advertised publicly that he intended to keep his airplane, a JN4D Jenny, in the air for twenty-four hours. Everybody knew he could not carry that much fuel; and in the morning, a huge crowd turned out at Long Beach Airport to see what he would do. At noon, while Dougherty's barker on the ground was selling rides like hotcakes, a second ship appeared in the air.

The crowd gasped; crouched on top of the Standard's upper wing was Wesley May, with a 5-gallon can of gasoline strapped to his back! The Standard, flown by Frank Hawks, a noted racing pilot, maneuvered into position alongside the Jenny. May stood up, bracing himself against the tearing wind, and reached up, just as Dougherty moved a wing in over him. He grabbed a wing skid and hung there, unable to pull himself up. Dougherty, seeing the look of sudden panic on May's face, adroitly dipped his wing to relieve the strain, and May quickly scrambled aboard. Dougherty flew low over the field, where the enthusiastic crowd roared approval as May calmly walked down the wing and poured the gasoline into the Jenny's gas tank. It was the world's first mid-air refueling flight.

Flying with the Gates Circus, May added other spectacular stunts to his repertoire; he was the first person to roller skate off the top wing, and once attempted to ride a bicycle along its full length on a beaverboard strip. May finally was killed when he slipped off a wing and his parachute failed to open. He fell into a graveyard and was smashed to death on a granite tombstone.

Movie actress Rosalie Gordon owed her life to Pangborn, when she fouled up an attempted parachute jump from his ship. It was an old pull-out-type chute, stuffed inside a canister carried between the wheels; but Miss Gordon's weight was not enough to pull it out when she stepped off the wing. Pangborn and Milton Girten, a wing-walker standing on the opposite wing, were shocked to see Rosalie swinging like a pendulum at the end of the shroud lines. Girten tried in vain to pull her back onto the wing, for the riser cords were quickly covered with oil from the engine.

A second plane flew up alongside Pangborn's, and Freddie Lund, another stunt pilot, made a plane-change to give Girten a hand. Lund finally slipped into the front cockpit as Pangborn, who was more muscular, clambered out. He and Girten finally got the thoroughly frightened girl back. It was a mid-air rescue that won nationwide publicity both for Miss Gordon and for the Gates Flying Circus.

Art Inman, manager of the Inman Brothers Flying Circus, panicked Des Moines one memorable night with a terrifying buzz job in a huge trimotor Boeing Clipper. Stuck with a thirty-day lease at Des Moines Municipal Airport, Inman decided that the only way to come out even was to roust the whole town out of bed and virtually drag them to the field to watch his night extravaganza.

Circling at 6,000 feet over the city, Inman waited for a big searchlight to stab upward, the signal to begin. Then down he came, trailing white smoke and all three engines roaring wide open. Pandemonium broke loose as the big ship zoomed and rolled and dove low across the rooftops. A cordon of motorcycle cops, sirens screaming, thundered from the state capital building to the airport as the searchlight, mounted on a truck, followed, holding Inman's ship like a butterfly on a pin. Thanks to Inman's drag with the governor's office, the night show was a sellout, and Inman raked in enough money, from flying passengers over the city in the trimotor, to settle the lease.

Harold S. Johnson, of Chicago, was another barnstormer who found it profitable to operate a big ship. Johnson won fame of a sort by being the first to stunt a Ford Trimotor, looping and rolling the big tin monster to attract the suckers to the airport for dollar rides.

Another wild man who barnstormed with a Ford Trimotor was a Texan known as Crazy John. Working a regular beat from Houston to Dallas, Crazy John, who was not too sharp a navigator, marked his compass with an arrow and the legend, "This Way to Dallas." One time, Crazy John caught a rube carving his initials on the side of his beautiful tin bird. In retaliation he followed the man to his nice new car and scratched "Crazy John" on the hood.

A friend of Crazy John was Carl Squier, a motorcycle racer who learned to fly at Rockwell Field in 1916 and who later became a Lockheed vice president. During the barnstorming years, Squier formed an air circus that featured a mock dogfight between himself in a Spad and his partner, Eddie Stinson, in a Sopwith Camel. The dogfight invariably drew big crowds, but Squier could not understand why the barker was not selling many ride tickets. He investigated and found out what was wrong—it was the spiel.

"Anybody else want to take a chance—fifteen dollars for five minutes?" the barker begged. Squier groaned and put him straight.

A favorite story of Squier's concerns another barnstormer friend of his, who went miles out of his way to land at a farm in the Midwest where, a few years before, he had been much more than congenially entertained by a farmer's beautiful daughter. She met him by the haystack—with a two-year-old boy who was a dead ringer for the pilot.

"Is that my son?" he asked, both shocked and pleased. When she nodded, he asked, "Then why didn't you write and tell me?"

The girl blushed, then admitted: "Daddy said he'd rather have a bastard in the family than a pilot!"

Squier's partner, Eddie Stinson, although a skilled pilot, once crashed a new ship through a fence upside down when his mechanic rigged the aileron wire backward. "Misfortune just hit me in the face," he groaned when Squier ran up to see what had happened.

Eddie Stinson was one of four brothers and sisters who made a name for themselves in aviation's hurly-burly days before World War I. The boys, Eddie and Jack, started out as mechanics and helpers to their flying sisters, Katherine and Margie. First to solo was Kathy, who learned to fly at the old Max Lillie Flying School, one of twenty struggling schools at crowded Cicero Field near Chicago, in 1912. Barely 5 feet tall, Kathy was only eighteen when she soloed, but quickly she became the darling of the skies. When the great Linc Beachey was killed in San Francisco, Kathy bought the wreckage of his plane and got a well-known airplane designer, E. M. ("Matty") Laird, to build a new ship around its Gnome rotary engine. With this ship, Kathy became the first woman to fly through a loop. After a whirlwind tour of the United States and Canada, Kathy became the first aviatress to perform in Japan. She spent the war years at San Antonio with her sister, Margie, training military pilots for the United States and Canadian governments.

While parachute jumps were standard fare at air circuses of the 1920's, a team of four Oklahomans hit the barnstorm trail as the Hunter Brothers Flying Circus and pulled sizable crowds by advertising their specialty—a "Thrilling Death Leap from an Airplane WITHOUT a Parachute!" The brothers, Walter, Albert, Kenneth, and John, were as rugged a bunch of grease-stained, leather-putteed flying gypsies as ever bored a hole through the sky. They capped their performance by buzzing low across the field, with Walter hanging by his knees from the axle of their Standard biplane, while one of the other three brothers flew at just above stalling speed. In a stiff wind, this might be only 20 miles an hour; but on calm days, Walt had to jump from the ship twice that fast. And the old adage, "it isn't the fall that kills you, it's the landing," was something they prepared for in advance. Walt timed his drop to land smack in a haystack.

Beating the bushes for ride customers was highly profitable right after World War I ended; but as time went on and the novelty of flying wore off, aerobatics played an increasing role in a successful barnstorming tour. Handsome young Doug Davis, a second lieutenant in the Air Corps, left out of a job when the Armistice was signed, decided to try his luck barnstorming, even though he was one of the worst pilots ever to come from Kelly Field.

Davis sunk his life savings—four hundred dollars—in a war-surplus clipped-wing Jenny and set up shop at Chandler Race Track, on the outskirts of Atlanta, Georgia. For a while things went well; the passengers did not know the difference when Davis slipped and skidded all over the sky. And they did not mind paying a dollar a ride while Doug literally taught himself to fly.

Competition appeared one day in the person of a cigar-chomping gypsy flier named Beeler Blevins, who fishtailed in to a landing on the race track infield, jumped out, and told Davis: "Sonny, the sky ain't big enough here for both of us!" Davis took a good look at Blevins, who towered a head taller than himself, and decided maybe he was right. He pulled stakes and began beating the back country for suckers—and found a gold mine.

"Tell you what," he would inform the rubes who gathered around his Jenny, when he slipped into a tiny field outside some Georgia hamlet, "the first man to step forward gets two rides for the price of one!" By taking aviation to the grass roots masses, Davis was tapping a limitless source of revenue, which he invested in more airplanes. Early in 1924, he rounded out a complete squadron of daredevil pilots, who flew under the banner of the Doug Davis Flying Circus.

Other loners, amazed at Davis' success, quickly joined his retinue. George Sheally, Johnny Kytle, Vivian Jones, Frank Ward, and Doug's brother Paul helped him take $1,400 from the crowd at Opelika, Alabama, on his first venture into that state. Things were all champagne and roses until the next spring, when the circus hit Birmingham. Practically nobody turned out. Puzzled, Davis investigated.

His problem was a girl. Not just an ordinary, everyday girl.

A very beautiful, amply endowed girl with golden hair and sky-blue eyes that could laugh or blaze in anger. They belonged to Mabel Cody, a nerveless flying hellion and wing-walker who had just put together her own air show. Mabel, Davis learned, liked to race a speedboat underneath a flying airplane and leap aboard, then clamber over the wings while the pilot performed all sorts of gyrations.

Like Katherine Stinson, another Southern girl, Mabel was one to believe that a woman's place was in the sky, not the kitchen. Other stunt pilots and acrobats were glad to join Mabel Cody's Flying Circus. She moulded them into as perfect a functioning aerobatic team as ever buzzed a hick town upside down. Among her stalwarts were such performers as Bonnie Rowe, a former smokestack painter who was also a war balloonist and a parachute jumper. Rowe was the first stunt man to make a plane-change with one hand tied behind him. Another of his favorite tricks was to hang from a trapeze bar swinging 15 feet below a speeding plane—by his toes!

Rowe frequently hocked his parachute to pay for a wild party, a practice that at times forced him to take extreme measures to go on with the show. He and his pals would sit up all night sewing bed sheets, stolen from their hotel, into a makeshift canopy. Occasionally one would rip open in mid-air, but Rowe never suffered more than a sprained ankle from the too speedy fall.

Curly Burns was Mabel's secret weapon. Burns, who was Mabel Cody's advance man, always saw that one of her pilots was starred over the others. Dressed in a snappy military uniform, this hero-for-a-day would outfly the others and work up the crowd to a great pitch of excitement. They would fight each other for the honor of flying with the great aviator, who personally autographed a certificate for them to hang on their walls at home, framed, a practical reminder if the circus came that way again.

If there was a buck to be made in the provinces, Curly saw to it that Mabel Cody made it. With shrewd timing, he built the crowds to a pitch of excitement with the finesse of an orchestra leader, while the airplanes zoomed and swooped through the sky overhead. Invariably they would line up to fly with the "ace" of the show, for such was Curly's power of suggestion and persuasion that the pilot might just as well have been Eddie Rickenbacker.

All this hoopla cut deeply into Doug Davis' pocketbook, and in desperation he tried to hire Mabel's top aerial performers away with salaries double what she paid them. But the Cody Circus stunt men remained loyal under the spell of Mabel and Curly's high-pressure salesmanship. Davis, not one to admit defeat, next plunged recklessly into a gigantic advertising campaign, plastering towns with gaudy billboards weeks in advance of a show. Again Mabel outsmarted him; she simply moved the Cody Circus in ahead of Davis' troupe and skimmed off the cream.

In desperation, Davis began adding newer and more dangerous stunts. His entire squadron of Standards and Jennys would roar into town over the rooftops, buzz the main street in line astern, and then go looping off to the airport. A few crashes were inevitable, but the business picked up. Mabel's boys began flying harder than ever; and she, too, began to feel the pinch when her pilots started crashing their way into Kingdom Come.

Then one day, Doug Davis played his trump card. He buzzed over the field where the Cody Circus was limping through its performance, flew low over the grandstand upside down, and tossed something at Mabel, who was standing beside her ship on the infield of the town's race track. Mabel ducked and let go a string of curses at Davis, who flew off waggling his wings in glee. This was too much; rivalry was rivalry, but to try and kill your competitor was something else! Then she picked up the object Davis had tossed at her and laughed. It was a champagne bottle with a note inside.

"Dear Mabel," it read. "We ain't doing each other much good fighting. What do you say we join forces? Sincerely yours, Douglas."

She showed the note to her boys at a pilot meeting and asked what they thought. Slim Culpepper, a former Navy pilot who was starring in the Cody Circus that day, spoke up. "Hell, Mabel, like we said in the Navy, if you can't lick 'em, join 'em!"

Curly Burns lit a fresh cigar and blew a thoughtful smoke ring. "He's right, Mabel. We're both losing money this way. We've skimmed off the cream. And besides—" he grinned and pulled a telegram out of his pocket "—the Curtis Candy Company wants to sponsor us. I think I can use this as a lever to get us a good deal with Davis!"

That evening, as the sun went down, the sky over eastern Alabama was filled with an incredible band of gypsy fliers. Mabel buzzed Davis' field, tossing the champagne bottle back with a new note: "Okay, sucker, but come up and fight first!"

Davis read the note and knew what Mabel meant. It was her way of accepting defeat. He told his pilots to follow and roared off into the crimson sky, where Mabel Cody and her boys waited like eagles ready to pounce on a flight of sparrows. For half an hour, the two flying circuses put on an impromptu show the likes of which had never been seen before—or since.

Davis and Mabel Cody drove toward each other at full throttle. On the ground, a group of perplexed farmers looked up and cried, "Mother of Jesus, they're gonna kill each other!" At the last second, as if by prearrangement, both Doug Davis and Mabel Cody executed half-snaps and shot past each other with their upper wings brushing, and staring each other in the eyes so close they could have reached out and touched hands.

The other pilots drew back to watch, for they knew that the two masters were out to prove who was the better stunt artist. Like two angry hornets, they came at each other again, and for the next few minutes they put on perhaps the wildest, most uninhibited dogfight ever seen. Mabel got on Doug's tail and would not get off. He looped, rolled, and stunted all over the sky, but she hung on like a barnacle. In desperation, Doug dove for the ground, flipped sideways, and flew between a row of tall poplars, like a knife slicing through butter. Mabel was right behind him. At the end of the road loomed a bridge. Doug flipped upside down and shot beneath it, his head inches above the muddy river. In his rear-view mirror he saw that Mabel had not budged.

Finally, Doug knew he had to do something really spectacular to show Mabel up. Down below, he spotted a freight train winding along the tracks like a big caterpillar. He grinned, dove for the train, and pulled up over the caboose. He eased off the throttle, adjusting his speed to that of the train, inched ahead to an empty flat car and dropped down for a three-point landing!

Pleased with himself, Davis crawled out of the cockpit and up over the boxcar behind him. There stood Mabel Cody, in front of her Standard, legs apart and hands on hips. "Okay, cowboy," Mabel laughed. "Now how do you propose we get these things off here?"

The merger of the two flying circuses took place then and there, atop a westbound freight, somewhere in Alabama. From that day on, they flew under one banner—"The Doug Davis–Baby Ruth Flying Circus"—to become the most famous barnstorming troupe in history.

It would be a fitting end to the story to relate that Mabel and Doug got married and lived happily ever after on a prolonged flying honeymoon, but that was not to happen. At the Cleveland Air Races in 1934, Davis entered the dangerous Thompson Trophy Race, flying a Wedell-Williams racer, No. 44, against one of the finest racing pilots in America, Colonel Roscoe Turner. For eight spine-chilling laps, Davis and Turner battled through the field virtually wingtip-to-wingtip. Then, in the backstretch, Davis pulled up suddenly to avoid overrunning Turner. His racer snap-rolled viciously and dived into the ground, exploding in a ball of flame.

Barnstormers were heroes to kids who grew up in America in the 1920's, just as the Astronauts are today's idols. My particular favorite was a handsome, carefree birdman named Skeet Sliter, who dropped into my life in a floatplane one glassy day at Canada Lake, New York. Skeet, famous in upstate New York as the Eagle of the Adirondacks, tossed out the Sunday papers before landing, so he could see the surface.

The girls just naturally flocked around Skeet, begging for rides; and I made up my mind then and there to become an aviator. Some of my enthusiasm dampened when I listened wide-eyed to Skeet's "hangar-flying" stories.

Sliter learned to fly in 1927—right after Lindbergh had made America air crazy with his hop to Paris—with an instructor named Red Harris. "Red liked to cut his initials in a wheat field," Skeet reminisced. "He'd buzz right through it, his propeller chewing out the letters. The *H* was easy but the *R* sometimes gave him a little trouble."

Skeet finally bought a Waco 10 with an OX-5 engine and began passenger-hopping at Dolgeville, New York, operating from a ball park with a 150-foot infield. Taking off and landing, he had to fly through a line of tall elm trees sideways, a feat that did not endear him to his customers.

When the 1929 depression began cutting into his passenger-hopping business, Skeet turned to running booze into New York, across the Canadian border. He had nine small fields to land in, but unfortunately the Coast Guard revenooers knew where they were and began lying in wait for him to come down. Twice they almost nabbed him; but he managed to spin his ship around and take off in the nick of time, showering them with a spray of dirt. He finally arranged with his bootlegger contact, a man named Lee Roth and now deceased, to lay out a sheet in the corner of the field that was safe to land in. But one time, when he was about to land a Pitcairn Mailwing, loaded down with twenty-two cases of Golden Wedding, Skeet saw a Model T Ford race out onto the runway with a big sign on top: "LAND AT ONCE!" He did—right on top of the Coast Guardsmen. It cost him a $500 fine and the loss of his cargo.

Another time, Skeet got into an argument as to whether a domesticated turkey could fly worth a damn. "We got one drunk and I took it up to a thousand feet and shoved it out. It flew fine!" he recalls.

During the 1929 American Legion Convention in Utica, New

York, Skeet rented a Trimotor Ford to hop passengers; but the day he brought the ship up the Mohawk River from New York, the whole Mohawk Valley was socked in. "I flew under the bridge at Fonda and tore down a high-tension line at Little Falls," he shudders. "Then I figured I must be somewhere near Utica and set her down between some trees and bounced right into a barn. By sheer luck it was the field I was looking for!"

In the 1930's, Skeet operated the Central Adirondack Aviation Corporation from Eagle Bay in Fourth Lake, taking fishermen back into the heart of the pickerel and bass country. He liked it so well he settled down and bought a camp on a pine-covered shore of West Lake, where he could lie on his back and look up at the clouds and contrails and buzzards and say, "To hell with it! That stuff is for kids!"

One of the "kids" who carried on was Milo Burcham, one of the greatest stunt pilots of all time. "He did everything with a Boeing 100 except completely disassemble it," commented a friend, Cy Caldwell. "And he may even do that before he gets through!"

Burcham, a burglar-alarm salesman in Long Beach, California, got into aviation when he sold an alarm to Lloyd O'Donnell, an airport operator. O'Donnell paid Burcham off with flying lessons. By 1933, Burcham was stunting all over the sky in a Fleet; and in August of that year, he decided to see how long he could fly upside down. He made it all the way from San Diego up the coast to Los Angeles in one hour and forty-seven minutes without once seeing the sun; but the next day Tito Falconi, an Italian stunt artist, beat that by flying upside down two hours and eight minutes.

Burcham swallowed enough aspirin to make his headache go away—inverted flying forces extra blood into your head—and upped Falconi's record to two hours and twenty minutes; but the intrepid Italian flew inverted from St. Louis, Missouri, to Joliet, Illinois, a three-hour-and-six-minute run, while Burcham was on his way to pick up a new ship, his Boeing 100, at Hartford, Connecticut. On December 29, Burcham set a new record for inverted flight that nobody cared to shoot at—four hours five minutes and twenty-two seconds. He accomplished it by installing his engine upside down, so that it would be in an upright position when he flipped over. The toughest part of the flight, he admitted afterward, was pumping forty gallons of fuel to the engine with a hand wobble pump, no mean feat upside down. During the war, Burcham risked his life once too often as a test pilot. He died at the controls of a P-80, America's first production jet fighter.

Perhaps the most satisfying crowd-pleaser in the stunt business was a masochistic character named F. F. ("Bowser") Frakes, who decided that the best way to beat the Depression slump in barnstorming was to give the suckers what they came to see—a real, honest-to-God crack-up! On January 26, 1931, at a time when Doug Davis and Mabel Cody were finding slim pickings in Alabama, Bowser Frakes staged his first deliberate crash before a throng of blood-thirsty spectators who jammed an abandoned field near Mobile in hopes of seeing real blood.

Gawking skyward, they watched expectantly as Frakes, circling the field in a tired old Stearman biplane, suddenly fell off into a sickening spin. Down it came, hell-bent for death, as the crowd shrieked. At 500 feet, Frakes went into a tight spiral dive over the fence. He hit the deck hard, screeched around in a dust-raising groundloop, and came to a stop. The crowd groaned when the dust cleared; Frakes' body hung limply half out of the cockpit, half in. But soon he moved, shook his head, and staggered out, cut and bleeding but alive. The crowd forgave him for that, and went away satisfied. They had seen a genuine plane crash and loved it.

Frakes found the gate large enough to buy a different ship for each crash, a necessity as they were usually demolished beyond repair. He bought second-hand junkers for as little as $500, and often his percentage of the gate ran to $7,000. Jennies, Swallows, Travel Airs, Wacos, Gypsy Moths, and De Havillands all ripped apart under his crushing performances. For his own protection, Bowser relied on a shoulder harness; but occasionally he wore a football helmet.

Planning each act with detailed care, Frakes would climb to

2,000 feet and go into a two- or three-turn spin, then switch to a spiral dive, falling leaf, or whipstall. Just as the ship prepared to smash to earth, Frakes bent forward, pulled up his legs, and waited for the impact. He varied his act by crashing through board fences, small buildings, and sheets of flame, sometimes heightening the illusion by setting off a dynamite explosion simultaneously.

Bowser Frakes tried hard to please the crowds; but one time he failed, when the crate he was flying simply would not gain enough altitude over Clinton Field, Knoxville, Tennessee, to crash properly. The crowd took things into its own hands and rushed the field, setting the ship afire almost before Bowser could leap away.

Only once was Bowser hurt badly, when he kicked a Jenny into a flat spin over Anderson, Indiana, and could not get it out. He tore into a clump of trees and was thrown out, landing with a wrenched back that hospitalized him for a week.

Frakes' flirtatious romance with Death almost got the better of him one day in 1937, when he staged a "grand slam" crash at the Oklahoma City State Fair, diving into a wooden building soaked in gasoline to catch fire when he flew through it. The trouble was he did not fly through; he was trapped in the demolished cockpit of the Stearman, enveloped by flames. Firemen played their hoses over the blazing ship and Bowser, by a superhuman effort, tore himself free, his shirt and pants ablaze and one shoe missing. Back to the hospital he went, with second-degree burns.

At Great Falls, Montana, Bowser convinced himself he could survive one of aviation's most terrifying accidents—a head-on collision with another plane. With sufficient cash inducement, he talked another stunt pilot, John Jabo, into flying the other ship; and on an August day in 1938 that might have been his last, Bowser piloted his Waco into position over the grandstand, while Jabo came at him on a collision course. The two ships swept past each other by inches—the buildup—and then circled into position for the "death" run. In the turn, perhaps luckily,

Frakes' wing suddenly buckled 100 feet above the ground. The Waco crashed to earth and out stepped Bowser—still alive.

All in all, Frakes deliberately crashed ninety-eight airplanes in acts that might well have passed for premeditated murder or suicide. His ninety-ninth crash was accidental; he nosed up a ship when his controls locked on landing at a Tennessee airport. Then, figuring that his 100th crash might be the final act for him, Bowser gave up plane-crashing and turned to a saner line of stunt work—climbing into a coffin with five sticks of dynamite and blowing himself up.

10

The King of Hollywood

IT LOOKED FOR ALL THE WORLD like a shaping air battle high above the Normandy coast, with snarling warplanes of the Royal Flying Corps and the German Air Force rushing together to join in the greatest aerial dogfight in history.

But World War I was already nine years past; and in the cold sky thousands of feet above San Francisco Bay, two score of the most skilled and daring pilots in the world were about to clash in a deliberate melee that would surpass in drama most of the great air battles over Europe.

Towering cumulus clouds formed the backdrop, a gigantic upheaval of swirling vapors piled like whipped cream against the cerulean blue of space. Breaking through the mists came a tight formation of weird biplanes, an aerial armada the likes of which had never before been seen. Snarling angrily and stinking of burning castor oil loomed the dawn patrol of oddball crates—SE-5's, Sopwiths, Snipes, Avros, Canucks.

At that instant, from the opposite direction came a second formation of warplanes—Fokker D-VII's, their coffinlike fuselages silhouetted against the massive cloud as they streaked into combat. In the lead fighter huddled a German pilot, garbed in black, a white scarf streaming back from his tight leather helmet. Quickly the pilot glanced over his left shoulder, his eyes flashing behind oval goggles. Below the cockpit's rim, in bold white letters, was emblazoned the dreaded name: *von Richthofen!*

The German killer raised a gloved hand in a signal to the others. Then the Fokker banked over, half-rolling into a screaming dive toward the formation of white enemy planes.

Frank Clarke, the greatest living stunt pilot, felt a strange exhilaration as he led his group into a rough-and-tumble melee that would make aviation—and cinematic—history. The sky was an erratic mélange of more than forty World War I fighters, suddenly mixing it up in a whirling, diving, screaming dogfight, more spectacular than any ever watched from the trenches of the Meuse-Argonne.

Hell's Angels, the most extravagant aerial epic ever to come from Hollywood, was building up to its triumphant climax. Unreal as the actual battle scene was, Clarke knew that death still lurked in the sky; not death from the sting of tracers from white-hot machine gun muzzles, but from imminent collisions in hairbreadth misses by the incredible flying of the craziest squadron of stunt pilots ever to shove a control stick and slam a rudder. One slip, one miscalculation could snuff out two lives.

For months, Clarke had led his motley crew of stunting birdmen through one scene after another of the flying extravaganza. He had felt rising anger and frustration, trying to coordinate the sky of contorting ships; each time something had gone wrong: the cloud background did not look right to Howard Hughes; the ships were out of camera range; cameras jammed; or half a dozen pilots would spiral earthward from the mock battle with all-too-realistic engine trouble.

Now, late in December, 1927, Clarke meant to wind up the titanic air fight with a dazzling display of in-fighting that would never be forgotten. As his black machine rolled over inverted and plunged down toward the "enemy" formation, he singled out the lead ship, an SE-5 flown by Roy Wilson, another pilot famed for his daring and recklessness in the sky.

The aerial cameramen did not want to miss this one; Clarke had a grudge to settle with Wilson, and anything might happen. The day before, Wilson had sliced away a part of Clarke's

Fokker's tail in mid-air by spinning down on top of him, and then had slipped off into a cloud unrecognized. Later, Clarke discovered Wilson's damaged SE-5 in the hangar at Oakland Airport. He was furious.

"Sure, you've got to get in close to make it look realistic," he shouted, "but damn it, Roy, you could have killed me!"

Wilson looked up from where he was sitting and grinned sardonically. "What's the matter, Frank?" he sneered. "You getting old?"

Clarke's reaction was violent. "Listen," he snapped, "any time you want to play chicken, just waggle your wings and let me know. And then get the hell out of the way!"

As the formations closed on each other, Clarke saw Wilson's wings suddenly waggle and remembered his own words. "Okay, Buster!" he yelled into the slipstream. Signaling his wingmen to break away, Clarke rolled swiftly right-side up and aligned his gunsight dead on Wilson's SE-5, approaching head-on.

Above and behind him, Harry Perry, Hollywood's top aerial cinematographer, was swinging his gyroscopically-mounted Akeley camera, following *von Richthofen* as the camera ship chased the swift Fokker. Clarke grinned as he thought of what Perry would be getting on film as he shot from the Thomas-Morse Scout piloted by Frank Tomick. Hughes had already poured $300,000 into getting this one single sequence; he was after the jackpot now.

The SE-5 loomed larger and larger in his sights as Clarke bored straight ahead. A nerveless man, lean, muscular, Clarke hunched his 6-foot frame and tensed. Beneath him was his parachute. Hughes had insisted his pilots wear them; and while Clarke felt that was for sissies, it also made him, for the first time in his unusual flying career, careless.

"Okay, move over!" he yelled explosively into the wind. "I'm comin' through!"

Wilson felt his mouth go dry as he saw Clarke's Fokker bearing down on him.

For Clarke to pull up now would mean a personal defeat. He knew that Wilson was tops, one of the best. But he preferred to have the two ships slam together in a head-on flaming crash than to swerve away.

Closing on each other at better than 200 miles an hour, the black and white enemy fighters seemed bent on suicidal destruction.

In his excitement, cameraman Perry stood up and forgot to turn the crank. "Pull up!" he cried. "Damn it, Frank, pull up!"

One fighter swerved—at the last split second. It was the white one.

Clarke felt the sudden sharp jolt as Wilson's landing gear slashed across his top wing, ripping the fabric. A second later and he had the Fokker pulling up through a steep Immelmann turn, climbing hard. Beneath his cowling, Clarke carried a Hall Scott L6 engine that gave him a power advantage over the Hispano-powered SE-5. His Fokker arched over the sky in a dramatic, silhouetted turn against the alabaster cloud; again he dove after Wilson, closing in on his tail now.

All around him, Clarke saw the sky filled with dogfighting airplanes, but he was intent on only one of them. Gradually, he closed the distance on Wilson, but Wilson was running scared. The SE-5 suddenly whipped its nose skyward and shot into a vertical climb. Clarke grimly hung on.

Wilson felt his ship slow, the controls grow sluggish; he was on the ragged edge of a stall. He jammed in full right rudder, kicking the SE-5 over through a violent stall-turn. And again he tried for the advantage, diving straight down at the climbing Fokker. Clarke hesitated one second, then yanked back the stick and kicked the Fokker into a whirling spin as the white biplane shot inches past him in its dive. He saw Wilson thumb his nose as he flashed past.

Clarke's Fokker gradually inched up on Wilson, easing out of the spin and sliding in close by cross-controlling. A moment later and he had locked wingtips with those of the SE-5.

"Okay! Okay!" Wilson shouted across to Clarke as they dove earthward in a tightening spiral. "You win!"

Laughing, Clarke pulled away and turned back into the thick of the dogfight. He saw with a shock that two fighters had collided directly above him and were spinning down, out of control. He recognized them as ones being flown by Ira Reed and Stuart Murphy. The latter abruptly hurled himself from the cockpit of his demolished SE-5; the body continued to fall as Murphy made a delayed drop to clear the tumbling wreckage. Reed's Fokker staggered off and disappeared.

Later, on the ground, Clarke met Reed walking home. He had flown his battered ship 40 miles before all the fabric ripped away from one wing, exposing two broken spars.

"Hey, Spooks," he yelled at Clarke. "I won't get fired, will I? I got her down okay."

"Hell, no," Clarke grinned at him. "You looked good on film!"

Clarke had won the nickname "Spooks" from Hughes because of a gag the millionaire producer had pulled on him one time during a table-tilting seance. Hughes slid a Coke bottle under one table leg and nearly choked laughing at Clarke's consternation when the table would not level itself.

Fun-loving, easy-going, Clarke was a man of strange contrasts. Seemingly completely relaxed, he was one of the coolest pilots ever to risk his neck flying before a camera. He loved his work and his men, and he felt a personal loss when three fellow pilots died in the filming of *Hell's Angels*.

First to die was Clem ("Little Phil") Phillips, who shared ownership of a Waco with Western actor Ken Maynard. Phil was told by Clarke to fly an SE-5 from Glendale Airport north to Oakland, where the big dogfight scene for *Hell's Angels* was to be shot; there were not enough clouds over San Fernando Valley to please Howard Hughes, the perfectionist. En route, Phil landed for gas in a small field; and on takeoff, his engine quit at an altitude of 100 feet. He spun in, breaking his neck in the crash.

The second *Hell's Angels* tragedy occurred when Al Johnson tore out some power lines, crashed, and was burned alive in the wreckage.

More horrifying was the death of a young mechanic, Phil Jones, who was running the smoke pots in the tail of a Sikorsky painted up to look like a German Gotha bomber, apparently on fire and spinning out of control.

Jones had volunteered to do the job for $100, which he needed to buy some medicine. The pilot was Al Wilson, a reckless devil-may-care stunt pilot, who agreed to fly the ship after both Clarke and Jimmy Angel, another sharp airman, had shaken their heads. The Gotha was in such bad shape that they figured it did not have a chance.

At 7,500 feet, Wilson kicked the big ship into a spin; as it swung through the first turn, Wilson heard a spar snap. He yelled to Jones to jump and bailed out. But Jones, huddled back over the big smoke pot, did not hear him. As Clarke followed the crippled ship down in his camera plane, he was startled to see the smoke stop and start up again. That meant Jones had started up the second pot, obviously unaware of disaster.

Clarke shoved over into a vertical dive, hoping to slam his wheels against the Gotha hard enough to alert Jones to his plight in time for him to jump. He was too late; the big ship spun all the way down into an orange grove and exploded. Jones died in a ball of flame.

Throughout Clarke's years of stunt flying, death was his constant companion. Somehow, through skill, careful planning, and luck, he managed to stay one jump ahead of the grim reaper. In general, Caddo Field, the movie airport Clarke built in San Fernando Valley and named for Hughes' production company, had high safety standards. Equipped as a complete military field, it employed several hundred ground crewmen and mechanics, who kept the old combat crates flyable. There were plenty of incidents to keep Clarke jittery, and even he paled one day when Hughes himself insisted upon personally flying a Thomas-Morse, with its infamous Le Rhone rotary engine.

At the age of twenty, Hughes was a "boy genius" who had already brought in a celluloid money-maker, entitled *Two Arabian Knights*, starring William Boyd and Louis Wolheim. Hughes defied box-office tradition by not using any females in the picture, and stunned everybody by bringing home a box-office smash.

Intrigued with aviation, Hughes learned to fly to get a better feel for the subject and then began assembling his *Hell's Angels* fleet. The first was the Sikorsky that took Jones' life; Roscoe Turner, the racing pilot, had brought it out from the East Coast.

The Thomas-Morse incident began with Hughes berating Ben Lyon, his male lead, for excessive flying. Lyon, a private pilot as well as an actor, laughed in Hughes' face. "I'll knock off flying if you will," he said.

Hughes accepted the retort as a personal challenge and stalked angrily inside the hangar. Moments later, he rolled out the Thomas-Morse, fired up the engine, climbed in, and took off. You did not just fly the vicious little ship; unaware of the overpowering gyroscopic torque of the spinning rotary engine, Hughes completely lost control in his first turn and spun wildly into the ground. Horrified, Clarke dashed out to the wreckage.

"Howard," he shouted as Hughes crawled out. "Are you all right?"

"I guess so," Hughes replied weakly.

"Thank God," Clarke sighed. "I thought for a moment we'd lost our meal ticket!"

Hughes grinned at him.

Frank Clarke served his apprenticeship as a fledgling pilot at the old Venice Field, a barley patch on the edge of Santa Monica Bay. This was the locale of the great ones; barnstormers and carnival flyers gathered there to try out new ways to cheat death for money in the good old wood-and-wire days of open cockpit flying. Venice, it is claimed, turned out more unique aerial acts than any other airport in the world, largely because of its proximity to Hollywood, the nation's film capital and West Coast center for worldwide newsreels.

In 1918, Clarke made his first solo flight. It was a bright Sunday morning, and no one could ever accuse Clarke of moving slowly in the barnstorming business. That same afternoon, he took up twelve passengers at ten dollars a head. Two of the best-known early birds, Al Wilson and Swede Meyerhofer, were his instructors, and what they failed to teach him he invented for himself.

For the first two years that Clarke flew at Venice Field, Lady Luck was kind; there were no fatalities and only the usual number of crack-ups. And then, as so often happens, tragedy came in bunches. Clarke watched six of his closest buddies killed before his eyes.

First to go was Joe Hoff, a Venice tailor who had built Clarke's first airplane, but who lacked skill as a pilot. He dove straight through the Venice pier while stunting on the deck one afternoon, killing a passenger as well as himself. A short time later, Herb Wilson and his mechanic drowned when their flying boat plunged out of control into the ocean. Then B.H. De Lay, flying with a close friend of Clarke, Ruel Short, tore the wings from his plane while trying to pull out of a vertical dive. Completing the run of bad luck, Swede Meyerhofer finally got it in grisly fashion—despite the hand-lettered sign over his hangar door that read: "Pilots may come and pilots may go, but the Swede goes on forever!" The Swede did not die in the air, however; he simply forgot to let go of the propeller, trying to start his Standard's engine one morning, and stumbled into it when the engine backfired. The blade sliced his body in two.

Frank Clarke maintained that a stunt pilot was born, not made; you could not make an eagle out of a duck. He once explained this philosophy to friends: "I never heard of a man coming to the flying field and saying, 'I want to learn to be a wing-walker.' Flying stunt men just *appear*." Such a man was Al Johnson, who became one of Hollywood's great stunt pilots, before losing his life in a simple stall-spin accident while flying for *Hell's Angels;* Johnson got started in the business simply by showing up at Venice Field one day and volunteering to execute a plane-change for ten dollars.

The first plane-change on record was brought off in 1919 by Lieutenant Omar Locklear, who startled an audience of Texans by stepping off the top wing of one airplane and climbing up a rope ladder to another, flying directly overhead. When word of Locklear's feat reached the stunt men at Venice Field, they

flatly refused to believe it could be accomplished. It was well
and good to crawl all over a single airplane in flight, but to leap
from one to another was so much hogwash. However, a producer at Famous Players–Lasky Studios heard about it, too,
and decided to use the routine in a Houdini movie; Lieutenant
Al Kennedy, spanking-fresh from the air war in Europe, agreed
to give it a whirl.

C.V. Pickup and Tommy Thompson discussed it with Clarke
and finally agreed to risk it, a decision they regretted. Flying in
tight formation over Venice Field, with a camera ship hovering
close by, the two airplanes locked wings. The two pilots fought
wildly at the controls but without avail. Helpless, they watched
their ships swing around to smash head-on, their propellers
grinding into each other like angry bulldogs. Thompson spun
crazily into a bean field a mile away and by a miracle survived
the crash. Pickup and Kennedy—the latter grimly clinging to his
rope ladder—glided down into a tomato field. They had their
second miracle of the day when both men walked away from
the wreckage without serious injury, although Kennedy looked
like a bloody mess, covered with mashed tomatoes.

Clarke hated to send men up on something he had not tried
out himself, and he announced he would make the next attempt. The only rope ladder he could find, however, was rotten,
and Clarke volunteered to attempt the trick bare-handed. No
one, including Locklear, had ever done that before.

At 3,000 feet, Clarke crawled out onto the wingtip of Howard
Patterson's Waco. Al Wilson flew a Standard above and behind
Patterson. But this was not going to be any easy job. . . .

Unexpected turbulence threw Wilson's judgment off badly.
His wingtips smashed Clarke on the jaw, sending him sprawling
10 feet back along the wing, his feet tearing through the fabric
of the center section. That little accident saved his life. Clarke
was out cold.

When he revived, Clarke's head was a pinwheel of bright
stars. But he started crawling back again, toward the wingtip.
Any other man would have called it quits and still have been
acclaimed a hero. But Clarke was blindly determined to go

through with the act. He stood up once more, precariously balanced in the tearing wind, and signaled Wilson to move his wing back into position for the change. With Wilson's wing skid directly overhead, Clarke reached up—and missed. He recovered his balance after nearly toppling off into space, and tried again. This time, his fingers closed around the metal skid on Wilson's wing, and he scrambled aboard!

In one way, that first plane-change might have been a bad mistake for Clarke; he had the fever now and he was eager to try out every stunt in the books—plus a few that he would invent himself. He began by taking up wing-walking, a peculiar form of suicide first accomplished the year before by Mark Campbell, a stunt man who worked the East Coast. Clarke left Venice Field on a barnstorming tour with his mechanic, Wally Timm, who was just learning to fly. Timm would later teach Art Goebel, winner of the Dole Race to Honolulu; but at this time he did not know how to take off or land.

Once they were airborne, Clarke would turn the controls over to Timm, who put the ship in a shallow dive while Clarke crawled back to the tail. Then, bracing himself, he leaped forward to land in the cockpit. This bit of nonsense scared the spectators on the ground, and other pilots as well.

It also frightened Timm, but for a different reason. "Don't ever miss that cockpit, Frank," Timm pleaded with Clarke. "Because if you do and fall off, how in hell am I going to land this thing?"

Clarke once *did* miss the cockpit, although by good fortune an experienced pilot, Ray Goldsworthy, was at the control instead of Timm. Clarke bounded forward from the tail and smashed through the turtleback behind the cockpit with the seat of his pants. Goldsworthy brought the ship down for a landing with Clarke still ignominiously stuck there.

Another time, Clarke decided to outdo himself with a spectacular stunt never tried before: he would leap from the ground and hang on to a speeding plane flying overhead. He had no intention of changing to the plane from a speeding car; he meant to accomplish the feat by running along the ground and snatching at a rope dragged by the airplane. His friends told him he was mad; Clarke agreed.

Airmail Pilot E. L. Remlin came across the field, flying low and at a slow speed, with the rope trailing. Clarke took off in a cloud of dust, sprinting to build up speed before the rope reached him. He grabbed it and hung on, then promptly was towed down the runway in enormous 100-foot strides that made him appear to be hurtling through the air in balloonlike leaps. But he could not get his body into position to climb the rope and finally, gasping for air, let go and rolled to a stop.

Continually plotting new stunts to draw crowds to his air shows, or to land a movie stunt job, Clarke reached some sort of pinnacle of nuttiness one day, terrifying an audience of thousands of people by taking off solo and then calmly climbing back onto the tail of the airplane! His idea was to fly the ship with a rope that ran through a pulley system to the control stick on the cockpit. It was a great idea, but Clarke never seemed to follow up his ideas with quality equipment. On his first attempt, sitting astride the tail as if he were riding the cruppers of a big horse, he tugged at the rope. It snapped. Immediately, with the weight of Clarke's body on the tail, the plane clawed upward into a violent whipstall. It hung there on the prop while Clarke dug his fingers into the fuselage and clung to it for his life, not knowing what would come next. With a wild plunge, the ship's nose dove under, snapping the tail back and almost throwing Clarke to his death. Finally settling down in a screaming power dive, the airplane steadied itself enough for Clarke, inching ahead sans parachute, to reach the cockpit and crawl back inside.

The next time he used a new rope. . . .

Frank Clarke finally crashed Hollywood, after making a name for himself on the barnstorming circuit, by coming up with a new stunt that nobody else had thought of. He dressed himself up in a cop's uniform and then chased Mark Campbell, in convict stripes, all over the ship—in flight, of course. There was no hidden pilot doing the flying, either; Clarke simply tied the controls in neutral with a length of rope, climbed out of the cockpit, and for the next few minutes, with the plane staggering all over the sky, he pursued Campbell out over the wings, down through the undercarriage and back up the other side!

After this episode, Clarke hit the barnstorming trail once more. He was particularly vexed with the public's behavior on the ground; folks getting their first look at a flying machine up close clambered all over his Jenny, into the cockpit, over the wings, punching holes in the fabric and stealing instruments from the instrument panel for souvenirs. At the Venice Pier Midway, Clarke borrowed a healthy rattlesnake from a side-show pal and carried it with him when he went out of town. Whenever he had to leave the ship unattended, he removed the snake from the box and left it free inside the cockpit. Then, whenever some stranger started to climb in with screwdriver and pliers, to take home a free air speed indicator or altimeter, an angry rattle from the pilot seat was guaranteed to send him running in a hasty retreat.

Even the best of the pilots, if they pursued the crazy career of a stunt specialist, inevitably ran up against the odds, and Clarke was no exception. His first crack-up came one day as a result of letting discretion be overcome by an urge to valor. Flying an old Canuck World War I trainer, Clarke attempted a loop close to the ground, pulling out under some trolley wires. Diving down the backside of the loop, he suddenly spotted a big electric signboard he had not noticed before. Veering desperately to miss the sign, Clarke plowed smack into the wires. The first person he saw when he crawled from the wreckage was smiling Charley Crawford, the happy junkman who ran a Venice junk yard at a nice profit—supported by fool pilots who supplied cracked-up ships with dependable regularity.

Flying at Venice Field was a feast or a famine for Clarke and his friends. There were the lean times when the weather turned sour or road-show bookings fell off, and there were the days of great fortune when Hollywood script writers relied on them to add zest to a movie with "something new and different." In 1920, Clarke was hired to fly in a super air melodrama called

Stranger Than Fiction, an action film starring Katherine Mac-
Donald. The script, Clarke decided after reading it, was a lot
stranger than fact. The scenarist was calling for stunts that had
not yet been invented!

Zaniest was one that called for a gang of villains to chase
the hero to the top of a skyscraper. And there, for some reason
the writer did not make too clear to Clarke, would be waiting
the hero's plane. The script called for Clarke, doubling the
hero, to leap into the cockpit, look over his shoulder at his pursuers, and then leap off the skyscraper roof into space. Nobody
had ever flown an airplane off the top of a skyscraper, although
others, like the great Lincoln Beachey, had flown either around
or through large buildings and lived to tell about it. But if anybody could accomplish the feat, Clarke figured, *he* could.

He visited downtown Los Angeles and looked over the city's
sky line; the tallest structure was the brand-new Los Angeles
Railway Building, a thirteen-story height-limit structure.
(Earthquake hazards for years stopped construction, ironically,
at the thirteenth floor.) The roof was 95 feet wide, obviously
not enough to give Clarke's Jenny a running start capable of
getting him airborne without toppling off the edge of the building into the crowded street below. He decided it would be im-
proper to solicit police approval, but the building's contractor,
a rugged type, said, "Sure, Frank. Go ahead. I'm finished with
the job!"

With a select crew, Clarke dismantled his Jenny and hoisted
it to the top, where he had built a plank runway just wide
enough for the wheels, with an incline at one end to help lift
the plane into the air at the end of its dangerously brief take-
off run. The Jenny, sitting atop the roof of the building, naturally attracted considerable attention. When the building's
owner, on the East Coast, heard about the mad stunt, he sent
off a frantic wire forbidding it. Clarke read the telegram,
shoved it into his pocket, and dismissed it from his mind. But
worried civic officials were beginning to protest, and Clarke
knew he would have to act as if the phoney movie chase were
for real—which it was.

Angry public safety officials were riding up the elevator at the moment Clarke hurriedly started the engine, climbed into the cockpit, and signaled the camera crews to start cranking. While two assistants held tightly to a rope tied to the tailskid, Clarke ran the engine up to full power. At his signal, they let go, and the Jenny rolled down the wooden track, gathering momentum all too slowly. Clarke shoved forward on the stick to pick up the tail and reduce drag, and then the Jenny struck the incline. It shuddered and jumped 30 feet into the air above the rooftop. Thousands of amazed pedestrians on the streets below cheered as Clarke dove down between the buildings to pick up flying speed. Flying down the concrete canyon, with his wingtips barely grazing the buildings on either side, he streaked past the Examiner Building, waggling his wings happily at the throngs and swung off toward the airfield in Hollywood.

Two glaring motorcycle cops were waiting for him when he landed. "You're under arrest!" they yelled in chorus.

"For *what?*" Clarke demanded, eyes wide in amazement.

There was a long pause; finally, the first cop scratched his head and admitted candidly: "Damned if I know." Then he added, as an afterthought: "But why in hell did you do it, Frank?"

Clarke grinned sheepishly. "You know, officer, I got to rolling and couldn't stop. It was a case of either take off or fall into the street and kill a lot of people. You wouldn't have wanted *that*, would you?"

Clarke grinned some more. The officers left in disgust. Clarke roared with glee.

The *Stranger Than Fiction* script writer, highly pleased with himself, called Clarke into his office and outlined an even wackier stunt, which had come to him in the middle of the night.

"You dive out of this airplane, see?" the writer began enthusiastically. Clarke interrupted. "Just a minute, I wear a parachute, don't I?"

"Well, I guess so," the genius said, frowning as if Frank were spoiling his dream. Then he brightened. "Then while you're falling down the sky, see, this second plane comes in from camera left, trailing a 3-foot barbed grappling iron."

Clarke gulped. He had a mental picture of the sharp hook snagging him in the seat of the pants, like an albacore. But the Hollywood arm-chair stunt specialist eased his mind on this point. "You yank the ripcord and jerk to a stop—wham!—and suddenly in comes this hook and grabs hold of the canopy. Now —get this, Frank—the big scene is where you climb up the rigging into the second ship and beat hell out of the pilot, who naturally is the villain."

He stopped, pleased with himself, waiting for Clarke's reaction. "Okay, let's do it," he grinned. "I'll fly the camera ship!"

A newcomer to Venice Field, broker than the others, agreed to try the stunt—for fifty dollars. It was a steep fee as fees went in those days, before the Motion Picture Pilots Association and the Screen Actors Guild were in existence; but the studio reluctantly agreed to it.

Clarke, flying the camera ship, circled around the new stunt man, Sergeant Ray Sauren, as he stepped over the side of his cockpit. A line fouled, one of those things that happen. Sauren's body plunged earthward as Clarke dove after him, the cameraman grinding furiously away. With amazing coolness, Sauren pulled his knife and cut away his main chute, then deployed his reserve canopy. Lieutenant Ray Robinson, the "villain" pilot of the second ship, failed to see this little train of events and bore down on Sauren. Clarke knew Sauren's danger—with no other reserve chute, another mistake would seal his doom. Clarke dove at full speed, directly across in front of Robinson's ship.

Angrily, Robinson pulled up, circled, waved Clarke away, and dove in again, the big grappling hook trailing menacingly behind him. Once again, Clarke risked his life to intercept him. Robinson veered away, the hook swinging dangerously close to Clarke's airplane. But Sauren finally got his feet back on the ground safely—ready to try again for his fifty bucks.

This time things went smoothly, until the anchor jerked

through Sauren's parachute canopy with brutal force; it snapped the riser cords and nearly broke Sauren's back. Grimacing with pain, Sauren, for the second time, managed to jerk the ripcord of his reserve chute and reach the ground alive. They never tried the stunt again—much to the screen writer's disappointment.

When movie work slackened again, Clarke and his gang swung to the open road on another barnstorming tour, this time as a Wild West Flying Circus. Their first stop was El Centro, California, and advance publicity had brought ranchers in from miles around. The pilots were perplexed to see them pull off the road a good distance from the airfield and climb on top of their vehicles to watch the forthcoming show—for free. Clarke's anger boiled; their deal called for a percentage of the take at the airport entrance, and this was strictly a no-profit deal.

Clarke did not mean to let a bunch of yokels outsmart him; landing inside the airport, he briefed his teammates on a plan to force the freeloaders inside the fence. They took off in line astern, hopped low over the fence, and then roared along the road, wheels only inches from the ground. Scores of frightened men and women leaped off their cars, just in time to avoid the snarling, flashing propellers that chewed across the parked vehicles like a swarm of mad hornets. They got the message, and headed quickly for the safety of the grandstands.

At Yuma, Arizona, promoters booked the Flying Circus for a death-defying free-for-all race from Los Angeles to the Arizona border. The hoopla raised the ante for the prize winners and had the whole town betting on who would win. Favorites were Clarke, Ray Goldsworthy, Howard Patterson, and Swede Meyerhofer, in that order. The night before the big race, they flew out of town, presumably for Los Angeles, but stopped half way there, at Palm Springs. Carousing until the wee small hours, they grabbed a few winks of sleep and at dawn straggled back into the air. They hedge-hopped lazily along over the cactus country until they had Yuma in sight; then with throttles wide open and racing almost wingtip-to-wingtip, they sprinted across the field, in full view of the cheering crowd, which did not know the difference, and in fact did not care. All it had come to see was the finish, anyway. They also cleaned up enough "prize" money to move on to Tucson with full tanks and bellies.

It was in that city that Clarke's cronies saw another—and delightful, to them—side of the ace pilot. Clarke was described as "a handsome dog with a pencil mustache, a fondness for Irish whiskey, and a penchant for pretty girls." In Tucson, he fell madly in love with a dark-haired cabaret singer, who lived on the top floor of a big hotel, smack in the center of town.

Following a wild party one night, Clarke wrote her a passionate love letter, crammed it into a pocket of his leather flying jacket, and at dawn stumbled off to his plane. He flew low back to town, then roared as gloriously as a knight on a white charger down the main street, straight at the hotel. At the last moment before crashing into it, he hauled back hard on the stick. His airplane shot vertically into the air; Clarke rolled his wheels up the side of the building and flipped the note into his beloved's window, which he had thoughtfully left open an hour before. He pulled away in a graceful Immelmann turn, leaving Tucson a nervous wreck.

Clarke's buddies decided that this reaction was just what they needed to have some fun with him. They went to see the sheriff, who was snowed under with complaints from irate citizens. In those days, there were no specific laws against flying up the sides of hotels; but nevertheless, he was happy to issue a fake warrant for Clarke's arrest. When the sheriff served him with the warrant, and then unexpectedly demanded payment of a $10 fine, Clarke's buddies hastily, and testily, interceded.

"Hell, Sheriff," they cried, "he's just an inexperienced pilot who doesn't know any better!"

The sheriff tightened his lips and set his jaw. "Ten dollars, please," he repeated.

Clarke eyed him without blinking. "Tell you what, Sheriff," he drawled. "I'll pay you off with a plane ride!"

"No, thanks!" the lawman cried. "Fine suspended!"

On another occasion, Clarke clattered noisily down a Tucson

residential street and buzzed a milk wagon. The sudden roar
and sight of the airplane so unnerved the horse that it dashed
a hundred yards and collapsed in a heap—stone dead. The irate,
shouting milkman came to the airport and demanded $150 for
the dead beast. It took all the eloquence Clarke could muster
to convince the man that his horse had simply died of a heart
attack.

As a barnstormer, Clarke was learning all the tricks of making a buck with an airplane, from hopping passengers at $10
a head to putting on air shows or flying up the sides of buildings. His first student pilot was a young Japanese who was
sadly lacking in proficiency, although his supply of money was
valid. For this reason, Clarke decided against washing him out;
and against his better judgment, he turned the student loose
solo one day.

It happened that the Japanese owned his own ship, a war-
surplus Fokker; he eagerly told Clarke he meant to fly it alone
clear to Fresno, 200 miles north of Venice, to visit relatives.

"Okay," Frank told him, "but be sure to send me a telegram
that you landed okay at Fresno."

The student nodded, gave Clarke a toothy grin, and clambered into the cockpit, adjusting his helmet and goggles. He
staggered off the field and headed generally north, as Clarke
winced; a brisk north wind was blowing, and his boy was not
noteworthy as a navigator. Hours passed, the stars came out,
and still no message. Clarke started chewing on his fingernails
until, at 11 P.M., a Western Union messenger rode up to the
field on his bicycle. Hastily, Clarke tore open the envelope and
read:

LANDED FRESNO OKAY. UPSIDE DOWN.

Atropos, the inflexible Greek goddess of Destiny, in whose
power rests the decision of where and when to cut the thread
of life, had a running love affair with Frank Clarke. There is no
other explanation of how or why he lived as long as he did, considering the temptations he offered her. There was the time he
decided to thrill a barnstorming audience by climbing all over

the outside of a speeding airplane—*while his wrists were hand-cuffed!*

He was at 2,500 feet in his madman's act, working his way out along the lower wing, when his foot slipped. Instinctively he grasped for a flying wire with his right hand, forgetting all about the handcuffs. It was almost a lethal lapse of memory. The sudden lunging motion jerked his left hand free from a strut, and Clarke toppled backward in the howling wind. His body fell against a drift wire, preventing him at the last second from tumbling to his death.

Each miraculous escape seemed only to urge Clarke on to other stunts that taxed his imagination. One of his most dramatic acts took place when he blindfolded Al Johnson, put him in the cockpit, and then had Johnson, *still blindfolded*, crawl out along the top wing and lie on his back, sticking his feet up in the air. As Johnson hung in this precarious position, Art Goebel flew in from the rear and maneuvered a wingtip hook to adroitly snag Johnson between the legs, which were tied together. Jerked off the wing, Johnson pulled off the blindfold with a heroic gesture and almost fainted at the sight. There was nothing below him but solid ground, thousands of feet down. Clarke slid in beneath him, just in case he dropped off, but Johnson miraculously swung up onto the wing and scrambled into the cockpit behind Goebel, white as a sheet.

Clarke never missed a chance to play a hilarious joke on his friends. During the filming of the picture *Eagle of the Night* Clarke flew Jerry Fairbanks, the producer-cameraman, and a friend on a sight-seeing trip along the California-Mexico border. Before taking off, he warned Fairbanks that he was subject to strange spells and every now and then was possessed with an uncontrollable urge to leap from the cockpit. Jerry laughed weakly and climbed aboard.

While his passengers were enjoying the sights, Clarke ducked down into the depths of the rear cockpit and started flying the ship by pulling with his hands on the control cables. He put the airplane into a dive, then suddenly pulled up. He repeated this maneuver a second time until Fairbanks looked around to see what was going on. With a shock, he stared at an empty cockpit; neither Fairbanks nor his friend knew how to fly! (And Clarke had removed the controls from the front cockpit anyway!)

While the two passengers clung to each other in sheer terror, Clarke put the ship into a wild tailspin. Fairbanks yelled goodbye to his friend and prepared mentally for certain death. Then, miraculously, the ship stopped spinning and went into a sudden climb, back to level flight. Had death taken a holiday? Or . . .

Fairbanks, suspicious, looked behind him. There sat Clarke, flying nonchalantly along with a poker face, totally unconcerned, as if nothing had happened.

Fairbanks did not speak to him for a month.

Clarke could not escape forever the accidents that plagued the barnstormers and stunt men of that glorious era. Sooner or later, he realized, his amazing luck was bound to change. Thus he was not particularly alarmed, one bitterly cold winter day, when his engine quit while he was flying in his Standard—a mile off the California coastline—with Jimmy Hester, his mechanic. Clarke looked quickly around and spotted a Japanese fishing boat; he glided deadstick toward the vessel and pancaked neatly onto the water, without damaging the ship.

Half awash and half frozen in the cold water, Clarke saw that Hester, his pockets filled with wrenches, was starting to sink. He threw him a line just as the fishing boat, its deck lined with jabbering sailors, pulled alongside. Clarke and Hester crawled back onto the airplane's tail to keep the engine out of the water, as the fishing vessel towed them to shore.

Dragging the ship ashore through the surf, they drained the carburetor, poured 5 gallons of borrowed gasoline into the tank, and took off again! The only aftereffect of the incident was a bad cold that plagued Clarke for a week.

In the early stunt-flying days, necessity mothered a multitude of inventions. Once, a wheel came loose and spun off the axle of a plane that Howard Batt was flying. Clarke and Al Johnson, witnesses to the accident, took off hurriedly in another plane, carrying along a spare wheel. Clarke strapped the wheel to his back and stood up on the top wing, while Johnson flew in underneath Batt's ship. Clarke grabbed Batt's undercarriage and swung himself up, then bolted the new wheel in place. The idea worked so well that it became a routine movie and newsreel stunt.

During his movie career, Clarke managed to tear apart quite a number of airplanes before the cameras without getting hurt, but only twice did he crack up airplanes strictly because of unintended accidents. One crash occurred during the filming of *The Woman with Four Faces.* Clarke took off from the top of the Santa Monica palisades, turning in the cockpit as he did to wave goodbye to actress Betty Compson. He smiled long and hard at Betty, and so failed to see the tree that loomed up before him—into which he flew at full throttle. The crash demolished the ship, and a disgusted Clarke crawled out from under. He sat down under another tree to calm his nerves with a cigarette and contemplate his own stupidity.

Miss Compson and the director, Herbert Brenon, ran over to the wreckage and began a frantic search for Clarke's body. After a while, Clarke got to his feet, walked over, and tapped Brenon's shoulder from behind.

"Looking for something?" he smiled.

Brenon whirled, turned chalk-white, and almost fainted.

Clarke's second crash—accidental, that is—virtually duplicated the first. Only this time the event occurred in a pine grove at Beverly Hills, then a far-out community next to nowhere. He walked away from that one also, and the plane suffered only a broken propeller and a bent wing.

An oil-field roughneck probably gave Clarke his biggest flying thrill, one which had nothing at all to do with stunting. Clarke was asked to fly a case of dynamite up to Point Conception, above Santa Barbara, to shoot a well. Clarke asked his friend Wally Timm to go along for the ride; Wally agreed. Not until he settled himself in the cockpit did Timm find out why Clarke really wanted him along.

"Here," Clarke said, dropping the wooden box in his lap, "see that this doesn't jog around, will you?"

Timm paled but grimly carried on as if he flew around every day with a case of dynamite in his lap. They flew north in almost zero weather, protecting their health by nipping at a quart of Irish whiskey. Finally, Clarke set the ship down in the soggy oil field, bounced over the rutted ground, and came to a stop only inches from a derrick.

"Hey, take it easy!" the gang boss yelled. "You want to blow up that rig?"

On the way back to Venice Field, Clarke's engine sputtered and quit over an Oxnard spinach farm. He stretched his glide and made it to a dirt road beyond the field, where he and Wally sat a long time, finishing off the whiskey and considering the happy fact that they were alive.

When a relative of Timm died some time later, he and Clarke decided to pay a final tribute to the deceased with an impromptu air show, tossing flowers over the grave from the air. Together they searched for and found the cemetery, located a group of mourners standing around an open grave, and then streaked in low, upside down, tossing out an armload of violets. The mourners looked startled, and it was not until Clarke and Timm landed that they learned they had buzzed the wrong funeral.

A Fourth of July celebration at Venice Field prompted Clarke to stage a brilliant fireworks show. It turned out to be a wild and gala occasion; people came in droves to watch the spectacle, and the liquor flowed freely. Clarke decided it would be much nicer and far more interesting if he watched the show from the air. Ed Remlin fired up a Canuck, and Clarke climbed up to sit on the top wing, clutching a bottle to his breast, while the Canuck flew in lazy circles through the exploding star shells.

It was not until the pyrotechnics were over that Clarke discovered he was blinded from the bright lights. He groped his way back to where he was sure the cockpit would be—and stepped off into space.

Frantically, Clarke flung out his arms, sacrificing what was left of the whiskey; and as he fell away from the airplane, his fingers gripped a wire. Superb coordination, great strength, and an unbelievable grip on his own fear enabled Clarke to hang on, and then to pull himself bodily against the wind back onto the wing. It was then he realized he had committed a near-fatal error in walking out on the right wing instead of the left.

The dazzling impact of brilliant lights at night came home to Clarke in yet another way, when he watched two pilots die because the man at the controls was blinded by pyrotechnics during a night movie sequence being shot at Cecil B. DeMille's field at Wilshire and Fairfax in Los Angeles. Omar Locklear, one of the greatest of the barnstormers and the man who had made the first plane-change, kicked his ship into a dizzy spin with Skeeter Elliott as passenger. Clarke dove alongside in the camera ship and was watching so intently he almost followed them into the ground. Locklear's ship smacked the airport and exploded just as Clarke veered away.

Al Wilson owed his life to Frank Clarke's quick thinking, when Wilson once attempted a plane-change without a parachute. He was hanging by his knees from the wing skid of Wally Timm's ship, while Clarke flew up from behind to pick him off. As he approached, Clarke spotted Wilson in trouble.

Just as Wilson lost his grip and plummeted away, Clarke rammed the throttle to the firewall and dropped into a desperate dive, directly beneath Wilson's falling body. Fifty feet below Timm's airplane, he made one of the most spectacular mid-air catches in all of aviation history. Wilson plunged head first through Clarke's upper wing and stuck there—5,000 feet above the ground. Clarke gently returned him to earth, where Wilson jumped to the ground and kissed it fervently.

To provide realism for the old airplane action serials, Clarke dreamed up an endless variety of tricks. On one occasion he rode a galloping horse alongside a plane speeding down the runway on take-off. Clarke did not just climb aboard—he leaped from the saddle onto the airplane's tail. In another sequence, he would hang from the axle of an airplane and drop onto a speeding passenger train in which the bad guys were carrying off the heroine, who kicked and shrieked appropriately.

Clarke was, in fact, the first movie pilot ever to land an airplane on a moving train. It was a feat infinitely more difficult than it seemed, due to the turbulence gusting up between the cars.

In 1937, Clarke made headlines in a unique accident. He broke an ankle while stepping off a 6-inch curbing.

In 1939, he narrowly escaped death at the National Air Races while looping in a tight formation billed as the Hollywood Aces. Following close on the wing of the leader, the great Paul Mantz, Clarke felt a tip vortex slam one wing so that it jammed between Mantz' left wing surfaces. By a miracle they pulled apart.

For more than three decades, Clarke laughed death in the face, defying all odds; but in the end, he pushed even his fabulous luck too far.

On Friday the thirteenth in June of 1948—a date that should have been a warning to Clarke—he flew a war-surplus BT-13 Vultee Valiant up to a mountain mine owned by his old flying buddy Frank Tomick. He had not seen Tomick for a long time, and he decided it would be great fun to surprise him by buzzing the mine shack. That way Tomick could drive out to the airport at Kernville and pick him up.

Clarke invited another friend, Mark Owen, to go along for the ride. For a final touch of genius, he loaded a sack of manure into the back seat. It was his plan to slow-roll over the mine and christen it with a rain of cow dung.

Tomick heard the characteristic high whine of the BT-13 as Clarke shoved the propeller into high pitch. He saw the ship dive straight at him.

"That has to be Clarke," Tomick grinned, shaking his head happily. He knew Clarke's penchant for the spectacular. Then his face froze. He watched in stark disbelief as the ship rolled over gracefully, hesitated inverted, and then plunged straight down into the ground.

Almost at Tomick's feet, the BT-13 exploded with a terrifying ball of flame and flying debris. Tomick ducked; and when he looked again, it was all over for Frank Clarke and his luckless passenger.

It was Clarke's own sense of humor that killed him, Tomick discovered later. The manure sack was found jammed behind the control stick, locking it.

All the old-timers showed up at Clarke's funeral, but there were not many tears. Clarke had died the way he would have wanted to go, pulling off a gag for a friend.

The only real tragedy was that Mark Owen had died with him. Clarke would have felt bad about that.

11

It's Only a Canvas Sky

HOLLYWOOD, California, mecca of stunt pilots in the 1920's, boasted more airports than movie studios back in the days when Charles Lindbergh was just another airmail pilot, when the Gish sisters were America's sweethearts, and when Volstead was a nasty word.

Barnstormers flying in from back East thus had a wide choice of landing fields to set their oil-streaked crates down on—Griffith Field in the Hollywood Hills; Dycer and Burdett Airports on Angelus Mesa, south of town; De Mille and Rogers Fields at Wilshire and Fairfax; Glendale, United, Wilson, and Metropolitan Airports in the Valley; others down by the sea. Mercury Field, at Fairfax and Melrose, was right in town.

On a clear day, they could flop down onto Clover Field in Santa Monica; at Mines Field, farther south in Inglewood; or at De Lay Field, near the mud flats of Venice. The last of these, which alternately lay knee-deep in water or parched under a broiling sun, was the home port of a nineteen-year-old gypsy barnstormer named Mort Bach, who would one day grow up to become a Lockheed vice president.

Bach did his share of stunting in the make-believe world of Hollywood's celluloid wings, but he is remembered around airports today as the guy who *almost* talked movie producer Thomas Ince out of $25,000 to sponsor a great Mexico-to-Siberia airplane race.

The great race might have become history's first international event, for the year was 1921, a good six years before Lucky Lindy found his way from New York to Paris. Bach got the idea for it in a Las Vegas speakeasy, where he and Clarence Prest, another unemployed World War aviator, were scrounging around for some way to make a fast buck—back before there were crap tables in Nevada.

Mort had a half-finished homebuilt airplane in a barn back at De Lay Field, and Prest scraped up $1,500 from trusting friends to pay for finishing it. The next step was to paint Ince's name on the top and bottom wings and on the side of their biplane in block letters.

But the day of their take-off, July 15, 1921, Ince heeded the warnings of rival airmen that the great race was a wild hoax; he stomped out to De Lay Field, down in the Venice swamps, and painted out his name.

"We came within an Ince of making that twenty-five grand," Bach grinned afterward. He and Prest flipped their last quarter to see who would buy the smokes and then started off on their wonderful flying adventure, broke and happy. They headed for the Mexican border at Tijuana, then turned around and flew back to San Bernardino, where Prest's father filled their gas tank to get them up to Las Vegas.

At Las Vegas, the gypsy pilots staged a glorious air show, looping and rolling all over the sky, and were honored at a "testimonial dinner" that raised $75, enough to get clear up to Salt Lake City. From there it was easy—daring flights to Pocatello, Butte, Great Falls, and into Canada at Sweet Grass, Montana. They hopped passengers, between aerobatics, and increased their poke to $500, the amount each needed to enter Canada legally to prove they were not grifters. Bach flew over the line, and that night slipped back and handed Prest the money. Prest followed in the morning.

Canadian regulations forbade them from flying for hire or taking money out of the country; but at Lethbridge, they teamed up with a couple of Canadian barnstormers, putting on a wild air show while their Canuck friends hopped the rubes.

And so their aerial odyssey rolled along through the summer months, and their ship, the *Polar Bear*, came at last to Hazelton, where they had been told there was a fine meadow to land in. The meadow was on the wrong side of the river for a safe take-off run; they dismantled the plane and paddled it across in an Indian dugout.

Eventually, the birdmen reached Prince Rupert Island, landing in a 300-foot ball park, where fickle fate tapped them. Unable to take off in so small a space, they got the city fathers to grade a slope that linked the ball park to an adjacent tennis court. At the far end, they stretched the tennis net across the end of the 350-foot runway, in case they missed—history's first arresting gear, long before the Navy thought of it.

While Bach was warming up for the take-off, an excited youngster ran up with bad news—the Northwest Mounties were on their way to arrest them for flying passengers for pay. Mort poured on the coal and zoomed off over the tennis net while Prest waved goodbye to their friends. Their goal was Siberia, by way of Rango, Alaska, where, they were told, there was a nice wide beach to land on. But at Ketchikan, they ran into strong headwinds that gently but firmly blew them backward, toward Prince Rupert.

Thus baffled by the elements, Bach and Prest turned their tail to the winds and sadly sped back to the ball park, where the red-coated mounties waited with their warrant. The mayor of Prince Rupert, however, pulled strings, contacting a Member of Parliament; and with international politics dangling dangerously, Bach and Prest were released and told to go home. But fate struck again—a windstorm rolled their ship up into a non-flyable ball of junk.

Meanwhile, back in Hollywood, as the script writers say, more riotous dissension was brewing among the growing horde of tramp pilots trying to cash in on their talents by risking their lives for money in front of the cameras. There were no pilot unions to protect them, until formation of the Association of Motion Picture Pilots in the 1930's, hence producers hired only the best of the stunt flyers and paid them off in peanuts. A wing-walker might make $25 on a plane-change, and crashing a ship into splinters was worth $100. Hollywood valued the lives of these foolhardy adventurers even less; few studios bothered to insure their aerobats. If they wanted to risk death to make a dollar, that was their business.

Among the wilder, more daring aerial stunt men was a select group of battle-scarred barnstormers like Omar Locklear, Frank Tomick, Frank Clarke, Ivan Unger, Art Goebel, Al Johnson, and Bobby Rose. Their bread-and-butter money came not from the old flying serials, but from the newsreels.

In the corner of a battered hangar at the Venice field, more thrilling stunts were dreamed up than anywhere else in the world, over a poker game that ran uninterrupted for four and a half years—until the day the hangar burned down.

Presiding over this game were two veteran newsreel cameramen—Pathé's Joe Johnson and International's Sam Greenwald. Whenever one of the stunt pilots went broke, all he had to do to get back into the game was to come up with a new idea.

"Sam," Ivan Unger would say, "how would it be if I jumped off the wing of Art Goebel's ship and grabbed onto Frank Clarke's tail? Then I climb forward and wrestle him out of the cockpit and we loop the loop with nobody at the controls."

"No parachute?" Sam would say, tossing a fifty-cent chip into the pot.

"No parachute."

"Okay. Ten bucks. I got a full house!"

Greenwald had learned the tough side of the newsreel business many years before coming to Hollywood, as a fresh young kid out of high school in Oakland, California, where he got his first newsreel job with Gaumont News.

"I bought me a $75 camera and four hundred feet of film and went out to cover my first assignment," Greenwald recalled. "It was a Memorial Day show at Sacramento . . . auto races, stunt flying, wrestling matches, the works. . . . I was real eager to do a good job, and started off with the flag raising. I spun my cap around and started cranking at the bottom of the flagpole, and followed that flag clear to the top. And there I ran out of film."

When the newsreel company fired him, Greenwald sent them a wire: "Recommend you hire veteran cameraman Joe Wilson." When they accepted the offer, Sam went back to work under his new name—Joe Wilson—at a $25 raise. "Their offices were back east, and they didn't know the difference," he admits.

The wildest idea-man in those days was unquestionably Bobby Rose, a diminutive youngster who started out as a jockey but quit when he figured he had pushed his luck farther than any rider in history. A black stud he was booting home in a big race at Calgary, Canada, had a heart attack on the final stretch. "I won the race on a dead horse," Bobby claims.

Eddie Polo, one of the early silent-serial stars, talked Bobby into coming to Hollywood. He knew of a job opening—Ruth Roland, the sad-eyed heroine of a thousand cliff-hangers, needed a double for some of the more dangerous stunts her writers were dreaming up. Doubling for a girl actor seemed easier to Bobby than falling off a dead horse. He was wrong.

Out at Universal Studios, in San Fernando Valley, the head rajah called Bobby into his office. "Why is it, Bobby," he inquired, "that the censors are after our Ruth Roland and Pearl White series but they never touch the Eddie Polo scripts?"

Rose grinned. "It's easy; you've got your girls all mixed up in dope dens, dungeons, and murders, but Eddie goes in for thrill situation comedy routines that are well-timed and clean. He builds the audience, gives them a letdown and then builds them back up again. You saturate your movies with so much violence the audience runs out of adrenalin after the first ten minutes!"

The executive's mouth dropped open. These were pearls of wisdom, coming from the handsome young stunt man. "You're hired, Bobby," he smiled. "But not as an actor. As a writer!"

Bobby's first Ruth Roland script was so thrill-packed the studio bosses shook their heads in disbelief. "This all reads great," they snapped, "but of course these stunts can't be done!" In disgust, Bobby quit his soft writing job and went out to Burdett Airport on Angelus Mesa, bought an OX-5 Standard biplane, and taught himself to fly.

His talents as a wing-walker were so monkeylike that Bobby found plenty of work at Vitagraph Studios, making parachute jumps only 75 feet above the Venice mud flats and otherwise risking his neck to learn the trade. Rose quickly became one of the most inventive and therefore most successful of the Hollywood "fall guys," while over at Universal, the Ruth Roland production company was bloodying up the landscape trying to film Bobby's script.

"They crippled four or five people, killed two men, and then decided to let the stunts go until they'd shot everything else," Rose recalls. "But finally the casting director called me in and asked if I really could do the stunts I'd written into the script. I agreed to do them if they let me have Woody Van Dyke for my director—he was the town's top action director, but was winding up a serial at another studio. When Woody agreed, I got busy."

The mad, mad, mad, mad sequence Bobby Rose had dreamed up was something he was sure nobody else would attempt, thus providing solid gold job insurance for himself. "I had Ruth in this car with a wireless set, calling to a pilot to fly over her and rescue her from the bad guys. Then she scrambles up this ladder, see? And the pilot sets her down on top of a speeding train. She scrambles down into the passenger section and gets into a gunfight over the weenie—the deed or whatever the hell it was —then she climbs back up on top of the train, up the ladder to the airplane, back down the ladder into the car, and tops it off by racing the train to a crossing, just ahead of the bad guys, who of course don't make it."

Bobby not only doubled Ruth Roland on the whole sequence, he played the part of a bad guy and nearly got himself killed, rolling a car down an embankment after finishing his race with the train in a tie, out on the desert near Mojave.

Later on Bobby concentrated on aerial stunts, like getting himself knocked off the wing of a biplane in a fight with another wing-walker. To make it look more horrible to the rubes,

Bobby devised a way to free-fall several hundred feet and then open his chute by yanking on a rope. It was the forerunner of the ripcord.

Bobby Rose always considered the great escape artist Harry Houdini to be the world's greatest stunt man. At Lasky Studios, where Bobby and Harry worked together, Houdini once told him: "Bobby, you can do anything in the world if you engineer it right!"

Ironically, Houdini failed to "engineer" a stunt properly and died of a ruptured liver, when he let a college athlete punch him in the stomach before he got set for the blow. But Bobby Rose lived on to become the dean of Hollywood's stunt men. In the summer of 1965, when he might have been home watching a Western on television, Bobby was still feeling the rush of the wind on his face, riding in the open cockpit of a jerry-built airplane, across the sand dunes of Yuma, Arizona, behind stunt pilot Paul Mantz. It was the big scene for a Twentieth-Century Fox Studios film, *Flight of the Phoenix,* in which Bobby and Paul doubled two actors playing the roles of an Air Force crew escaping from the Sahara Desert in a makeshift machine, built up from parts of a bomber crash.

Bobby had worked in many films with Mantz since the old thriller *Men With Wings,* and this job seemed relatively simple. In the early morning, before the sun heated up the air in Buttercup Valley, Mantz and Rose flew several orbits, simulating a take-off from a sand dune. On the last pass, Mantz turned and yelled to Bobby, *"We'll get her this time!"*

"Over the wind blast and the roar of the engine I couldn't hear him," Bobby remembers. "So I grinned and waved at him to go ahead. I was half out of the tiny cockpit right behind him, but Paul sat low down, out of sight. We came in on power and touched the wheels down right by the number one camera. But when he went to pull up, something went wrong; one of the skis hooked on a sand hummock and we flipped. We were almost on our back when I acted automatically—I flipped my safety belt loose and jumped off to one side.

"When I came to I was pretty bloody, lying down in a helicopter. A marine was holding an oxygen mask over my face. I asked him what had happened.

" 'You were just in one hell of an airplane accident,' he told me.

" 'How's the other fellow?' I asked him.

"He shook his head and turned his thumb down. 'He's gone.' "

Of all the strange characters who drifted into the old Venice Field hangar looking for stunt work, International Newsreel cameraman Sam Greenwald rates Chief Whitefeather, a full-blooded Cherokee Indian who showed up one day in the early 1920's, as the strangest. He had thick black hair braided down his back.

"Half a dozen pilots and cameramen were sweating out the big poker game in a corner of the hangar, when Chief White-feather came in and told us he wanted to hang under a ship by his hair, for fifty dollars," Greenwald remembers.

To make sure he could really do it, they interrupted their game long enough to string the Indian up by the hair, to a rope thrown over a rafter. "We forgot all about him until that night," says Greenwald. "When we went back he was pretty sore, but in good shape."

The next day, Frank Clarke flew a Standard biplane over town at 2,000 feet, while Sam shot newsreel pictures of the chief swinging happily from the landing gear by his hair. Clarke was happy too—he had visions of a veritable fortune rolling in, touring the nation with Whitefeather and sponsored all the way by a hair-restorer company.

Such was not to be, for Whitefeather wanted to try an even riskier stunt first—a spectacular cutaway parachute fall wearing *ten* chutes, which he intended to open one at a time, cutting them loose as they opened, until he would land with the tenth. The stunt worked fine, up to the sixth cutaway. Then, as cameraman Joe Johnson cranked furiously in a following airplane, he saw Whitefeather plunge all the way into a barley patch, his last four chutes unopened.

About this time a daredevil pilot named Art Goebel began

making headlines with a series of thrilling antics that were the envy of the Venice Field gang.

Working with stunt man Ivan Unger, whose father, Ed Unger, was a veteran circus balloonist, Goebel became a regular on the old Pathé News, making pickups from speedboats, mid-air plane-changes while inverted, and replacing a lost landing wheel in the sky. One shot that earned Joe Johnson a bonus from Pathé showed Art Goebel flying under a span of the Colorado Street Bridge near the Rose Bowl, in Pasadena, with two stunt girls, Gladys Ingalls and Shirley Calishak, standing on the top wing of his Standard.

Goebel, who gained international fame in 1927 by winning the tragic, death-studded Dole Race from Oakland to Honolulu, became one of Hollywood's most imitated birdmen, a situation that resulted in a long-standing, bitter feud with a famed movie stunt team, the Thirteen Black Cats. Although he once posed for a photograph with seven members of the group, while wearing a black sweater with the "13 Cats" insignia, Goebel insists he never stunted as one of them.

The Black 13, which included newsreel cameraman Sam Greenwald, actually was born at Burdett Field in 1924, on a Friday the thirteenth. "It was a newsreel gimmick," Greenwald says. "We each juggled our names to include thirteen letters; it kept us all eating pretty regularly."

Original members of the Black 13 flying team included Spider Matlock, Bon MacDougall, and Ken ("Fronty") Nichols. Others who joined later, to make up the unlucky number, included Greenwald, actor Reginald Denny, Paul Richter, Jr. (who later became a TWA executive), "Wild Bill" Lind, Morrison Stapp, Al Johnson, Ivan Unger, Frank Lockhart, Herd McClellan and—according to a group picture that appeared in the International Newsreel Corporation's house organ in November, 1925—Art Goebel.

One time, Greenwald wired a card table to the top wing of Bon MacDougall's Standard biplane and asked for two volunteers to sit there playing cards, dressed in cowboy costumes, at 3,000 feet above Los Angeles. Fronty Nichols jumped at the chance to make $10 in such an easy manner, but the other Cats decided to remain in the real game going on in the hangar. A newcomer, Al Johnson, volunteered and thus became a member of the stunt team.

Not all of the hazards that the Black Cats faced were up in the air. Herd McClellan figured he was safe on the stage of a Los Angeles theater, with his wife firing point-blank at him with a rifle, for he was encased in what a policeman friend had assured him was a bullet-proof vest. He was wrong. Mrs. McClellan, with unusual accuracy, kept hitting the same spot over Herd's liver, thirty-nine times. The fortieth and last shot penetrated the weakened vest and killed him.

War pictures were considered anathema in Hollywood until King Vidor made *The Big Parade* at M-G-M Studios, a breakthrough that prompted Famous Players–Lasky to gamble on a spectacular film, transferring the action of war background from the soggy trenches to the sky. They bought a John Monk Saunders story, *Wings*, hired a hero of the Lafayette Escadrille, William Wellman, to direct it, and engaged a stunt pilot named Dick Grace to do the crashes.

The picture was a $2,500,000 epic, thanks to the loan of the entire Army Air Service at Kelly Field, Texas, courtesy of the Secretary of War, and to Dick Grace, who broke his neck in three places busting up a Fokker D-7 in front of the cameras.

By the time Grace got out of his cast, Colleen Moore was ready to star in First National's war film *Lilac Time*. Grace agreed to handle the flying, if he could organize his own squadron of stunt flyers. He hand-picked his men, building a tight unit of seven hard-flying barnstormers, who became known as the Buzzards. Each Buzzard had to prove his mettle by following Grace through a harrowing afternoon of wild aerobatics without once getting off his tail.

In another picture, called *Wide Open*, Grace risked his life in a remarkable plane-change with no parachute—actually dropping from one ship to the other in mid-air! For this stunt, he hired the best pilots he could find: Art Goebel, Frank Clarke, and Frank Tomick.

*Skeet Sliter, "Eagle of the Adiron-
dacks," poses with a glamour gal of
the 1920's, while on a barnstorming
stop at Dolgeville, New York. Skeet, a
ladies' man, also flew booze over the
border from Canada.*
(Photo courtesy Skeet Sliter)

*While barnstorming in upper New York State in the 1920's, Skeet
Sliter often flew fishermen into bush country.*
(Photo courtesy Skeet Sliter)

Walter Hunter (left), with his three brothers Albert, Kenneth and John, barnstormed as the Hunter Brothers Flying Circus, did death-defying stunts in Standard biplane. Walter's act was to drop from undercarriage into a haymow without a parachute. Picture was taken at Scott Field, Ill., April 1924. (Walter Hunter photo)

13 Black Cats was early Hollywood stunt-pilot team that performed hair-raising feats for newsreels and movies. Here Spider Matlock flies Curtiss Jenny with two "Cats" hanging on wingskids—minus parachutes. (Hank Coffin photo)

Ivan Unger, one of the greatest Hollywood stunt pilots, was a founder of the 13 Black Cats team. Ivan's dad, Ed, was well-known balloonist; his sister, Mildred, a stunt artist herself. Ivan made his first parachute jump at the age of thirteen.

(Ivan Unger collection)

Gladys Ingalls, poised atop wing of Bon MacDougall's "13 Black Cats," gets ready to leap onto wing of Art Goebel's ship. This was a newsreel stunt of 1920's. (Ivan Unger collection)

These helmeted heroes, wearing Army britches and high boots, were the flying wild men of Hollywood in the 1920's. In the center, standing before propeller, is handsome Frank Clarke. Second from left is Frank Tomick, who taught Amelia Earhart to fly, performed in Hell's Angels and other flying movies. Left to right are: J. V. Sandblum, Frank Tomick, Kenneth W. Montee, Burgess Kreeth, Mrs. Emery Rogers (wife of Rogers Field owner), Frank Clarke, Hubert Kittle, Maurice Murphy, Eddie Bellande, Jack Kalbenschlag. Boy and dog are not identified. Picture was taken at Rogers Field, at the corner of Wilshire and Fairfax, Los Angeles, in 1922.

(Security First National Bank collection)

Frank Clarke—the King of Hollywood! Greatest of the Hollywood stunt pilots, Clarke learned his tricks at Venice Field, packed a lifetime of adventure in his years before the camera.

(Author's collection)

Frank Clarke in a World War I ship he flew in thriller Wings, *in which he played role of Baron Manfred von Richthofen.* (Author's collection)

Frank Clarke flies his Curtiss Jenny off the roof of a Los Angeles skyscraper. (Author's collection)

Hollywood dogfight! Howard Hughes released this picture of skyful of war planes to promote film Wings, *but the stunt pilots found it a little too realistic—midair collisions, uncontrolled spins and forced landings brought death and injury to men of the* Wings *squadron.*
(Author's collection)

Movie pilot Ira Reed escaped death in mid-air collision with pilot Stuart Murphy filming dogfight for Wings. *Reed flew ship safely to emergency landing with one wing nearly gone. Murphy had to bail out.* (Author's collection)

Hank Coffin "goes to war" in biplane painted up like a Fokker for dogfight scene in Wings. (Hank Coffin photo)

Mort Bach and Clarence Prest ignominiously ferry their ship across a Canadian river on great "Mexico-to-Siberia" dash. The field wasn't big enough to take off from, so they pulled wings and took it across river in Indian dugout to bigger field. (Author's collection)

Mort Bach and Clarence Prest's great Mexico-to-Siberia dash almost ended at Prince Rupert Island—but they took off from tennis court! (Author's collection)

Hollywood stunt man Bobby Rose invented the plane-to-train stunt for early Mabel Normand serial. (Author's collection)

Veteran stunt pilot Hank Coffin flies through a building with greatest aplomb. (Hank Coffin photo)

Hank Coffin clips top of steeple, while two stunt men down below jump for their lives, in scene for Lilac Time. (Hank Coffin photo)

Hank Coffin picks up Cliff Winters from car in auto-to-plane change for movie. (Hank Coffin photo)

Movie stunt men Frank Clarke, Roy Wilson, and Frank Tomick per-
form thrilling Bomb Burst maneuver at Los Angeles Air Fiesta, 1931.
(L. A. International Airport photo)

Paul Mantz tears wings off a Stearman in a crash stunt for film When Johnny Comes Marching Home. *Arrow points to Mantz.*
(Tallmantz Aviation photo)

Paul Mantz and Frank Clarke perform amazing wheel-to-wheel flyby at Los Angeles air show.

Movie stunt pilot Paul Mantz flies through open hangar in early movie. Mantz began stunting in 1930, was killed in front of camera in July 1965 after 3½ decades of precision flying.

(Tallmantz Aviation photo)

Stunt man Jimmie Goodwin poses with "batman" rig he used to fly like a bird from plane flown by Hank Coffin, movie pilot. Hank claims Jimmie once soared all the way from Big Bear Lake to Alhambra Airport, 75 miles. (Hank Coffin photo)

In the high sky, Grace clambered out to the wingtip of the ship Goebel was flying, wrapped his legs around the wing skid and hung there, head down, waiting for Tomick to move his ship into position beneath him, while Clarke flew alongside with the camera ship. When the blur of Tomick's propeller slid in beside and below, Grace unlocked his knees, preparing to drop onto the leading edge of Tomick's wing.

What happened next Grace told dramatically in his autobiography, *I Am Still Alive:*

"My whole mind and body were concentrated on grasping the top wing of that ship below. Then, in a split second, while falling through the air, I realized that I had misjudged! It might have been because of the whipping clothes that bothered and hampered me in leaving, or it might have been that the rush of blood to my eyes had affected my judgement. But from whatever the cause I realized that I would fall in front of Tomick's ship—not by mere inches but by at least a foot and a half!

"It is impossible to convey the sense of horror that gripped me. In the short distance I had to go I couldn't wriggle into a position which would swing my body back that far. It was too late for Tomick to gun the ship enough to cover me. My decision was not to try to divert my body from its course but to try to catch a cabane wire as I passed the leading edge of the top wing.

"I swung my right hand backward, and made one attempt to grasp the thin, small wire. For a long second I thought I had missed. Then the two forefingers touched and slid over it—and closed! They closed with all of the strength of a man in such circumstances, which at most times would be impossible to command.

"My body turned a complete forward somersault; still those fingers held. With a sudden jolt my feet hit the second bay strut and I hung on in front of the plane. . . . Finally I recovered enough to climb to the top wing, where I finished the action required for the picture."

Grace claimed he owed his life to rigorous physical training that kept him in top shape as a stunt pilot through the long, active years of his career, which finally ended in death in 1965.

Drop in on any bull session of the Quiet Birdmen's Hollywood hangar at the Roosevelt Hotel and you will be sure to heard brand-new stories told by or about the great movie pilots of yesterday and today.

That nice little guy over there in the corner, having a drink with Colonel Chuck Yeager, chief of the USAF's Aerospace School and first supersonic airman, is Hank Coffin, a movie stunt pilot for the past thirty-five years. Hank has thrilled millions with his aerial antics in *Hell's Angels, Lilac Time, Wings, Dawn Patrol, Pylon, The Spirit of St. Louis*, and, more recently, *Beach Blanket Bingo.*

Once, Hank got the cops sore at him for buzzing under the Colorado Street Bridge, in Pasadena, with a Waco 10, towing a huge sign that read: "EAT AT LUCCA'S." They raced after him on their motorcycles; but by the time they reached nearby Alhambra Airport, Hank had hidden the sign and played innocent.

"Did you ever try to hide a 60-foot sign in two minutes?" he grinned.

Another time Hank and his son, Bud Coffin, now a Western Air Lines jet jockey, flew a replica of Lindbergh's *Spirit of St. Louis* out to sea from Santa Barbara, to simulate the Lone Eagle's departure from America for Paris. "They planned to flip the film over to make it look like we were flying east," he explained. When radio contact failed, the Coffins, unsure whether the camera ship had gotten what it needed, simply kept on flying into darkness, then finally turned around and flew back.

"A little longer and we'd have flown right on to Honolulu," Hank laughs painfully.

Standing at the Q.B.'s bar is Colonel Jerry Phillips, another veteran MPPA (Motion Picture Pilots Association) member, who frequently is called in as technical advisor on flying films. One time, Jerry was barnstorming down in Arizona and was asked by a distraught woman if he would take her deaf son up and make a power dive with him to see if it would cure him.

"I climbed up to five thousand in this Jenny," Jerry is telling the boys. "Then I shoved the nose straight down. I wanted to make it good. We went full bore all the way. But when I pulled out, off came the wings! We crashed into a bunch of trees, utterly demolishing the Jenny.

"I ran over to where the boy sat staring at me with wide eyes, shaking his head. 'Sonny!' I yelled at him. 'Are you all right?' He said, 'What? What?' You know what? He *still* couldn't hear worth a damn!"

Another group of hangar flyers soberly discusses the late Cliff Winters, a Johnny-come-lately to Hollywood, who plunged to his death after a low-level snap roll at the Chino Air Show in 1962. Cliff had left the 82nd Airborne Division to learn flying under the G.I. Bill, then broadened his activities to become one of Hollywood's most versatile stunt men as a wingwalker, batman, and sky diver. Once Cliff wore a strait jacket on a jump and pulled the ripcord with his teeth, but almost died the second time he tried it, when the ripcord D-ring blew away from his mouth. He flipped over and finally found it. Another time, when a plane he was flying through an acrobatic sequence at 5,000 feet collided with another ship, during the filming of a *Ripcord* television sequence, Winters found himself spinning violently earthward minus a wing—with his parachute on the back seat. He reached back and grabbed it, stepped out into space, and buckled it on while falling at 120 miles an hour!

And then there is Frank Tallman, whose handsome, tanned face just naturally belongs under a leather helmet, narrowed eyes squinting at danger ahead. Once Frank flew a twin Beech through a billboard to please Stanley Kramer, producer of *It's a Mad, Mad, Mad, Mad World.* Tallman flies to work every day at Orange County Airport, near Santa Ana, California, where he opened an air museum with another movie pilot, Paul Mantz.

In the course of a day, Tallman may wring out a 1918 German Fokker D-7, loop a frail little Blériot monoplane or race a hot-air balloon across Catalina Channel. Like a kid with a new toy to play with every day, Tallman lives life to the hilt. Even a tragic accident in the summer of 1965 did not stop him—pushing his son in a go-cart, Frank twisted and broke a leg. Complications necessitated a leg amputation; but even as the surgery healed, Tallman was back in the sky, flying a rudderless Ercoupe.

Tallman's accident precipitated another tragedy, indirectly, when his partner, Mantz, came out of retirement to fly a tough scene with stunt man Bobby Rose in the movie, *Flight of the Phoenix.* As told earlier, a shocking crash before the grinding cameras snuffed out Mantz' life at the height of a long career as one of movietown's smoothest precision flyers.

12

Wine, Women and Wings

BACK IN THE CAREFREE, open-cockpit era of aviation's thundering youth, when leather-helmeted sky pilots sang their songs of mudholes, whiskey, and wild, wild women, a playboy pilot named Jimmie Mattern blazed a unique trail across the sky as a hard-flying glamour boy, whose world spun through a cosmos of wine, women, and wings.

Jimmie had plenty of guts, and as a first-rate stunt pilot he flew with finesse. He seemed to bring a new quality to aviation that had not been there before. To the smell of wet leather and gas fumes and airplane dope Jimmie added the headiness of champagne and roses. In contrast with the rough-and-tumble, grease-stained airport bums, who would fly an ironing board in a windstorm to make a fast buck, Mattern had class. It was only natural that Jimmie would turn out to be the catalyst who brought aviation and Texas oil money together to create a jazz-age aerial odyssey never approached before or since.

There was the time Jimmie Mattern was awakened in the middle of the night by a jangling telephone. He took the receiver off the hook and replaced it, rolling over to go back to sleep. But the caller was insistent, and Jimmie finally answered it. He recognized the voice and sat bolt upright. It was a wildcatter who had just struck it rich.

"Jimmie!" the voice yelled. "How long will it take us to blow two million dollars?"

Mattern whistled. "At least a year!"

"Okay!" the wildcatter shouted. "Get your pants on and let's go! What are we waitin' for?"

Mattern obligingly kept the oil man's identity anonymous, but the bender they went on together is still talked about with considerable awe in hangars all over the world.

That all happened just before the Thirsty Thirties, when Celebrity Night at Chicago's noisy College Inn was the hottest show between Roxy's and M-G-M. Jammed six nights a week with World's Fair visitors, this Jazz-Age waterhole all but ran dry on Wednesday nights, when the most incredible private talent parties in show business swung into high pitch.

Jimmie Mattern swung in the middle of it, as a close pal of Frank Bering, the owner of Chicago's Hotel Sherman, where the College Inn outshone the Bal Tabarin during the height of its Wednesday night jamborees.

Ben Bernie's band was just the starter. The fun began when Bering locked the doors to keep the tourists out and turned the joint over to his special guests, who leaped to the stage to put on million-dollar talent shows for the hell of it.

Mattern knew everybody who was anybody, because they all came to the College Inn sooner or later. Buddy Rogers, Jack Benny, Milton Berle, Gary Cooper, Will Rogers, John Barrymore, and Edmund Lowe might show up to put on one evening's vaudeville spectacular in the small, smoke-filled cabaret.

The girls were there too—Jeanette MacDonald, Bea Lillie, Ruth Chatterton, Sally Rand, the Duncan sisters, and a pretty dancer Jimmie eventually married.

Mattern was on friendly terms with them all—the troupers and the new stars who got their start there, like a skinny, scared elevator operator from Marshall Field's, who turned out to be Dorothy Lamour.

As a handsome young aviator, curly-haired Jimmie Mattern quickly became the favorite hero of the fabled, and ruined a good number of tablecloths drawing up plans on them for one of the most action-packed adventures in the history of flying.

Taking a tip from show business, which he watched at close range night after night at the College Inn, Mattern knew that advance publicity and a little hoopla were in order to make the first round-the-world solo flight a financially solid venture.

Jimmie Mattern was not just money-hungry. Aviation was big business, a force that was changing the map of the world, a place where an ambitious hustler could make his mark. He wanted in. Mattern had two sides to his character. One was the reckless barnstormer who loved adventure, the sting of the wind in his face, and the thrill of testing his nerves by cheating death in shocking combat with the elements; the other was the boy who meant to go first class. And did.

Jimmie Mattern, in fact, traveled first class all the way through aviation's splendid years of wine and roses, outflying, outliving, outloving the daring, fun-loving flyboys who blazed brightly but briefly in the heavens, and then died like falling stars.

Fate often dimmed Mattern's incredible achievements, so that today the world has forgotten that he holds more world records than many another living pilot. But it was not the records that Jimmie wanted; Mattern was a trail-blazer who set performance standards in the sky for others to shoot at.

In the spring of 1933, Jimmie Mattern was already an aviation hero; he and Benny Griffin, who later would become the director of Washington's International Airport, high-balled across the Atlantic Ocean to Berlin in seventeen and a half hours, the fastest Atlantic crossing recorded at that time, little more than half the time Charles Lindbergh took to reach Paris. The flight also was the longest instrument trip on record, at a time when the experts swore you could not fly the gauges for more than an hour at a stretch without getting into serious trouble.

Mattern and Griffin had been shooting at the Post-Gatty eight-and-a-half-day round-the-world record in a Lockheed Vega, a sister ship to Wiley Post's *Winnie Mae;* but a hatch cover tore loose over Russia, and they were forced to crash land. Jimmie and Benny became the first American fliers interned behind the Iron Curtain, but finally got outside in a cloak-and-dagger adventure.

It was then that Mattern set up shop beside a champagne bucket at the College Inn and made plans to rebuild the Vega for a top secret world flight. Jimmie's table-hopping buddies became enthusiastic over his project and chipped in to swell his kitty, which would become the bankroll for a $50,000 world flight, organized on a shoestring and a crazy dream during the black post-depression bank holidays.

The world flight would be a milestone on Mattern's path to the stars that had started in Hawaii in the early 1920's; he crashed the first time he ever got off the ground, as a hitch-hiker in an Army Jenny. Jimmie crawled from the wreckage miraculously unhurt.

"I'm sorry, Jimmie," the crestfallen pilot apologized.

"Sorry?" Mattern laughed. "Hell, I thought that was how you were supposed to land!"

Jimmie admired the pilot's snappy uniform and decided to enlist. When his hitch ended in 1925, Mattern, who had come to appreciate a uniform's appeal to the ladies, found a new outlet for his extroversion as a band leader. This time his uniform was a pair of ice-cream slacks, a blue jacket, and a polka-dot tie.

The Jimmie Mattern Jazz Band roamed the blue Pacific on moonlit decks of pleasure cruisers of the Dollar and Pacific Steamship Lines, playing sentimental love songs to romantic school teachers bound for Alaska, Tokyo, and Hong Kong to escape the mundane world of classrooms and text books. It was great for a while, but life was too easy—a pushover. He missed competition, adventure, danger, excitement. He wanted to fly.

Lindbergh had made the nation air-minded in 1927 with his fabulous flight from New York to Paris, and Mattern naturally gravitated to the Ryan School of Aeronautics in San Diego, the home of the *Spirit of St. Louis*. There, Mattern won his civilian wings. With money saved up from his jazz band days he moved on to Troy, Ohio, and paid cash for a swift little Waco 10.

At the Waco factory, Mattern met another flying hero, Freddie Lund, America's leading stunt pilot at the time. Lund said he was headed for California, so Jimmie invited him to go with him in the Waco. Things went well until they reached the little town of Vaughn, New Mexico. A motorist tooling along over the washboard road was startled to see an airplane parked alongside a ditch. Beside it stood two handsome aviators, thumbing a ride.

"What happened?" the driver asked Mattern.

Jimmie laughed. "The ground ran into us!"

It was true; crossing the Continental Divide with an overload—Jimmie and Freddie had brought along their golf clubs and bags and other paraphernalia—the Waco was boring along, minding its own business as a good airplane should, at ceiling altitude. But the ground kept getting higher and higher, and they simply ran out of sky.

Under Freddie Lund's tutelage, Mattern learned to wring out the Waco in thrilling aerobatic maneuvers—loops, rolls, Immelmann turns, chandelles and Cuban eights—that gave him a new-found release for his enormous store of energy. He learned stunt flying just in time to sign on with Frank Clarke for a pilot role in Howard Hughes' air epic *Hell's Angels*, and for another in *Lilac Time*. What Mattern lacked in experience he made up in native skill and judgment, figuring his odds with slide rule precision. After all, his entire fortune was wrapped up in the Waco.

Jimmie got into the one and only flat spin he ever tangled with quite by accident, while flying for the *Hell's Angels*. His Waco, painted up to look like a World War I fighter, stalled at the top of a loop, flipped over, and began falling earthward in an uncontrollable vortex plunge, with all the helplessness of driving a car down an expressway with a broken steering column and no brakes. Mattern made a hairbreadth escape and somehow landed his ship in one piece. He crawled out, pale and trembling from the experience.

The producer ran up to Jimmie and grabbed his shoulders. "That was great, Mattern!" he cried. "But why didn't you tell us what you were going to do? Our cameras weren't loaded! I'll pay you an extra ten bucks to do it again!"

Mattern told him where to go.

Dogfighting, stunting, and buzzing Hollywood was fun, but it rang too much of phoniness for Mattern. He sold his Waco (it is still flying in the movies, incidentally) and went down to Kelly Field, Texas, for a course of Army flight training. The rigid discipline sharpened his flying skills even more, and then there was the old appeal of the uniform that pleased him. There were plenty of pretty girls living in San Angelo, which he adopted as his "official" home town, replacing Freeport, Illinois, as his birthplace on his pilot's license.

Graduating with honors, Jimmie moved up from the action-packed cadet period into the big time. Texas he liked, and the way the millionaire oil operators lived he liked even better. An unemployed aviator with a champagne appetite on a beer drinker's budget, Mattern began looking around for a way to make a fast buck. He bought a ten-gallon hat, a pair of shiny leather boots, and a brace of pistols, and waited for Texas to discover him. It did not take long.

Carl Cromwell, a tough wildcatter with sharp blue eyes and calloused hands, had just discovered the black gold of the fabulous Big Lake oil field, a stretch of prairie land so vast he figured he needed a flying machine to get around from one gushing well to another. He and Mattern just naturally teamed up; and with Cromwell's backing, Jimmie started up his own airline, flying between San Angelo, Fort Worth, and Dallas. But tragedy struck; Cromwell was killed instantly in an auto crash. The accident shook Jimmie up badly, for he had come to love Cromwell like a father. He inherited two airplanes, free and clear, but now he felt he needed another angel. Running an airline cost money he did not have. He had blown his money earned while working for Cromwell as fast as he had earned it.

Then fortune smiled on Jimmie Mattern a second time, when a wildcatter, as mentioned earlier, who had overnight become superfluously burdened with riches called him in the middle of the night and begged him to help spend them. Tossing a suitcase loaded with greenbacks into his Vega, Mattern and his pal took off for a whirlwind tour of the nation. They made a strange pair, Jimmie, the smooth, fast-talking, handsome aviator, and his party-loving parvenu pal. More than once, Jimmie had to dig into the suitcase for funds to bail his anonymous friend out of jail, after a particularly wild evening, financed from the same cardboard cornucopia. Cost was of no concern; if the wildcatter was pleased with the events of the night, a $500 tip was the rule. There was always more where that came from.

Trying to spend $2 million in a year—a theme reminiscent of *Brewster's Millions*—was an almost overwhelming challenge. That was more than $5,000 a day, Jimmie figured, but he did his best. It was something to dream about—an endless parade of parties from coast to coast, with plenty of funds to pay for it all. Jimmie's assignment was to keep his friend out of jail as often as possible, and to settle for the fantastic breakage that was left in the wake of their cyclonic tour de farce.

On the ground, the wildcatter's limitless funds were an open sesame. His riches could buy anything—and did.

But in the sky, Jimmie Mattern was boss. After all, he figured, he only had one life, and that to him was worth considerably more than $2 million. He could put up with a lot of nonsense on the ground, but in an airplane Mattern was all business. His patience left him one day while flying the oilman through the turbulence of San Gorgornio Pass, near Palm Springs, en route from El Paso to Los Angeles. When Mattern complained that both of them were too exhausted for the trip, the wildcatter pulled a six-shooter and pointedly insisted that Jimmie keep his side of their bargain; the Texan claimed he had a date with Clara Bow and meant to get to Hollywood fast. Jimmie resignedly went along with him until, flying through the pass toward the haze-locked Los Angeles Basin, his pal dropped into the cockpit, tapped Mattern on the shoulder, and motioned for him to get out.

"I'm gonna fly this thing, Jimmie!" the Texan said thickly. "You all get back there now and have yourself a drink!"

Jimmie's impulse was to grab the gun away from him and

bust him on the jaw, but he suddenly had had enough. He left his seat and called the oilman's bluff. "Okay, sucker," he snapped. "You asked for it. Now fly it!"

Turning white, the Texan grabbed at the controls and began pushing and pulling. The Vega, responding like a runaway horse, bolted all over the sky. Mattern hung on grimly until the ship fell into a wrenching spin, then took over. The oilman was as sober as a judge by the time they landed. He forgot all about his date with Clara Bow, and after that left the flying to Mattern.

Through his Texas oil business contacts, Mattern landed finally in Chicago, as official "Air Ambassador" for the Chicago World's Fair, which was managed by Rufus Dawes, the brother of Henry Dawes, president of Pure Oil Company. Everybody liked Jimmie's smiling demeanor, including Frank Bering, the owner of the Hotel Sherman, who figured that Mattern was just the likable young flyboy hero who might take the gangster onus off his hostelry. In the Prohibition days, Al Capone's mob had made a practice of hanging out there uninvited. Jimmie moved in and became the boy wonder of the College Inn crowd.

Mattern's Chicago friends were not all in show business; there were a couple of tough cops to whom Mattern became firmly attached. Jimmie's wealthy oil-field buddy had hired two Windy City detectives, named Durry and Howe, as personal bodyguards, to help Mattern keep him out of trouble on his nightly forays into the gin joints of Chicago's Loop district. To Mattern, this was a new kind of excitement, riding around in a prowl car with the detectives who liked nothing better than to shoot up a gangster hangout for the hell of it.

All this was fun, but Jimmie was planning an even bigger adventure—his solo flight around the world. He wanted to be the first man to do it. Even Magellan, he mused, had not accomplished a true circumnavigation of Earth, having been killed by natives near the island of Cebu, in the Philippines. And certainly no lone pilot had made such a trip by air. The promotional possibilities that Jimmie saw were simply breathtaking, endorsing round-the-world watches, soft drinks, and engine fuels, and then personal appearances . . .

At last, on June 3, 1933, Jimmie Mattern's rebuilt Lockheed Vega roared off the runway at Floyd Bennett Field to begin a record-breaking flight, the longest solo hop ever flown—4,300 miles from New York to Norway, and the first flight between those two countries. For danger and excitement, the flight was just what Mattern liked best. Just as he and Benny Griffin had flown the Atlantic to Berlin on instruments some months before, now he was again on the gauges, this time alone, with no relief pilot to spell him when fatigue left him red-eyed and aching from long hours of sitting in one position.

Halfway across the ocean, Mattern felt his Vega begin to lose altitude, the controls grow mushy. In alarm, he glanced out at his wing; the leading edge was growing bulbous with rime ice. He dove the Vega down in a tight spiral to get below the icing level and break the ice free before his wings stalled out completely and left his airplane uncontrollable. Less than 500 feet above the whitecaps of the North Atlantic, Mattern broke into the clear, and gradually the ice melted away.

Sighing with relief, Mattern climbed back to cruising altitude for better fuel consumption, but there ran into unexpected headwinds, blowing from east to west! He had counted on the prevailing westerlies to assist him on the crossing, but now it appeared that the gods had turned against him. His Vega, the *Century of Progress*, so named to promote the World's Fair, began bucking and yawing all over the sky, buffeted by upper-air turbulence.

The Atlantic crossing was only the start of Mattern's amazing journey. Where Lindbergh, six years earlier, had called it quits at Le Bourget Field, Paris, Mattern droned on to Norway, made a harrowing landing on a rocky beach, then gassed up and roared off again to complete history's first New York-to-Moscow flight—5,150 miles in twenty-nine hours and forty-five minutes. It also was the first solo flight of an American aircraft into Russia.

Mattern racked up record after record as he sped on across

the vastness of Russia's interior, the first solo pilot to transnavigate that region. It was not all a breeze, the way it looked on the tablecloths back at the College Inn in Chicago. There were unbelievable hardships and unforeseen obstacles. He literally lost his tail when he hit a stump in a small Russian "airport," battled raging storms, inaccurate Russian maps, and worse fuel to finally reach Khabarovsk, the last gas stop before Nome, Alaska.

Mattern, who had done some crazy things in his lifetime, now became involved in an adventure plot as intriguing as any Hollywood movie he had stunted in. One-eyed Wiley Post's *Winnie Mae*, grounded by weather, was sitting back at Floyd Bennett Field in New York, a late starter in what still could become a race to be the first round-the-world solo. An accident, a mechanical breakdown, might delay the *Century of Progress* or even put it out of the race, if Post got off soon.

Already near exhaustion, Mattern decided to push on. He roared off the muddy field at Khabarovsk and groggily swung the ship's nose toward Alaska, 3,000 miles away. It would be a grueling leg, and Jimmie was not too sure he was up to it. Sleep was heavy in his eyes, but he fought it with black coffee and kept on. Fighting against the hypnotic drone of the engine, he watched the Russian landscape as though in a dream. In the dream, he watched an old scene played again, the time he and Freddie Lund ran out of sky over the Continental Divide in his old Waco 10. Mattern suddenly started—it was no dream; the towering, snow-capped mountains of Kamchatka were rising higher and higher before him, to 16,000 feet. The ceiling of his struggling ship was only half that high, for he still carried a big load of gasoline. He threaded his way through awesome chasms, and then ran into a virtual wall of ice in the sky. The violence of the black storm Mattern encountered was the worst he had ever experienced. It would be folly to try and punch his way through on instruments, for already he was lost in the mountain fastness. Frustrated, he swung the ship around and flew back to Khabarovsk, ending a heartbreaking, 1,600-mile flight that got him nowhere.

Any pilot who has ever been forced to execute a "one-eighty" turn in foul weather knows the disappointment Mattern experienced; but for Jimmie it was even worse, for there were no alternate airports between Khabarovsk and the Kamchatka Peninsula. But after a night's sleep, he was determined once more to try and punch through the weather barrier. This time, the gods gave Jimmie a break, and he sneaked through the mountain passes feeling the worst was behind him. He was so wrong.

The needle on Mattern's oil temperature gauge began creeping dangerously toward the red line; his engine was losing rpm's. Mattern could smell the Russian oil breaking down, filling the cockpit with a cloud of blue smoke. He looked out the window; below him stretched an endless stratus layer, blanketing the Russian coast line along the Bering Sea. Jimmie was not sure whether he was over land or water.

The temperature gauge needle stuck against the red line, indicating to Mattern that his straining engine was about to seize up and quit. Within 600 miles of his goal in Alaska, Mattern already was past the point of no return. He had forced the Vega to the limit of her endurance. To attempt a flight across the Bering Sea with an engine about to quit would be suicidal. Mattern dove down through the clouds and deliberately crashlanded on a small island in the Anadyr River, a lonely outpost in the heart of the tundra region, forbidding in its vast emptiness under the midnight summer sun.

Philosophically, Mattern figured his chances. He must get word out, by telegraph. He still had friends back at the College Inn in Chicago who could bring a new ship up to Nome. He could still finish the trip, meet his sponsors' commitments, and perhaps even beat Wiley Post back to New York. But how?

For long weeks, Mattern lived on the tiny island, surviving the bitter cold winds by huddling in the shelter of his cockpit and living off the land—berries, fresh water, and small game he shot and trapped. Then one day in late July, he saw people, real, live people! A band of Eskimo reindeer hunters moved slowly along the distant river bank, but they did not see him.

In desperation, Mattern poured gasoline onto the tundra and set it afire. Flames leaped high and quickly spread, driven by the wind. Soon the whole island—including his wrecked Vega, was a mass of seething flame. Mattern waded into the icy water and began to swim for shore.

The startled Eskimos gave Jimmie some warm clothes and proudly escorted him into Anadyr, a small village where he finally made contact with the outside world. To his astonishment, Mattern learned he had been given up for dead. He soon put the facts straight, and in a few days got the message he had hoped would come—a new ship was on its way to Nome.

The news was not all good; Wiley Post had taken off and was even then racing after him on his way around the world, alone with the *Winnie Mae*. Time was of the essence now to Mattern, but not to the Russians. Here was a chance for a great propaganda beat—they were sending their own flying ace, handsome Sigmund Levenesky, to "rescue" him! Mattern groaned; it would take precious days for Levenesky to get to Anadyr from the Black Sea with his flying boat, a 5,000-mile trip. There was nothing to do but wait.

Jimmie Mattern was disconsolately riding as a passenger with Levenesky, en route to Nome, when the Russian pilot handed him the headset, grinning proudly. The world was hailing the "rescue" as a great achievement in international "understanding," with one hero helping out another. Then came another news flash—Wiley Post was at that moment streaking home from Alaska in the *Winnie Mae!*

He handed the earphones back to Levenesky, who did not speak English. "Thank you, Sigmund!" he said, smiling broadly. "I hope you choke!"

Levenesky returned the smile and thanked Jimmie in Russian for being such a nice guy.

In Nome, Mattern picked up his new ship and headed homeward to complete the job he had set out to do. His great achievement, his hatful of records and his great adventure in Siberia, were dimmed by the wild welcome New York was giving Wiley Post, but he was not about to quit. At Edmonton,

Canada, he found out that the world had not forgotten him. He was still a hero. The local telegraph operator dumped a bushel basket of telegrams in his lap, welcoming him back.

Excitedly, Mattern dug through the pile of telegrams looking for a special one that would carry the code word "Shaggy." That would be from his business manager. He finally located it and tore it open. He read it, grinning broadly, and shoved it into his pocket. Then he faced the crowd of newsmen and radio reporters, who were pushing and shoving to get their microphones in close for his thrilling story of survival in the Arctic.

Mattern smiled politely, pushing his way silently to the rear of the group, where a radio reporter stood holding his mike, labeled: "NBC."

"Welcome back, Jimmie!" the NBC man cried suddenly, before the others could get into position. Mattern smiled back and grabbed the mike.

"Hand me a Lucky!" he cried. While Wiley Post was back in New York broke, Mattern already was cashing in. He had just made himself $10,000 by speaking four words.

All Mattern's College Inn training was paying off big now, because of his shrewd advance planning. By the time he had completed the round-the-world flight and returned to Hollywood to consider some big movie offers, he was eager to try for still another spectacular.

Through polo-playing buddies at Santa Monica's Uplifters Club, Mattern met and became fast friends with the great humorist Will Rogers. He had known Rogers briefly back at the College Inn, but now Rogers invited him to his Santa Monica hideaway to hear all about Jimmie's world flight at first hand.

"Jimmie," Rogers finally said, "when I finish this picture I'm working on, how about you and me making that trip?"

Mattern agreed. Rogers had become a great aviation enthusiast; and besides having the pleasure of making such a flight with as nice a guy as Will Rogers, there would be even more exploitation possibilities in it. Together the two men huddled over Rogers' globe. Jimmie showed the cowboy-actor a new route they could fly by seaplane, tracing his fingers from

Los Angeles north to Point Barrow, Alaska, and then on to Kamchatka, Tokyo, Hong Kong, Manila, Singapore, and around India up into Europe, Africa, South America, Texas, and home.

Jimmie Mattern still has that trip marked on his own globe but the trip never took place; Will Rogers could not get away from Hollywood that season, and Jimmie Mattern accepted an offer from the Pure Oil Company for a lucrative promotional tour of the nation to sell the Chicago World's Fair.

As an oil company pilot, Jimmie Mattern held down one of the four softest aviation berths in the nation; every stunt pilot dreamed of getting on what came to be called the "Panhandle gravy train" with Mattern, Jimmy Doolittle at Shell, Frank Hawks at Texaco, and Al Williams at Gulf. He claimed to know every back yard in America and extended his contacts to include governors, mayors, and business leaders in each of the forty-eight states.

Mattern next went out to the Lockheed factory in Burbank, California, to help Clarence (Kelly) Johnson design and build the world's plushiest executive aircraft for Mike Benedum, a Texas oilman of almost mythical achievements, who was world-famed as The Great Wildcatter. Nothing was too good for the twin-engine Lockheed 12, which boasted the world's first white sidewall airplane tires, the finest radio equipment, and the longest range of any ship in the world. Benedum's lounge was the livin' end of luxury, all who viewed it admitted.

When another millionaire oilman, Howard Hughes, got a look at Benedum's ship, he canceled plans for a round-the-world hop in a flying boat, scrapped that craft, and ordered a new ship like the one Jimmie Mattern had dreamed up. Hughes later circled the globe in three and a half days, but this did not bother Jimmie. He had even bigger ideas.

For some time now, Mattern had been planning a spectacular world flight nonstop, by using mid-air refueling. It was a daring scheme for 1937, but then Mattern was one to come up with novel ideas. Mike Benedum handed him a blank check and told him to go ahead and complete the ship any way he pleased. It cost him $120,000.

Among his past accomplishments, Mattern already had gained experience flying refueling ships in Alaska, in 1929; he had the details for his projected nonstop global flight all carefully worked out. Governor Aldred of Texas christened the ship *The Texan* and everything was in readiness for the great flight, when Amelia Earhart and Fred Noonan vanished somewhere in the South Pacific. The State Department denied Mattern permission to go.

Mattern stormed Washington with the lieutenant governor of Texas, leading an irate delegation demanding to clear *The Texan* for the world nonstop flight. The government finally relented, and the trip was rescheduled for the following spring.

Mattern got another jolt; Sigmund Levenesky, the Russian ace who had flown him out of Siberia, was lost somewhere in the Arctic on a North Pole flight. The Russian Embassy figured that Jimmie owed them a favor; they appealed to him to go find him; Mattern had the only long-range ship available for the job.

Mattern was on a spot; he felt sorry for Levenesky, but the Russian had cost him the chance to be the first solo round-the-world pilot. He agreed to go, but put the price high.

"I'll go for fifty thousand dollars cash, plus two hundred fifty thousand dollars insurance on *The Texan* and twenty-five thousand dollars insurance on my trimotor Ford refueling ship," he wired, expecting to get turned down. The Russians readily accepted, and the Hollywood Western Union girl thought Mattern was joking when he wired back:

DEPARTING FOR NORTH POLE IN MORNING. MATTERN.

On the hop from Oakland to Fairbanks, Alaska, Mattern set a nonstop record, then kept his word to conduct an extended search over the treacherous ice packs at the top of the world. Another pilot brought the Ford north, but crashed it landing in an ice fog, eliminating the chance of conducting a more widespread hunt for Levenesky.

Jimmie failed to locate the downed Russian, but he did come back with another exclusive story—the tragic crash of Wiley Post and Will Rogers, who died in the plunge of a blood-red seaplane in a shallow river at Walakpi, Alaska, on August 15, 1935. Jimmie got the facts from the lips of a famed bush pilot, Joe Crosson, who had talked with Post just prior to the accident. Crosson was later killed, and Mattern felt that he alone was left with the true story.

Things began moving even more swiftly for Mattern now. He flew actor Jimmy Stewart to the 1937 National Air Races, in Cleveland, through full storm conditions that proved *The Texan* was a good instrument ship. But *The Texan* was soon destroyed in a Miami hangar fire, and Mattern, concerned that America was moving relentlessly toward world war, joined Lockheed as a test pilot of new military fighters and bombers.

An era was slipping by and a new one was beginning; the war years had arrived. Veteran pilot Jimmie Mattern, who was number twelve in seniority among the Lockheed test pilots when he signed on, too quickly advanced to the top of the list as the others tragically died.

Turning down an opportunity to become a commissioned Air Force officer, Mattern felt he could better serve his country as a project pilot on the radical new P-38 Lightning, a twin-boomed monster fighter so secret she was designed in an abandoned distillery in Burbank. Mattern's assignment was to find out why bloody training accidents were destroying P-38's almost as fast as Lockheed built them. He knew the Lightning was a dream ship, despite a wave of applications asking to transfer from fighters to bomber units.

After much interrogation of Lightning crewmen, Mattern uncovered what amounted to a weird "psychological sabotage" campaign that made pilots look on her as a flying death trap, with the result that their flying skill suffered. Major General Barney M. Giles, Assistant Chief of Air Staff, called Mattern into consultation.

"Jimmie," said the general, "I'm giving you carte blanche to break that jinx! Can you do it?"

Mattern readily agreed, and soon was putting P-38's through unheard of maneuvers. All his stunt pilot training was put to good use as Jimmie feathered one engine and performed all sorts of gyrations the Army pilots had considered fatal, even with two engines running. After each such demonstration, Mattern jumped to the ground and told the military pilots: "That ought to prove she's a lady—if an old man like me can handle her!"

The Lightning was the hottest thing on wings for her time at the war's outset and Mattern ironically set a score of new world records doomed to secrecy; there was a war on, and we were not telling the enemy what the ship could really do.

Mattern lowered the transcontinental speed record by three hours and racked up innumerable intercity records, and then, amazingly enough, became the first pilot to touch the sound barrier, in 1940, seven years before Colonel Chuck Yeager blasted through it for the first time, in 1947, in Rocket Ship X-1A. In a screaming terminal dive, Mattern shuddered the Lightning against the "barrier" until his tail almost shook off, and came back to tell others what lay ahead.

Jimmie did more; he conceived the piggy-back concept for single-seater fighter trainers, which meant that instructors could ride with students, a revolutionary step ahead in the nation's accelerated flight training program. For this, Mattern won official thanks from the Pentagon.

Jimmie Mattern slowed down some in later years, and as one of the few old-bold pilots still hurried about the country as an airline passenger on business trips. Not too long ago, on a trip to a national meeting of the OX-5 Club in Kansas City, Jimmie, white-haired and distinguished looking, leaned back to watch the latest in-flight movie and sip a glass of champagne. His mind went back to all he had gone through . . . the round-the-world flight . . . the survival epic in Siberia . . . the time he had once flown over bandit-infested country in Mexico, as chief pilot of a cargo line . . . his war years . . . three decades of hell-for-leather, adventurous aviating. Those were the stunt years, and he smiled thinking about them. He looked up, startled, as someone touched his arm. A pretty stewardess smiled down on the kindly faced man with the crinkled eyes and thinning hair.

"Beg your pardon, sir," she said reassuringly. "We hope you are enjoying your flight. Have you ever flown before?"

Jimmie Mattern laughed. "A couple of times," he admitted.

Times had changed, but even the stewardess could not know that he was still three years ahead of them all; early in 1959, before the first all-jet transport, Boeing's 707, went into scheduled operation, Jimmie Mattern had been invited to sit at her controls and comment on her performance. He had flown them all, Jennies to jets, and he had left his mark on aviation—a hallmark of considerable fame and good fortune rare among stunt men.

13

Gold Mine in the Sky

Jimmie Angel felt the chill wind of death swirling through the cockpit of his ancient biplane despite the stifling jungle heat shimmering above the limitless rain forests of the upper Orinoco.

It was an incredible sight—an endless green sea of teak, mahogany, and climbing vines that formed the impenetrable barrier he was now flying over, toward the towering majesty of Auyán-tepuí—Devil Mountain—in a land that time forgot.

Jimmie lifted his goggles and wiped away the sweat that stung his eyes; and for a moment he remembered another time, another place, when he had momentarily been blinded and had come very close to death. He was barnstorming with his brother, Eddie, his partner in Jimmie Angel's Flying Circus. . . . It was night, high above the Pasadena Rose Bowl, and his muscles ached from flying, in a Hisso Standard, one of the hardest shows of his life. He rolled inverted, split-essed around through a half loop, with Eddie standing on the top wing.

"Go!" he shouted, and Eddie fell away into the screaming wind, clutching two giant flashlights that stabbed the blackness of the night with long, probing fingers. He remembered what Eddie had told him: "Jimmie, I'll give them the thrill of their lives! I ain't gonna pull the ripcord until I can see ground with my flashlights!" Down Eddie spiraled in a sickening free-fall, until it seemed that he would crash in a heap on the 50-yard line. Then Jimmie saw Eddie's canopy open, a second before he landed.

His engine coughed, and Jimmie Angel snapped back from his reverie. Startled, he hit the fuel pump, and breathed easier when the emergency passed. A forced landing in the jungle would mean death.

In the front cockpit Jimmie saw Bob Williamson, a grizzled, ancient prospector, turn and grin, jerking his thumb toward the left. Williamson was an almost legendary character, an Old Man of the Forest. He was guiding Jimmie over the uncharted Orinoco country from memory.

Nobody but a damn fool would risk his life flying over such country, Jimmie thought. Maybe he was a damn fool, but had not the Spaniards risked their lives for the fabled treasure of the Incas? Ahead, to the left of his nose, loomed Auyán-tepuí. Rising 10,000 feet from the jungle floor, it jutted into billowing rain clouds overhead, a vast, unexplored fortress of a mountain, a lost world where no man had ever set foot.

Jimmie caught Williamson's excitement now. If what the old prospector said was true . . .

Jimmie Angel thought back to when he had first met Williamson, in a hot, evil-smelling saloon in Panama City, where Jimmie was relaxing from his last job, flying mining company payrolls over bandit-infested country back of Tampico. Known throughout Central America as a tough, hard-fighting but likable Americano who flew like a fool, Jimmie was out to make a fortune as a wedding present for his fiancée, Marie, back in the States.

That is why Jimmie's eyes glinted when he saw the old prospector pull out a chamois bag and dump a handful of gold nuggets on the bar.

"Gimme fourteen brandies, six inches apart!" the oldster roared. At the other end of the 7 feet of drinks, Jimmie Angel picked up a brandy glass and tossed it off.

"If you're gonna drink with me," the prospector glowered, "you'll have to drink faster than that!"

It was a tie.

Glowing warmly inside, both men shook hands and introduced themselves. Jimmie set up another 7 feet of drinks.

"Where'd those nuggets come from?" Jimmie finally asked, his curiosity exceeding normal reticence.

"From a mountaintop," Williamson replied softly. "From a beautiful, mysterious mountaintop, where nobody on this earth had ever been before! In a lost world, beyond the jungles, 'way back in the Gran Sabana!"

Jimmie twisted his glass. He knew a little of the Venezuela wilderness, back from the oil camp at Ciudad Bolivar, on the Orinoco. But back to the Gran Sabana, thousands of miles of green hell extended from horizon to horizon, a vast green curtain beyond which no one knew what lay. No one, perhaps, except Williamson.

"How much did you bring out?" Jimmie asked.

"All I could carry. But there's plenty more there! There's a hidden valley up there, paved with gold! The ancient mother lode of the lost treasure of the Incas!"

Jimmie started to answer but stopped. A stranger had moved in between them. A sailor, ugly, scar-faced. He gripped a knife. "I'll take that bag!" he spat.

"Go ahead," Jimmie said abruptly. "Give it to him!" The old man slowly extended his hand toward the sailor, a look of deep hurt on his face, as if he thought Jimmie was in on the holdup.

"A hell of a way to . . ." Williamson began. He never finished. Jimmie waited until the sailor's greedy eyes were riveted to the gold sack; then he acted. With a swift jujitsu twist on his knife hand Jimmie caught him off balance. The sailor flew through the air and crash-landed on the floor.

"Let's get the hell out of here!" Jimmie yelled to the old man. They hit for the street and ran down an alley, followed by a crowd of yelling, cursing waterfront characters. Later, Jimmie and Williamson sat in the old man's small hotel room, over a candle, fingering the nuggets and talking.

"How much is that gold worth?" Jimmie asked.

"About five thousand here."

"Okay. Put that up for a bond and I'll put up my ship! You and I will fly back to that mountain, and whatever we find we split." They shook hands.

That is how it was that Jimmie Angel and the old prospector were flying over the deadly jungle, a green carpet that hid death in many forms—poisonous snakes . . . piranha fishes . . . insects . . . Jivaro head-hunters.

Angel added power and climbed the little ship up through the clouds. There he came upon the lost world of Auyán-tepuí, seeming to float in the sky. For about 25 miles, the tabletop mountain stretched, crisscrossed with fantastic gorges. The old man motioned this way and that, and finally jumped excitedly, almost falling out of the cockpit in his eagerness.

"Down there!" he yelled to Jimmie. "Land down there!"

Jimmie Angel took one look and shuddered. This was worse than he had bargained for. A tiny clearing the size of a baseball diamond, set in the middle of a rocky bowl through which a stream wandered.

He had come this far, and he had a $5,000 guarantee if they crashed. But could they ever get out? Jimmie thought about Marie. He set his jaw, banked around, chopped the throttle, and cross-controlled, throwing the ship into a steep, violent forward slip. Down they slid, until it appeared they would crash into the mountaintop valley, two miles high in the thin, chill air. But Jimmie made it.

By now, thunderheads were gathering above them. Jimmie knew they would have to get out within thirty minutes or never. The ship would bog down in the wet ground; and even if they did get off, battling the raging storm atop Devil Mountain would be catastrophic.

Already, Williamson was on the ground, frantically scooping up gravel and pouring it into a gunny sack. Jimmie watched in awe.

"Look!" Williamson cried, holding something in his hand. A nugget. Big as a walnut!

"Hurry up!" Angel said. "We've got to get out of here!"

Excitedly, the two men literally scooped a fortune from the gold mine in the sky; and as the first drops of rain fell, they thundered off the little clearing, bounced through branches of scrub, and were gone. Jimmie had done it again.

Tragedy ended the strange partnership when Bob Williamson fell ill in Panama City. "I'm gonna die, Jimmie," the old man told him. "The mine's yours. But don't draw any maps. They'll steal it from you. Think you can find it again from the air?"

"I hope so," Angel said.

Jimmie Angel was wrong. Try as he might, he could not relocate Williamson's mother lode. The vast back country of La Gran Sabana looked all alike to him from the air.

Angel set up a base camp at Ciudad Bolivar and for months flew endless searches over the back country. Once, he was startled to see a great waterfall plunging from the top of the mountain in the clouds, into a sea of mist at the jungle floor, thousands of feet below. The oil-field roughnecks at Ciudad Bolivar had laughed at his story of the lost gold mine in the sky, but maybe they would believe the waterfall!

Jimmie flew across the top of the falls and checked his altimeter. Then he glided down through the turbulent air and dove out along the valley floor through the spray, hedge-hopping dangerously along the river. He could not believe his eyes, but the altimeter did not lie—the water plunged down for more than a mile!

For months, everyone called it "Angel's Fairy Story," until Jimmie finally flew in a government official and showed him the falls were real. "Magnificent!" the official cried to Jimmie. "This is the Eighth Wonder of the World! It shall bear your name— Angel Falls!"

Jimmie Angel was still restless. A waterfall was fine, but he was broke. He needed ready cash to continue his search for the lost mine. He returned to Mexico to resume flying payrolls over bandit country. On one flight, the guard riding in the front cockpit turned and thrust a gun in Jimmie's face, commanding him to land. Angel yanked back hard on the stick, forcing the gunman back into his seat. Then he shot the guard through the head—he had recognized him as the leader of the *bandidos!*

The time came when Marie became impatient and flew down to Mexico to join Jimmie. They were married and settled down in Managua, Nicaragua, where Jimmie was trying to set up a commercial airline linking Managua and San José, Costa Rica.

The Angels moved to San José just in time to be caught in a revolution seeking to overthrow the President, Teodoro Picado. Jimmie was used to violence—he had scored five kills in the World War, flying with the Royal Flying Corps—but Marie was living in a hotel adjacent to the presidential palace. Bullets whined in the streets. Jimmie had to get her out.

The revolutionists offered Jimmie $50,000 to bomb the palace and kill Picado. He thought of his wife. If he turned down the job, they would only hire another pilot. He accepted. That night, Jimmie finally wangled a ride out of town for Marie in a friend's airplane. It was none too soon—the revolutionists, realizing that Jimmie had tricked them, paid another flyer to bomb the palace. Marie's room was shattered.

Back in Panama City, Jimmie told Marie about the lost gold mine in the sky. She laughed, but saw from his seriousness that he would never be happy until he had found it again. She agreed to join him in a new effort. Back at Ciudad Bolivar, the Angels set up a new camp, then flew back to the foot of Auyán-tepuí and established an advance base. Day after day, Jimmie and Marie searched the vast mountaintop for Williamson's lost mine.

One day, Jimmie landed and told Marie excitedly he thought he had found it. With them in the camp were three men, Gustavo Heny, an explorer; Miguel Angel Delgado, a friend; and Captain Felix Cardona, another explorer.

Captain Cardona stayed behind the next day, as the Angels, Heny, and Delgado took off in Jimmie's new ship, an eight-place, single-engine Fokker, the *Flamingo*. Higher and higher they soared on the jungle thermals, rising through the clouds to the top of the mountain the natives prayed to, where endless thunder shook the basaltic cliffs until they trembled, where mysterious animal, bird, and plant life existed as nowhere else on earth.

And then they crashed.

Jimmie had picked what looked like a smooth landing area; it was a thin crust over a hidden bog. The *Flamingo*'s wheels broke through and the plane flipped over, where it remains to this day. Worse, Jimmie realized he had picked the wrong valley. They faced a serious problem—getting down the cliff alive.

From the top of the lost world, the three men and one girl began a tortuous, twenty-one-day odyssey of struggle against the hell of Auyán-tepuí. Nights were bitterly cold. Food was scarce. Unknown dangers waited at every turn. Through the misty clouds, they stumbled and fell, crossing frightening crevasses, toward the majesty of Angel Falls. They found strange plants and scurrying, apelike animals, beasts that had lived apart from the outside world since before history began. It was a naturalist's paradise, one that would be explored later by the American Museum of Natural History.

Using ropes, the party worked its way down sheer cliffs, sleeping through the long nights on narrow ledges in agonizing downpours of rain, attacked by vicious insects—mosquitoes as big as wasps, and experiencing the cold fear of the unknown.

Exhausted and ill, they finally staggered into their base camp, where Cardona nursed them back to health. A rescue plane, called in by radio, flew them back to the outside world, where Jimmie Angel, sullen and quiet, realized Auyán-tepuí had defeated him. The secret of the lost gold mine in the sky remained locked in the misty wonderland atop Devil Mountain, where, if it really exists, it remains today.

Who knows whether it really exists? Only Jimmie Angel and Bob Williamson had gazed at its wonders. Williamson was dead, and Jimmie, his fortunes again dwindling, sent his wife to Santa Barbara, California, to live and raise their two sons.

I met Jimmie in 1956, at Whiteman Airpark, in Pacoima, California, an older man now, but with a strange, haunted look still in his eyes.

"Come with me and write the story," Jimmie grinned. "I'm really gonna find it this time!"

He had a map, he told me, a map drawn for him by an Indian who had guided Williamson to the mother lode so many years ago. And there was new mining excitement in Venezuela; diamonds had been discovered, and uranium. But Jimmie had one thing only on his mind.

Backed by San Francisco financiers, Jimmie Angel set off on his last quest for the glittering bonanza with a brand new ship, a Cessna 180, which he hoped to land atop the mystery mountain.

"Meet me in Panama," he said. "I'm picking up a short-wave radio there, to use on the mountaintop."

By the time I reached Panama, Jimmie Angel was dead.

Hindi Diamond, a capable reporter from the *Panama American*, told me what had happened.

"He landed in a bad wind," she said. "It was not too serious an accident, but the ship flipped over and Jimmie banged his head. He suffered a concussion."

For long days, Hindi sat by Jimmie's side in the hospital. Several times, Jimmie tried to tell her something—perhaps where the map was. But finally, he closed his eyes for the last time.

There are skeptics who say the whole story was phoney, that Jimmie Angel never visited Auyán-tepuí, that his gold mine in the sky did not exist.

But Jimmie did find Angel Falls, a living monument to one of the last of the barnstormers, who died chasing a dream. Was it real? The *Flamingo* still sits there. Maybe you have seen it in *Cinerama*, for Lowell Thomas sent a crew down there specifically to photograph it.

And Marie Angel remembers too well the terrifying hardships she endured climbing down the mountain after their crash. "Jimmie wouldn't have risked our lives for nothing," she says. "Of course it was no dream!"

14

The Wild Blue Yonder

BLUSHING FURIOUSLY under the stares of the crowd, Army Lieutenant Benjamin D. Foulois clambered awkwardly into the small seat of America's first military airplane, a frail wood-and-wire Wright pusher, and fumbled with the football helmet on his head. The time was January, 1910; the scene, Chicago's Fifth Annual Electric Show. The event was the Army's public unveiling of *Aeroplane Number One, Heavier-than-air Division, United States Aerial Fleet,* a handsome flying machine that had passed all flight tests and won acceptance only a few months earlier, on August 2, 1909.

Lieutenant Foulois felt rather foolish, sitting there in full view of the cheering crowd, waving to the kids and blowing kisses to the pretty girls. The Army had insisted on this display of courage beyond the call of duty as a demonstration of the potential of air power. But damn it, they might have let him at least fly the thing; the biplane was ignominiously *suspended by a cable* from the ceiling of the Electric Show Auditorium!

The moment came to open the show; the lights dimmed, except for a spotlight on Foulois and another on the bandstand, where a soprano belted out the opening lines of the national anthem: *Oh, say can you see . . . !* Foulois pressed a button, and suddenly the airplane's propellers began to whir, powered by an electric motor. Foulois adjusted his goggles and pretended to soar away into the wild blue yonder, but by now the crowd was no longer cheering—they were laughing like crazy. The windstorm from the propellers was blowing the sheet music from the grandstand and drowning out the soprano's voice.

Its first air show a decided failure, the Army forthwith retreated from public exhibition "flying" and left sky-stunting to civilians like Linc ("Loop-the-Loop") Beachey, who made a fortune capitalizing on the stunt first performed by a Russian airman named Nesterov on August 20, 1913, and later by the Frenchman Adolphe Pegoud.

After World War I, military flight demonstrations were largely confined to participation in the Pulitzer Prize Races; but behind the scenes, both the Army and the Navy were polishing up something excitingly new—the first formation aerial demonstration teams.

At 3:22 P.M. on the afternoon of September 13, 1928, a crowd of 40,000 spectators at Mines Field, California, watched the Army's crack stunt team, the Three Musketeers, thundering across the grandstands roped together in a tight vee. The Army pilots—Lieutenants W. L. Cornelius, J. A. Woodring, and J. J. Williams—looped and barrel-rolled across the sky as one ship.

Not to be outdone, the Navy's Sea Hawks, D. W. Tomlinson, W. V. Davis, and A. P. Storrs, amazed the military observers at the National Air Races by flashing over the field *inverted*, the Wasp engines of their Boeing F-2B's never missing a beat. The engines had been specially modified for inverted flight as a result of research by the Navy's great engineering test pilot Alford Williams.

On December 12, 1935, the Army Air Corps' 1st Pursuit Group, from Selfridge Field, shocked the people of Miami with the first public demonstration of an aerobatic maneuver that today is a standard part of most shows of that type—the Bomb Burst. High above the field appeared the formation of Army ships, coming straight down in a thundering power dive. Women screamed as the ships plunged earthward, seemingly bent on crashing. But at the last second, they broke away from each other, pulling out of their dive to all points of the compass like an inverted fleur-de-lis.

Commented an observer: "It was extremely regrettable that the bursting bomb maneuvers of this unit (1st Pursuit Group) resulted in a number of airplanes flying over the grandstand at a very low altitude on the first day of the meet. While the action of the Department of Commerce official in grounding the Commander and Leader of the Pursuit Unit could be taken easily, the imposition of a fine of $100 upon our kind host, the City of Miami, left a feeling of regret. . . ."

Other dazzling performances by other military stunt teams at the Miami Air Races got a warmer welcome. The Navy Hell Divers, commented the *Miami Herald*, "followed with one intricate maneuver after the other in rapid succession," while the Army's Three Mugs of Beer—Lieutenants Karl Voelter, Charles P. Darnes, and L. A. Heard—drew even stronger praise: "The aerial antics of this team was crazy. They shot their small planes around the field in a series of loops, nose dives and wing wobbling spurts of what not to do in flying—they were spectacular!"

But the outstanding air show, the *Miami Herald* affirmed, was a breathtaking aerobatic demonstration put on by the Three Men on a Flying Trapeze, an Army team led by a leather-faced officer, Major Claire L. Chennault. With his wingmen, Lieutenants J. H. Williamson and William E. McDonald, Major Chennault had already been putting on eye-opening aerobatic exhibitions for a little over a year to promote interest in the role of fighter aviation.

"There was a great surge of approval when the crowd recognized the Army's team as they speeded over the edge of the airport," commented the *Herald*. "These expert Army fliers from Maxwell Field again staged the stunts which brought world fame to themselves and renown to the military service they represent. Their work included the longest series of maneuvers ever presented in Miami. One spectacular feat was a roll within a roll in which the planes revolved around each other while barrel rolling individually. The expertness of this maneuver brought cheers from the crowd. Then, too, there were the half rolls while completing a loop and Immelmann turns. These marvelous turns, at the top of a loop, pulled in

V-formation, were amazing. They ended their work by speeding across the field in a very tight formation. . . ."

For their performance, Chennault's Three Men on a Flying
Trapeze won the Miami Trophy for Acro-Flying and left the
nation soberly thinking about what the future of military combat would be like. "They demonstrated the ultimate in Element
Team Work," the *Miami Herald* editorialized. "Some of the
maneuvers executed by this team required timing in terms of
tenths of seconds, while others required perfect flying technique at high speeds. The application of such timing and technique to the tactical formation exercises should produce an
organization of maximum effectiveness in combat."

Seven years later, the astuteness of this report was borne out
when Chennault, Williamson, and McDonald took discharges
from the Army and traveled to China to train Generalissimo
Chiang Kai-shek's pilots and to form the American Volunteer
Group, which later became world famous as the Flying Tiger
squadron. Chennault's pursuit tactics, developed during eighteen years of Army aerobatic flying, paid off victoriously.

One admirer wrote a poem, dedicated to Chennault's aerobatic team, which appeared in the *Cleveland Plain Dealer:*

> *Oh, they float through the air just as straight as a rule,*
> *These gallant young men from the Tactical School;*
> *They have ten times the kick of the old Army mule,*
> *And the fair hearts they've stolen away!*

In 1946, America was a nation tired of war, in a time when
swift demobilization and a return to peaceful pursuits was on
everyone's mind. It was also a time when the Army Air Force
saw an opportunity to become autonomous, a move that had
been under discussion since 1942. What better way to sell the
nation on a "United States Air Force" than to put on a spectacular air show?

General Carl Spaatz, Chief of the Army Air Force, in July
sent a note over to Lieutenant General Elwood P. ("Pete")
Quesada, head of the Tactical Air Command at Langley Field,
Virginia, suggesting formation of a special demonstration team

to be designated Squadron Z. The following month, Squadron Z was created with Colonel Kenneth R. Powell as leader and hand-picked airmen as wingmen.

By late November, Squadron Z had completed a whirlwind tour of the nation, putting on 17 air exhibitions featuring the new "propellerless" P-80—Lockheed's all-jet Shooting Star. General Quesada himself led the hot-shot Squadron Z to Mexico City on a nonstop flight from Salina, Kansas, thrilling thousands of Latins attending the inaugural of President Miguel Alemán.

In all, more than half a million people got their first look at jet aircraft during Squadron Z's four-month existence, before the outfit was deactivated in late November.

The aerobatic team of Fenton & Fitzgerald burst upon the scene about the same time that Squadron Z retired; and for the next two years, they stunned air-show crowds with a display of precision flying unequalled for its daring conception and execution. The pilots were two young Reservist lieutenants from Mitchell Field, Bill Fenton and Bob Fitzgerald, who worked up an act using two T-6 trainers and soon had the spectators gasping.

Fenton and Fitzgerald at first had no intention of putting on aerial demonstrations; they were just a couple of guys who happened to be clowning around one afternoon and decided to work out some intricate aerobatic maneuvers together. They were good—so good, in fact, that soon offers came in from other fields to put on their show at open houses.

At the National Air Races, from 1947 to 1949, Fenton and Fitzgerald were a howling success; the public had never seen anything like it. Fenton would approach the field on a low, fast pass from the north, while Fitzgerald closed in from the south. At mid-field, barely off the ground, it appeared that a head-on crash was inevitable. Screams pierced the air and women closed their eyes to blot out the bloody collison, but those who kept their eyes open saw Fenton and Fitzgerald's ships break suddenly into flick rolls, snapping around each other as they passed. Formation spins and precision rolls were others in their repertoire of aerobatic maneuvers, which have been called "the most spectacular exhibition of skill and timing ever seen" by a man who should know—Captain Robert D. Janca, picked by the Air Force in April, 1959, to fly as a member of its superb Thunderbirds air demonstration team, born in the summer of 1953.

Four years earlier, on March 21, 1949, a highly skilled group of jet pilots from Williams AFB, Arizona, who flew together as the Acrojets, had been officially recognized as the first Air Force Jet Demonstration Team with a simple mission: "To assure the maximum amount of favorable publicity for the Air Force and to provide appropriate cadet recruiting data before and during the aerial display." There was another, unstated mission—to convince cadets at "Willie Air Patch" that the wild tales they were hearing about the new F-80's flight characteristics were so much prop-wash from disgruntled pilots of conventional aircraft.

Organized in June, 1948, the Acrojet team included Major Howard W. Jensen, leader; Captain Benjamin F. Yeargin, right wing; Lieutenant Michael Smolen, left wing; Captain Robert C. Tomlinson, slot; and Major Jones E. Bolt, alternate. The outbreak of the Korean War, in June, 1950, cut short the Acrojets' public career as the USAF's official demonstration team, but there was still a job to do; until May, 1953, the team continued actively performing its beautiful aerial ballets at other pilot training bases to give their cadets confidence in what a jet could do.

Overseas, a thundering team of F-84E Thunderjets, organized at the 36th Fighter Bomber Wing, Fürstenfeldbruck Air Base, Germany, in May, 1949, by Major Harry K. Evans, began a series of 257 shows under the name Skyblazers. Other members were Lieutenants Buck and Bill Patillo, Lawrence Damewood, and Captain Vince Gordon. By the time they rotated back to Stateside in the summer of 1952, the Skyblazers were considered so valuable a demonstration of American air power that USAF Commander General Lauris Norstad saw to it that the tradition was continued by the 86th Fighter Bomber Wing at Neubiberg Air Base, Germany. During the single year the

86th flew, more than 3 million Europeans thrilled to their aerobatics. Their finest hour was a brilliant show they put on over Paris, for the 20th International Air Exhibition, on July 5, 1953. Half a million spectators, including France's President Vincent Auriol, yelled themselves hoarse.

In the three years from 1957 through 1959, flying a diamond formation of F-100C jets as Europe's first supersonic aerial demonstration team, the Skyblazers played to 8 million spectators in 114 shows, with such spectacular success that they were banned from European competitions for being "too professional." They disbanded in January, 1962.

Major Vince Gordon, one of the original Skyblazer pilots, in August, 1952, organized a brand-new jet aerobatic team—the Sabre Knights—at Hamilton AFB in California, as part of the 325th Fighter Interceptor Squadron. Gordon's original wingmen were Captain Dick Hellwege, left wing; Captain Bruce Jones, right wing; and Lieutenant James F. Low, slot. During their 5-year existence, the Sabre Knights showed their stuff to an estimated 500,000 awed spectators. Of particular interest was the team's skill in flying the heavier F-86D all-weather interceptors through precision maneuvers with apparently effortless ease.

Of all the military aerial demonstration teams ever to stun an audience, the Four Horsemen were without doubt the most unusual. No sleek fighter craft flew in this team; it was composed of 50-ton C-130 turbo-prop cargo craft! Formed at Ardmore, Oklahoma, in 1957, the team pilots were Captains Hubert E. Chaney, William H. Hatfield, James F. Akin, and Donald L. Moore.

Naturally, loops and flick rolls were out, but the Four Horsemen nevertheless drew thunderous applause from audiences throughout America, and overseas in Europe and in Japan. Their act included diamond-formation high-speed flybys, a modified bomb-burst and a fan break for landing, all executed with the fluid grace of a trained elephant troupe under a circus tent. The show was formed to draw attention to the role of the troop-carriers. Said Captain Chaney: "Ever notice how spectators at a troop drop keep their eyes fixed on the parachutes? Nobody ever notices the aircraft!"

Many National Guard units joined the craze to put on aerial demonstrations to help charity drives, recruitment programs, and holiday celebrations; and one of the greatest was South Dakota's ANG demonstration team, organized by former Marine ace Joe Foss. In the South Pacific, Major Foss had been an advocate of team tactics in combat against Jap pilots, whose stunt flying looked pretty but set them up as easy targets. His ANG demonstrations were colorful playbacks of those deadly duels over the Solomons.

Another ANG demonstration team of the 1950's were The Minutemen, organized in 1955 at Buckley Field, Colorado, by Lieutenant Colonel Walter E. Williams. Within a year The Minutemen were so hot that the National Guard Bureau adopted them as its official team, sending them off to Hawaii, Mexico, Bermuda, and Central America to carry its air-power-for-peace message in flashing maneuvers with bright red F-86C's and F-86F's.

The Minutemen pilots, Colonel Williams, Major Wynn Coomer, and Captains John T. Ferrier and Robert Cherry, had their own special number that was so outlandish no other team ever tried to duplicate it—the Corkscrew Roll. Slashing past the spectator area at low level, the leader and slot man held their normal positions while the two wingmen, trailing spiraling smoke, *rolled simultaneously in opposite directions around their teammates!*

As glamorous as these performers were, The Minutemen were disbanded in 1960 by Chief of Staff General Curtis Le May, who wanted only a single Air Force demonstration team on stage—the incredible Thunderbirds.

Original team leader of the Thunderbirds, formed at Luke Air Force Base, Arizona, was Major Dick Catlege, who selected Buck and Bill Patillo, just back from a tour of Europe with the Skyblazers, as his wingmen, and Captain Bob Kanaga as slot man. On June 16, 1953, USAF Chief of Staff General Hoyt Vandenberg witnessed their first show, a breath-catching display of skillful airmanship in four huge Republic F-84G's. By 1965, the Thunderbirds had staged more than a thousand performances throughout the United States, Central and South America, Europe, and the Far East, witnessed by more than 60 million people.

In June, 1956, the Thunderbirds moved their home base to Nellis AFB, Nevada, equipped themselves with the new F-100C Super Sabre, and became the world's first supersonic precision flying team. Perhaps not so maneuverable as the F-84F swept-wing Thunderstreak they had gone to in October, 1954, the Super Sabres, painted wildly in red, white, and blue markings of the Indian Thunderbird, are breathtakingly beautiful to behold in tight formation flight.

On such a day, sitting in the stands with your head on a swivel and your heart in your mouth, you will hear the driving voice of the team narrator, Captain Russ Goodman, drawing your attention to four flashing jets streaking vertically skyward, trailing smoke, as one ship:

"Watch now as the aircraft approach the top of their climb for this maneuver, the spectacular Thunderbird Bomb Burst! . . . Seconds ago the four aircraft were streaking upward in a tight diamond formation . . . now the aircraft break away from each other to the four points of the compass, trailing white smoke much like a bursting rocket. . . . Climbing vertically is Captain Bob Morgan, leaving the bomb burst with a vertical roll. . . . Now streaking away from each other the pilots will complete a half roll each, then simultaneously each aircraft will half-roll on its back, dive through a Split-S maneuver straight down, pulling up at minimum altitude. . . .

"Leveling off, the four aircraft will fly *directly toward each other* and cross over at low altitude! Keep your eyes on all four of them—if you can! The T'Birds are coming in now from four different directions at speeds up to 600 miles an hour. . . . The timing of this maneuver is critical . . . each man correcting for wind, turbulence, speed, drift, and altitude to properly execute the crossover. . . . *Here they come!* . . . each pilot jockeying for position while closing at high speed . . . (A deafening roar drowns out his voice as the four Thunderbirds shoot past, like four runaway autos slamming through an intersection at the same time.) . . . Major Paul Kauttu, the leader, has pulled up and over through a half Cuban-8 to the rear. . . . Captain Hank Canterbury is completing an overhead loop directly in front of us, to dive back into his slot position. . . . The wingmen, Captains Chuck Hamm and Bill McGee, have pulled up sharply to the right and the left, to rejoin on their leader's wing from either side, reforming their diamond formation."

And so the show goes . . . change-over rolls . . . the bon ton roulle . . . six-ship wedge victory roll . . . graceful whifferdill turns, and finally the tactical pitchup and landing. Afterward, you fly the back seat with Chuck Hamm to get the feel of supersonic aerobatic flight, the crushing force of an afterburner sprint, and the sudden, violent five-G pitchup, and you think how different, how gloriously different, from the old Stearman trainer of a quarter-century ago, when you first learned about these things! In a way, you miss the open-cockpit days, but the Thunderbirds you admire and respect as the greatest of all.

Or are they the greatest? Don't say that around a Navy ship, son! Didn't you ever hear of the Blue Angels?

Among all flight demonstration teams, the Blue Angels are the coziest; they do not just maintain a "broomstick" clearance between wingtips—they *overlap* almost their complete wings while zooming around the atmosphere at speeds up to 500 miles an hour! There is an iron-clad rule among the Blue Angel pilots that "thou shalt not stick thy wingtip closer than 36 inches to my canopy, Sir!" This makes for a 14-foot overlap, which seems ridiculous, when you think of it.

It has been two full decades since the Blue Angels, officially known as the U.S. Navy Flight Demonstration Team, first began trying to elbow each other out of the big, beautiful sky, where, it seems, there is plenty of room for all. Lieutenant Commander Roy M. ("Butch") Voris was the first leader of this apparently suicide-bent group, who put on their first air show flying Grumman F6F Hellcats at the Southeastern Air Show in June of 1946. That first show was a lulu, but decidedly unfair.

They sent up a poor, defenseless Yellow Peril primary trainer, painted up like a Jap Zero, and then calmly went about shooting it down. The trainer spiraled earthward trailing black smoke and out jumped the pilot, who parachuted to earth only to be captured—by Marines, of course. While carrying out this mock battle, the original Blue Angels claim to have invented the diamond formation, now their trademark.

Today, the Blue Angels perform their miraculous man-and-machine maneuvers in supersonic Grumman F11A Tigers, lovely swept-wing ships with Coke-bottle bellies and thundering voices, utilizing two basic formation structures—the echelon, with the planes stacked down and back from the leader at a 45-degree angle, and the diamond formation. For some reason known only to the Navy, the Blue Angels consider it beneath their station to be found more than 5 feet apart; take-offs, rolls, and landings are all performed as if there were not too much sky around to fly in. The team also claims to have invented the "back-to-back" formation, with the top man inverted and the other flyboy snuggled in underneath him, right side up, making faces at his buddy.

It all makes for high living.

15

Your Father Is a Stunt Pilot!

As James Gilbert, associate editor of *Flying* magazine, has stated: "Make no mistake about it, competition aerobatics today is nothing like the pre-war image of some mad flying fool in a superannuated rattletrap trying to impress a gullible crowd by missing death by inches. It is a cool and calculated activity performed by cool and calculated specialists in specially built or rebuilt airplanes that have been coolly and calculatedly stressed for the punishment they receive. . . ."

Without question, a natural resentment exists among professionals against their being portrayed as rugged, carefree individuals, bluffing their way through life with more bravado than brains. Jet-Age engineering test pilots will hoot down the helmeted hero of a "Test Pilot" movie thriller, who screams earthward baring his teeth, pulls the wings off his boss' ship, and then marries his daughter.

And so it is with modern aerobatic fliers who put in long, tiring (but thoroughly enjoyable!) hours perfecting their graceful sky ballets, making the most difficult maneuvers look so easy that audiences are inclined simply to take them for granted.

Whenever one of the few remaining hell-for-leather stunt pilots crashes in a ball of flame, fellow Quiet Birdmen dim the lights, fill their glasses, and drink a silent toast to "those of us who have gone west." The QB's have a long and bloody honor roll, where you will find names like Paul Mantz, Tex Rankin, Frank Clarke, Dick Grace, Milo Burcham, and Rolly Cole, men who shared something in common; all were great performers in the sky, and each died with his flying boots on.

Few people would deny that Jimmy Doolittle was one of the great stunt pilots of all time; a cooler, more calculating precision flier never lived than this man who performed the first outside loop on May 27, 1927. Doolittle was one of the first aerobatic pilots really to become a part of his ship, in the same sense that Lindbergh thought of himself and his Ryan NX-211 —the famed *Spirit of St. Louis*—as "we." Doolittle's flashing Hawk P-1 pursuit ship was a classic mount for the diminutive airman, who shocked the crowds at the 1929 National Air Races, in Cleveland, by stripping off his wings, bailing out, and then completing his aerobatic routine in another plane.

During the years that Doolittle flew with the Air Corps as an aerobatic pilot, transcontinental speed flyer, and pioneer of instrument flight, the Navy's Lieutenant Alford Williams, in his famed Curtiss Gulfhawk, was blazing his own epic trail across the skies as that service's greatest racing and precision aerobatic pilot. A keen rivalry existed between Doolittle and Williams; Jimmy was an amateur boxer, while Williams grew up in the Bronx and was signed by the New York Giants, shortly before World War I.

Like Doolittle, Al Williams became a specialist in outside loops and upside-down flight, winning in 1929 the Distinguished Flying Cross for his work as a test pilot in assessing the effects on aircraft of inverted flying maneuvers, for their potential value in military combat. Heavily instrumenting his Gulfhawk, Lieutenant Williams provided engineers with their first solid information on both positive and negative load factors, data that made possible today's precision aerobatics as opposed to the old-style, death-defying antics.

Harold Krier, whose red and white swept-wing Great Lakes Special is rated one of the finest special-purpose aerobatic ships ever built, considered Freddie Lund as the leading civilian aerobatic flyer of the Roaring Twenties, a period when military pilots like Doolittle and Williams ruled the skies. One of the last of the old Flying Circus performers, Lund entered the lists of modern aerobatic exhibitions and, says Krier, was the first to equip his ship, a red, white, and blue Waco Taperwing, with a smoke-generator device "so that the spectators could follow the course of his flight and the perfection of his maneuvers." Lund became the first civilian pilot to duplicate Jimmy Doolittle's outside loop. In 1931, the same year that Doolittle won the first Bendix Trophy Race from Burbank to Cleveland, Lund was killed after colliding with another racer in a pylon event at Lexington, Kentucky.

The outside loop, in which the pilot rides on the outside of the maneuver, is a punishing stunt, because the centrifugal forces send blood rushing to the brain. Paul Mantz once flew a Fleet biplane through 46 consecutive outside loops, as a demonstration of that ship's airworthiness; but this record was eclipsed by another Hollywood stunt pilot, Tex Rankin, who performed 131 outside loops on a single flight.

At a time when other pilots were thrilling the crowds with the old standard stunts like loops, slow rolls, and spins, Tex began building an entirely new repertoire strictly by trial and error; once, he slammed the stick forward and booted full left rudder on the top of a loop to see what would happen. The result was a wild gyration in which the horizon spun around crazily and Tex felt himself half thrown from the cockpit. It was history's first recorded outside snap roll from an inverted position, a maneuver which today rates fifteen points in the Championship Aerobatic rules laid down by the Fédération Aeronautique Internationale in Paris.

In 1937, Tex worked up a routine of twenty-five different aerobatic maneuvers crowded into ten minutes, the prescribed time limit for a competitive performance. Then, at St. Louis' Lambert Field, Rankin left the crowd gasping, by flashing his low-wing monoplane through the sequence to win the International Aerobatic Contest with 282.7 points out of a possible 297, nosing out the Rumanian Air Force ace Captain Alexandro Papana and Paul Mantz for second and third places.

Lieutenant Alford Williams, greatest of the Navy aerobatic pilots, was awarded the Distinguished Flying Cross in 1929 for his research in inverted flight. His favorite ship was the Gulfhawk.

(U. S. Navy photo)

General Claire L. Chennault, leader of the famed Army aerobatic team, Three Men on a Flying Trapeze, applied his skill to train Chinese Air Force, formed Flying Tigers, who flew with tactics he had developed in long stunt career. (National Archives)

The USAFE aerobatic team, the Skyblazers, perform precision flying over France. They were stationed at Chaumont Air Force Base, France, at time of picture, October 18, 1955.   (U. S. Air Force)

The USAF Thunderbirds perform the spectacular Bomb Burst in their F-100 Supersabres. (U. S. Air Force)

Blue Angels. (U. S. Navy)

Blue Angels in "back-to-back" formation, with the top man inverted.
(U. S. Navy)

Movie stunt pilot Cliff Winters dives into a prop building during motion-picture filming with a mockup of a German ME-109, World War II vintage.

Shades of the past—one of the grand old aircraft from World War I, a German Fokker D-VII. Cliff Walker is hanging from strut; Frank Tallman is pilot.

A daring young man on a real flying trapeze. Stunt pilot and aerialist Cliff Winters put on a thrilling show at the 1961 Aero-Rama at Borrego Springs, Calif.

Cliff Winters in the cockpit of First World War vintage Fokker D-VII which he flew against stunt pilot Frank Tallman in Sopwith Camel, thrilling audiences at California air shows. Winters was killed in the crash of stunt plane at Chino, Calif., 1962.

(Author's collection)

Tex Rankin, champion stunt pilot, held record for outside loops—131 in 131 minutes! (Hank Coffin photo)

Aerobatic performer Sammy Mason flies inverted so much he painted his name upside down on side of ship. (Rudy Profant photo)

Aerobatic pilot Bill Adams in 1959 flew with National Championship Air Show. Adams placed third in 1959 National Aerobatic Championships at Ottumwa, Iowa. (Rudy Profant photo)

Brothers Duane, Marion and Lester Cole trail smoke from their Stearman aerobatic ships, tracing graceful patterns against the sky.
(Cole Brothers Air Show photo)

Which way is up? Marion Cole flies inverted while wing rider Lloyd Stoner hangs beneath ship on top wing. Cole Brothers Air Show used this picture as a trade mark for over thirteen years.

(Cole Brothers Air Show photo)

Marion Cole, of the Cole Brothers Air Show, cuts ribbon while flying inverted at 20 feet off the deck.   (Cole Brothers Air Show photo)

Mickey Seaver transfers from speeding car to rope ladder of plane flown by Rolly Cole.
(Cole Brothers Air Show photo)

Rolly Cole flies Mickey Seaver on target for handkerchief pickup.
(Cole Brothers Air Show photo)

Judy Cole stands on top wing of Stearman as her 23-year-old son Rolly taxis out for take-off. Rolly died in Stearman crash shortly afterward. (Cole Brothers Air Show photo)

Judy Cole rides the top wing of Rolly Cole's 450-hp Stearman, as the only woman ever to participate in a mother-and-son aerobatic team. (Cole Brothers Air Show photo)

Rolly Cole, considered the "most promising" of the young aerobatic pilots, died tragically when the engine of his Stearman stunt plane tore out in recovery from a power dive. Rolly tried to jump, too late, and died with his passenger, Mel Stickney.

(Cole Brothers Air Show photo)

Not all of Rankin's stunts were so skillfully flown; at a Walla Walla aerobatic contest, Rankin, tied for first place with Basil Russell, attempted a vertical sideslip over a row of trees from an altitude of 500 feet. Rankin waited a split second too long and fell off into a vicious tailslide. He recovered from that but snapped into a spin, finally landing at the edge of the field in a hard stall-down that left him shaking but alive. One of the judges ran over to Tex and shook his hand. "You win, Rankin!" he cried. "Russell says he will *not* try a tailspin landing!"

Tex grinned weakly. "Hell, that was an accident, not a stunt!" He and Russell split the prize money, and Rankin won the trophy on the toss of a coin. Death caught up with Rankin in 1947, after wartime service as a flight school operator, when an amphibian he was demonstrating crashed on take-off from a field at Klamath Falls, Oregon. This time there was no room to recover.

Captain Alex Papana, the Rumanian flyer who placed second behind Rankin in the St. Louis international competition in 1937, introduced a new style of aerobatic flying to America, along with a smart little stunt plane that had all the other pilots drooling—a smoothly cowled, swept-wing biplane that flew as responsively as a race horse with wings, the German-built Bucker-Jungmeister.

Papana's ship, which drew crowds of admirers wherever it performed, was brought to America by Papana aboard the dirigible *Hindenburg* in 1936 and subsequently was sold to M.C. ("Mike") Murphy, one of the country's outstanding aerobats of the 1930's, who won the National Aeronautic Association-sponsored U.S. Aerobatic Championship three years in a row—1938, 1939, and 1940-41. In doing so, Murphy retired the Freddie Lund Trophy at the All-American Air Races in Miami, Florida.

Mike Murphy was an ambivalent sort of guy who not only captured almost every aerobatic competition in sight in the late 1930's but invented a new stunt each year he appeared at the Cleveland Air Races under contract to the Henderson Brothers. Mike recalls: "In 1937 I introduced the aircraft landing on a moving automobile; in 1938, the use of pontoons to take off and land on the ground without assistance; 1939, the aircraft equipped with two landing gears, which took off upside down and landed right side up. . . ." When things got dull, Mike liked to stop his engine in flight, climb out, and recrank it to life, or maybe bring his ship to a complete stall and drop it to the ground with a parachute. During World War II, Colonel Mike Murphy led the historic glider invasion of Normandy; and in the 1960's, when the newly activated Aerobatic Club of America was formed, they naturally picked Mike for president.

Beverly ("Bevo") Howard, the first pilot to outside-loop a light plane (a 37-horsepower Piper Cub, in 1938), watched Murphy perform in the Bucker-Jungmeister at Miami in 1941 and decided he belonged in its cockpit. "Mike let me fly it," Howard recalled. "I knew I just had to own that airplane. The control pressures were perfect and its ability to execute any routine I asked of it was something out of a dream." (He bought it for $10,000.)

Not long ago, a graduating class of USAF cadets stood with their eyes wide and mouths open watching Bevo, the "Old Man" of Spence AFB, Moultrie, Georgia, salute them with a demonstration of what a man can do with a plane if he is inspired. Don Kinsey, who stood amongst them, stared in awe as "it whirled through a series of crushing outside loops, pullups from vertical dives and violent snaprolls. Suddenly I saw it stand on its tail and climb vertically into what I presumed was a complete stall when, lo and behold, it looped sharply with a double snap roll at the top, flipped on its back for a let-down circle of the field, and made a low-level power approach to the runway, still inverted. Over the fence the plane rolled right side up and the wings came straight and level at almost the exact instant its wheels touched in a three-point landing. . . ."

Harold Krier, 1965 winner of the U.S. Aerobatic Championship competition, flown under F.A.I. rules at Reno, Nevada, recently authored a handbook titled *Modern Aerobatics;* he colorfully describes the way he starts his complex routine:

"As the controls come to life we hold the airplane on the runway a bit longer than usual . . . we're going to need that extra speed! Now, slight right-stick . . . the left wheel leaves the runway, and then the right one. Back slightly on the stick, with a little left rudder—and watch the right lower wingtip as it clears the runway. . . . As we roll past vertical, feed in slight forward-stick and, at the 20-foot level, we are in inverted flight. You may be fairly sure that everyone is watching now!"

In case everyone is *not* watching now, Krier climbs on up through a series of slow rolls and boots his ship through an outside Horizontal-8, a fancy maneuver that the late Tex Rankin adapted from the Cuban-8, introduced to the United States by a Cuban aerobat, Captain Lem Povey. From there, Krier follows a cockpit chart through a total of fifteen precise maneuvers—chain loops, outside snaps from knife-edge flight, roller coasters, inside and outside snap rolls, outside loops, low-level inverted flight (while waving to the crowd—"Look, no hands!"), an inverted ribbon pickup 20 feet off the ground, and finally an inverted approach and a landing—right side up of course, not having wheels on the top wing like Mike Murphy's ship!

Krier, who polished his act while flying with the Ray Doan Sky King Air Shows, rates Rod Jocelyn, Bevo Howard, Roy Timm, Charlie Hillard, and Woody Edmunson as among the best aerobatic performers of this generation. "There are others," he qualifies; "in fact, there may be more unusually skilled precision and acropilots today than ever before."

As always, inventiveness plays a major role in any aerobatic performance, although today practically everything that can be done with an airplane has been done and is catalogued in a list of 87 aerobatic maneuvers compiled by the NAA. There are, however, over 350 variations of these basic maneuvers.

Almost every pilot who has "checked out" on aerobatics has his own favorite, which may be simply a graceful wing over, a Cuban-8, or an inverted spin. I remember sitting in the ready room at Falcon Field, Arizona, during the war years, hangar-flying with a fellow flight instructor, Alvin Algee, who had had

considerable aerobatic experience before the war in a Great
Lakes trainer.

"Al," I said, "what do you think would happen if you started
a snap roll to the right, then, as soon as it breaks, you shoved
the stick clear up to the firewall with full left aileron?"

Algee flipped away his cigarette, grabbed his chute, and
said, "There's one way to find out! Let's go!"

Our Royal Air Force cadets lined the ramp as we climbed a
Stearman primary trainer out of the pattern and headed for
Superstition Mountain, east of Phoenix, where no other ships
would be practicing. It was a beautiful Arizona morning, the
sun just rising and the smell of sage strong in the air. At 3,000
feet Algee said, "Okay, let me try it first!"

He shoved the nose down, picking up speed, then hauled
back to raise it above the horizon in a gentle climb. WHAM!
We were suddenly snapping to the right—Al wore size twelve
shoes and knew how to use them—and as we flashed inverted,
I felt the stick torn from my hand. It socked forward into the
corner of the cockpit. "Hang on!" Al yelled.

There was a sudden shudder, a blast of exhaust in our faces;
and with a wrenching lurch, the Stearman half-outside snapped
to the *left*—with full right rudder still on! Al expertly stopped
the outside flick with wings level, then turned and grinned.

"Go ahead, it's yours," he yelled. I repeated the maneuver—
with the same amazing results. I knew we had something special, and that night, at the Wagon Wheel saloon in Phoenix,
we began lining up suckers from Thunderbird Field, up in
Paradise Valley, a USAF training school which operated with
somewhat more formality than Falcon.

"Ten bucks says we can do a snap roll to the left with full
right rudder," Al would challenge the Thunderbird instructors
at the bar. "Put up or shut up!"

The following dawn, at 3,000 feet over the black tarmac
of an isolated auxiliary field behind Camelback Mountain, with
T'Bird instructor Jimmy Netser in the front seat, Algee ran
through our wonderful "in-and-outer" while a dozen primary
trainers buzzed around watching. It worked fine except for

one thing—with a noise like a shotgun blast, the fabric ripped wide open on Al's upper wing. The stunt was prohibited after that, but we won $50 anyway.

After the war, a former Polish pilot and hero of the Battle of Britain, Jan Zurakowski, invented a stunt described as the "first entirely new aerobatic maneuver in twenty years"—the Zurabatic Cartwheel. In effect, it is a sideways cartwheel tumble, which Zurakowski first worked out carefully with a slide rule.

In executing it, Zurakowski puts a twin-engine Gloster Meteor into a vertical climb, and when the speed falls to between 60 and 70 knots, he shuts down one engine. The asymmetric power thrust throws the ship into a cartwheel; and after three quarters of a turn, he chops off the remaining engine. The Meteor continues to cartwheel through one and one-half turns, ending up nose down and entering a spin. "And anybody can get out of a spin," Zurakowski grins.

Considered by pilots to be the most spectacular maneuver of all time is a spine-chilling something or other originated in the early 1960's in Czechoslovakia, a country that produces some of today's finest aerobatic pilots. It is called the *Lomcevak*, a Czech word that has been roughly translated as: "I've had too much slivovitz brandy and all of my gyros have tumbled!"

In the *Lomcevak*, the airplane is rolled inverted, then pushed into a vertical climb at full throttle. The pilot now executes an inverted snap roll with full forward elevator, full left rudder, and full right aileron. The climb stops, and suddenly the nose swings wildly around the horizon through 360 degrees, while the ship hovers. Then the nose drops and gyroscopic forces, acting 90 degrees from the point of application, change the axis of rotation. With a sickening plunge, the aircraft tumbles completely, tail over nose. Again the axis of rotation changes because of the gyroscopic forces, and, if left alone, the ship falls into an inverted spin. Simple as that!

Team aerobatics, brought to perfection through the years by the military, occasionally have been used effectively at air shows by civilian pilots performing rudimentary loops, figure-8's and bomb bursts, the latter a crowd-pleaser which

Frank Clarke, Frank Tomick, and Roy Wilson demonstrated with spectacular success at the 1931 Los Angeles Air Fiesta.

Thus, thousands of expectant citizens of Kewanee, Illinois, turned out on the hot afternoon of July 28, 1946, to watch the first performance of the Cole Brothers Air Show, which had advertised a demonstration by "Colonel Joe Jet and His Fighting Wingmen."

Duane Cole, who put the show together with his brothers, Marion and Lester, and a dozen or so pilot friends, after a professional flying circus failed to appear for the opening of the new airfield, announced the spectacular at 4 P.M., but only a single Piper Cub appeared in the sky. The door opened and out flew three Guinea hens to spiral down into neighboring barnyards. There were boos and grumbling over false advertising, but the crowd's humor returned when Cole hurriedly staged a "pants race"—the contestants were to fly six miles around the pylon course, land, and take off their pants in front of the grandstand. Then, after three more laps, they were to land, put their pants back on, and jump back into their ships to finish the race. But on the second landing, the pilots found that somebody had tied their pants in knots and tossed them against the fence in front of the stands.

While the crowd roared at their antics, a farmer came driving out onto the field in a John Deere tractor, pop-popped to a halt, and then stole a Piper Cub. Clowning all over the sky, the farmer—Marion Cole—wound up his performance by buzzing the freeloaders on a back road, to the delight of the paid onlookers. But one of the outsiders, failing to see the humor of the snarling Cub diving at him, let fly with a rock. It scored a direct hit, caving in a wing strut which so badly warped the wing that Marion almost crashed getting back to the field.

For seventeen years, the Cole Brothers Air Show thrilled millions of spectators across the country; it was the longest run of any flying circus in history. There were lean years and fat years; there were laughter and tears. There was the time Marion tried to land on top of Duane's auto with a Clipped Wing Cub; just as the Cub's wheels touched, the car dropped two feet into a hidden ditch in the tall grass. The Cub bounced off in front of the car, the car hit the Cub and the act ended in a splintering crash. The Coles staged a pitched battle with newsmen to keep them from taking pictures of the wreck, for there had been a recent outcry against "foolhardy" air circuses when a first lieutenant from Denver flubbed a slow roll and crashed into the grandstands at Flagler, Colorado, killing twenty-two spectators.

Then there were the times when Duane Cole introduced his son, Rolly, to the world of the airman from the back seat of his Clipped Wing Cub, and, later, flying in two-ship formation. Duane remembers: "My cross-country flights with Rolly afforded a close relationship between father and son denied most families. Whether over the Canadian bush with its myriad shimmering blue lakes, the quilted patchwork of grainfields in the midwest, the majestic Rockies with their snow-capped peaks and deep awesome canyons, or the colorful rolling mountains of Pennsylvania, we flew side by side, pointing out rare sights of nature's handiwork to each other. Occasionally, one of us would spot a moose or antelope, a fox or coyote, then we would drop down for a better look. . . ."

Like my own son, Donl, who, as a lad, slept peacefully cradled in the canvas instrument hood of the family Vultee BT-13 on cross-country flights, Rolly Cole grew to manhood in the sky. It was Rolly's dream to fly as well as his father, and some day to lead the Cole Brothers Air Show to thrill a new generation of audiences. Rolly was good—so good that Lindsay Parsons, a member of the 1965 United States Aerobatic Team, called him "the most promising young aerobatic pilot in the country, whose energy, experience and remarkable ability represent the exact ingredients for success in aerobatic competition."

By 1962, Rolly was on his way. At the Experimental Aircraft Association's International Aerobatic Championship, at Phoenix, Arizona, Rolly placed third among seventeen entries. His father won the championship, and Rod Jocelyn nosed him out for second place.

Then, on a Thursday afternoon, August 1, 1963, Rolly Cole
went after new honors at the Rockford, Illinois, E.A.A. fly-in,
flying the finale of a day-long display of top aerial showmanship. "It was a superb exhibition," his father wrote with pride,
after it was all over. "Etching each intricate maneuver with
white smoke against a blue sky in graceful rhythm, he held the
audience spellbound. . . ."

The next day, Rolly took up a passenger, Pan American Captain Melvin Stickney, to run through his routine once more.
From the ground, his Boeing A75N1 Stearman was a flashing
thing of beauty, pulling up through a graceful loop. At the top,
7,000 feet above the Illinois cornfields, Rolly throttled back the
big 450-horsepower Pratt & Whitney engine and entered a
near-vertical, high-speed dive. The wind screamed through the
struts with the same song of death that had been the last thing
the great Lincoln Beachey had heard almost half a century
earlier.

Rolly began his pull-out between 1,000 and 2,000 feet above
the ground, as his father, Duane Cole, watched with his practiced eye. There was a sudden sound of the engine misfiring,
followed by a surge of power. Some incalculable force gripped
the engine and wrenched it from its mount. Pieces of metal
slammed back into the right wing, tearing away 4 feet of the
upper panel. Rolly battled desperately, with all the skill at his
command. It was no use; the gargantuan centrifugal forces of
the spinning ship were overpowering. He and Stickney tried
to jump—too late.

Stunned, Duane Cole ran to the wreckage, his face drained.

"Suddenly," he remembers, "it is quiet. Only the rustle of an
orange and white parachute canopy draped as if by a gentle
hand over the tall stalks of corn may be heard. Beneath the
canopy lies the lifeless, broken body of my son, Rolly. Thirty
feet away, trapped in the twisted wreckage of the red and white
Stearman, is the remains of his friend, Mel. Thus was a dream
shattered . . . a family broken . . . a way of life gone forever. . . .
Why?"

It is a tragic question, one which others have asked a thousand times; needless, because flying was Rolly's chosen way of life, and the accident unpredictable. Said the Federal Aviation Agency investigators:

"Examination of the engine, which was located 30 feet west and 95 feet south of the main wreckage, revealed evidence of a near-instantaneous failure while substantial power was being developed. . . ."

On that day when Rolly died, Duane Cole folded the wings of the Cole Brothers Air Show. With his wife, Judy—the show's star wing-rider—Duane wrote a touching book about Rolly Cole, entitled *To A Pilot*. And then he went back to flying, as Rolly would have wanted him to.

One windy October day in 1965, I watched Duane Cole perform again in a new aerobatic ship, a Clipped Wing Taylorcraft, at Boulder City, Nevada, where severe gusts slammed across Hoover Dam to stiffen the field's wind sock.

Air shows were coming back, and Duane Cole, the old master, needed to be among friends. Neat and trim, his little ship sat on the line with an array of sleek new home-builts and reconditioned World War II fighters, modest and unassuming.

Through the hot afternoon the crowd cheered the star performers—Bob Downey, careening through a *Lomcevak* like a tumbler pigeon . . . Myra Slovak, the Czechoslovakian "Poor Refugee" who escaped from behind the Iron Curtain to stunt across the free skies of America in his Bucker-Jungmeister . . . racing pilots Chuck Lyford and Darryl Greenamyer—Mustang versus Bearcat—flashing past red and white pylons.

And then Duane Cole, his face lined with the sadness of personal tragedy, went into action. The crowd hushed. Duane's Taylorcraft lifted into the breeze, gained altitude with inverted climbing turns, executed so gently it seemed the only way to fly. Then up, over, down, and back through a square outside loop, with a roll on each side! . . . outside-inside Cuban eights with full rolls . . . and—amazing for a Taylorcraft, even the way Cole had stripped all unneeded weight from it—a vertical climb, slow-rolling higher and higher into the blue sky where his son Rolly had lived, and died.

This was a new kind of aerobatic show—flying by the numbers, carefully charted "Aerocryptographic System" curlicues on his cockpit panel. The notation system was the invention of Spain's Count José L. Aresti, adopted by the Fédération Aéronautique Internationale to give aerobats the world over a common language, like mathematics or music. A whole new world of competitive flying was opening, and Duane Cole was still its master.

Few of the grandstand spectators knew the story of the man in the cockpit, and still fewer were aware that the very simplicity and ease with which he flew were the brush strokes of the professional performer. The day of violence, of flirting with death, was in decline; in its place was a rebirth of the same "inspirational finesse of movement" that Elbert Hubbard had once seen in the skill of Lincoln Beachey.

Lovely to look at, like a beautiful woman, Aresti Aerobatics have a more practical, mundane side, in making pilots safer by giving them a confidence and skill of handling an aircraft in some grotesque attitude of flight. This skill once saved Duane Cole's life, when he found himself and a student pilot flipped upside down in a 250 Comanche by wild, unseen vortiginous air, the violent wake of a United DC-7 that had just landed ahead of them at Fort Wayne, Indiana. "Instinctively I grabbed the wheel and executed a half-roll to the upright position," Cole remembers. "Had I not been capable of slow-rolling, we would have been killed."

I recalled Duane Cole's words later that day at Boulder City, when a hard-flying racing pilot, Robert P. Abrams, a cargo-drop specialist back from the war in Vietnam, slammed his Mustang down the back stretch of the pylon course, trailing smoke. In trouble, he dropped his gear and pulled through a sharp, dangerous down-wind turn, in a desperate attempt to land before fire broke out. Abrams' P-51 crashed and exploded.

Flying from Boulder City Airport that night, looking down at the seared, blackened desert floor where Abrams had died, the tragedy seemed needless, and yet symbolic, marking the end of a wild, slam-bang world of exhibition flying, and the birth of another—the new world of precision aerobatics.

A tumbleweed, driven by the desert wind, rolled across the scarred earth, the only moving thing. I thought about Linc Beachey, and Spooks Clarke, and Rolly Cole, and all the other men who flew for the love of it, who conquered the sky with their skill in 3-D flying, and had gone West.

I dipped a wing and flew home.

Index

ZIARNO
PRAWDY

MROCZNA SERIA

ZYGMUNT MIŁOSZEWSKI

ZIARNO
PRAWDY

wydawnictwo
w.a.b

Dla Marty

W każdej legendzie kryje się ziarno prawdy.
powiedzenie ludowe

Pół prawdy to całe kłamstwo.
przysłowie żydowskie

*Obowiązkiem prokuratora jest dążenie
do ustalenia prawdy.*
Zbiór Zasad Etycznych Prokuratora

Rozdział pierwszy

środa, 15 kwietnia 2009

Żydzi uroczyście świętują siódmy dzień święta Pesach i wspominają przejście przez Morze Czerwone, dla chrześcijan to czwarty dzień Oktawy Wielkanocnej. Dla Polaków – drugi dzień trzydniowej żałoby narodowej ogłoszonej po pożarze w Kamieniu Pomorskim. W świecie wielkiej piłki Chelsea i Manchester United awansują do półfinału Ligi Mistrzów, w świecie polskiej piłki kilku kibiców ŁKS zostaje oskarżonych o nawoływanie do nienawiści na tle różnic narodowościowych poprzez noszenie koszulek z napisem „Śmierć żydzewskiej kurwie". Komenda Główna Policji ogłasza raport o przestępczości w marcu – w porównaniu do marca 2008 wzrosła o 11 procent. Policja komentuje: „Kryzys będzie zmuszał ludzi do popełniania przestępstw". W Sandomierzu już zmusił ekspedientkę z mięsnego do sprzedawania spod lady papierosów bez akcyzy, kobieta została zatrzymana. W mieście zimno jak w całej Polsce, temperatura nie przekracza 14 stopni, ale to i tak pierwszy słoneczny dzień po lodowatej Wielkanocy.

1

Duchy na pewno nie przychodzą o północy. O północy trwają jeszcze wieczorne filmy w telewizji, nastolatkowie myślą intensywnie o swoich nauczycielkach, kochankowie zbierają siły przed następnym razem, stare małżeństwa odbywają poważne rozmowy o tym, co się dzieje z naszymi pieniędzmi, dobre żony wyciągają ciasto z piekarnika, a źli mężowie budzą dzieci, próbując po pijaku otworzyć drzwi do mieszkania. Zbyt wiele jest o północy życia, aby duchy zmarłych mogły zrobić należyte wrażenie. Co innego przed świtem, kiedy przysypiają nawet pracownicy stacji benzynowych, a brudne światło zaczyna wydobywać z mroku byty i przedmioty, których istnienia nie podejrzewaliśmy

Dochodziła czwarta nad ranem, słońce miało wstać za godzinę, a Roman Myszyński walczył ze snem w czytelni Archiwum Państwowego w Sandomierzu, otoczony przez zmarłych. Wokół niego piętrzyły się dziewiętnastowieczne księgi parafialne i mimo że większość wpisów dotyczyła radosnych momentów życia, mimo że chrztów i ślubów więcej było niż aktów zgonu – to i tak stale czuł towarzyszący mu odór śmierci, nie potrafił pozbyć się myśli, że wszystkie te noworodki i wszyscy ci nowożeńcy od co najmniej kilkudziesięciu lat gryzą ziemię, a z rzadka odkurzane i przeglądane księgi są jedynym świadectwem ich istnienia. Choć akurat oni i tak mieli szczęście, biorąc pod uwagę to, jak z polskimi archiwami obeszła się wojna.

Było cholernie zimno, w termosie skończyła się kawa, a jedyną myślą, jaką potrafił skonstruować Myszyński, było besztanie się za idiotyczny pomysł, żeby założyć firmę zajmującą się poszukiwaniami genealogicznymi, zamiast wziąć asystenturę. Na uczelni dochód niewielki, ale stały, ubezpieczenie opłacone – same plusy. Zwłaszcza w porównaniu z posadami w szkołach, na które trafili jego koledzy z roku, tak samo źle płatnymi, ale wzbogaconymi o wieczną frustrację i groźby karalne ze strony uczniów.

Spojrzał na rozłożoną przed sobą księgę i na zdanie ładnie wykaligrafowane przez księdza z parafii w Dwikozach w kwietniu 1834 roku: „Stawający i świadkowie czytać nie umieją". To by właściwie było na tyle, jeśli chodzi o szlacheckie pochodzenie Włodzimierza Niewolina. A gdyby ktoś jeszcze miał wątpliwości, że być może przynoszący do chrztu rodzic prapradziadka Niewolina miał po pępkowym gorszy dzień, to rozwiewał je jego zawód – włościanin. Myszyński był pewien, że jak już doszpera się do aktu ślubu, okaże się, że wzmiankowana w akcie urodzenia Marjanna Niewolinowa – piętnaście lat młodsza od małżonka – była dziewką służebną. A może jeszcze mieszkała przy rodzicach.

Wstał i przeciągnął się energicznie, potrącając palcami wiszące na ścianie stare, przedwojenne zdjęcie sandomierskiego rynku. Poprawił je, myśląc, że plac z pocztówki wygląda jakoś inaczej niż dziś. Skromniej. Wyjrzał przez okno, ale widoczna w perspektywie ulicy pierzeja rynku zasłonięta była ciemną mgłą przedświtu. Co za bzdura, dlaczego stary rynek miałby wyglądać inaczej, po co w ogóle o tym myśli, musi wziąć się do roboty, jeśli chce zrekonstruować przeszłość Niewolina i zdążyć na trzynastą do Warszawy.

Co go jeszcze może spotkać? Nie powinien mieć trudności z aktem ślubu, także akty urodzenia Jakuba i Marjanny muszą gdzieś być, szczęśliwie Kongresówka była dla badaczy archiwów dość łaskawa. Od początku XIX wieku w Księstwie Warszawskim dzięki kodeksowi napoleońskiemu wszystkie akta metrykalne musiały być sporządzane przez parafie w dwóch egzemplarzach i przekazywane do archiwum państwowego – później zasady uległy zmianie, ale i tak było nieźle. W Galicji – gorzej, a już Kresy to prawdziwa genealogiczna czarna dziura, w Archiwum Zabużańskim

11

w Warszawie leżały jedynie jakieś szczątki akt. Czyli z Marjanną, urodzoną około 1814 roku, nie powinno być problemu. Jeśli chodzi o Jakuba – końcówka XVIII wieku to ciągle nieźle, księża byli lepiej wykształceni i poza wyjątkowo leniwymi parafiami księgi są raczej kompletne. W Sandomierzu pomagał fakt, że w czasie ostatniej wojny nie puścili go z dymem ani Niemcy, ani Sowieci. Najstarsze akta pochodziły z lat osiemdziesiątych XVI wieku. Wcześniej i tak ślad się urywał, dopiero na soborze trydenckim w XVI wieku Kościół wpadł na pomysł, żeby swoje owieczki spisywać.

Potarł oczy i nachylił się nad rozłożonymi aktami. Czyli potrzebne są mu akta ślubu z Dwikoz z ostatnich dwóch lat i może od razu poszuka matki. Z domu Kwietniewska. Hmm. W głowie badacza zadzwonił alarmowy dzwoneczek.

Mijały dwa lata od chwili, kiedy wbrew radom wszystkich założył firmę Złoty Korzeń. Na który to pomysł wpadł, gdy w czasie zbierania materiałów do doktoratu w Archiwum Głównym Akt Dawnych zaczął spotykać ludzi z szaleństwem w oczach, nieporadnie szukających informacji o przodkach i próbujących wyrysować swoje drzewo genealogiczne. Jednemu chłopakowi pomógł z litości, jednej dziewczynie ze względu na obezwładniająco piękny biust i w końcu Magdzie, bo była rozkoszna ze swoją wielką planszą genealogiczną, przypominającą Drzewo Jessego. Skończyło się tak, że Magda i jej plansza mieszkały u niego przez pół roku. O pięć miesięcy za długo, wyprowadzała się ze łzami w oczach i wiedzą, że praprababka Cecylia była bękartem, bo w 1813 roku do chrztu podawała ją akuszerka.

Wtedy postanowił, że można wykorzystać ten genealogiczny szał i sprzedawać swoją umiejętność korzystania z archiwów. Rejestrując działalność, był bardzo podniecony wizją zostania detektywem historii i nie przyszło mu do głowy, że nazwa Złoty Korzeń sprawi, że każdy – dosłownie każdy – klient najpierw zapyta, czy ma coś wspólnego ze słynnym pływakiem, a potem wysili się na niewybredny żart.

Niczym w powieściach *noir*, na początku głównie czekał na telefon i gapił się w sufit, ale w końcu klienci się pojawili. Od przypadku do przypadku i od polecenia do polecenia było ich coraz więcej, w większości niestety nie długonogie brunetki w pończochach. Przychodziły przede wszystkim dwa typy. Typ pierwszy to zakompleksieni okularnicy w pulowerkach, o wyrazie twarzy „no ale co ja ci zrobiłem?", którym w życiu nie wyszło tak bardzo, że mieli nadzieję znaleźć jego sens i wartość w dawno rozłożonych przodkach. Z pokorą i ulgą, jakby spodziewali się tego ciosu, przyjmowali informację, że są potomkami nikogo znikąd.

Typ drugi – typ Niewolina – od początku dawał do zrozumienia, że nie płaci za informację, iż wywodzi się z rodu pijanych furmanów i przechodzonych dziwek, tylko za doszukanie się herbowej szlachty i miejsca, gdzie można zawieźć dzieci i pokazać, że tutaj stał dwór, w którym pradziadek Polikarp leczył rany odniesione w powstaniu. Jakimkolwiek powstaniu. Na początku Roman był do bólu szczery, potem uznał, że jest jednak prywatną firmą, a nie instytutem badawczym. Skoro szlachta oznaczała premie, napiwki i kolejnych klientów – niech będzie szlachta. Gdyby ktoś miał wyrobić sobie opinię na temat przeszłości Polski tylko po wynikach jego śledztw, łatwo doszedłby do wniosku, że wbrew pozorom nie jest to kraj prymitywnych chłopów, lecz dystyngowanych panów, w ostateczności dobrze prosperujących mieszczan. Mimo różnych nagięć Roman nigdy nie kłamał – po prostu zwykle dotąd szperał w bocznych odnogach, aż znalazł jakiegoś pana na zagrodzie.

Najgorzej było trafić na Żyda. Argumenty historyczne, że w międzywojennej Polsce dziesięć procent mieszkańców stanowili Żydzi, w związku z czym zwłaszcza na terenach Kongresówki i Galicji można odnaleźć przodka wyznania mojżeszowego, do nikogo nie trafiały. Dwa razy mu się to zdarzyło – za pierwszym razem został zbluzgany, a za drugim mało nie dostał po gębie. Najpierw nie mógł wyjść ze zdziwienia, potem podumał kilka dni, a w końcu doszedł do wniosku, że klient nasz pan. Zwykle poruszał sprawę w czasie pierwszej rozmowy i jeśli się okazywało, że temat budzi nadmierne emocje – gotów był zamieść ewentualnego Icka pod dywan. Zdarzało się to jednak niezmiernie rzadko – Zagłada ścięła koronę izraelskiego drzewa genealogicznego.

A teraz proszę, pojawiła się w dziewiętnastowiecznych dokumentach Marjanna Niewolin, de domo Kwietniewska. To nie musiało być regułą, ale nazwiska wzięte od nazw miesięcy często były nazwiskami przechrztów, przyjmowanymi od miesiąca, w którym odbył się chrzest. Podobnie nazwiska zawierające w sobie dni tygodnia, albo zaczynające się od „Nowa". Także nazwisko Dobrowolski mogło wskazywać na to, że jakiś przodek dobrowolnie przeszedł z wyznania mojżeszowego na chrystusowe. Roman lubił wierzyć, że za takimi historiami stała miłość. Że ludzie, mając do wyboru religię albo uczucie, wybierali to drugie. A jako że katolicyzm był w Najjaśniejszej religią panującą, zwykle w tę stronę odbywały się konwersje.

Właściwie Roman mógł porzucić ten trop, i tak był zaskoczony, że udokumentowane korzenie Niewolina sięgają tak daleko. Ale po pierwsze, był ciekaw, a po drugie, zdenerwował go ten buc wymachujący sygnetem z miejscem na herb.

Roman uruchomił w laptopie jedno ze swoich podstawowych narzędzi – zeskanowany *Słownik geograficzny Królestwa Polskiego i innych krajów słowiańskich*, monumentalne dzieło z końca XIX wieku, gdzie opisano właściwie każdą wioskę znajdującą się w granicach przedrozbiorowej Rzeczpospolitej. Odszukał hasło Dwikozy, aby dowiedzieć się, że była to wieś i folwark poduchowny, licząca 77 domów i 548 mieszkańców. Ani słowa o gminie żydowskiej, co naturalne, biorąc pod uwagę, że zwykle obowiązywał zakaz osiedlania się Żydów w dobrach kościelnych. Czyli jeśli Marjanna pochodziła z okolicznej rodziny przechrztów, trzeba szukać w Sandomierzu albo Zawichoście. Przejrzał skany i dowiedział się, że w Sandomierzu było 5 domów zajezdnych żydowskich, synagoga, 3250 katolików, 50 prawosławnych, 1 protestant i 2715 Żydów. Za to w Zawichoście na 3948 dusz do religii mojżeszowej przyznawało się 2401 osób. Sporo. Spojrzał na mapę. Intuicja mówiła mu, że Zawichost to lepszy strzał.

Przegonił myśl, że marnuje czas, wstał, zrobił kilka przysiadów, skrzywił się, słysząc trzaski w kolanach, i wyszedł z czytelni. Pstryknął przełącznikiem w ciemnym korytarzu, ale nic się nie stało. Pstryknął jeszcze dwa razy. Ciągle nic. Rozejrzał się niepewnie. Choć był weteranem spędzania nocy w archiwach – poczuł niepokój. Genius loci, pomyślał i westchnął litościwie nad swoją skłonnością do fantazjowania.

Zniecierpliwiony jeszcze raz wcisnął przełącznik i po kilku błyskach klatkę schodową zalało trupie światło jarzeniówek. Roman spojrzał w dół na gotycki portal, prowadzący z części administracyjnej do archiwum. Wyglądał jakoś tak, jak by to powiedzieć, groźnie.

Odchrząknął, żeby zabić ciszę, i ruszył w dół, myśląc, że ciekawego smaczku dodaje sprawie Niewolina i jego prapra de domo przechrzcie Kwietniewskiej fakt, że sandomierskie archiwum mieści się w budynku osiemnastowiecznej synagogi. Czytelnia i pokoje pracowników znajdowały się w dolepionym do świątyni budynku kahału, siedzibie gminnej administracji. Same akta zajmowały główne pomieszczenie modlitewne synagogi. Było to jedno z najciekawszych miejsc, jakie widział w swojej karierze pradetektywa.

Zszedł na dół i pchnął ciężkie, nabijane ćwiekami żelazne drzwi. Uderzył go orzechowy zapach starego papieru.

Stara sala modlitewna miała kształt dużego sześcianu, który w interesujący sposób zaadaptowany został na potrzeby archiwum. Pośrodku pomieszczenia zbudowano ażurową kostkę, złożoną ze stalowych chodniczków, schodków i – przede wszystkim – półek. Kostka była nieznacznie mniejsza od sali, można było ją okrążyć wzdłuż ścian, można było wejść do środka, w labirynt wąziutkich korytarzy, lub wspiąć się na wyższe poziomy i tam zagłębić w stare akta. Konstrukcja czyniła z tego rusztu jakby przerośniętą bimę, w której zamiast Tory studiowało się dokumenty informujące o urodzinach, ślubach, podatkach i wyrokach. Biurokracja jako święta księga ery nowożytnej, pomyślał Roman. Nie zapalając światła, okrążał ruszt; wodził dłonią po chłodnym tynku. Doszedł tak do wschodniej ściany, gdzie jeszcze kilkadziesiąt lat temu we wnęce zwanej aron ha-kodesz przechowywano zwoje Tory. Roman zapalił latarkę, światło przecisnęło się przez gęsto unoszące się w powietrzu drobinki kurzu i wydobyło z ciemności złotego gryfa, trzymającego tablicę z hebrajskim pismem. Podejrzewał, że to jedna z Tablic Przymierza. Skierował światło wyżej, jednak polichromie znajdujące się bliżej sklepienia tonęły w mroku.

Wszedł na najwyższy poziom po stromych ażurowych schodkach, przy akompaniamencie metalicznego echa. Znalazł się tuż pod sklepieniem. Chodząc między pełnymi akt półkami, zaczął oglądać w świetle latarki zdobiące górną część sali przedstawienia znaków zodiaku. Przy krokodylu zmarszczył brwi. Krokodyl? Spojrzał na sąsiedni – strzelec – i zrozumiał, że krokodyl to skorpion. Być może miało to uzasadnienie. Pamiętał jedynie, że w judaizmie nie wolno było przedstawiać ludzi. Podszedł do bliźniąt. Wbrew tej wiedzy, przedstawione były jako ludzkie postaci, tylko pozbawione głów. Wzdrygnął się.

Pomyślał, że starczy już tej wycieczki, na dodatek dostrzegł owiniętego wokół okulusa lewiatana. Duch śmierci i zniszczenia otaczał plamę szarego światła, jakby to było wejście do jego podwodnego królestwa, i Romanowi zrobiło się nieswojo. Poczuł nagłą potrzebę opuszczenia archiwum, ale wtedy kątem oka dostrzegł za okrągłym oknem ruch.

Wsunął głowę do wnętrza potwora, lecz nie mógł za wiele dostrzec przez brudne szyby.

Po drugiej stronie sali skrzypnęła deska, Roman się poderwał, boleśnie uderzając głową o mur. Zaklął i wypełzł z okulusa. Znowu skrzypnięcie.

– Halo? Jest tam kto?

Świecił latarką we wszystkie strony, ale widział tylko akta, kurz i znaki zodiaku.

Tym razem skrzypnęło tuż obok niego. Roman krzyknął cicho. Chwilę mu zajęło uspokojenie oddechu. Doskonale, pomyślał, powinienem sobie zafundować jeszcze mniej snu i jeszcze więcej kawy.

Energicznym krokiem skierował się stalowym chodniczkiem w stronę stromych schodów, od ciemnej dziury ziejącej pomiędzy nim a ścianą oddzielała go wątła barierka. Ponieważ najwyższy poziom rusztu był zarazem poziomem doświetlających salę okien, mijał przedziwne konstrukcje, służące do ich otwierania i mycia. Były to jakby zwodzone pomosty, obecnie podniesione do pionu. Aby dostać się do okna, należało odblokować grubą linę i opuścić pomost w ten sposób, aby sięgnął do wnęki okiennej. Roman pomyślał, że jest to mechanizm dość kuriozalny, w końcu ani ruszt z aktami, ani tym bardziej grube mury synagogi nigdzie się nie wybierały, można je było połączyć na stałe. Teraz przypominało mu to okręt z podniesionymi trapami, gotowy do wypłynięcia. Omiótł instalację światłem latarki i podszedł do schodków. Zestawił jedną stopę, kiedy potężny huk wypełnił pomieszczenie, przez stopnie przeszedł wstrząs, a on stracił równowagę i nie spadł na dół tylko dlatego, że obiema rękami złapał się barierki. Latarka wypadła mu z ręki, odbiła się dwa razy od podłogi i zgasła.

Wyprostował się, serce biło mu w zawrotnym tempie. Szybko, w lekkiej histerii, zlustrował otoczenie. To spadł mostek, obok którego przechodził. Patrzył na niego, ciężko dysząc. W końcu się roześmiał. Musiał coś niechcący naruszyć.

Fizyka tak, metafizyka nie. Proste. W każdym razie ostatni raz pracuje po zmroku wśród tych wszystkich pratrupów.

Trochę po omacku podszedł do zwodzonego mostka i chwycił linę, żeby podnieść go do pionu. Oczywiście był zaklinowany. Klnąc na czym świat stoi, na kolanach wszedł do okiennej wnęki. Okno wychodziło na te same krzaki, co strzeżony przez lewiatana okulus.

Świat na zewnątrz stanowił teraz jedyne źródło światła, a było to światło nad wyraz liche. Wewnątrz nie dało się zobaczyć praktycznie nic, na zewnątrz przedświt zamieniał się w wiosenny, nieśmiały jeszcze świt, z mroku wyłaniały się drzewa, dno otaczającego sandomierską starówkę parowu, wille pobudowane na przeciwległej stronie skarpy i mur dawnego klasztoru franciszkanów. Czarna mgła zamieniała się we mgłę szarą, świat był nieostry i mętny, jakby odbity w wodzie z mydlinami.

Roman spojrzał w miejsce, gdzie wcześniej widział ruch – w krzaki tuż pod pozostałościami obronnego muru. Wytężył wzrok – od morza szarości odcinało się tam coś sterylną bielą. Przetarł rękawem szybę, ale istnienie wyrafinowanego mechanizmu zwodzonego mostu najwyraźniej nie skłoniło nikogo do jej częstego mycia, tylko rozmazał kurz na szkle.

Otworzył okno, zamrugał, twarz omiotło mu zimne powietrze.

Jak porcelanowa laleczka pływająca we mgle, pomyślał Myszyński, patrząc na leżące pod synagogą zwłoki. Były nienaturalnie, niepokojąco białe, świeciły brakiem koloru.

Z tyłu z hukiem trzasnęły ciężkie drzwi do starej synagogi, jakby wszystkie duchy wyleciały zobaczyć, co się stało.

2

Prokurator Teodor Szacki nie mógł zasnąć. Świtało, a on przez całą noc nie zmrużył oka. Co gorsza, ta mała nimfomanka też nie zmrużyła. Chętnie sięgnąłby po książkę, zamiast tego leżał bez ruchu i udawał, że śpi. Poczuł drapanie za uchem.

– Śpisz?

Mlasnął kilka razy i mruknął coś na odczepnego.

– Bo ja nie śpię.

Musiał zebrać całą siłę woli, żeby nie westchnąć głośno. Cały napięty czekał, co się wydarzy. Bo coś się wydarzy – tego był pewien. Ciepłe ciało za jego plecami poruszyło się pod kołdrą i mruknęło jak postać z kreskówek, która właśnie wymyśliła plan zdobycia władzy nad światem. A potem poczuł bolesne ukąszenie w łopatkę. Zerwał się z łóżka, ciężkie przekleństwo w ostatniej chwili zatrzymało mu się na zębach.

– Zwariowałaś?!

Dziewczyna oparła się na łokciu i spojrzała na niego zaczepnie.

– No właśnie, straszna ze mnie wariatka, bo jakoś tak sobie pomyślałam, że może jeszcze raz zrobisz mi dobrze. Dżizas, ja to jednak jestem niemożliwa.

Szacki w obronnym geście uniósł ręce do nieba i uciekł do kuchni na papierosa. Był już przy zlewie, kiedy dobiegło go zalotne „czekam". Niedoczekanie, pomyślał, wkładając polar. Zapalił papierosa i włączył czajnik. Za oknem ciemnoszare dachy odcinały się od jasnoszarych błoń, oddzielonych od bladej nicości Podkarpacia ciemniejszą wstęgą Wisły. Przez most przejechał samochód, dwa lejki światła przesuwające się przez mgłę. Wszystko w tym obrazie było monochromatyczne, włącznie z białą ramą okna, pokrytą łuszczącą się farbą, odbiciem bladej twarzy Szackiego, jego mlecznych włosów i czarnej bluzy.

Co za pieprzona dziura, pomyślał Szacki i zaciągnął się papierosem. Czerwony ognik sprawił, że świat przestał być monochromatyczny. Co za pieprzona dziura, w której siedział już kilka miesięcy, i gdyby ktoś spytał się go, jak to się stało – wzruszyłby bezradnie ramionami. Na początku była Sprawa. Zawsze jest jakaś sprawa. Akurat ta – niewdzięczna i upierdliwa. Zaczęło się od zabójstwa ukraińskiej prostytutki w burdelu na Kruczej – niespełna sto metrów od biura Szackiego zresztą. Zwykle w takich przypadkach znalezienie trupa było końcem sprawy. Wszyscy alfonsi i dziwki ulatniali się w kwadrans, świadków z oczywistych przyczyn nie znaleziono, a ci, którzy się zgłosili, niczego nie pamiętali i można było mówić o szczęściu, jeśli w ogóle udało się zidentyfikować zwłoki.

Tym razem zdarzyło się inaczej. Pojawiła się przyjaciółka zmarłej, zwłoki zyskały imię Irina, alfons nawet przystojną twarz na portrecie pamięciowym, a wątek świętokrzyski pojawił się, kiedy sprawa była już rozkręcona. Szacki dwa tygodnie jeździł po okolicach Sandomierza i Tarnobrzega razem z Olgą, tłumaczem i przewodnikiem, aby znaleźć miejsce, gdzie dziewczyny przetrzymywano po przyjeździe ze Wschodu. Olga opowiadała, co widziała z różnych okien i czasami zza szyb samochodu, tłumacz tłumaczył, przewodnik zastanawiał się, gdzie to może być, jednocześnie snując doprowadzające Szackiego do białej gorączki sielskie gawędy. Lokalny policjant prowadził i każdym mięśniem mimicznym dawał do zrozumienia, że jego czas jest marnowany, bo – jak stwierdził na początku – jedyny burdel w Sandomierzu zlikwidowali latem, a razem z nim panią Kasię i panią Beatę, które dorabiały ciałem po pracy w sklepie i przedszkolu. Reszta to małe cichodajki z technikum spożywczego. W Tarnobrzegu czy w Kielcach – tam to co innego.

Mimo to znaleźli w końcu dom na uboczu, w przemysłowej części Sandomierza. Ten dom. W przerobionej na sypialnię szklarni dogorywała wyniszczona przez grypę żołądkową drobna blondynka z Białorusi, poza tym nie było nikogo. Dziewczyna powtarzała bez przerwy, że pojechali na targ i że oni ją zabiją. Jej strach zrobił wielkie wrażenie na reszcie wycieczki – na Szackim żadnego. Za to słowo „targ" dało mu do myślenia. Sypialnia w szklarni była naprawdę spora, poza tym na posesji stał duży dom, warsztat, magazyn. Szacki wyobraził sobie Sandomierz na mapie Polski. Mieścina z dwiema prostytutkami amatorkami. Kościół koło kościoła. Cicho, sennie, nic się nie dzieje. Na Ukrainę blisko. Na Białoruś niedaleko. Dwieście kilometrów do stolicy, jeszcze mniej do Łodzi i Krakowa. W sumie niegłupie miejsce na punkt przerzutowy i hurtownię żywym towarem. Targ.

Okazało się, że był targ, i to nielichy. Wielki bazar zwany przez miejscowych targowicą, giełda absolutnie wszystkiego pomiędzy Starym Miastem i Wisłą, tuż przy obwodnicy. Odpytał policjanta, co się tam dzieje. Ten odpowiedział, że wszystko, ale Ruscy załatwiają interesy między sobą, jak się w to wtrącić, to tylko statystykę się zabagni. Czasami zgarną jakiegoś dzieciaka z lewymi płytami albo z trawką, żeby nie było, że się nie interesują.

Z jednej strony wydawało się mało prawdopodobne, że istnieją mafiosi tak głupi, żeby handlować ludźmi na bazarze. Z drugiej – jest jakiś powód, dla którego nie zderzają hadronów i nie wprowadzają spółek na giełdę. No i bazar był właściwie eksterytorialny.

Wzięli słaniającą się, chorą dziewczynę, pojechali i znaleźli. Dwie wielkie furgonetki pomiędzy stoiskami z konfekcją, teoretycznie z ciuchami, praktycznie z dwudziestoma skutymi dziewczynami, które przyjechały do lepszego świata. To był największy sukces sandomierskiej policji od czasu, kiedy odzyskali skradziony rower ojca Mateusza, lokalne gazety przez miesiąc nie pisały o niczym innym, a Szacki został na chwilę małomiasteczkowym celebrytą. Jesień była piękna.

I spodobało mu się tu.

I pomyślał: a może?

Pili w pizzerii Modena nieopodal prokuratury, miał już w czubie i spytał z głupia frant, czy nie mają wakatu. Mieli. Zdarza im się to raz na dwadzieścia lat, ale akurat mieli. Miał zacząć nowe wspaniałe życie. Podrywać dziewczyny w klubach, biegać co rano nad Wisłą, rozkoszować się powietrzem, przeżywać przygody i uniesienia, a w końcu znaleźć najprawdziwszą miłość swojego życia i zestarzeć się przy niej w obrośniętym winem domku gdzieś koło Piszczeli. Tak żeby krótkim spacerem można było dojść na rynek, usiąść w Małej albo w Kordegardzie i napić się kawy. Kiedy się tutaj sprowadzał, obraz ten był tak żywy, że nawet trudno było go nazwać planem lub marzeniami. To była rzeczywistość, która wkroczyła do jego życia i zaczęła się dziać. Po prostu. Pamiętał dokładnie moment, kiedy wygrzewał się na zamkowych ławkach w jesiennym słońcu i zobaczył swoją przyszłość tak wyraźnie, że prawie łzy stanęły mu w oczach. W końcu! W końcu wiedział dokładnie, czego chce.

Cóż, delikatnie mówiąc, mylił się. Mówiąc niedelikatnie, utopił w szambie swoje przez lata budowane życie dla popieprzonej mrzonki i teraz został tak bardzo z niczym, że nawet dawało to poczucie oczyszczenia. Absolutnie i dokładnie z niczym.

Zamiast gwiazdy stołecznej prokuratury budzący nieufność obcy w prowincjonalnym mieście, które co prawda od osiemnastej było wymarłe – ale niestety nie dlatego, że mieszkańcy się pomordowali. Oni w ogóle się nie mordowali. Nie usiłowali mordować. Nie gwałcili. Nie organizowali się w przestępczych celach. Z rzadka napadali na siebie. Kiedy Szacki przeleciał w myślach katalog spraw, którymi się zajmuje, poczuł w gardle lekką zgagę. To nie mogła być prawda.

Zamiast rodziny – samotność. Zamiast miłości – samotność. Zamiast bliskości – samotność. Kryzys wywołany żałosnym – a także krótkim i nikogo niesatysfakcjonującym –

22

romansem z dziennikarką Moniką Grzelką zepchnął jego małżeństwo do dołu, z którego nie miał szans się wygrzebać. Trochę się jeszcze wozili, że niby dla dobra dziecka, ale to już było tchórzliwe dogorywanie. Zawsze myślał, że to on zasługuje na więcej, a Weronika ciągnie go do dołu. Tymczasem nie minęło pół roku od ostatecznego rozstania, kiedy zaczęła się umawiać z młodszym od siebie o rok wziętym adwokatem. Ostatnio lakonicznie go poinformowała, że postanowili zamieszkać wspólnie w jego domu w Wawrze i że chyba powinien spotkać się i porozmawiać z Tomaszem, który teraz będzie wychowywał jego córkę.

Właściwie przegrał wszystko, co było do przegrania. Nie miał nic i nikogo, na dodatek z własnej woli został wygnańcem na nielubianej i nielubiącej go ziemi. Zadzwonienie do Klary, którą przed miesiącem poderwał w klubie i spławił po trzech dniach, gdyż w świetle dnia nie wydała mu się ani ładna, ani mądra, ani interesująca – było aktem desperacji i ostatecznym dowodem jego upadku.

Zgasił papierosa i powrócił do monochromatycznego świata. Tylko na chwilę – na jego polarze pojawiły się długie czerwone paznokcie. Zamknął oczy, żeby ukryć irytację, ale nie potrafił zdobyć się na brutalność wobec dziewczyny, którą najpierw uwiódł, a teraz jeszcze dał jej fałszywą nadzieję, że coś może między nimi być.

Poszedł grzecznie do łóżka, żeby uprawiać nudny seks. Klara wiła się pod nim, jakby w ten sposób usiłowała nadrobić brak czułości i fantazji. Spojrzała na niego i widocznie dostrzegła w jego twarzy coś, co kazało jej się bardziej starać. Wierzgnęła i zaczęła jęczeć.

– Och tak, rżnij mnie, jestem twoja, chcę cię czuć głęboko.

Prokurator Teodor Szacki próbował się powstrzymać, ale nie dał rady i wybuchnął śmiechem.

3

Żadne zwłoki nie wyglądają dobrze, ale niektóre wyglądają gorzej. Leżąca w parowie pod średniowiecznymi murami Sandomierza denatka należała do drugiej kategorii. Jeden z policjantów litościwie okrywał nagość kobiety, kiedy na miejscu zbrodni pojawił się prokurator.

– Nie zakrywaj jeszcze.

Policjant podniósł głowę.

– Daj spokój, znałem ją od przedszkola, nie może tak leżeć.

– Też ją znałam, Piotrze. To naprawdę nie ma dziś znaczenia.

Prokurator Barbara Sobieraj delikatnie rozgarnęła bezlistne gałęzie i ukucnęła przy zwłokach. Ich obraz rozmyły łzy. Widywała nieraz ciała zabitych, najczęściej wyciągnięte z wraków aut przy obwodnicy, czasami nawet martwych ludzi znanych z widzenia. Nigdy jednak nikogo, kogo znałaby osobiście. A już na pewno nie wieloletniej przyjaciółki. Wiedziała, na pewno lepiej od innych, że ludzie popełniają przestępstwa i że można paść ich ofiarą. Ale to – to nie mogła być prawda.

Odchrząknęła, żeby przeczyścić gardło.

– Grzesiek już wie?

– Myślałem, że ty mu powiesz. Wiesz przecież...

Barbara spojrzała na niego i już miała wybuchnąć, ale zrozumiała, że Marszałek – jak nazywano w Sandomierzu tego policjanta – ma rację. Od wielu lat była przyjaciółką szczęśliwego domu Elżbiety i Grzegorza Budników. Nawet kiedyś plotkowano, że gdyby Ela swego czasu nie wróciła z Krakowa, to kto wie, niektórzy już słyszeli zapowiedzi. Plotki i stare dzieje, ale faktycznie, jeśli ktoś miał poinformować Grześka, to tylko ona. Niestety.

Westchnęła. To nie był wypadek, to nie było pobicie ani napad czy gwałt dokonany przez pijanych żuli. Ktoś musiał sobie zadać dużo trudu, żeby ją zabić, potem dokładnie rozebrać i ułożyć w tych krzakach. I jeszcze to... Barbara próbowała nie patrzeć, ale jej wzrok co chwila wracał do zmasakrowanej szyi ofiary. Wielokrotnie przecięte w poprzek gardło przypominało skrzela, wąskie listki skóry, pomiędzy którymi widać było fragmenty żył, krtani i przełyku. Twarz nad makabryczną raną była za to dziwnie spokojna, nawet lekko uśmiechnięta, w połączeniu z niezwykłą, gipsową bielą skóry sprawiało to wrażenie nierealności, posągowości. Barbara pomyślała, że może ktoś zamordował Elżbietę we śnie albo kiedy była nieprzytomna. Uchwyciła się tej myśli, naprawdę chciała w to wierzyć.

Marszałek podszedł do niej i położył jej rękę na ramieniu.

– Strasznie mi przykro, Basiu.

Skinęła głową, żeby zakryć zwłoki.

4

Takie dziury mają swoją dobrą stronę: wszędzie jest blisko. Zaraz po otrzymaniu telefonu od szefowej Szacki z westchnieniem ulgi zostawił Klarę i opuścił wynajmowaną kawalerkę w kamienicy na Długosza. Mała, brzydka i zapuszczona, miała jedną zaletę – położenie. Na Starym Mieście, z widokiem na Wisłę i zabytkową szkołę średnią, którą założyli w XVII wieku jezuici. Wyszedł z budynku i szybkim krokiem dotarł do rynku, ślizgając się na wilgotnych kocich łbach. Powietrze było jeszcze po zimowemu rześkie, ale czuło się, że to już ostatnie takie chwile. Mgła przerzedzała się z każdym krokiem i Szacki miał nadzieję, że ten dzień będzie pierwszym z pięknych, wiosennych dni. Naprawdę, potrzebował w swoim życiu pozytywnej emocji. Słonecznego ciepła na przykład.

Przeszedł przez kompletnie opustoszały rynek, minął gmach poczty, usadowionej w pięknej kamienicy z podcieniami i doszedł do Żydowskiej, widząc już z daleka poświatę błyskających szklanek. Poruszyło to w nim jakąś czułą strunę, ten widok policyjnych kogutów we mgle był częścią rytuału. Poranny telefon, wygrzebywanie się z ciepłych ramion Weroniki, ubieranie się po omacku w przedpokoju, przed wyjściem jeszcze całus w ciepłe czoło śpiącego dziecka. Potem jazda przez budzącą się do życia stolicę, gasnące latarnie, nocne autobusy zjeżdżające do zajezdni. Na miejscu sceptyczny uśmieszek Kuzniecowa, potem trup, kawa na placu Trzech Krzyży. I starcie ze zrzędzącą szefową w prokuraturze. „Nasze gabinety są chyba w różnych wymiarach czasoprzestrzeni, panie prokuratorze".

Mdliło go z tęsknoty, kiedy minął budynek synagogi i przytrzymując się gałęzi, zszedł po skarpie. Rudą czuprynę piczki-zasadniczki Sobieraj poznał od razu. Stała ze spuszczoną głową, jakby przyszła odmawiać modlitwę za zmarłych, zamiast prowadzić śledztwo. Otyły gliniarz trzymał rękę na jej ramieniu, łącząc się z nią w bólu. Tak jak Szacki przypuszczał – miasto, w którym było więcej kościołów niż barów, musiało odciskać na mieszkańcach bolesne piętno. Sobieraj odwróciła się do Szackiego, zbyt zaskoczona jego widokiem, aby ukryć wypełzający na twarz grymas niechęci.

Skinął wszystkim głową na powitanie, podszedł do zwłok i bezceremonialnie podniósł okrywającą je folię. Kobieta. Między czterdziestką a pięćdziesiątką. Paskudnie poderżnięte gardło, innych obrażeń nie widać. Nie wyglądało to na napad, raczej na dziwaczną zbrodnię w afekcie. No, w końcu porządny trup. Już chciał ponownie przykryć ciało, ale coś nie dawało mu spokoju. Obejrzał je jeszcze dwa razy od stóp do głów, zeskanował wzrokiem miejsce zbrodni. Coś było nie tak, coś było zdecydowanie nie tak, a on nie miał pojęcia co, i to uczucie było bardzo niepokojące.

Odrzucił foliowy worek, część policjantów zawstydzona odwróciła wzrok. Amatorzy.

Już wiedział, co jest nie tak. Biel. Nierealna, niespotykana w naturze biel ciała denatki. Ale coś jeszcze.

– Przepraszam, to jest moja znajoma – powiedziała za jego plecami Sobieraj.

– To była pani znajoma – odburknął Szacki. – Gdzie technicy?

Cisza. Odwrócił się i spojrzał na grubego policjanta, łysego i z sumiastymi wąsami. Jaką on miał ksywkę? Marszałek? Jakże oryginalnie.

– Gdzie technicy? – powtórzył.

– Marysia zaraz będzie.

Wszyscy tu byli po imieniu. Sami przyjaciele, psia ich mać, małomiasteczkowa sekta.

– Wezwijcie też ekipę z Kielc, niech zabiorą wszystkie swoje zabawki. Zanim przyjadą, ciało okryć, otoczyć teren w promieniu pięćdziesięciu metrów, nikogo nie wpuszczać. Gapiów trzymać jak najdalej. Jest już oficer operacyjny?

Marszałek podniósł rękę, patrząc na Szackiego jak na kosmitę i pytająco na Sobieraj, która stała oszołomiona.

– Świetnie. Ja wiem, że mgła, ciemno i gówno widać. Ale wszyscy z tych kamienic – wskazał ręką na domy przy Żydowskiej – i z tamtych domów – odwrócił się i pokazał wille po drugiej stronie parowu – mają zostać przesłuchani. Może ktoś cierpi na bezsenność, może ma chorą prostatę, może jest szaloną kurą domową i gotuje zupę przed wyjściem do roboty. Ktoś mógł coś widzieć. Jasne?

Marszałek pokiwał głową. Tymczasem Sobieraj odzyskała rezon, podeszła i stanęła tak blisko, że czuł jej oddech. Była wysoka jak na kobietę, ich oczy znajdowały się prawie na tym samym poziomie. Na wsi zawsze dorodne dziewczyny, pomyślał Szacki, czekając spokojnie, co się wydarzy.

– Przepraszam, to pan teraz prowadzi tę sprawę?

– No.

– A mogłabym wiedzieć dlaczego?

– Niech zgadnę. Bo wyjątkowo nie chodzi o pijanego rowerzystę ani kradzież komórki w podstawówce?

Ciemne oczy Sobieraj zrobiły się czarne.

– Idę prosto do Misi – wysyczała.

Szacki sięgnął do nigdy nieużywanych najgłębszych pokładów siły woli, żeby się opanować i nie parsknąć śmiechem. Boże przenajświętszy, oni naprawdę nazywali swoją szefową Misią.

– Im szybciej, tym lepiej. To ona wykopała mnie z wyra, gdzie w wariacko interesujący sposób spędzałem czas, i kazała się tym zająć.

Sobieraj przez chwilę sprawiała wrażenie, jakby miała wybuchnąć, ale odwróciła się na pięcie i odeszła, kołysząc biodrami. Wąskimi i mało atrakcyjnymi biodrami, ocenił Szacki, odprowadzając ją wzrokiem. Odwrócił się do Marszałka.

– Ktoś z dochodzeniówki będzie? Czy zaczynają pracę o dziesiątej?

– Jestem, synku, jestem – dobiegło go zza pleców.

Za nim na rozkładanym wędkarskim krzesełku siedział jakiś dziadek z wąsami – oni tutaj prawie wszyscy mieli wąsy – i palił szluga bez filtra. Nie pierwszego. Po jednej stronie krzesełka leżało kilka oderwanych filtrów, po drugiej kilka kiepów. Szacki opanował zdziwioną minę i podszedł do niego. Miał całkiem siwe, krótko obcięte włosy, pobrużdżoną twarz, niczym z autoportretu Leonarda, i jasne, wodniste oczy. Dobrze utrzymane skromne wąsy były natomiast kruczoczarne, co nadawało dziadkowi demoniczny, niepokojący wygląd. Musiał mieć z siedemdziesiątkę. Jeśli miał mniej, to widać w jego życiu wiele było zaskakujących zwrotów akcji. Dziadek patrzył ze znudzoną miną, Szacki stanął przy nim i wyciągnął rękę.

– Teodor Szacki.

Stary policjant pociągnął nosem, odrzucił peta na właściwą stronę krzesełka i nie wstając, podał mu dłoń.

– Leon.

Przytrzymał rękę Szackiego i skorzystał z jego pomocy, żeby się podnieść. Był wysoki, bardzo szczupły, pod grubą kurtką i szalikiem wyglądał zapewne jak laseczka wanilii – chuda, wiotka i pomarszczona. Szacki puścił dłoń dziadka i czekał na dalszą część prezentacji. Która nie nastąpiła. Staruszek zerknął w stronę Marszałka, na co tamten podbiegł w podskokach, jakby był na gumce.

– Panie inspektorze?

To chyba pomyłka. Za wysoka szarża na psa z prowincjonalnej dochodzeniówki.

– Zróbcie, co prokurator powiedział. Kielce będą za dwadzieścia minut.

– Spokojnie, to prawie sto kilometrów – zaoponował Szacki.

– Wezwałem ich godzinę temu – mruknął dziadek. – A potem czekałem, aż się państwo prokuratorstwo zwlecze. Dobrze, że krzesełko wziąłem. Kawa?

– Słucham?

– Kawę czy pan prokurator pija? Ciżemkę otwierają o siódmej.

– Bylebyśmy tam nic nie jedli.

Dziadek pokiwał głową z uznaniem.

– Młode to, przyjezdne, a uczy się szybko. Idziemy. Chcę tu być, jak dzieciaki z zabawkami się pojawią.

5

Sala restauracyjna w Ciżemce, jak nazywano znajdujący się w najlepszym turystycznie miejscu miasta – w rynku, przy drodze do katedry i zamku – hotel Pod Ciżemką, była wszystkim tym, czym restauracje w cywilizowanych miejscach przestały być dekadę temu. Wielka nieprzyjazna przestrzeń, stoły nakryte obrusem i serwetą, obite pluszem krzesła z wysokimi oparciami. Na ścianach kinkiety, pod powałą kandelabry. Stukająca obcasami kelnerka musiała przemierzyć tak wielki dystans, że Szacki był pewien: kawa wystygła po drodze.

Nie wystygła, wyczuwalna w niej za to była odległa nuta brudnej ścierki – znak, że ekspres nie był w tym reprezentacyjnym sandomierskim przybytku pierwszy na liście rzeczy do codziennego czyszczenia. Czy to mnie dziwi? – pomyślał Teodor Szacki. Wcale.

Inspektor Leon pił bez słowa, gapiąc się przez okno na attykę ratusza, Szackiego mogłoby tu w ogóle nie być. Postanowił dostosować się do tempa dziadka i poczekać cierpliwie, aż się dowie, po co został tu wyciągnięty. Policjant w końcu odstawił filiżankę, kaszlnął i oderwał filtr od papierosa. Westchnął.

– Pomogę panu. – Miał nieprzyjemny, jakby źle naoliwiony głos.

Szacki spojrzał pytająco.

– Mieszkał pan kiedyś poza Warszawą?

– Dopiero teraz.

– Czyli gówno pan wie o życiu.

Szacki nie skomentował.

– Ale to nie grzech. Każdy małolat gówno wie o życiu. Ale ja panu pomogę.

W Szackim narastała irytacja.

– Czy ta pomoc obejmuje tylko wykonywanie pańskich obowiązków, czy coś ekstra? Nie znamy się, trudno mi ocenić, jak dobre ma pan serce.

Leon dopiero teraz popatrzył dłużej na prokuratora.

– Mało dobre – odparł bez uśmiechu. – Ale bardzo jestem ciekaw, kto zaszlachtował i wrzucił w krzaki żonę tego pajaca Budnika. Intuicja mi mówi, że pan się tego dowie. Ale pan nie jest stąd. Z panem każdy będzie rozmawiał, ale nikt panu nic nie powie. Może to i dobrze, mniej informacji to czystszy umysł.

– Więcej informacji to prawda – wtrącił Szacki.

– Prawda to prawda, od pływania w szambie zbytecznej wiedzy nie robi się bardziej prawdziwa – zaskrzypiał inspektor. – I niech pan mi nie przerywa, młody człowieku. Czasami będzie pan usiłował zrozumieć, kto naprawdę z kim i dlaczego. Wtedy ja panu pomogę.

– Przyjaźni się pan z nimi wszystkimi?

– Ja się słabo zaprzyjaźniam. I niech mi pan nie zadaje pytań, które nie mają znaczenia, bo stracę o panu dobre zdanie.

Szacki miał kilka pytań znaczących, ale zostawił je na później.

– I wolałbym, żebyśmy pozostali przy formach grzecznościowych – zakończył policjant, a Szacki nie dał po sobie poznać, jak bardzo mu się podoba ta propozycja. Kiwnął potakująco głową.

6

Gapiów było coraz więcej, na szczęście stali grzecznie. Szacki wyławiał z prowadzonych półgłosem rozmów nazwisko Budnik albo Budnikowa. Przez chwilę się zastanawiał, czy wiedza o tym, kim była denatka, jest mu teraz potrzebna. Uznał, że nie. Teraz potrzebne są dokładne oględziny miejsca i ciała. Reszta może poczekać.

Razem z inspektorem, który tymczasem wzbogacił się o nazwisko Wilczur, stali przy ciele otoczonym parawanem, kielecki technik fotografował zwłoki. Szacki wpatrywał się w precyzyjnie porozcinane gardło, które wyglądało jak przygotowane do sporządzenia anatomicznego preparatu, i szlag go trafiał, że ciągle nie potrafi nazwać nieznośnego brzęczenia w głowie. Coś było nie tak. Oczywiście, dowie

31

się co, ale wolałby to zrozumieć, zanim przyjdzie do przesłuchań i szukania biegłych. Podszedł do nich szef zespołu oględzinowego, sympatyczny trzydziestolatek o wyłupiastych oczach i wyglądzie judoki. Po dokonaniu prezentacji zawiesił rybi wzrok na Szackim.

– Skąd się pan desantował, panie prokuratorze, tak z ciekawości? – zapytał.

– Ze stolicy.

– Z samej warszawki? – Nie starał się ukryć zdziwienia, jakby następnym pytaniem miało być to, czy Szackiego wypieprzyli za pijaństwo, narkotyki, czy molestowanie.

– Jak mówię: ze stolicy. – Szacki nie cierpiał słowa „warszawka".

– Ale przeskrobał pan coś czy tak jakoś?

– Tak jakoś.

– Aha. – Policjant przez chwilę oczekiwał dalszego ciągu serdecznej rozmowy, ale dał spokój. – Poza ciałem nic nie ma, nie znaleźliśmy żadnych ciuchów, torebek, biżuterii. Śladów wleczenia nie ma, śladów walki też nie. Wygląda na to, że została tu przyniesiona. Zrobiliśmy odlewy śladów opon z dołu i odcisków buta, które były świeże. Wszystko będzie w protokole, ale nie liczyłbym na zbyt wiele, chyba że z oględzin zwłok.

Szacki pokiwał głową. Nie żeby był jakoś szczególnie przejęty. Wszystkie swoje sprawy rozwiązał, opierając się na dowodach osobowych, nie rzeczowych. Oczywiście, przyjemnie byłoby znaleźć w krzakach narzędzie zbrodni i dowód osobisty mordercy, ale już dawno zrozumiał, że przyjemnie to nie jest w życiu Teodora Szackiego żadna codzienność.

– Panie komisarzu! – wydarł się jeden z buszujących po krzakach na skarpie techników.

Wyłupiastooki dał znać, żeby zaczekali, podbiegł w kierunku resztek średniowiecznego muru, który kiedyś szczelnie opasywał miasto, a dziś służył głównie do obalania w jego cieniu tradycyjnego polskiego wina. Szacki podążył śladem technika, który kucnął pod murem, rozgarniając bezlistne jeszcze gałązki i zeszłoroczną trawę. Wyłupiastooki sięgnął dłonią w rękawiczce i podniósł coś ostrożnie do góry. Słońce akurat przedarło się przez chmury i błysnęło ostro w tym przedmiocie, oślepiając Szackiego na chwilę. Dopiero kiedy mrugnął kilka razy, aby rozwiać latające przed oczami ciemne płatki, mógł dostrzec, że technik trzyma dziwaczny nóż. Ostrożnie schował go do hermetycznego worka na dowody i wyciągnął w ich stronę. Narzędzie musiało być jednak diablo ostre, bo od samego ciężaru ostrze przekłuło worek i spadło na ziemię. To znaczy, spadłoby, gdyby przykucnięty technik nie złapał go w ostatniej chwili za rękojeść. Złapał i spojrzał na nich.

– Mogłeś zostać bez palców – powiedział spokojnie Wyłupiastooki.

– Mogłeś zafajdać swoją krwią narzędzie zbrodni, kretynie – powiedział spokojnie Wilczur.

Szacki spojrzał na starego policjanta.

– Skąd pan wie, że to narzędzie zbrodni?

– Domniemywam. Skoro znajdujemy pod jednym krzakiem rozpłatane precyzyjnie gardło, a pod drugim ostrą jak samurajski miecz brzytwę, to może istnieć między nimi jakiś związek.

„Brzytwa" to było dobre słowo na określenie noża, który Wyłupiastooki wkładał do kolejnej torebki, tym razem ostrożniej. Miał prostokątną, lśniącą niczym lustro klingę, bez ostrego czubka, bez żadnych krzywizn na linii ostrza. Rękojeść z ciemnego drewna była w stosunku do klingi bardzo delikatna, wręcz nie na miejscu. Samo ostrze natomiast było potężne. Długie na około trzydzieści centymetrów, szerokie na dziesięć. Brzytwa, brzytwa do golenia dla olbrzyma, który ma gębę wielkości furgonetki. Zarówno klinga, jak i rękojeść – przynajmniej na pierwszy rzut oka – były pozbawione zdobień. To nie była kolekcjonerska zabawka, ale narzędzie. Narzędzie być może zbrodni, ale przede wszystkim narzędzie z jakimś zastosowaniem. Innym niż golenie nóg pięćdziesięciostopowej kobiety.

– Daktyloskopia, mikroślady, krew, wydzieliny, materiał DNA, chemia – wyliczył Szacki. – Tak szybko, jak się da. A dziś chcę mieć szczegółowe zdjęcia tego cacka. Wręczył Wyłupiastookiemu swoją wizytówkę. Tamten schował ją do kieszeni, patrząc podejrzliwie na dużą brzytwę.

Wilczur znów oderwał filtr od papierosa.

– Nie podoba mi się to – skomentował. – Za bardzo wydumane.

7

Prokurator Teodor Szacki nie miał szczęścia do szefowych. Poprzednia była technokratyczną suką, zimną i urodziwą jak wygrzebane spod śniegu zwłoki. Niejednokrotnie, siedząc u niej w gabinecie, nasiąkając dymem i cierpiąc, że starała się na nim zrobić kobiece wrażenie osoba kompletnie z kobiecości wyprana, zastanawiał się, czy można trafić gorzej. Złośliwy los niedługo później odpowiedział na to pytanie.

– Naprawdę proszę spróbować. – Maria Miszczyk, ku przerażeniu Szackiego zwana przez wszystkich, z nią samą włącznie, Misią, podetknęła mu pod nos paterę z ciastem. Składało się z warstwy czegoś w rodzaju bajaderki, biszkoptu i chyba bezy.

Przełożona uśmiechnęła się do niego promiennie.

– Pod bezę dałam cieniutką warstwę powideł śliwkowych. Mam jeszcze trochę z jesieni. No, proszę.

Szacki nie chciał, ale serdeczny uśmiech Miszczyk był jak wzrok kobry. Pozbawiona kontroli umysłu ręka sięgnęła po ciasto, zgodnie z wolą kobiety wzięła kawałek i wepchnęła go Szackiemu do gęby. Uśmiechnął się krzywo, obsypując kruszynkami garnitur.

– No dobrze, Basiu, powiedz nam, o co chodzi – powiedziała Miszczyk, odstawiając paterę.

Sobieraj siedziała sztywno na skórzanej sofie w stylu „Konstancin lata osiemdziesiąte", od Szackiego, umoszczonego w fotelu od kompletu, oddzielał ją szklany stolik. Jeśli Miszczyk chciała stworzyć w swoim gabinecie domową atmosferę, biorąc za wzorzec przeciętne wyposażenie sześcianu polskiego, to osiągnęła sukces.

– Chciałabym zrozumieć – Sobieraj nie potrafiła albo nie próbowała ukryć pretensji w głosie – dlaczego prowadząc od siedmiu lat własne śledztwa w naszej prokuraturze, zostaję odsunięta od zabójstwa Eli. I chciałabym wiedzieć, dlaczego ma je prowadzić pan Teodor, którego osiągnięć nie neguję, ale który nie zna jeszcze za dobrze miasta i jego specyfiki. I chciałabym powiedzieć, że było mi przykro dowiedzieć się o tym w ten sposób. Mogłaś mnie chociaż uprzedzić, Misiu.

Twarz Miszczyk zrobiła się autentycznie po matczynemu zatroskana. Biło z niej takie ciepło i zrozumienie, że Szacki poczuł zapach przedszkolnej stołówki. Był bezpieczny, pani przedszkolanka na pewno rozwiąże ten problem tak, żeby nikomu nie było smutno. A potem ich przytuli.

– No wiem, Basiu, przepraszam. Ale kiedy dowiedziałam się o Eli, musiałam działać szybko. Normalnie taka sprawa czekałaby na ciebie. Ale nie jest normalnie. Ela to twoja bliska przyjaciółka, Grzegorz był z tobą związany. Przyjaźniłaś się z nimi, spotykałaś. Jakiś adwokat mógłby to wykorzystać przeciwko nam.

Sobieraj zagryzła wargę.

– Poza tym emocje nie pomagają w śledztwie – dobił ją Szacki, wziął drugi kawałek ciasta i odpowiedział uśmiechem na mordercze spojrzenie.

– Gówno pan wie o moich emocjach.

– Błogosławiona to niewiedza.

Miszczyk klasnęła w dłonie i spojrzała na nich, jakby chciała powiedzieć „oj, dzieci, dzieci, naprawdę dałybyście już spokój". Szacki zmusił się, żeby nie spuścić wzroku i wytrzymać wyrzut w jej łagodnych, rozmaślonych, matczynych oczach.

– Potem sobie podogryzacie, kochani. Teraz wam powiem, jak wygląda wasza sytuacja zawodowa.

Sobieraj drgnęła i szybko zaczęła mówić. Ileż to Szacki widział takich neurotycznych lasek w życiu? Legion.

– Mam nadzieję, że...

– Basiu – wpadła jej w słowo Miszczyk. – Chętnie wysłucham waszych opinii i propozycji. Zawsze słucham chętnie, wiesz o tym, prawda? Ale teraz powiem, jak wygląda wasza sytuacja zawodowa.

Sobieraj zamknęła się błyskawicznie, a Szacki spojrzał uważnie na Miszczyk. Ciągle była mamuśką o łagodnych oczach, uśmiechu dziecięcej terapeutki i głosie, w którym pobrzmiewał zapach waniliowy i proszek do pieczenia. Ale gdyby odrzeć ostatni komunikat z formy – zostawało stanowcze usadzenie podwładnej i przyjaciółki.

Miszczyk dolała wszystkim herbaty.

– Znałam Elę Budnik, znam też Grześka, zresztą jak wszyscy tutaj. Nie musimy go lubić albo się z nim zgadzać, ale trudno go przeoczyć. To będzie, już jest, wielkie i głośne śledztwo. Sytuacja, kiedy prowadzi je przyjaciółka denatki...

– I głównego podejrzanego – wtrącił Szacki.

Sobieraj parsknęła.

– Proszę uważać na słowa. Nie zna pan tego człowieka.

– Nie muszę. Jest mężem denatki. Na tym etapie to czyni go głównym podejrzanym.

– I właśnie o tym mówię. – Sobieraj triumfalnie uniosła ręce do góry. – Dlatego powinien się trzymać od tej sprawy z daleka.

Miszczyk odczekała chwilę, aż znowu zapanuje cisza.

– Właśnie dlatego prokurator Szacki nie dość, że nie będzie trzymał się od tej sprawy z daleka, to jeszcze będzie prowadził to śledztwo. Ponieważ chcę uniknąć sytuacji, kiedy zwłoki, podejrzani i śledczy to grupa przyjaciół, którzy jeszcze wczoraj umawiali się na grilla. Ale masz rację, Basiu, że pan Teodor jest tutaj nowy. Dlatego będziesz służyła mu radą, pomocą i wiedzą o wszystkim, co dotyczy miasta i jego mieszkańców.

Szacki odetchnął z ulgą, gdy wielki kawał ciasta jednak przecisnął się przez przełyk. Szykuje się szampańska zabawa, pomyślał. Sobieraj tkwiła nieruchomo na kanapie, zamieniając się w gigantyczny foch. Miszczyk zerknęła matczynym okiem na filiżanki i paterę. Przekręciła ją o sto osiemdziesiąt stopni.

– Z tej strony jest więcej powideł – szepnęła teatralnie i wzięła kawałek.

Szacki odczekał chwilę, uznał, że audiencja jest skończona, i wstał. Miszczyk dała mu znak ręką, że jak tylko przełknie, to jeszcze coś powie.

– Spotykamy się tutaj o dziewiętnastej. Chcę zobaczyć pierwsze protokoły i dokładny plan śledztwa. Wszystkie media wysyłacie do mnie. Jeśli uznam, że prywatne animozje przeszkadzają wam w tej sprawie...

Sobieraj i Szacki zgodnie zawiesili wzrok na wydatnych, pokrytych okruszkami wargach szefowej. Uśmiechnęła się do nich ciepło.

– ...urządzę wam piekło, którego nigdy nie zapomnicie. A z dostępnych prac w instytucjach państwowych zostanie wam mycie podłóg w pierdlu. Czy to jasne?

Szacki pokiwał głową, ukłonił się obu paniom i położył rękę na klamce.

– Rozumiem, że mam przekazać komuś swoje pozostałe sprawy.

Miszczyk uśmiechnęła się miękko. Zrozumiał, że w ogóle niepotrzebnie pyta. Wręcz obraża ją myślą, że mogła o tym nie pomyśleć. Już na pewno wszystko jest załatwione, a sekretarka wynosi akta z jego gabinetu.

– Oszalał pan chyba. Do roboty.

8

Prokurator Teodor Szacki stał w swoim gabinecie, patrzył przez okno i myślał, że prowincja ma swoje dobre strony. Miał tylko dla siebie wielki gabinet, z którego w Warszawie wykrojono by trzy dwuosobowe pokoje. Miał ładny widok na zieleń, willową zabudowę i wieże Starego Miasta w oddali. Miał dwadzieścia minut spacerem z domu do roboty. Miał szafę pancerną, a w niej akta swoich ośmiu bieżących spraw – dokładnie dziewięćdziesiąt siedem mniej niż w Warszawie pół roku wcześniej. Miał tę samą pensję, co w stolicy, a wyborna kawa w ulubionej kafejce na Sokolnickiego kosztowała go ledwie pięć złotych. No i w końcu – wstydził się tego, ale nie potrafił ukryć zadowolenia – miał porządnego trupa. Nagle ta koszmarna senna dziura wydała mu się całkiem znośnym miejscem.

Trzasnęły drzwi. Szacki się odwrócił, dodając myśl, że ma też partnerkę, która z PMS-a uczyniła sposób na życie. Automatycznie przywdział swoją chłodną, zawodową maskę prokuratora, obserwując, jak piczka-zasadniczka Sobieraj podchodzi do niego z teczką w dłoni.

– Właśnie przyszło. Powinniśmy to obejrzeć.

Wskazał dłonią miejsce na kanapie (tak jest, miał w gabinecie kanapę) i usiedli obok siebie. Zerknął na jej dekolt, nie dostrzegł tam niczego ciekawego, bo zasłonięty był kompletnie aseksualnym czarnym golfem. Otworzył teczkę. Pierwsze zdjęcie przedstawiało zbliżenie rozpłatanego gardła denatki. Sobieraj głośno zaczerpnęła powietrza i odwróciła

38

wzrok, a Szacki już miał to skomentować, ale zrobiło mu się przykro i zachował złośliwość dla siebie. Ani ich wina, ani wada, że wszyscy tutaj razem wzięci przez całe życie widzieli tyle trupów, co on w ciągu roku.

Odłożył na bok zdjęcia zwłok.

– I tak musimy zaczekać na oględziny. Pójdzie pani na Oczki?

Spojrzała bez zrozumienia.

– Przepraszam. Do szpitala. Na sekcję.

W jej oczach błysnął lęk, ale szybko się opanowała.

– Myślę, że powinniśmy być tam razem.

Szacki przytaknął i rozłożył na stole kilkanaście zdjęć dokładnie obfotografowanej brzytwy. Wedle rozłożonej pod nią miarki brzytwa miała ponad czterdzieści centymetrów, z tego samo prostokątne ostrze około trzydziestu. Rękojeść pokrywało ciemne drewno, na mosiężnej oprawie było coś wygrawerowane. Szacki poszukał zbliżenia. Wytarty napis głosił: C.RUNEWALD. Na jednym ze zbliżeń dostrzegł odbijającą się w wypolerowanej, gładkiej jak lustro klindze dłoń fotografa. Pani fotograf, mężatki, sądząc po obrączce. Błękitne ostrze było pozbawione plam, zadrapań i szczerb. Niewątpliwie arcydzieło sztuki metalurgicznej. Zabytkowe arcydzieło.

– Sądzi pan, że to narzędzie zbrodni?

Szacki sądził, że te grzecznościowe formy już są męczące, a w trakcie śledztwa staną się nie do zniesienia.

– Sądzę, że to wszystko dziwne i teatralne. Nagie zwłoki z rozpłatanym gardłem, porzucona obok zabytkowa brzytwomaczeta, żadnych śladów walki czy szamotaniny.

– Ani krwi na ostrzu.

– Dajmy im się wykazać w laboratorium. Myślę, że będzie krew, jakieś mikroślady, DNA. Więcej nam powie nóż, niż chciałby ten, kto go podrzucił.

– Podrzucił?

– Taki czysty, wymuskany, nietknięty? Ktoś to zrobił specjalnie. Nawet przy brudnych zabójstwach w afekcie każdy pijany żul pamięta, żeby zabrać ze sobą narzędzie zbrodni. Nie wierzę, żeby został w tych krzakach przez przypadek.

Sobieraj wyjęła z torebki okulary do czytania i zaczęła uważnie przeglądać zdjęcia. Do twarzy jej było w grubych brązowych oprawkach. Szacki pomyślał: jeśli brzytwomaczeta jest wiadomością, to trzeba znaleźć kogoś, kto potrafi ją odczytać. Cholera jasna, jaki biegły może się tym zajmować? Od broni białej? Od militariów? Od metalurgii? Od dzieł sztuki?

Sobieraj podała mu zdjęcie ze zbliżeniem obłożonej drewnem rękojeści i zdjęła okulary.

– Trzeba poszukać biegłego od broni białej, najlepiej jakiegoś muzealnika. Może zna tę firmę.

– C. Runewald? – zapytał Szacki.

Sobieraj parsknęła śmiechem.

– Grünewald. Może najwyższa pora na okulary, panie prokuratorze.

Szacki postawił na spokój. Żadnych uśmieszków, żadnych nerwów, żadnych ripost.

– Najwyższa pora, żeby mi pani opowiedziała o denatce i jej rodzinie.

Sobieraj zmarkotniała.

9

Prokurator Teodor Szacki był niezadowolony. Opowieść Sobieraj o Budnikach przyniosła dużo informacji, ale też wiele uczuć. Denatka przestała być dla niego efektem czynu zabronionego, za który ktoś musi zostać pociągnięty do odpowiedzialności i ponieść karę. Mąż denatki przestał być podejrzanym numer jeden. Dzięki barwnej, emocjonalnej opowieści Sobieraj za bardzo stali się osobami z krwi i kości, granica między informacją a interpretacją została przekroczona. Wbrew sobie Szacki, myśląc o denatce, widział uśmiechniętą nauczycielkę, prowadzącą zielone lekcje w czasie wycieczek rowerowych. Jej mąż był nie tylko kandydatem do odsiadki, ale też społecznikiem, który potrafił do upadłego walczyć w każdej najdrobniejszej sprawie, jeśli tylko oznaczało to dobro miasta. Szacki wątpił, aby gdzieś indziej w Polsce istniał bezpartyjny radny, który potrafił skłonić całą radę do jednogłośnego głosowania – dla Sandomierza. Basta, basta, basta, nie chciał myśleć o Budnikach, dopóki nie porozmawia ze starym policjantem, który już dał do zrozumienia, że nie jest najlepszego zdania o tych świeckich świętych.

Próbował zająć myśli, szukając informacji o tajemniczej brzytwomaczecie, i to był jego drugi powód do niezadowolenia. Teodor Szacki w ogóle nie miał zaufania do ludzi. Ale do ludzi z hobby – w szczególności. Pasję i poświęcenie się pasji, zwłaszcza zbieraczej, uważał za zaburzenie, a ludzi skłonnych tak zafiksować się na jednym temacie – za potencjalnie niebezpiecznych. Widział samobójstwa spowodowane utratą numizmatycznej kolekcji, widział też dwie żony, których przewiną było podarcie najcenniejszego znaczka i spalenie pierwszego wydania *Panien z Wilka* i *Brzeziny*. Obie nie żyły. Mężowie-mordercy czuwali przy ich zwłokach, płakali i powtarzali, że nie rozumieją.

Tymczasem świat noży okazał się światem miłośników i kolekcjonerów, istniał nawet periodyk „Sztych", którego misją jest – jak zapewniali autorzy – „dostarczenie Ci, drogi Czytelniku, rzetelnych informacji na temat wysokiej jakości noży oraz tematów im pokrewnych. Nie zabraknie także ciekawostek, przykładem będzie w następnym numerze «Bat», wydawałoby się, egzotyczny, a przecież pleciony od dawna w Polsce. Oczywistym będzie seria artykułów o długiej białej broni".

Baty, szable i rzeźnickie noże – naprawdę urocze hobby, zżymał się Szacki, zagłębiając w forach pełnych dyskusji o klingach, rękojeściach, sposobach ostrzenia, wykuwania, kucia i kłucia. Czytał wynurzenia jednego pisarza, który własnoręcznie wyrabiał miecze samurajskie, czytał o „Ojcu Nowoczesnego Damastu", który opanował technologię wytwarzania stali damasceńskiej, oglądał zdjęcia wojskowych kordzików, myśliwskich noży do sprawiania zwierzyny, mieczy, bagnetów, rapierów i pałaszy. Nie przypuszczał, że ludzkość wyprodukowała tyle rodzajów ostrych przedmiotów.

Ale brzytwomaczety nie znalazł.

W końcu w akcie desperacji zrobił komórką kilka zdjęć prawdopodobnego narzędzia zbrodni i wysłał do redakcji „Sztychu" mail z pytaniem, czy coś im to mówi.

10

Wiosna przyszła i poszła, wieczorem Teodor Szacki dokuczliwie odczuwał chłód, idąc ulicą Mickiewicza w kierunku pizzerii Modena, gdzie umówił się z Wilczurem. Stary policjant nie dał się namówić na spotkanie w rynku, twierdząc, że „nie cierpi tego pierdolonego muzeum", a Szacki mieszkał już w Sandomierzu na tyle długo, żeby zrozumieć, o co chodzi.

Sandomierz składał się właściwie z dwóch, a nawet trzech miast. Trzecie to tak zwana huta po drugiej stronie rzeki, memento czasów, kiedy czerwoni usiłowali zmienić mieszczański, kościelny gród w przemysłowe miasto i postawili tam ogromną hutę szkła. Ponura i brzydka była to dzielnica, strasząca nieczynną stacją kolejową, paskudnym kościołem i ogromnym fabrycznym kominem, który o każdej porze dnia i nocy mordował panoramę Podkarpacia widoczną z wysokiego lewego brzegu Wisły.

Miasto numer dwa to był Sandomierz, w którym faktycznie toczyło się życie. Tutaj było niewielkie osiedle na szczęście niezbyt inwazyjnych bloków, tutaj były dzielnice domków jednorodzinnych, szkoły, parki, cmentarz, jednostka wojskowa, policja, dworzec autobusowy, mniejsze i większe sklepy, biblioteka. Ot, polskie powiatowe miasteczko, może trochę bardziej zadbane i ładniej – bo na wzgórzach – położone od innych. Nie wyróżniałoby się jednak na tle niepoliczonych polskich dziur, gdyby nie miasto numer jeden.

Miasto numer jeden to był pocztówkowy Sandomierz ojca Mateusza i Jarosława Iwaszkiewicza, usadowiony na skarpie cukiereczek, którego panorama zachwycała niezmiennie każdego i w której zakochał się swego czasu Szacki. Ciągle potrafił przejść się na most tylko po to, żeby zobaczyć piętrzące się na zboczu kamieniczki, dostojny gmach Collegium Gostomianum, wieże ratusza i katedry, renesansowy szczyt Bramy Opatowskiej, bryłę zamku. W zależności od pory roku i pory dnia widok ten za każdym razem wyglądał inaczej i za każdym razem tak samo chwytał za serce.

Niestety, co Szacki wiedział dziś aż za dobrze, był to widok, który tylko z oddali sprawiał wrażenie bardzo włoskie, toskańskie. Wewnątrz Starego Miasta wszystko było już bardzo polskie. Za daleko był Sandomierz od Krakowa i przede wszystkim za daleko od Warszawy, aby stać się kurortem w rodzaju Kazimierza Dolnego. Na co zasługiwał stokroć bardziej, będąc pięknym miastem, a nie wiochą z trzema renesansowymi kamienicami i paroma tuzinami hoteli, żeby każdy polski prezes miał gdzie rżnąć kochankę. Położenie na uboczu szlaków sprawiało, że na ślicznych staromiejskich uliczkach Sandomierza tchnęło nudą, pustką, polską beznadzieją i „pierdolonym muzeum". Po południu znikały szkolne wycieczki, starzy lokatorzy kamieniczek zamykali się w domach, niedługo potem zamykano nieliczne sklepy, chwilę później knajpy. Już o osiemnastej zdarzało się Szackiemu przejść od zamku do Bramy Opatowskiej, nie napotykając żywego ducha. Jedno z najpiękniejszych miejsc w Polsce było opustoszałe, wymarłe i przygnębiające.

Szacki naprawdę poczuł się lepiej, kiedy zszedł Sokolnickiego w dół i zaczął maszerować wzdłuż Mickiewicza do Modeny. Pojawiły się samochody, ludzie, pełne jeszcze o tej porze sklepy, dzieciaki uwieszone komórek, ktoś jadł pączka, ktoś biegł do autobusu, ktoś krzyczał do kobiety po drugiej stronie, że zaraz, zaraz, jeszcze chwila. Szacki głęboko odetchnął, bał się samemu sobie do tego przyznać, ale bardzo brakowało mu miasta. Tak bardzo, że nawet ta jego skromna namiastka, jaką był Sandomierz, sprawiała, że krew szybciej krążyła w żyłach.

Modena była śmierdzącą piwem powiatową mordownią, ale – to im trzeba przyznać – dawali tu najlepszą pizzę w Sandomierzu, a dzięki pysznej romantice, uzbrojonej w podwójną mozzarellę, cholesterol Szackiego już nieraz podskoczył. Inspektor Leon Wilczur psim zwyczajem siedział w najczarniejszym kącie, plecami do ściany. Bez kurtki wydawał się jeszcze chudszy i Szackiemu przypomniały się salony krzywych zwierciadeł w wakacyjnych wesołych miasteczkach. To niemożliwe, żeby człowiek był aż tak wąski, jak spreparowana głowa nasadzona dla żartu na stare ciuchy.

Usiadł bez słowa naprzeciwko starego policjanta, przeleciał w głowie zestaw pytań.

– Wie pan, kto to zrobił?

Wilczur spojrzeniem zaakceptował pytanie.

– Nie. Nie mam też pojęcia, kto mógłby to zrobić. Nie znam nikogo, kto by chciał. Nie znam nikogo, kto na tej śmierci zyskuje. Powiedziałbym, że to nikt stąd, gdyby nie to, że to musi być ktoś stąd. Nie wierzę w nieznajomych przybłędów, którzy zadają sobie tyle trudu.

To właściwie dawało odpowiedź na kluczowe pytania Szackiego, nawet jeśli zamierzał na każde z nich odpowiedzieć osobiście. Pora przejść do pomocniczych.

– Piwo czy wódka?

– Woda.

Szacki zamówił wodę, a także colę i romanticę. Po czym zaczął słuchać skrzypiącego głosu Wilczura, tworząc w głowie protokół rozbieżności pomiędzy opowieścią starego policjanta a ckliwym przekazem Sobieraj. Suche informacje były takie same. Grzegorz Budnik był „od zawsze", czyli od 1990 roku, sandomierskim radnym z niespełnionymi burmistrzowskimi aspiracjami, jego świętej pamięci żona, Elżbieta, młodszą o piętnaście lat nauczycielką angielskiego w słynnej „jedynce", czyli ogólniaku zajmującym gmach starego jezuickiego kolegium, prowadziła artystyczną świetlicę dla dzieci i udzielała się we wszystkich możliwych lokalnych imprezach kulturalnych. Mieszkali w domku przy Katedralnej, niegdyś podobno zamieszkiwanym przez Iwaszkiewicza. Niezbyt majętni, bezdzietni, starzejący się społecznicy. Bez barw politycznych. Jeśliby na siłę szukać etykietek, to on byłby czerwony przez swoją przeszłość w Radzie Narodowej, ona czarna przez zaangażowanie w kościelne inicjatywy i lekko manifestowaną katolicką wiarę.

„To w pewien sposób symbol tego miasta – opowiadała Sobieraj. – Ludzie o bardzo różnych poglądach, o różnej historii, teoretycznie z dwóch stron barykady. Ale zdolni dogadać się zawsze, gdy chodziło o dobro Sandomierza".

– To w pewien sposób symbol tej dziury – mówił Wilczur. – Najpierw czerwoni i czarni mieli na zmianę coś do udowodnienia, w końcu uznali, że się dogadają dla dobra interesu. Nie na darmo urząd miasta jest w starym klasztorze dominikańskim, z widokiem na synagogę i dzielnicę żydowską. Żeby nie zapomnieli, co jest dobre dla geszeft – zażydłaczył. – Nie będę panu robił wykładu z historii, ale mówiąc w skrócie, za czerwonych miasto było be. Cacy był Tarnobrzeg z siarką, ewentualnie huta za rzeką, a tutaj to wydziwianie wykształciuchów, w sutannach na dodatek. W Warszawie nawet drogowskazy były na Tarnobrzeg. Bida tu była, nędza i pierdolony skansen. Przyszło nowe, ludzie się ucieszyli, ale na krótko, bo nagle się okazało, że to nie miasto, tylko świecka narośl na zdrowej tkance Kościoła. Kino zamienili na Dom Katolicki. Na rynku zaczęli odprawiać nabożeństwa. Na błoniach ustawili Jana Pawła wielkości latarni morskiej, żeby potem mieć pretekst, że żadnej imprezy tam zrobić nie wypada, to teraz tylko psy srają. No i zrobił się znowu pierdolony skansen, więcej kościołów niż knajp. A potem czerwoni wrócili do władzy i po chwili konsternacji się okazało, że jak jest dobry geszeft, to ajwaj, ajwaj, wszyscy mogą skorzystać. Że jak się na odzyskanych kościelnych gruntach postawi sklep albo stację benzynową, to wszyscy będą zadowoleni.

– Budnik brał w tym udział?

Wilczur zawahał się, zamówił następną wodę gestem godnym maltowej whisky.

– Pracowałem wtedy w Tarnobrzegu, ale ludzie gadali.

– To Polska, zawsze gadają. Słyszałem, że nigdy nie był w nic zamieszany.

– Oficjalnie nie. Ale Kościół nie musi organizować przetargów, może sprzedać, co chce, za ile chce i komu chce. To było dość dziwne, że najpierw miasto chętnie oddaje, w ramach naprawy komunistycznych krzywd, działki Kościołowi, a ten je zaraz potem sprzedaje pod stację benzynową albo supermarket. Nie wiadomo komu, nie wiadomo po jakiej cenie. A Budnik był wielkim orędownikiem tego, żeby Bogu, co boskie, Żydowi, co żydowskie.

Szacki wzruszył ramionami. Nudził się, męczyło go, że wszystkie wypowiedzi Wilczura były negatywnie nacechowane, przesycone polskim jadem, lepkie jak stoły w Modenie.

– Takie biznesy jak Polska długa i szeroka, co to ma za znaczenie. Narobiło Budnikowi wrogów? Komuś nie załatwił? Załatwił nie tak, jak trzeba? Dogadał się z mafią? Na razie mi to wygląda na wioskowe przekręty, podnieta dla lokalnej gazetki szkolnej. Ale nic, za co się podrzyna gardło czyjejś żonie.

Wilczur podniósł do góry cienki, pomarszczony palec.

– Może tutaj grunty nie są tyle warte, co na Marszałkowskiej, ale nikt ich za darmo nie daje.

Zamilkł i zamyślił się. Szacki czekał, obserwując policjanta. Próbował o nim myśleć jak o lokalnym doświadczonym glinie, ale było w inspektorze coś, co go odrzucało. Wyglądał jak menel, a było to menelstwo tak z nim zrośnięte, że jakkolwiek by się ubrał i cokolwiek by pił, to zawsze będzie wódczanego menela przypominał. Nie było ku temu żadnych racjonalnych powodów, ale kredyt zaufania Szackiego topniał z minuty na minutę. Brakowało mu Kuzniecowa. Bardzo brakowało.

– Pan widzi, jak to miasto wygląda – kontynuował Wilczur. – Może jest ciągle senne, ale to cukiereczek, jakiego nie ma w Polsce, z zadatkami na nowy Kazimierz Dolny albo i lepiej. Zbudują przystań, postawią parę spa, obok będzie szła autostrada z Warszawy do Rzeszowa i dalej na Ukrainę. Kawałek w drugą stronę autostrada ze stolicy do Krakowa. Pięć lat i tutaj będą korki z beemek w każdy piątek w każdą stronę. Jakie będzie przebicie na działkach? Dziesięciokrotne? Dwudziestokrotne? Stukrotne? Nie trzeba geniusza, żeby to przewidzieć. I teraz proszę pomyśleć. Zna pan Sandomierz, ma dużo pieniędzy i wielkie plany. Hotele, restauracje, dzielnice willowe, atrakcje turystyczne. W tej ziemi są naprawdę miliardy. I pan to wie, ale może pan co najwyżej postawić budę w ogródku swojej willi, bo miejskie grunty inwestycyjne w glorii chwały wracają do kurii, żeby potem po cichu trafić do najbardziej zaufanych i znających, kogo trzeba. Gdzie pan mieszka?

– Wynajmuję na Długosza.

– A sprawdzał pan, ile kosztuje tutaj mieszkanie? Albo dom? Albo działka?

– Jasne. Mieszkanie sześćdziesiąt metrów około dwustu tysięcy, dom trzy razy tyle.

– W Kazimierzu mieszkanie tej wielkości kosztuje od pół miliona do miliona, dom właściwie bez górnej granicy, ale rozmowa zaczyna się od miliona w wypadku ruder na obrzeżach.

Szacki wyobraził sobie, że bierze najwyższy możliwy kredyt i kupuje tutaj trzy mieszkania, żeby zostać za kilka lat szczęśliwym rentierem. Miłe, bardzo miłe.

– Okej – powiedział wolno. – Następne pytanie: kto jest najbardziej wkurwionym budowniczym psiej budy w ogródku swojej willi?

Wilczur w odpowiedzi oderwał filtr od papierosa i zapalił.

– Musi pan jedną rzecz zrozumieć – powiedział. – Budnika nikt tutaj nie lubi.

Szacki zaczął się wiercić, spodziewał się przenikliwego, lokalnego policjanta, a miał do czynienia z paranoikiem.

– Dopiero co namalowano mi obraz państwa Budników w samych pastelowych barwach, ulubieńców wszystkich, świeckich świętych. To prawda, że on sprowadził tu ojca Mateusza?

– Prawda. Mieli kręcić w Nidzicy, ale Budnik znał kogoś w TVP i namówił ich na Sandomierz.

– Prawda, że dzięki niemu krzaczory na bulwarze Piłsudskiego zamieniają się w park i przystań?

– Najprawdziwsza prawda.

– Prawda, że wyremontował Piszczele?

– Sama prawda. Nawet na mnie to zrobiło wrażenie, byłem pewien, że nie ma mocnych na ten wąwóz imienia morderców i gwałcicieli.

Szacki pomyślał, że nie słyszał o żadnych sandomierskich mordercach i gwałcicielach, nie licząc lokalnych knajp, gdzie smaki były mordowane, a podniebienia brutalnie gwałcone. Zachował uwagę dla siebie.

– To o co chodzi? – spytał.

Inspektor Wilczur wykonał nieokreślony gest, mający dać do zrozumienia, że stara się oddać coś nieoddawalnego w słowach.

– Zna pan typ głośnego społecznika, nieznoszącego sprzeciwu, bo zawsze jest w trakcie jakiejś krucjaty?

Szacki przytaknął.

– To był ten typ. Wszystko jedno, czy miał rację, czy jej nie miał, zawsze był nieprzytomnie wkurwiający. Znam ludzi, którzy głosowali po jego myśli, żeby już tylko dał spokój. Żeby nie mędził, nie wydzwaniał po nocach, nie latał po gazetach.

– Mało – skomentował Szacki. – Wszystko mało. Irytujący społecznik, kręcący jakieś swoje małe prowincjonalne lody; to wszystko mało. Jemu nie pocięli opon w samochodzie, nie zbili szyby, nie zabili psa. Jemu w okrutny, nieprzypadkowy sposób zarżnęli żonę.

Sobieraj oceniała denatkę jednoznacznie. Wspaniała, dobra, pozbawiona wad, z sercem na dłoni, nawet jeśli jej mąż bywał w swoich krucjatach zbyt agresywny i budził złość, to przy niej wszyscy mięknęli. Ona pomagała, ona radziła, ona załatwiała sprawy. Chodząca dobroć z ustami, kibicią i sercem pełnymi wszystkiego, co najlepsze. Pani prokurator Sobieraj wygłosiła absolutnie pozbawiony obiektywizmu pean na jej cześć, po czym się rozbeczała. To było żenujące. Ale mimo wszystko wiarygodne. Tymczasem z relacjami Wilczura Szacki miał problem. Coś nie grało. Nie wiedział jeszcze co, ale coś było nie tak.

– Matka Elżbieta od Aniołów, tak ją nazywali – powiedział Wilczur.

– Wariatka?

Wilczur pokręcił głową.

– Kompletnie nie. Ucieleśniona dobroć.

– W opowiadaniu to była wariatka.

– To pan wie i ja, i ona też wiedziała i nienawidziła tej ksyw-
ki. Ale tak ją nazywali, myśleli, że to komplement. I będę z panem szczery: nie była z mojej bajki, lecz zasłużyła na każdy
komplement. To naprawdę była dobra osoba. Nie będę się
powtarzał, ale na pewno wszystko, co pan o niej usłyszał i co
o niej jeszcze usłyszy, to prawda.

– Może też była irytująca? Za bardzo społecznikowska? Za
bardzo katolicka? Nie wiem, za mało kupowała na jarmar-
kach ludowych? To Polska, musieli ją za coś nienawidzić,
obrabiać dupę za plecami, zazdrościć czegoś.

Wilczur wzruszył ramionami.

– Nie.

– Nie i już? Koniec błyskotliwej analizy?

Policjant przytaknął i oderwał filtr od papierosa, a Szacki poczuł obezwładniającą rezygnację. Chciał do Warszawy.
Teraz. Zaraz. Natychmiast.

– A relacje między nimi?

– Ludzie zazwyczaj dobierają się w pary w tej samej li-
dze, zna pan na pewno tę zasadę. Piękni z pięknymi, głupi
z głupimi, rozrzutni z rozrzutnymi. Tymczasem Budnikowa była tak ze dwa, trzy szczebelki wyżej niż jej mąż. Jak
by to panu wytłumaczyć... – Wilczur zamyślił się, przez co
jego twarz nabrała upiornego, trupiego wyrazu. W mdłym
świetle pizzerii, za zasłoną papierosowego dymu, wyglądał
jak nieudolnie animowana mumia. – Ludzie znoszą go tylko
dlatego, że Budnikowa go wybrała. Myślą, że trudno, niech
sobie będzie oszołomiony, ale w sumie ma rację, a jeśli przy
jego boku stoi taka kobieta, to nie może być zły. I on to wie.
Wie, że to wbrew naturze.

Sobieraj powiedziała: „Chciałabym, żeby jakiś mężczyzna
był we mnie tyle lat tak zakochany. Chciałabym widzieć codziennie takie uwielbienie w czyichś oczach. Z zewnątrz

mogli wydawać się niedobrani, ale to była wspaniała para. Każdemu życzyłabym takiej miłości, takiego uwielbienia".

– Uwielbiał ją, ale było w tym uwielbieniu coś brudnego – sączył swój jad Wilczur – coś zaborczego, lepkiego, powiedziałbym. Moja była pracowała w szpitalu kilkanaście lat temu, kiedy stało się jasne, że Budnikowa nie będzie mieć dzieci. Ona rozpaczała, on wcale. Powiedział, że przynajmniej nie będzie się musiał nią dzielić. To była pasja, na pewno. Ale wie pan, jak to jest z pasjonatami.

Szacki wiedział, ale nie chciał się zgadzać z Wilczurem, ponieważ coraz mniej go lubił i wszelkie bratanie się z tym osobnikiem wydało mu się wstrętne. Nie chciał też przeciągać tej dyskusji. Dwie osoby opowiadały mu dziś o Budnikach, a miał wrażenie, że wciąż gówno wie, po nic mu ta nacechowana emocjonalnie ćwierćwiedza.

– Przesłuchał pan Budnika? – zapytał na koniec.

– Jest w strasznym stanie. Zadałem mu kilka technicznych pytań, resztę zostawiam panu. Jest pod dyskretną obserwacją.

– Gdzie był wczoraj?

– W domu.

– A ona?

– Też w domu.

– Słucham?

– Tak twierdzi. Oglądali telewizję, przytulili się, usnęli. Wstał nad ranem, żeby napić się wody, jej nie było. Zanim zdążył się na dobre zaniepokoić, dostał telefon od Baśki Sobieraj.

Szacki nie wierzył własnym uszom.

– To jakaś bzdura. Najgłupsze łgarstwo, jakie słyszałem w karierze.

Wilczur pokiwał potakująco głową.

11

Prokurator Teodor Szacki wyrzucił do śmieci resztki wędliny i serów, które zalegały w lodówce, zjedzony do połowy pasztet z puszki, kawałek pomidora, chwilę wahał się nad zawartością patelni, ale w końcu przedwczorajszy sos bolognese też wylądował w śmieciach. Większa część tego, co przyrządził. Cały czas gotował za dużo, tyle, że starczyłoby dla trzyosobowej rodziny i przygodnych gości. W Sandomierzu nie miał rodziny, nie miał przyjaciół ani znajomych i gości, czasami zmuszał się, żeby ugotować coś dla siebie, ale rytuał samotnego stania przy kuchni i samotnego jedzenia był potworny; próbował jeść przy włączonym radiu albo telewizji, lecz ta podróbka cudzej obecności tylko pogarszała sprawę. Nie mógł przełknąć ani kęsa, jedzenie stawało mu w gardle, zaczęło się kojarzyć z czynnością tak ciężką i depresyjną, że po każdym posiłku musiał długo dochodzić do siebie. I szło mu to coraz mozolniej.

Do sklepów szedł jak za karę. Uczył się kupować mniej i mniej. Na początku – tak jak z gotowaniem – odruchowo brał tyle, co zawsze. Przyzwyczajony, że ile by kupił, to i tak wszystko zniknie z lodówki. Ktoś sobie zrobi kanapkę, ktoś wróci głodny, coś się przekąsi przy wieczornej telewizji. Tutaj był tylko on. Najpierw zrezygnował ze wszystkiego, co paczkowane. W paczkach wędlin i serów było za dużo dla jednej osoby, codziennie coś wyrzucał. Zaczął kupować na wagę, ale ciągle za dużo. Dwadzieścia deka wędliny, piętnaście, dziesięć. Któregoś dnia stanął przy kasie obskurnego sklepu społemowskiego w rynku. Jedna kajzerka, serek wiejski, mały kartonik soku pomarańczowego, pięć deka baleronu, pomidor. Ekspedientka zażartowała, że apetyt nie dopisuje. Wyszedł bez słowa, jeszcze jakoś trzymał się po drodze, ale w domu płakał, robiąc sobie śniadanie, a kiedy usiadł nad talerzem z dwiema kanapkami, histerycznie szlochał, nie

52

mógł przestać, łzy i smarki rozmazywały mu się na twarzy. A on wył, kiwając się w przód i w tył, nie mogąc oderwać zamglonego wzroku od kanapek z baleronem. Ponieważ zrozumiał, że stracił wszystko, co kochał, i nigdy tego nie odzyska.

Po wyprowadzce z Warszawy schudł piętnaście kilo. Tutaj go nie znali, myśleli, że zawsze był chudzielcem. Ale garnitury na nim wisiały, przy kołnierzykach pojawił się nadmierny luz, w paskach musiał wypalić rozgrzanym nad gazem gwoździem dodatkowe dziurki.

Myślał, żeby rzucić się w wir pracy, ale tutaj nie było tyle pracy. Myślał, żeby wrócić do Warszawy, ale nie miał do czego wracać. Myślał, żeby znaleźć do towarzystwa kogoś, kto nie byłby jedynie wkładem do łóżka, ale nie miał na to siły. Dużo leżał, dużo rozmyślał. Czasami wydawało mu się, że już jest lepiej, że już stoi na twardym gruncie, ale wtedy grunt się osypywał, znowu musiał zrobić krok do tyłu. Nie widział, co tam jest, ale ten krok robił. Po drugiej stronie rozpadliny było jego dawne życie, kręciła się Weronika, Helcia, Kuzniecow, przyjaciele. Światło, gwar, śmiech. U niego była z jednej strony ciemność, a z drugiej rozpadlina. Kolejny dzień, kolejne osuwisko, kolejny krok w tył. W końcu ciemność otaczała go z każdej strony, a on i tak codziennie robił krok w tył. Pogodził się, że tak to już będzie.

Nalał trochę wody do patelni po sosie i odstawił ją na kuchenkę. Pozmywa kiedyś.

Nie może tak być, pomyślał, odpychając od siebie świadomość, że to przeświadczenie nawiedza go codziennie. Nie może tak być. Ludzie żyją po rozwodach w zgodzie, przyjaźnią się czasami, razem wychowują dzieci, Demi Moore była na ślubie Bruce'a Willisa i odwrotnie, nie trzeba spać w jednym łóżku, mieszkać w jednym mieszkaniu, żeby tworzyć rodzinę. Przecież on, Weronika i Helcia zawsze będą rodziną, bez względu na to, co się wydarzyło i co się wydarzy.

Sięgnął po telefon, ciągle miał Weronikę pod szybkim wybieraniem. Tyle że teraz była Weroniką, a nie – jak kiedyś – Kotkiem.

– Tak?

– No cześć, to ja.

– No cześć, widzę przecież. Co chcesz?

Mogła być niemiła. Rozumiał to.

– A tak dzwonię, czy wszystko okej. Co u ciebie, co u Helci.

Chwila milczenia.

– Znowu?

– Jak to znowu? A to, przepraszam, jest jakiś okres, kiedy mogę dzwonić i dowiadywać się, co u mojej córki?

Westchnienie.

– Wszystko w porządku u twojej córki, zaganiam ją do odrabiania lekcji, jutro ma klasówkę. – Miała zmęczony, zniechęcony głos, jakby spełniała przykry obowiązek, Szacki poczuł, że w gardle rośnie mu kula agresji.

– A z czego klasówkę?

– Z przyrody. Teo, chcesz coś konkretnie? Przepraszam, jestem trochę zajęta.

– Konkretnie chciałem się dowiedzieć, kiedy moja córka tu przyjedzie. Mam wrażenie, że utrudniasz jej kontakt ze mną.

– Nie bądź paranoikiem. Wiesz, że nie lubi tam przyjeżdżać.

– Bo co? Bo jak zacznie, to wtedy jej ojczym będzie miał konkurencję i twój nowy wspaniały związek nie będzie taki wspaniały?

– Teo...

– No tak, ale chyba musi zrozumieć, że ja teraz mieszkam tutaj.

Nienawidził się za to, że w jego głosie pojawiły się płaczliwe tony.

– Wytłumacz jej to sam.

Nie wiedział, co na to odpowiedzieć. Helcia niechętnie z nim rozmawiała, niechętnie słuchała. Lubiła swój nowy dom, oddalonej o dwieście kilometrów kawalerskiej nory swojego ojca – nie. Kiedyś próbowała ten niesmak ukrywać, ostatnio przestała.

– Dobrze, to może ja przyjadę.

– Może. Jak chcesz. Teo... błagam, jeśli nie masz nic konkretnego...

– Nie, dzięki, ucałuj mojego borsuczka. Dobra?

– Dobra.

Czekała, czy jeszcze coś powie, czuł jej niechęć i zniecierpliwienie. Łowił dźwięki dobiegające z drugiej strony. Grał telewizor, szczęknął garnek, ktoś się zaśmiał, dziecko. Weronika odłożyła słuchawkę, a w małym mieszkaniu na Długosza w Sandomierzu zapanowała niezmącona cisza.

Szacki musiał coś zrobić, żeby nie myśleć. Praca, w końcu przecież ma normalną sprawę. Musi zrobić plan śledztwa, zastanowić się, przygotować etapy działania, wpisać wszystko w kalendarz. Dlaczego tego nie robi? Normalnie miałby już trzy zeszyty zapisane notatkami. Gwałtownym gestem otworzył laptop, żeby poszukać informacji, przygotować się do jutrzejszego przesłuchania Budnika. Musiał się dużo udzielać w mediach, i on, i jego żona. Trzeba przejrzeć jakieś komentarze, plotki, sprawozdania z posiedzeń Rady Miejskiej. Wszystko. Charakterystyczny dźwięk teleportacji z Mysta poinformował go o nadejściu nowej wiadomości.

From: redakcja@sztych.com.pl
Subject: Re: Prokurator pyta o brzytwomaczetę
To: teodor.szacki@gmail.com
Date: 15 kwietnia 2009 19:44 CET

Witam!

Nieźle mnie Pan wystraszył z tym prokuratorem, już myślałem, że naruszyliśmy jakiś paragraf, pokazując zdjęcia zbyt wielkich noży :-) A tak w temacie, to musiałem spytać kilku poważnych kolekcjonerów, żeby potwierdzić własne rozpoznanie, i wszyscy są zgodni, że Pańska „brzytwomaczeta" to chalef, czyli nóż do rytualnego uboju zwierząt, używany przez szojcheta – żydowskiego rzeźnika.

Po rozmiarach można wnioskować, że przeznaczony jest do szlachtowania bydła (mniejsze są do drobiu i jagniąt), a po kondycji, że spokojnie mógłby być użyty jeszcze w niejednej koszernej rzeźni. Powinien pan wiedzieć, że noże do rytualnego uboju muszą być w idealnym stanie, eliminuje je najmniejsza rysa, szczerba albo nierówność, ostrze sprawdza się paznokciem przed każdym użyciem i po użyciu. Chodzi o to, że tylko perfekcyjnie ostry nóż może jednym cięciem przeciąć przełyk, krtań, główną żyłę szyjną i tętnicę, a takie są warunki rytualnego, koszernego uboju. Żydzi wierzą, że to najbardziej humanitarny i bezbolesny sposób zabijania (ile w tym prawdy, to inna sprawa).

Mam nadzieję, że pomogłem i że nóż – swoją drogą, bardzo podoba mi się określenie „brzytwomaczeta" – nie został użyty w jakichś niecnych celach ;-)

Serdecznie,
Janek Wiewiórski
redaktor

Szacki przeczytał mail kilkakrotnie, nie myśląc już zupełnie o swoich prywatnych problemach. W kościelnym mieście z antysemicką przeszłością miał prowadzić śledztwo w sprawie zabójstwa znanej działaczki społecznej, którą rytualnie zaszlachtowano, jak krowę w żydowskiej rzeźni.

Ktoś zapukał.

Będzie naprawdę niezła jatka, pomyślał Szacki, ganiąc się jednocześnie za niefortunny dobór słów, i otworzył drzwi. Klara stała za nimi golusieńka, jak ją Pan Bóg stworzył. Spojrzał na jej śliczne, jędrne ciało, spojrzał na sterczące, młode piersi, na rozlewające się po szyi kasztanowe loki. I uśmiechnął się szczęśliwie i zachęcająco, nie czując do niej absolutnie nic.

Ale uśmiech był szczery. Prokurator Teodor Szacki miał sprawę i bardzo był z tego powodu szczęśliwy.

Rozdział drugi

czwartek, 16 kwietnia 2009

Dla Żydów w diasporze to uroczyście świętowany ostatni dzień Pesach, dla chrześcijan piąty dzień Oktawy Wielkanocnej, dla Polaków ostatni dzień żałoby narodowej. Wojsko Polskie obchodzi Dzień Sapera, Alina Janowska – 86. urodziny, a warszawska giełda – osiemnaste. We Włocławku straż miejska zgarnęła pijanych w sztok i agresywnych księdza w szatach liturgicznych i jego ministranta. Okazali się świeckimi, którzy świsnęli stroje matce jednego z nich, krawcowej. Brytyjska spółka znajduje pod Poznaniem ogromne złoże gazu, a brytyjska prasa podaje, że najczęściej granym utworem na pogrzebach jest *My Way* Sinatry, wysoko na liście jest *Highway to Hell* AC/DC. W rewanżach ćwierćfinału Pucharu UEFA wygrywają i w półfinale podejmą bratobójcze boje Dynamo i Szachtar oraz Werder i Hamburger. Sandomierz oburzony przenosinami zieleniaka, który musi zwolnić miejsce parkingowi pod nowym stadionem. Mieszkańcy, niezależnie od poglądów w sprawie bazaru, doświadczają wspólnie kolejnego chłodnego dnia. Temperatura nie przekracza 14 stopni, ale przynajmniej słonecznie, nie pada.

1

Prokurator Teodor Szacki nie lubił zimna, głupich spraw, niekompetentnych adwokatów i prowincjonalnych sądów. Tego ranka dostał wszystko w uderzeniowej dawce. Spojrzał w kalendarz: wiosna. Spojrzał za okno: wiosna. Włożył garnitur, płaszcz, togę przerzucił przez ramię i postanowił orzeźwić się spacerem do budynku sądu. Już na Sokolnickiego, ślizgając się na oszronionych kocich łbach, zorientował się, że to był kiepski pomysł. W okolicach Bramy Opatowskiej zdrętwiały mu uszy, przy wieży ciśnień nie czuł palców, kiedy w końcu skręcił w Kościuszki i wszedł do zgniłozielonego budynku sądu, przez kilka minut dochodził do siebie, chuchając w zgrabiałe dłonie. Biegun zimna, cholerna wiocha, wygwizdów, szlag by to trafił.

Sąd był brzydki. Jego bryła mogła się wydawać nowoczesna, kiedy powstawała w latach dziewięćdziesiątych, teraz przypominała cygański pałac, przerobiony na gmach użyteczności publicznej. Schodki, chromy, zielony kamień, połamane płaszczyzny – budynek nie pasował ani do otaczającej go architektury, ani do samego siebie, w jego zielonym kolorze było coś przepraszającego, jakby próbował ukryć własną brzydotę na tle cmentarnych drzew. Sala rozpraw konsekwentnie rozwijała stylistykę gmachu, najbardziej rzucającym się w oczy elementem pomieszczenia, przypominającego salę konferencyjną w podrzędnej korporacji, były zielone wertikale.

Skrzywiony, zniesmaczony Szacki wyrzekał w myślach na otoczenie, nawet kiedy już w todze usiadł na miejscu przeznaczonym dla prokuratora. Po drugiej stronie miał oskarżonego i jego adwokata. Hubert Huby był miłym siedemdziesięciolatkiem. Miał gęste, jeszcze szpakowate włosy, okulary w rogowych oprawkach i uroczy, skromny uśmiech. Jego obrońca, zapewne z urzędu – obraz nędzy i rozpaczy. Toga niedopięta, włosy nieumyte, buty niewypastowane, wąsy nieprzystrzyżone, budził podejrzenie, że śmierdzi. Tak jak cała sprawa, myślał z rosnącą irytacją Szacki, dla którego dokończenie wszystkich spraw poprzednika było warunkiem otrzymania posady w Sandomierzu.

W końcu pojawiła się sędzia. Siksa, wyglądała, jakby dopiero co zrobiła maturę, ale przynajmniej proces się zaczął.

Panie prokuratorze? – Sędzia uśmiechnęła się do niego miło po dopełnieniu formalności, w Warszawie żaden sędzia się nie uśmiechał, jeśli już to złośliwie, kiedy przyłapał kogoś na nieznajomości przepisów.

Teodor Szacki wstał, odruchowo poprawił togę.

– Wysoki sądzie, urząd prokuratorski podtrzymuje tezy z aktu oskarżenia, oskarżony przyznał się do wszystkich zarzucanych mu czynów, jego wina nie budzi wątpliwości w świetle jego własnych zeznań i zeznań poszkodowanych kobiet. Nie chcę przedłużać sprawy, wnoszę o uznanie oskarżonego winnym, że kierując się podstępem, doprowadził wielokrotnie inne osoby do poddania się innej czynności seksualnej, co wyczerpuje znamiona czynu opisanego w artykule sto dziewięćdziesiątym siódmym paragraf drugi kodeksu karnego, i wnoszę o wymierzenie kary sześciu miesięcy pozbawienia wolności, co, zaznaczam, jest dolną granicą kary przewidzianej przez ustawodawcę.

Szacki usiadł, sprawa była ewidentna, chciał tylko, żeby to się skończyło. Specjalnie zażądał najniższego możliwego wyroku, nie miał ochoty na dyskusje. W myślach bez przerwy układał plan przesłuchania Budnika, żonglował tematami i pytaniami, zmieniał ich kolejność, starał się przewidzieć scenariusze rozmowy, przygotować się na wszystkie warianty. Miał pewność, że Budnik kłamał w sprawie ostatniego wieczoru, jaki spędził z żoną. Ale wszyscy kłamią, to ich jeszcze nie czyni mordercami. Mógł mieć kochankę, mogli się pokłócić, mogli mieć ciche dni, mógł pić z kumplami. Wróć, kochankę trzeba skreślić, jeśli Sobieraj i Wilczur mówili prawdę, to był najbardziej zakochanym człowiekiem świata. Wróć, niczego nie można skreślić, to jakiś małomiasteczkowy zblatowany układ, nie wiadomo kto, dlaczego i po co mu coś opowiada. Wilczur nie budzi zaufania, Sobieraj była przyjaciółką rodziny.

– Panie prokuratorze – ostry głos sędzi wyrwał go z letargu, zdał sobie sprawę, że słyszał co trzecie słowo z mowy obrońcy.

Wstał.

– Tak, wysoki sądzie?

– Mógłby się pan ustosunkować do stanowiska obrony?

Kurwa mać, nie miał najmniejszego pojęcia, jakie jest stanowisko obrony. W Warszawie, poza wyjątkowymi przypadkami, sąd nie pytał o zdanie, wysłuchiwał znudzony stron, znikał, wydawał wyrok, załatwione, następny, proszę.

W Sandomierzu sędzia była litościwa.

– Żeby zmienić kwalifikację czynu na artykuł dwieście siedemnasty, paragraf pierwszy?

Szackiemu wyświetliła się przed oczami treść przepisu. Spojrzał na obrońcę jak na wariata.

– Ustosunkuję się, że to chyba żart. Pan mecenas powinien zapoznać się z podstawowymi interpretacjami i orzecznictwem. Artykuł dwieście siedemnasty dotyczy naruszenia nietykalności cielesnej i właściwie stosuje się go tylko do łagodnych bójek lub kiedy jeden polityk trzaśnie drugiego po gębie. Oczywiście rozumiem intencje obrony, naruszenie nietykalności jest ścigane z oskarżenia prywatnego, a zagrożenie karą to najwyżej rok. Nie ma porównania z molestowaniem, za które grozi od pół roku do ośmiu lat. A to właśnie robił pański klient, panie mecenasie.

Obrońca wstał. Spojrzał pytająco na sędzię, dziewczyna skinęła głową.

– Chciałbym też przypomnieć, że w wyniku mediacji prawie wszystkie poszkodowane wybaczyły mojemu klientowi, co powinno skutkować umorzeniem postępowania.

Szacki nie czekał na pozwolenie.

– Jeszcze raz: proszę przeczytać kodeks, mecenasie – warknął. – Po pierwsze, „prawie" robi wielką różnicę, a po drugie, umorzenie w wyniku mediacji ma zastosowanie tylko do przestępstw zagrożonych karą do trzech lat pozbawienia wolności. Pan może co najwyżej wnioskować o nadzwyczajne złagodzenie kary, która i tak jest śmiesznie niska, biorąc pod uwagę wyczyny pańskiego klienta.

Mecenas uśmiechnął się i rozłożył ręce w geście zdziwienia. Za dużo filmów, za mało fachowych lektur, skomentował w myślach Szacki.

– Ale czy komuś stała się krzywda? Czy komuś było nieprzyjemnie? Ludzkie sprawy, dorośli ludzie...

Szackiemu spłynęła na oczy czerwona zasłona. Policzył w myślach do trzech, żeby się uspokoić. Zaczerpnął powietrza, wyprostował się, spojrzał na sędzię. Przytaknęła, zaciekawiona.

– Panie mecenasie, urząd prokuratorski jest zdumiony zarówno pańską nieznajomością prawa, jak i cywilizowanych obyczajów. Przypominam, że oskarżony Huby przez wiele miesięcy chodził po domach w powiecie sandomierskim, wyposażony w kitel oraz torbę lekarską, podając się za lekarza. Już to jest karalne. Podawał się za specjalistę od, cytuję, „mammografii palpacyjnej" i proponował badanie profilaktyczne, chcąc doprowadzić kobiety do obnażenia się i udostępnienia mu swoich wdzięków. Co podchodzi pod definicję gwałtu. I chciałbym też przypomnieć, że większość „pacjentek" zapewniał o dobrym stanie ich biustów, co nie musiało być prawdą i mogło doprowadzić do zaniechania badań profilaktycznych i poważnych problemów zdrowotnych. Zresztą jest to główny powód, dla którego jedna z poszkodowanych nie zgodziła się na mediację.

– Ale u dwóch pań wyczuł guz i skłonił je do leczenia, które w konsekwencji uratowało im życie – zaripostował z emfazą adwokat.

– To niech te panie ufundują mu nagrodę i przysyłają paczki. Tutaj zajmujemy się tym, że oskarżony dopuścił się czynu zabronionego i ma ponieść konsekwencje, ponieważ nie wolno chodzić po domach, okłamując i obmacując kobiety. Tak samo jak nie wolno chodzić po ulicach i wybijać ludziom zębów w nadziei, że potem u stomatologa zostaną wykryte i wyleczone poważniejsze problemy.

Widział, że sędzia powstrzymała parsknięcie śmiechem.

– I sprawa przyczyniła się w województwie do poważnej dyskusji o profilaktyce i konieczności badań mammograficznych – mecenas był nieugięty.

– Ale czy to jest wniosek formalny? – Szacki poczuł znużenie.

– To są okoliczności, które powinny być wzięte pod uwagę.

– Wysoki sądzie? – Szacki pytająco spojrzał na ubawioną sędzię.

– Zamykam posiedzenie, ogłoszenie wyroku w poniedziałek o dziesiątej. A pana, panie prokuratorze, zapraszam na chwilę do mojego gabinetu.

Gabinet pani sędzi, która po sprawdzeniu wokandy stała się Marią Tatarską, był brzydki jak cały budynek, równie nieprzyjemnie utrzymany w zgniłych zieleniach, ale przynajmniej przestronny. Szacki zapukał i wszedł po zaproszeniu w chwili, kiedy sędzia Tatarska zdejmowała togę. Na szafce już szumiał elektryczny czajnik.

– Kawy? – zapytała, odwieszając sędziowski mundur.

Szacki chciał odpowiedzieć, że chętnie, jedna łyżeczka, bez cukru, dużo mleka, ale w tejże chwili sędzia Tatarska odwróciła się do niego i prokurator musiał skoncentrować się na tym, żeby żaden z objawów emocji nie pojawił się na jego twarzy. I żeby teatralnie nie przełknąć śliny. Sędzia

Tatarska pod togą była regularną seksbombą, o ciele dziewczyny z rozkładówki, a dekolt jej fioletowej bluzki zostałby uznany za odważny nawet w nocnym klubie.

– Chętnie, jedna łyżeczka, bez cukru, dużo mleka.

Porozmawiali chwilę o sprawie, w czasie kiedy robiła dla nich kawę. Small talk, nic ciekawego. Przypuszczał, że ściągnęła go tu w jakimś celu. Innym niż przyjemność obcowania z jego służbowym chłodem, wychudzoną sylwetką i siną twarzą faceta, który za kilka miesięcy kończy czterdziestkę, a zima upłynęła mu na depresji i zaniedbywaniu tężyzny fizycznej. Wiedział, że wygląda jak urzędnik państwowy. Zwykle miał to gdzieś, ale teraz chciałby wyglądać lepiej. Chciałby też, żeby przeszła do rzeczy, musiał wyjść w ciągu pięciu minut.

– Słyszałam trochę o panu, o pańskich sprawach, koledzy ze stolicy opowiadali. – Przyglądała mu się uważnie. Szacki milczał, czekał na dalszy ciąg. Co miał powiedzieć? Że też ją zna ze słyszenia? – Nie powiem, specjalnie żeśmy podpytywali, jak poszła plotka, że pan zostaje. Pewnie już się pan zorientował, że zmiany kadrowe to nie jest na prowincji codzienność. Z pańskiej perspektywy nie było pewnie tego widać, ale w środowisku to stało się małą sensacją.

Ciągle nie wiedział, co powiedzieć.

– Szukałam też w prasie, czytałam o pańskich sprawach, niektóre to pierwszoligowe kryminały, głośne historie. Zaintrygowała mnie ta z morderstwem w czasie ustawień Hellingera.

Szacki wzruszył ramionami. Hellinger, szlag by trafił, gdyby nie tamta sprawa, nie romans, nie stare esbeckie historie, pewnie by teraz jadł jajko w sosie nomen omen tatarskim w alei Solidarności i umawiał się z Weroniką, kto odbierze dziecko ze szkoły. Gdyby nie Hellinger, miałby teraz życie.

– Swojego czasu dużo interesowałam się Hellingerem, nawet pojechałam do Kielc na ustawienia, ale odwołali, nie chciało mi się jechać po raz drugi. Wie pan, samotna kobieta, długie wieczory, za dużo myśli. Myśli, że może z nią coś nie tak, może potrzebuje terapii. Głupie.

Szacki nie wierzył własnym uszom. Ona go podrywała. Ta seksbomba z prawniczym wykształceniem go podrywała. Spiął się, stary małżeński nawyk. Spiął się na myśl o flircie, o schadzkach, kłamstwach, wysyłanych potajemnie esemesach, wyciszonych komórkach, biurogodzinach zmarnowanych na spotkania na mieście.

I zrozumiał, że małżeński nawyk to tylko nawyk, druga natura, ale ciągle druga. Był wolny, swobodny, miał mieszkanie z widokiem na Wisłę. Mógł się umówić i zerżnąć prowincjuszkę w kuchni na stojaka. Tak po prostu. Bez wyrzutów sumienia, bez kombinowania, bez podchodów i owijania w bawełnę przyjaźni i niewinnej znajomości.

Musiał lecieć. Ale umówił się na wieczór. Hellinger, oczywiście, to dopiero była sprawa, chętnie jej opowie.

Tylko trzeba będzie spławić Klarę.

2

PROTOKÓŁ PRZESŁUCHANIA ŚWIADKA. Grzegorz Budnik, urodzony 4 grudnia 1950 roku, zamieszkały w Sandomierzu przy ulicy Katedralnej 27, wykształcenie wyższe chemiczne, przewodniczący Rady Miejskiej miasta Sandomierz. Stosunek do stron: mąż Elżbiety Budnik (ofiary). Niekarany za składanie fałszywych zeznań.

Uprzedzony o odpowiedzialności karnej z art. 233 kk zeznaję, co następuje:

Elżbietę Szuszkiewicz poznałem zimą 1992 roku w czasie akcji „Zima w mieście", przyjechała z Krakowa, żeby prowadzić warsztaty teatralne dla dzieci. Nie znałem jej wcześniej, choć dzieciństwo spędziła w Sandomierzu. Ja koordynowałem wtedy wszystkie imprezy w ratuszu. Zwróciłem na nią uwagę, bo dla niektórych tego typu akcje to pańszczyzna, a ona zrobiła z dziećmi takie przedstawienie na koniec ferii, że ludzie bili brawo na stojąco, *Opowiadania dla dzieci* Singera. Była młoda, nie miała wtedy trzydziestu lat, piękna, pełna energii. Zakochałem się bez pamięci, bez nadziei na cokolwiek – prowincjonalny urzędnik i wielkomiejska dziewczyna po PWST. Ale dwa lata później wzięliśmy ślub w katedrze sandomierskiej w Białą Niedzielę. Niestety nie dorobiliśmy się dzieci, chociaż bardzo chcieliśmy. Kiedy się okazało, że musielibyśmy przechodzić te wszystkie procedury medyczne, rozważaliśmy adopcję, ale w końcu uznaliśmy, że dalej będziemy zajmować się dziećmi społecznie. Ja mniej ze względu na obowiązki w radzie, Ela całkowicie się temu oddała. Uczyła w szkole, ale przede wszystkim organizowała imprezy, ściągała artystów, wymyślała najbardziej odjazdowe warsztaty. To było nasze wspólne marzenie, żeby zrobić takie specjalne miejsce, ośrodek artystyczny dla dzieci. Gdzie moglibyśmy organizować całe obozy, takie w stylu amerykańskim. Ale ciągle to odkładaliśmy, zawsze jakaś bieżączka była do załatwienia. Mieliśmy ruszyć na dobre w tym roku, poszukać nieruchomości, wziąć kredyty.

Nasze pożycie układało się dobrze, kłótnie miały miejsce sporadycznie, prowadziliśmy życie towarzyskie, teraz może trochę mniej, zima długa, a u nas najlepiej siedzieć w ogrodzie.

Szacki czuł się wyczerpany. Krótki protokół był wynikiem trzygodzinnej rozmowy. Budnik wpadał w dygresje, w milczenie, czasami płakał, co chwila czuł się w obowiązku zapewnić, jak bardzo kochał swoją żonę, opowiedzieć anegdotę z ich wspólnego życia. Bywał tak autentyczny, że Szackiemu krajało się serce. Ale tylko bywał, poza tym prokuratorski nos czuł brzydki zapach kłamstwa. Budnik w jednej sprawie na pewno mówił prawdę, jego uczucie do żony było poruszająco prawdziwe. Ale poza tym łgał jak z nut.

Ostatnie dni w większości spędziliśmy z żoną wspólnie. Zimą dużo pracowaliśmy, dlatego Wielkanoc postanowiliśmy spędzić we dwójkę. Zresztą nie mieliśmy gdzie jechać ani kogo zapraszać. Moja siostra pojechała odwiedzić brata, który mieszka w Niemczech, rodzice Eli pojechali do Zakopanego. Wszyscy mieli przyjechać teraz, w niedzielę, na piętnastą rocznicę ślubu, chcieliśmy zrobić przyjęcie, drugie wesele jakby. Od soboty z nikim się nie spotykaliśmy, to znaczy, widzieliśmy znajomych na święconym, poszliśmy nie do katedry, tylko do Świętego Pawła, żeby się przejść trochę. Potem już nikogo, w niedzielę zaspaliśmy na rezurekcję, zjedliśmy skromne, ale uroczyste śniadanie, trochę czytaliśmy, trochę gadaliśmy, trochę oglądaliśmy telewizję. Wieczorem poszliśmy na spacer, po spacerze zajrzeliśmy do katedry, ale nie na mszę, tylko pomodlić się trochę. Nie pamiętam, czy był ktoś jeszcze, pewnie tak. Poniedziałek właściwie cały spędziliśmy w łóżku, Elżunię bolało gardło, strasznie było zimno w te święta. We wtorek ciągle źle się czuła, nie mieliśmy żadnych obowiązków, więc zostaliśmy w domu. Odwołaliśmy na wszelki wypadek wizytę u znajomych, Olgi i Tadeusza Bojarskich. Nie pamiętam, ale chyba na pewno dzwoniła do nich żona, w poniedziałek wieczorem albo we wtorek rano. Ja we wtorek na chwilę wpadłem do urzędu, widziało mnie tam parę osób. Przyszedłem po południu, przyniosłem nam jedzenie z Trzydziestki, Ela czuła się lepiej, wyglądała całkiem dobrze i nawet żałowaliśmy, że odwołaliśmy spotkanie. Wieczorem oglądaliśmy jakiś film z Redfordem na jedynce, o więzieniu, nie pamiętam tytułu. I poszliśmy spać. Bardzo wcześnie, bolała mnie głowa. Nie wstawałem w nocy. Nie mam problemów z prostatą. Jak się obudziłem, Eli nie było. Zanim zdążyłem się zaniepokoić, zadzwoniła Basia Sobieraj.

Cieszę się, że pan mnie przesłuchuje. Dla Basi mogłoby to być trudne.

– Przesłuchuję, ponieważ prowadzę śledztwo. Względy emocjonalne nie mają tu nic do rzeczy.

Grzegorz Budnik pokiwał w milczeniu głową. Wyglądał strasznie. Po wysłuchaniu wszystkich opowieści o legendarnym radnym Szacki spodziewał się zażywnego jegomościa z wąsami lub szpakowatą brodą, postępującą łysiną i kamizelką opinającą się na brzuchu, słowem, takiego posła albo burmistrza z telewizji. Tymczasem Grzegorz Budnik był typem emerytowanego maratończyka: niski, szczupły, żylasty w charakterystyczny drapieżny sposób, jakby w jego ciele nie było ani jednej komórki tłuszczowej. W normalnych warunkach zdolny zapewne pokonać na rękę niejednego osiłka z prowincjonalnej siłowni, dziś wyglądał na osobę, która właśnie przegrała długą walkę ze śmiertelną chorobą. Krótka ruda broda nie była w stanie ukryć zapadniętych policzków, spocone i nieumyte włosy przyklejały się do czaszki. Oczy miał podkrążone, czerwone od płaczu, mętne, zapewne od środków uspokajających. Zgarbiony i zamknięty w sobie, bardziej przypominał Szackiemu przesłuchiwanych niemal codziennie stołecznych menelików niż nieugiętego radnego, przewodniczącego Rady Miejskiej, postrach urzędników i przeciwników politycznych. Obraz nędzy i rozpaczy dopełniał nierówno przyklejony na czole wielki plaster. Grzegorz Budnik bardziej wyglądał jak bezdomny włóczęga niż jak urzędnik.

– Co się panu stało w czoło?

– Potknąłem się, uderzyłem o garnek.

– Garnek?

– Straciłem równowagę, machnąłem ręką, uderzyłem w rączkę patelni, patelnia podskoczyła i wyrżnęła mnie w głowę. Nic poważnego.

– Będziemy musieli zrobić obdukcję.

– Nic poważnego.

– Nie dlatego, że się o pana martwimy. Musimy sprawdzić, czy to nie wynik bójki albo zranienia.

– Nie wierzy mi pan?

Szacki tylko spojrzał. Nikomu nie wierzył.

– Pan wie oczywiście, że może odmówić zeznań lub odpowiedzi na konkretne pytania?

– Tak.

– Ale woli pan kłamać. Dlaczego?

Budnik wyprostował się dumnie, jakby to mogło dodać prawdy jego zeznaniom.

– Kiedy po raz ostatni widział pan żonę? – Szacki nie pozwolił mu dojść do głosu.

– Mówiłem...

– Wiem, co pan mówił. Teraz proszę powiedzieć, kiedy naprawdę po raz ostatni widział pan żonę i dlaczego pan skłamał. Jeśli nie, zatrzymam pana na czterdzieści osiem godzin, postawię zarzut zabójstwa małżonki i wystąpię do sądu o areszt. Ma pan trzydzieści sekund.

Budnik zgarbił się jeszcze bardziej, czerwone oczy, nieprzyjemnie kontrastujące z bladą cerą, pokryły się łzami, Szackiemu przypomniał się Gollum z *Władcy pierścieni*.

– Dwadzieścia.

Gollum, syczący my precious, nieistniejący bez swojego skarbu, uzależniony od rzeczy, która nigdy nie mogła być jego. Czy tak wyglądał związek Grzegorza i Elżbiety Budników? Prowincjonalny Gollum, społecznik-brzydal i miastowa dziewczyna, piękna, mądra i dobra, gwiazda ekstraklasy na gościnnych występach u trampkarzy. Dlaczego została? Dlaczego za niego wyszła?

– Dziesięć.

– Przecież mówiłem...

Szackiemu nie drgnął ani jeden mięsień, wystukał numer na telefonie, jednocześnie wyciągnął z biurka formularz postanowienia o postawieniu zarzutów.

– Mówi Szacki, poproszę z inspektorem Wilczurem.

Budnik położył rękę na widełkach.

– W poniedziałek.

– Dlaczego pan kłamał?

Budnik zrobił taki gest, jakby chciał wzruszyć ramionami, ale zabrakło mu siły. Szacki przysunął do siebie protokół, pstryknął długopisem.

– Słucham?

Zmieniam zeznania. Ostatni raz swoją żonę, Elżbietę, widziałem w Poniedziałek Wielkanocny około godziny czternastej. Rozstaliśmy się w niezgodzie, zaczęliśmy się kłócić o nasze plany, ona twierdziła, że czas ucieka, że jesteśmy coraz starsi i jeśli chcemy zrealizować nasze marzenia o ośrodku, musimy wreszcie zacząć. Ja wolałem zaczekać do wyborów samorządowych w przyszłym roku, kandydować na burmistrza, gdyby się udało, wszystko byłoby łatwiejsze. Potem jak to w kłótni, zaczęliśmy sobie wyrzucać. Ona mnie, że wszystko odkładam na później, że tak samo politykuję w urzędzie, jak w domu. Ja jej, że jest odrealniona, myśli, że wystarczy bardzo chcieć i wszystko się staje faktem. Krzyczeliśmy, obrażaliśmy się nawzajem.

Boże, jak sobie pomyślę, że ostatnie słowa, jakie jej powiedziałem, to żeby zabrała swoją chudą dupę z powrotem do Krakowa... – Budnik zaczął cicho szlochać. Szacki czekał, aż się uspokoi. Chciało mu się palić.

W końcu wzięła kurtkę i wyszła bez słowa. Nie goniłem jej, nie szukałem, byłem wściekły. Nie chciałem przepraszać, nie chciałem się kajać, chciałem być sam. Ma mnóstwo znajomych, podejrzewałem, że poszła do Barbary Sobieraj. Nie kontaktowałem się z nią w poniedziałek ani we wtorek. Czytałem, oglądałem telewizję, piłem trochę piwa. We wtorek wieczorem zacząłem już tęsknić, film z Redfordem był dobry, ale przykro mi go było oglądać samemu. Duma nie pozwalała mi zadzwonić wieczorem, pomyślałem, że rano pójdę do Barbary Sobieraj albo do niej zadzwonię. Fakty te zataiłem, ponieważ przestraszyłem się, że kłótnia i fakt, że jej nie szukałem, będą źle wyglądać i obciążą mnie przed organami ścigania.

A nie wpadł pan na to, że te fakty mogą mieć znaczenie dla śledztwa? Znalezienie mordercy nie jest dla pana ważne?

Budnik znowu nieomalże wzruszył ramionami.

– Nie jest. Nic teraz nie jest dla mnie ważne.

Szacki dał mu protokół do przeczytania, jednocześnie zastanawiając się, czy go zamknąć, czy nie. Zwykle słuchał intuicji w takich sprawach. Ale jego kompas głupiał. Budnik był politykiem, prowincjonalnym, ale politykiem, czyli zawodowym kłamcą i ściemniaczem. I Szacki miał pewność, że z jakichś powodów, które na pewno jeszcze pozna, nie powiedział mu całej prawdy. Mimo to jego smutek wydawał się autentyczny. Pełen rezygnacji smutek po nieodwracalnej stracie, nie rozdygotany, pełen strachu smutek mordercy. Szacki miał zbyt wiele okazji obserwować obie te emocje, nauczył się je rozpoznawać.

Wyciągnął z szuflady teczkę ze zdjęciami, wypełnił nagłówek protokołu okazania.

– Widział pan kiedyś to narzędzie?

Na widok zdjęcia brzytwomaczety Budnik pobladł, a Szacki zdumiał się, że to w ogóle możliwe przy jego kredowej cerze.

– Czy to...

– Proszę odpowiedzieć na pytanie.

– Nie, nie widziałem nigdy takiego narzędzia.

– Czy wie pan, do czego służy?

– Nie mam pojęcia.

Około szesnastej w słonecznym świetle w końcu pojawiła się jakaś nuta ciepła, nieśmiała zapowiedź wiosny. Prokurator Teodor Szacki wystawił twarz do słońca i popijał colę z puszki. Nie istniała dla niego inna cola.

Po przesłuchaniu Budnika spotkał się z Wilczurem, kazał znaleźć wszystkich, którzy mogli ich widzieć w Wielkanoc. W kościele, na spacerze, w knajpie. Każdy element przesłuchania musiał być potwierdzony, każdy znajomy odpytany. Kuzniecow dostałby palpitacji w połowie listy żądań, inspektor Wilczur tylko kiwał swoją wychudzoną głową, w czarnym garniturze wyglądał jak śmierć odbierająca zamówienie na żniwa. Szacki czuł się nieswojo w obecności starego policjanta.

Czekał teraz pod budynkiem policji na Sobieraj, żeby z nią odbyć romantyczny spacer do sandomierskiego szpitala. Swoją drogą, zdziwił się, że mają tutaj zakład patomorfologii, był pewien, że trzeba będzie jechać do Kielc albo Tarnobrzega.

Otworzył leniwie jedno oko, słysząc trąbienie. Sobieraj machała do niego z jakiejś bezosobowej fury. Westchnął i zwlókł się z ławki. Opel Astra.

– Myślałem, że się przejdziemy.

Czemu zawsze tak jest, że im mniejsza dziura, tym częściej wszyscy wszędzie jeżdżą samochodami?

– Trzy kwadranse w jedną stronę? Chyba nie mam ochoty. Nawet z panem, panie prokuratorze.

W trzy kwadranse to ja do Opatowa dojdę i każdą wieś po drodze zwiedzę – miał na końcu języka Szacki, ale wsiadł do auta. Samochód pachniał odświeżaczami powietrza i kosmetykami do plastiku, musiał mieć kilka lat, a wyglądał, jakby wczoraj wyjechał z salonu. Popielniczka była pusta, z głośników leciał jakiś smooth, nigdzie nie było żadnych okruszków i papierków. Czyli bezdzietna. Ale mężatka, za-obrączkowana, musiała mieć ze trzydzieści pięć lat. Nie chcą? Nie mogą?

– Dlaczego Budnikowie nie mogli mieć dzieci?

Spojrzała na niego podejrzliwie, włączając się do ruchu na Mickiewicza. Jechali w stronę wyjazdu na Warszawę.

– On nie mógł, prawda? – ponaglił Szacki.

– Prawda. Czemu pan pyta?

– Intuicja. Nie wiem dokładnie dlaczego, ale to istotne. Sposób, w jaki Budnik o tym wspomniał, niby mimochodem, niby lekko. Tak mówią mężczyźni, którzy tyle razy słyszeli, że to nieważne, że prawie uwierzyli.

Spojrzała na niego uważnie. Minęli budynek sądu.

– Mój mąż też nie może mieć dzieci. Też mu mówię, że to nie ma znaczenia, że liczą się inne rzeczy.

– A liczą się?

– Mniej.

Szacki milczał, objechali rondo i przejechali obok paskud-nego nowoczesnego kościoła, stosu czerwonej cegły ułożo-nego na kształt wrót piekieł, brzydkiego, przytłaczającego, kompletnie niepasującego do otoczenia i do miasta.

– Mam jedenastoletnią córkę. Mieszka w Warszawie z mamą. Mam wrażenie, że z dnia na dzień jest coraz bar-dziej obca, blaknie.

– I tak panu zazdroszczę.

Szacki milczał, spodziewał się wszystkiego, tylko nie takiej rozmowy. Dojechali do tak zwanej na wyrost obwodnicy, skręcili w stronę Wisły.

– Mieliśmy kiepski początek – powiedziała Sobieraj, cały czas nie odrywając wzroku od drogi. Szacki też na nią nie patrzył. – Myślałam o tym wczoraj, że jesteśmy więźniami stereotypów. Jestem dla pana głupią prowincjuszką, pan dla mnie aroganckim bucem z Warszawy. I oczywiście możemy w to grać dalej, tyle tylko, że ja naprawdę chcę znaleźć mor-dercę Eli.

Zjechała z obwodnicy w boczną uliczkę i zaparkowała pod zaskakująco wielkim budynkiem szpitala. Kształt litery L, sześć pięter, lata osiemdziesiąte. Lepiej niż myślał.

– Pan się może śmiać, że to małomiasteczkowa egzaltacja, ale ona była inna. Lepsza, jaśniejsza, czystsza, trudno mi to opisać. Znałam ją, znałam wszystkich, którzy ją znali, znam to miasto lepiej, niżbym chciała. A pan, cóż, nie czas na ściemy, wiem, ile razy panu proponowali przejście do okręgowej, do apelacyjnej, jaką przepowiadali karierę. Znam pańskie sprawy, znam opinie i legendy o białowłosym Teodorze Szackim, herosie Temidy.

W końcu spojrzeli na siebie. Szacki wyciągnął do niej rękę, którą Sobieraj delikatnie uścisnęła.

– Teodor.

– Baśka.

– Zaparkowałaś na miejscu dla niepełnosprawnych.

Sobieraj wyciągnęła z bocznej kieszeni drzwi tabliczkę z niebieskim logo, zaświadczającą inwalidztwo, i położyła na desce rozdzielczej.

– Serce. Dwa zawały. Pewnie i tak nie dałabym rady urodzić.

4

Artur Żmijewski powinien tu zamieszkać – powiedział Szacki, rozglądając się po zadbanej izbie przyjęć sandomierskiego szpitala. – Mógłby jeździć na rowerze ze swojej parafii prosto do Leśnej Góry.

– I tak tu bywa – odpowiedziała Sobieraj, prowadząc go schodami do piwnicy. – Jak kręcili *Ojca Mateusza,* to uchlał się tak, że wymagał hospitalizacji. Musieli mu wyrównać elektrolity. Znana sprawa, naprawdę nie słyszałeś?

74

Wykonał ręką nieokreślony gest. Co miał powiedzieć? Że nie słyszał, bo nie udzielał się towarzysko, że przeżywał w samotności swoją depresję? Zwekslował rozmowę na szpital. Naprawdę był zaskoczony, spodziewał się ponurego budynku śmierdzącego pleśnią, jakichś starych koszar w centrum, a ten co prawda czuć było latami osiemdziesiątymi, ale w środku zrobiony był już prawie na ładnie. Skromnie, miło, lekarze uśmiechnięci, pielęgniarki młode, jakby kręcili reklamówkę NFZ-etu. Nawet sala sekcyjna nie budziła obrzydzenia, do warszawskiej trupiarni zawalonej zwłokami miała się jak uroczy pensjonat do baraku w obozie pracy. Na jedynym stole leżały alabastrowe zwłoki Elżbiety Budnik.

Prokurator Teodor Szacki próbował myśleć o niej jako o żonie Budnika, ale nie potrafił. Nigdy nikomu się do tego nie przyznał, ale w obecności zwłok nie potrafił myśleć o nich jak o jeszcze do niedawna żywym człowieku, jedynie traktowanie ich jak kawałka mięsa pozwalało mu nie zwariować, choć ze śmiercią tak wiele miał do czynienia. Wiedział, że to samo działo się w głowach patologów.

Patrzył na niepokojąco białe zwłoki i oczywiście dostrzegał poszczególne elementy. Ciemnoblond włosy, lekko zadarty nos, wąskie usta. Była drobnej budowy, miała małe stopy, wąskie biodra o wystających kościach miednicy, niewielkie piersi. Pewnie wyglądałaby inaczej, gdyby urodziła dzieci. Czy była ładna? Nie miał pojęcia. Zwłoki zawsze są tylko zwłokami.

Jego wzrok nieustannie wracał do gardła wielokrotnie rozpłatanego nieomalże do kręgosłupa – zdaniem Żydów, pewnie też Arabów, to był najbardziej ludzki sposób zadania śmierci. Czy to znaczy, że nie cierpiała? Szczerze wątpił, humanitarność koszernych ubojni też do niego nie przemawiała.

Trzasnęły drzwi, Szacki odwrócił się i jakimś cudem udało mu się po pierwsze, nie zrobić zdziwionej miny, po drugie, nie cofnąć o krok. Ubrany w anatomiczny fartuch przybysz był przedstawicielem jakiejś humanoidalnej rasy olbrzymów. Dwa metry wzrostu, tyleż w barach, postura niedźwiedzia, dłońmi mógłby ładować węgiel do kotła szybciej niż łopatą. Do ogromnego ciała przytwierdzona była głowa, o dobrodusznej, zaróżowionej twarzy, słomkowe włosy upięte zostały z tyłu w małą kitkę. Rzeźnik z wielopokoleniowego rodu rzeźników, którzy w genach mają rąbanie półtuszy. Czyż mogło być dla niego lepsze miejsce?

Pokonując lęk, Szacki zrobił krok do przodu i wyciągnął rękę na powitanie.

– Teodor Szacki, prokuratura rejonowa.

Olbrzym uśmiechnął się sympatycznie i nieśmiało, zawijając dłoń Szackiego w ciepłą górę mięsa, którą miał przytwierdzoną do przedramienia.

– Paweł Rzeźnicki, bardzo mi przyjemnie. Basia o panu opowiadała.

Nie wiedział, czy to żart, więc na wszelki wypadek wziął to za dobrą monetę. Olbrzym wyciągnął z kieszeni fartucha gumowe rękawiczki i naciągnął je z trzaskiem, podchodząc do stołu. Prokuratorzy wycofali się na plastikowe krzesełka pod ścianę. Lekarz klasnął w dłonie, fala uderzeniowa sprawiła, że drzwi zadygotały.

– Kurczaki, z moimi dzieciakami właśnie przedstawienie robiła.

– Przykro mi, Pawle. Zawiozłabym ją gdzie indziej, ale do ciebie mam zaufanie. Jeśli to za trudne... Wiem, że znałeś Elę...

– To już nie Ela – odpowiedział Paweł, wciskając guzik dyktafonu. – Jest 16 kwietnia 2009 roku, oględziny zewnętrzne i otwarcie zwłok Elżbiety Budnik, lat czterdzieści cztery, przeprowadza Paweł Rzeźnicki, biegły w zakresie medycyny sądowej, w zakładzie anatomopatologii Samodzielnego Publicznego Zespołu Zakładów Opieki Zdrowotnej w Sandomierzu. Obecni prokuratorzy Barbara Sobieraj i Teodor Szacki. Oględziny zewnętrzne...

Na szczęście Rzeźnicki swoją posturą zasłaniał większość przeprowadzanych przez siebie czynności, Szacki i Sobieraj mogli pogrążyć się w rozmowie. Nie było sensu dręczyć olbrzyma, dopóki nie wiedział więcej niż oni. Szacki zrelacjonował Sobieraj swoją rozmowę z Budnikiem. Rzecz jasna, denatka nie dotarła do niej ani w poniedziałek, ani nigdy, ostatni kontakt miały ze sobą w niedzielę, kiedy składały sobie świąteczne życzenia przez telefon.

– Skąd wiedziałeś, że kłamie? Intuicja?

– Doświadczenie.

Potem opowiedziało swojej korespondencji ze „Sztychem". W miarę opowieści krew odpływała jej z twarzy, a oczy robiły się coraz większe.

– Powiedz, że żartujesz – wydusiła w końcu.

Zaprzeczył, zdziwiony jej reakcją.

– Nie masz pojęcia, co to znaczy, prawda? – musiała podnieść głos, w tle hałasowała piła, którą Rzeźnicki przecinał mostek.

– To znaczy, że ten, kto podrzucił ten nóż, miał nadzieję, że sprawa wycieknie do mediów i że rozpęta się tradycyjna polsko-żydowska histeria, a w histerii będzie nam trudniej pracować, bo więcej czasu będziemy spędzali na konferencjach prasowych niż na czynnościach. Spokojnie, nie przez takie burze przechodziłem. Media wszystkim się nudzą po trzech dniach.

Sobieraj słuchała go, jednocześnie kręcąc głową. Skrzywiła się, słysząc nieprzyjemne chrupnięcia. To Rzeźnik przecinał żebra denatki.

– To nie będzie zwykła histeria – powiedziała. – Tutaj tygodniami będą się kręcić dziennikarze. Sandomierz to centrum legendy o krwi, a historia stosunków polsko-żydowskich to na zmianę albo miła kohabitacja, albo oskarżenia i krwawe pogromy, ostatnie antysemickie zabójstwa zdarzyły się tu już po wojnie. Jeśli ktoś, nie daj Boże, użyje sformułowania „mord rytualny", to koniec.

– Mord rytualny to bajka – odpowiedział spokojnie Szacki. – I każdy wie, że to bajka, którą się opowiadało dzieciom, żeby były grzeczne, bo inaczej przyjdzie zły Żyd i je zje. Nie histeryzujmy.

– Nie taka bajka. Żyd to nie wilk i nie zła królowa, to prawdziwa osoba, do której można zgłosić pretensje. Wiesz, jak to wyglądało. Matka-chrześcijanka nie upilnowała dzieciaka, to dalej w krzyk, że Żydzi porwali, zabili. Od słowa do słowa się okazywało, że w sumie to mało kto tych Żydów lubi, ktoś im wisi kasę i skoro się znalazł taki pretekst, to nie byłoby źle puścić z dymem dzieciobójcom parę chałup i warsztatów.

– Dobrze, w takim razie nie bajka, ale zamierzchła historia. Żydów nie ma, warsztatów nie ma, oskarżać kogo nie ma, palić też nie. Ktoś, kto podrzucił tę brzytwę, zapewne bardzo chce, żebyśmy poszli tym tropem.

Sobieraj głośno westchnęła. W tle Rzeźnicki monotonnie dyktował do protokołu, że wszystkie kolejne narządy nie noszą znamion urazów ani zmian patologicznych.

– Obudź się, Teodorze. Sandomierz to jest wszechświatowa stolica mordu rytualnego. Miejsce, gdzie oskarżenia o porywanie dzieci i związane z tym pogromy były regularne jak pory roku. Miejsce, gdzie Kościół firmował to bestialstwo, nieomalże je zinstytucjonalizował. Miejsce, gdzie do dziś wisi w katedrze obraz przedstawiający mordowanie przez Żydów katolickich dzieci. Jako część cyklu o chrześcijańskim męczeństwie. Miejsce, gdzie zrobiono wszystko, aby tę część historii zamieść pod dywan. Teraz, jak o tym myślę, Boże, to wyjątkowo obrzydliwe...

Szacki patrzył na stół sekcyjny odsłonięty przez Rzeźnickiego, który na stoliku obok kroił narządy wewnętrzne Elżbiety Budnik. Nie użyłby słowa „obrzydliwe", obraz przed jego oczami – otwarte zwłoki ze zwisającą na boki skórą, z wystającymi z klatki piersiowej białymi końcówkami żeber – był okropny, ale nie obrzydliwy. Śmierć w jej ostateczności cechowała fizjologiczna elegancja. Spokój.

– Obrzydliwe, że ktoś próbuje to połączyć z Elą i Grześkiem.

Spojrzał pytająco.

– Grzesiek całe życie walczył z tym zabobonem, walczył, żeby mówić o tym w sposób właściwy, jako o czarnej karcie naszej historii, a nie swego rodzaju ekscentrycznej tradycji przodków. Długie lata próbował zdjąć obraz albo przynajmniej opatrzyć go odpowiednią tablicą, że zostaje tutaj jako memento polskiego antysemityzmu, przypomnienie, do czego może prowadzić nienawiść.

– I co?

– Kościół załatwia takie sprawy po swojemu. Ani nie zdjęli, ani tablicy nie powiesili. Jak się zrobiło za głośno, to zasłonili zasłonką, na zasłonce powiesili portret papieża i udają, że nie ma sprawy. Gdyby to nie był obraz, tylko mozaika na posadzce, pewnie przykryliby dywanem.

– Bardzo ciekawe, ale to wszystko nie ma znaczenia. Ktoś, kto podrzucił rytualny nóż, chce, żebyśmy się tym zajęli. Obrazami, historiami, legendami, żebyśmy zaczęli łazić po kościołach, siedzieć w czytelniach i rozmawiać z naukowcami. To ściema. Nie mam wątpliwości. Martwi mnie jedynie, że to dobrze przygotowana ściema. Że jeśli ktoś zadaje sobie tyle trudu, żeby wpuścić nas w te koleiny, może być za mądry, żeby ta sprawa w ogóle została rozwiązana.

Rzeźnicki podszedł do nich, w swojej gigadłoni miał plastikową torebkę z małym metalowym przedmiotem. Jego fartuch był zaskakująco czysty, nieomalże bez śladów krwi.

– Mój asystent ją zszyje. Chodźmy pogadać.

Pili kawę z plastikowych kubków. Była tak wstrętna, że koniec końców wszyscy pacjenci musieli tutaj trafiać na gastrologię. Szacki był tego pewien. Rzeźnik – okazało się, że naprawdę ma taką ksywkę, bardzo zaskakujące – przebrał się, w szarym golfie wyglądał jak wielki głaz z różową piłką na szczycie.

– Wszystko wam dokładnie opiszę, ale sprawa jest praktycznie ewidentna. Ktoś jej poderżnął gardło bardzo ostrym, chirurgicznym wręcz narzędziem. Jednak nie skalpelem i nie żyletką, ponieważ cięcia są za głębokie. Wielka brzytwa, którą mi pokazaliście na zdjęciach, nadałaby się doskonale. To wszystko się stało, kiedy jeszcze żyła, ale musiała być nieprzytomna, inaczej broniłaby się, nie wyglądałoby to tak – przez chwilę szukał słowa – precyzyjnie. A niewątpliwie jeszcze żyła, ponieważ nie ma w niej krwi. Przepraszam za szczegóły, ale to oznacza, że w momencie przecięcia tętnicy szyjnej w układzie krwionośnym jeszcze przez chwilę było ciśnienie, zdolne wypompować krew z organizmu. Ma też zastygłą krew w uszach, co zapewne oznacza, że w momencie śmierci wisiała do góry nogami, jak – przez twarz Rzeźnika przebiegł bolesny wyraz – jak, za przeproszeniem, krowa w ubojni, co za pieprzony zwyrodnialec musiał to zrobić. Zadał też sobie trud, żeby ją umyć, była zapewne cała we krwi.

– Musimy szukać krwi – pomyślał na głos Szacki.

– Musicie też dowiedzieć się, co to jest – powiedział Rzeźnik, podając im foliową torebkę na dowody. Szacki przyjrzał się uważnie, przełknął ślinę, od torebki bił mięsny zapaszek prosektorium. W środku był metalowy znaczek o przekątnej około centymetra, taki, jakie się nosi w bluzie albo klapie marynarki. Nie z agrafką, lecz z grubym sztyftem, na który od wewnątrz trzeba nakręcić docisk. Wyglądał staro. Sobieraj nachyliła się, żeby obejrzeć dowód, jej rude włosy połaskotały Szackiego w policzek. Pachniały rumiankiem. Prokurator spojrzał na jej zmarszczone w skupieniu czoło, na gęste piegi, którym udało się wydostać na wolność spod warstwy makijażu. Było w tym widoku coś, co go rozczuliło. Ruda dziewczynka, która dorosła, dojrzała, ale ciągle chce ukryć piegi na nosie.

– Gdzieś to widziałam – powiedziała. – Nie wiem gdzie, ale na pewno widziałam.

Znaczek był czerwony, prostokątny. Bez żadnych napisów, jedynie biały, geometryczny symbol. Wyglądał jak wydłużona litera S, tyle tylko, że bardzo zgeometryzowana, dwa krótsze odcinki przylegały do dłuższego pod kątem prostym, wyglądało to idealnie jak połówka swastyki. Od dolnego, krótszego końca dodatkowo odchodził w górę mały dzyndzel.

– Miała to w zaciśniętej dłoni. Musiałem połamać jej palce, żeby to wyciągnąć – powiedział Rzeźnik jakby do siebie, łagodne spojrzenie niebieskich oczu zawisło na jakimś punkcie za oknem, być może na jednej z zabytkowych wież Sandomierza.

Szacki za to patrzył na sympatyczny profil piczki-zasadniczki Sobieraj, na kurze łapki koło jej oczu, na mimiczne zmarszczki w kącikach ust, które mówiły, że dużo się uśmiechała i miała dobre życie. I zastanawiał się, dlaczego Budnik nie chciał, żeby przesłuchiwała go Sobieraj. Bo nie chciał, żeby jej było ciężko? Bzdura. Nie chciał, żeby coś zauważyła. Tylko co?

5

Kiedy w świetle jarzeniówek sandomierskiego prosektorium asystent Rzeźnika wkładał zmięte gazety do białego trupa najbardziej przez wszystkich ukochanej obywatelki Sandomierza, prokuratorzy Teodor Szacki i Barbara Sobieraj siedzieli na kanapie w gabinecie swojej szefowej i zjadali po trzecim kawałku murzynka, choć nie mieli ochoty nawet na drugi.

Opowiedzieli jej o przesłuchaniu Budnika, o sekcji, o znaczku z dziwnym symbolem, o nożu, który – być może – był narzędziem do rytualnego uboju. Misia wysłuchała ich z matczynym uśmiechem, nie przerywała, czasami coś wtrąciła, żeby pomóc im w relacji, jak wzorowa absolwentka kursu aktywnego słuchania. Skończyli, a ona zapaliła zapachową świeczkę, aromat wanilii rozszedł się po gabinecie, razem z zapadającym za oknem zmierzchem i bursztynowym światłem lampy na biurku stworzyło to miłą, świąteczną atmosferę.

Szacki nabrał ochoty na herbatę z sokiem malinowym, ale nie był pewien, czy mimo wszystko nie przegnie, jeśli o nią poprosi.

– Czas śmierci? – zapytała Miszczyk, wyciągając okruchy z miękkiego, zużytego zapewne przez kilkoro dzieci dekoltu. Szacki twardo patrzył jej w oczy.

– Z tym jest pewien problem, widełki są dość duże – odpowiedział. – Na pewno więcej niż pięć–sześć godzin, biorąc pod uwagę stężenie pośmiertne, czyli zamordowano ją najpóźniej we wtorek około północy. A najwcześniej? Patolog twierdzi, że mogła być martwa nawet od Wielkiego Poniedziałku. Krew ze zwłok została spuszczona, czyli nie można wnioskować na podstawie plam opadowych. Zimno było jak diabli, więc żadne procesy gnilne się nie zaczęły. Będziemy wiedzieli więcej, jeśli się okaże, że ktoś ją widział.

Na razie w grę wchodzi okres od opuszczenia domu w poniedziałek do północy następnego dnia. Oczywiście zakładając, że Budnik mówi prawdę. Równie dobrze może być martwa od niedzieli.

– A mówi?

– Nie. Nie wiem, kiedy dokładnie nie mówi prawdy, ale na pewno nie mówi. Jest pod stałą obserwacją, zobaczymy, co wyjdzie z przeszukania domu i posesji. Na razie jest głównym podejrzanym. Okłamał nas, nie ma alibi. Może i ona była święta, ale podobno nie działo się między nimi najlepiej.

– Ludzie zawsze tak gadają, jak komuś się układa – zaprotestowała Sobieraj.

– W każdym gadaniu jest ziarno prawdy – zripostował Szacki.

– A inne wersje?

Sobieraj sięgnęła do swoich papierów.

– Wykluczamy wstępnie mord na tle rabunkowym i seksualnym. Nie ma śladów gwałtu, na napad to za bardzo wydumane. Sprawdzam wszystkich, z którymi robiła wspólne akcje, rodzinę, znajome środowisko artystyczne. Zwłaszcza to ostatnie, Ela była związana z teatrem, a przyznacie, że ma to w sobie coś z przedstawienia.

– Fałsz – skomentował Szacki. – Ale to na razie drugorzędne. Przede wszystkim szukamy krwi. Musimy znaleźć ślady tych kilku litrów, które z niej wypłynęły. Policja będzie przetrząsać miejsca publiczne w mieście i pod miastem, także każdy prywatny lokal, który pojawi się w śledztwie, będzie sprawdzany pod tym kątem.

– Skoro mówimy o krwi – Miszczyk zawiesiła głos i westchnęła, poruszenie tego tematu przyszło jej z trudem – co z wątkiem mordu rytualnego?

– Oczywiście zgarniamy wszystkich Żydów z okolicy – powiedział z kamienną twarzą Szacki.

– Teodor żartuje – szybko wtrąciła Sobieraj, zanim wybrzmiała ostatnia głoska ze zdania Szackiego.

- W życiu bym nie przypuszczała. Że tak szybko przejdziecie na ty. Macie całkowity zakaz rozmów z prasą na temat śledztwa, zwłaszcza prokurator Żartowniś, wszystkich odsyłacie do mnie. Ja się postaram, żeby to śmierdzące jajo się nie stłukło.

Szacki miał wyrobione zdanie na ten temat, nie po to ktoś zadał sobie tyle zachodu, żeby to nie wypłynęło. Postawiłby duże pieniądze, że rano trudno się tu będzie przepchać między wozami transmisyjnymi. Ale skoro Miszczyk bierze prasę na siebie, cóż, nie jego cyrk, nie jego małpy. Zachował te przemyślenia dla siebie, podobnie jak te, że pani prokurator rejonowa właśnie wpisała się w wielowiekową polską tradycję zamiatania pod dywan. W Kościele zrobiłaby błyskawiczną karierę.

6

Być może było tak dlatego, że Oleg Kuzniecow był zupełnie inny. Zwalisty, rubaszny, jowialny, próbujący w każdym zdaniu zawrzeć jakiś głupi dowcip. Być może było to kwestią tego, że z Kuzniecowem przez lata się znali, że razem pracowali, razem pili, razem spotykali się po domach. A być może było to kwestią tego, że Kuzniecow był jego prawdziwym przyjacielem i że prokurator Teodor Szacki kochał go jak brata. I z tego powodu nie potrafił, nie mógł, nie chciał polubić inspektora Leona Wilczura.

Inna sprawa, że inspektor Wilczur słabo nadawał się do lubienia. Umówił się z nim w Ratuszowej, potwornej mordowni w suterenie kamienicy przy rynku, śmierdzącej szlugami, które przez dekady wsiąkały tu w każdy element wystroju, pełnej dziwnego typu klientów i dziwnych kelnerów. Szacki był pewien, że na zapleczu dziwni kucharze dziwnie preparują dziwne mięso, dlatego ograniczył się do kawy i sernika. Sernik czuć było starą kanapą, na której każdy siada, a której się nikomu nie chce uprać. Kawa była sypana. Wilczur wyglądał jak demon. W półmroku, w papierosowym dymie, jego głęboko osadzone żółte oczy świeciły chorobliwie, ostry nos rzucał cień na pół twarzy, policzki się zapadały przy każdym chciwym zaciągnięciu się papierosem.

– Panowie, może po kieliszeczku? – Ton kelnera był grobowy, jakby chodziło o kieliszeczek świeżej krwi.

Odmówili. Wilczur zaczekał, aż kelner odejdzie, potem zaczął mówić, co jakiś czas zaglądając do leżących przed nim papierów albo do małego laptopa. Który na początku zadziwił Szackiego. Inspektor wyglądał raczej na typ człowieka, któremu należałoby oszczędzić tortury tłumaczenia, czym są esemesy.

– Znamy wersję Budnika, możemy ją teraz uzupełnić o różne zeznania. W niedzielę na pewno byli w katedrze około osiemnastej, na pewno wyszli przed mszą, która zaczyna się o siódmej. Mamy na to dwóch niezależnych świadków. Potem byli na spacerze, kwadrans po siódmej złapała ich kamera na Mariackiej.

Wilczur obrócił komputer. Na krótkim nagraniu widać było niewyraźne sylwetki idącej pod rękę pary. Szacki powiększył obraz, pierwszy raz mógł zobaczyć Elżbietę Budnik żywą. Była tego samego wzrostu, co jej mąż, ciemnoblond włosy rozsypywały się po sportowej kurtce, nie miała czapki ani kapelusza. Musiała coś opowiadać, jedną ręką gwałtownie gestykulowała, w pewnej chwili zatrzymała się, żeby poprawić cholewkę kozaczka, przez ten czas Budnik przeszedł kilka kroków. Dogoniła go w trzech małych podskokach, jak dziewczynka, a nie dojrzała kobieta. Przy ubranym w brązową jesionkę i filcową czapkę poważnym Budniku wyglądała jak jego córka, a nie żona. Zrównała się z mężem na granicy widzenia kamery, wsunęła mu rękę do kieszeni. Potem zniknęli.

– Wszystko w porządku, prawda? – Wilczur oderwał filtr od kolejnego papierosa.

Szacki wiedział, o co mu chodzi. Nie było widać między nimi napięcia, kłótni ani upartego milczenia. Ot, para na spacerze w wielkanocny wieczór. To świadczyło na korzyść wersji Budnika, że spędzali jak zwykle święta, poprztykali się, ona wyszła i... i właśnie, i co?

– Nie złapała jej ta kamera w poniedziałek albo wtorek? – zapytał.

– Nie, posadziłem dwójkę ludzi, żeby przejrzeli od tego momentu do znalezienia zwłok wczoraj rano. Każdą minutę. Nie ma jej. Sprawdziliśmy tę kamerę i drugą przy zamku, jeśli chce się wyjść z Katedralnej do miasta, trzeba przejść obok jednej z nich. Inna droga to tylko przez krzaki albo przez mur i ogród katedry w stronę Wisły.

– Sąsiedzi?

– Zero. Ale proszę spojrzeć na to.

Drugie nagranie było z kamery na rynku, obejmującej fragment knajpianej pierzei, przy której mieściły się Ciżemka, Staromiejska, Trzydziestka i ta kawiarnia, co to Szacki zapomniał, jak się nazywa, bo nigdy do niej nie zaglądał. Cyferki pokazywały, że był wtorek, godzina szesnasta z minutami. Nic się nie działo, kręcili się pojedynczy przechodnie. Otworzyły się drzwi do Trzydziestki i wyszedł z nich Budnik, w przezroczystej foliowej torebce miał dwa „laptopy" – styropianowe pojemniki na jedzenie. Energicznie ruszył w stronę Mariackiej, szybko wyszedł z pola widzenia kamery.

Szacki doskonale wiedział, dlaczego Wilczur pokazał mu ten film.

– Ciekawe, prawda? – stary policjant odchylił się na krześle, wciskając się tak daleko w ciemny kąt pomieszczenia, że częściowo musiał już być na następnej posesji.

– Bardzo. Bo jeśli prawdą jest wersja, że żona opuściła Budnika w poniedziałek...

– To po co niósł jej obiad we wtorek?

– Co by się, owszem, zgadzało, ale z jego pierwszą wersją, absolutnie nieprawdopodobną, którą nawet on porzucił. Wilczur pokiwał głową – w mroku ruszał się wystający, blady nos. Szacki myślał. Wypalił dziś tylko jednego papierosa, więc zostały mu jeszcze dwa. Intuicja mówiła, że warto je sobie zachować na spotkanie z Tatarską, poza tym przez sam pobyt w tym pomieszczeniu wypalił półtorej paczki. Mimo to wyjął papierosa, Wilczur podał mu ogień. Nawet jeśli był zaskoczony, że prokurator w ogóle pali, nie dał tego po sobie poznać. Milczał, kiedy Szacki układał w głowie możliwe scenariusze. Puzzle wirowały w jego wyobraźni, ale każdy z innego kompletu, czuł, że dopasowuje je na siłę.

Jeszcze w niedzielę byli razem. Potem on pojawia się we wtorek w knajpie i kupuje dwa obiady. A ona – dopiero w środę, jako alabastrowe zwłoki w krzakach koło starej synagogi. Co się wydarzyło?

Załóżmy, że faktycznie pokłócili się w poniedziałek. Ona wyszła, wściekła ruszyła przez pola w kierunku Wisły, niezauważona przez kamery. Tam dorwał ją tajemniczy szaleniec, zamordował. Tylko dlaczego w takim razie Budnik następnego dnia kupił dwa obiady? Dlaczego na ciele denatki nie ma żadnych śladów walki, ucieczki, nie ma śladu po uderzeniu?

Załóżmy, że pokłócili się w poniedziałek tak bardzo, że Budnik zatłukł swoją żonę. Wróć, na ciele nie ma śladów. Załóżmy, że pokłócili się bardzo, wieczorem przycisnął ją poduszką. W piwnicy zamordował, spuścił krew. Wróć, nigdzie w domu nie ma śladów krwi. W takim razie wywiózł w ustronne miejsce, tam zamordował, wróć, kamery nie odnotowały, żeby Budnik wyjeżdżał samochodem. Wyniósł szczelnie zawiniętą – bo znowu nie ma śladów – przez krzaki w ustronne miejsce, zamordował, spuścił krew. Dla niepoznaki, że niby wszystko normalnie, poszedł we wtorek do biura, wziął dwa obiady, żeby mieć alibi. W nocy, znowu przez krzaki, zaciągnął ją na drugi koniec starówki, zostawił. Czy to brzmi wiarygodnie? Absolutnie, po tysiąckroć nie.

To może załóżmy, że miał plan przygotowany od dawna. Że miał motyw, o którym na razie nic nie wiedzą. Pracuje w urzędzie, zna system bezpieczeństwa, układ kamer. Przedefilował w niedzielę przed kamerą, potem wyciągnął ją na spacer w jakieś miejsce w pobliżu tego, gdzie znaleziono zwłoki. Żeby nie trzeba było ciągać trupa przez całe miasto. Ogłuszył, zamordował, wykrwawił. Jak było po wszystkim, podrzucił.

– Jak by nie patrzył, gówno widać, co nie? – zaskrzypiał Wilczur ze swojej ciemności.

Szacki przytaknął. Niestety, nie było widać motywów ani dowodów, a narzędzie zbrodni okazało się sterylne jak przygotowane do operacji narzędzie chirurgiczne.

– To jeszcze jeden odcinek – Wilczur podsunął prokuratorowi laptopa.

Obraz na ekranie był kompletnie biały, kontury kamienic tak blade, że praktycznie niewidoczne, Szackiemu przypomniało się Silent Hill.

– Gdzie to jest?

– Żydowska. Kamera wisi na ścianie synagogi – Szacki odnotował, że Wilczur nie użył słowa „archiwum" – ustawiona w stronę zamku. Po prawej jest parking, za parkingiem krzaki, w których znaleźli Budnikową. Nagranie ze środy rano, kilka minut wcześniej, zanim dostaliśmy zgłoszenie. Proszę patrzeć.

Szacki patrzył, mijały sekundy, minuty, cienka mgła troszkę zrzedła, przejaśniło się, widać było już, że kamera wisi nad ulicą, a nie jest zanurzona w misce z mlekiem. Nagle na dole ekranu pojawiło się czarne półkole, Szacki się wzdrygnął. Półkole ruszyło do przodu w dół ulicy, w miarę jak oddalało się od kamery, okazywało się, że półkole to tak naprawdę górna część kapelusza o kształcie melonika, tylko z bardzo szerokim rondem. Pod kapeluszem znajdował się sięgający ziemi czarny płaszcz, na tyle długi, że nie było widać nóg ani butów. Efekt był upiorny, czarna zjawa w kapeluszu lewitowała przez moment w szarym mleku, by po chwili zniknąć zupełnie. Szacki cofnął obraz, wcisnął pauzę. Bardzo chciał, żeby kojarzyło mu się to z czymś innym, ale nie było rady – we mgle zakrywającej ulicę Żydowską w Sandomierzu płynęła zjawa chasyda.

Spojrzał na Wilczura.

– Pan wie oczywiście, co tam było w tych krzakach, gdzie znaleźli Budnikową – zaskrzypiał policjant.

– Mury miejskie?

– Po pierwsze, wyżej, po drugie, dawno i nieprawda. Kirkut. Jej trup leżał dokładnie pośrodku starego cmentarza żydowskiego.

Zimne wieczorne powietrze było jak lekarstwo, antidotum na Ratuszową. Szacki odetchnął pełną piersią, Wilczur obwiązał szyję szalikiem i zapalił papierosa. Z tyłu trzasnęły drzwi, jeden z meneli wyszedł i teraz patrzył niepewnie.

– Panie władzo...

– Dajcie mi spokój, Gąsiorowski. Który to już raz? I zawsze się tak samo kończy, prawda?

– No wiem, panie władzo, ale...

– Ale co?

– Ale to już tydzień, jak Anatola nie ma.

– Gąsiorowski, zlitujże się nad nami. Policja przegania włóczęgów, nie szuka. A już na pewno nie takich z innego powiatu.

– Ale...

– Ale nie ma o czym mówić, do widzenia.

Menel schował się za drzwiami, Szacki spojrzał pytająco. Wilczur nie kwapił się z wyjaśnieniami, a on uznał, że nie musi znać wszystkich bolączek prowincjonalnej policji. Pożegnali się zdawkowo.

– Musimy się dowiedzieć, gdzie jest krew Elżbiety – powiedział Szacki, zapinając kołnierz płaszcza. Znowu było lodowato.

– W macy – mruknął Wilczur i rozpłynął się w ciemnościach.

7

Okna były pootwierane, szedł z nich niewielki chłodek i zapach nocy. Rogi jelenie spały na ścianach, a pod stolikami, na wieszakach i na lustrach czaiły się niebieskie plamy. Twarz w lustrze zamajaczyła jak na dnie jeziora. Wie, że nie może tutaj zostać, z każdym drgnieniem wskazówek zegara w przedpokoju ryzykuje bardziej, całe ciało wbrew rozumowi rwie się do ucieczki. Mimo to musi wytrzymać do soboty. Jeśli wytrzyma do soboty, jeśli do niedzieli nic się nie wydarzy, jeśli w niedzielę wieczorem będzie na wolności – to naprawdę ta Niedziela Miłosierdzia Bożego zasłuży na swoją nazwę.

8

Kupno porządnej butelki wina na najpiękniejszej polskiej starówce okazało się niewykonalne. W zapyziałych sklepach były tylko jakieś dziwne kwasy i w końcu uznał, że najszybciej będzie zbiec schodami ze skarpy i kupić butelkę frontery w Orlenie przy obwodnicy. Jak pomyślał, tak zrobił, chciał przy okazji kupić pudełko z torcikiem wedlowskim, co wydało mu się sympatycznym warszawskim upominkiem, niestety torcika nie było, wziął więc jakąś bombonierkę, która wręcz wyła, że kupiono ją na stacji benzynowej, i pudełko prezerwatyw. Wrócił na górę, starając się nie spocić za bardzo, ponieważ intuicja mówiła mu, że jeszcze dziś wystąpi bez ubrania. Druga półkula, ta racjonalna, tłumaczyła, że intuicja zawsze to podpowiada każdemu facetowi i że często się to nie sprawdza, ale i tak pilnował, żeby nie podbiegać.

Teraz stał w salonie sędzi Marysi Tatarskiej w jej domu na Żeromskiego i się dziwił. Bardzo się dziwił.

Wystrojowi wnętrza, to raz. Zrozumiał już, że brak, który odczuwa, odwiedzając sandomierskie mieszkania, to brak Ikei. W Warszawie nie do pomyślenia było, żeby przeciętne mieszkanie przedstawicieli klasy średniej nie miało przynajmniej połowy wystroju ze szwedzkiej firmy. Tutaj w lepszych domach obowiązywał styl krakowsko-mieszczański, czyli mnóstwo tkanin z ilością kurzu zdolną zamordować alergika, kredensy i mętne lustra. Zamożniejsi mieszkańcy bez rodowodu mieszkali w willach o wystroju boazeryjno-wypoczynkowym. Biedota to mieszkania w blokach, a w nich brązowe meblościanki i mebelki przywleczone z targowicy. Po Tatarskiej spodziewał się zakurzonego mieszczaństwa, ewentualnie pastelowej nowoczesności, podrabianej Ikei. A zobaczył... hmm, było w tym pomieszczeniu coś z sali szpitalnej. Biel, chrom, lustra i szkło. Salon był biały, bez żadnej przenośni biały, do tego stopnia biały, że książki na kilku półkach pieczołowicie obłożono w biały papier, na którym ręcznie wypisano tytuły i autorów.

Wystrojowi gospodyni, to dwa. Sędzia Maria Tatarska miała na sobie prostą, czerwoną koktajlową sukienkę i czerwone szpilki. Nie żeby spodziewał się zobaczyć ją w polarze i japonkach, ale jej strój był zbyt wystawny na niezobowiązujący wieczór przy winie. W białym wnętrzu wyglądała jak plama krwi, być może efekt był zamierzony. Szacki w duchu wzruszył ramionami, świadom, że go obserwuje. Lubił normalnie i zwyczajnie, efekciarstwo nie robiło na nim wrażenia, co najwyżej wywoływało żal, że są osoby zdolne włożyć tyle czasu i wysiłku w sprawy nieistotne.

Wystrojowi podwórka, to trzy. Tak, przede wszystkim wystrojowi podwórka, ponieważ ogródek sędzi Marii Tatarskiej był cmentarzem. Nie w przenośni, dosłownie. Szacki zawsze oglądał go od drugiej strony, od głównego wejścia, przechodząc lub przejeżdżając ulicą Mickiewicza. Piękna, zadrzewiona nekropolia rozciągała się prawie do położonej niżej ulicy Żeromskiego. Gdzie stały różne warsztaty kamieniarskie i dom sędzi Tatarskiej. Salon na piętrze znajdował się ciut powyżej poziomu nagrobków, tuż przy murze. Wystarczyło bijące z domu światło, żeby Szacki mógł się zabawiać czytaniem wyrytych w kamieniu nazwisk. Z niepokojem zauważył, że było tam troje czterdziestolatków. Równo czterdziestolatków. A jemu zostało kilka miesięcy do urodzin.

Odwrócił się, sędzia siedziała na kanapie z kieliszkiem wina w dłoni, biel i czerwień z trupami w tle, jakże to narodowe, pomyślał Szacki.

– Memento mori – powiedziała, stopę w czerwonej szpilce postawiła na kanapie. Nie miała majtek.

Rozdział trzeci

piątek, 17 kwietnia 2009

Dla katolików szósty dzień Oktawy Wielkanocnej, chrześcijanie prawosławni obchodzą Wielki Piątek, Żydzi zaczynają szabat o zachodzie słońca, w Sandomierzu to 18.31. Według hipotezy Molnara mija dokładnie 2015 lat od narodzin Jezusa, świeczki na torcie dmuchają też Jan Borysewicz, Apoloniusz Tajner i Victoria Beckham. W Polsce nudy, premier zyskuje poparcie, rząd traci poparcie, prezydent traci poparcie. Wałęsa przysięga, że nie był agentem i niech go szlag trafi, jeśli kłamie. Na świecie Biały Dom ujawnia, że Bush pozwalał torturować więźniów, UE donosi, że liczba udanych i nieudanych ataków terrorystycznych spada, szkocka policja dzieli się informacją, że pracuje w niej dziesięciu wyznawców jedi, a Watykan wyraża ubolewanie, że rząd Belgii krytykuje Benedykta XVI za krytykę stosowania prezerwatyw. W kinach premierę mają *Vicky Cristina Barcelona* Woody'ego Allena i niedoceniony *Generał Nil* ze świetną rolą Olgierda Łukaszewicza w roli Fieldorfa. Legia wygrywa w Gliwicach z Piastem 1:0 i zostaje liderem ekstraklasy. W powietrzu czuć wiosnę, w Sandomierzu maksymalna temperatura dochodzi do 20 stopni, niestety, to nie zasługa słońca, jest pochmurno i leje.

1

Prokurator Teodor Szacki odebrał klasyczne wykształcenie i wiedział, że Eros z Tanatosem od zawsze chodzą pod rękę, znał legendę Tristana i Izoldy, czytał Morsztyna, *Brzezinę* i *Kochanków z Marony*, był nawet okres, kiedy nie zasnął, dopóki nie wsączył w siebie paru kropel erotycznego przygnębienia Iwaszkiewicza. Ale nigdy te dwa pierwiastki nie połączyły się w jego życiu tak dosłownie i w sposób tak przejmujący. Obudził się z posmakiem winnego kaca na języku i zanim zdał sobie sprawę, gdzie jest, poczuł, że do świadomości przywróciło go nie pragnienie, lecz nieznośny, pulsujący ból członka. W miarę odzyskiwania świadomości, powracały wspomnienia wczorajszego wieczoru, kiedy to Tatarska wymęczyła go na sposoby, których wcześniej nie widział nawet na pornosach. Głupio mu było się ulotnić, bo najwidoczniej ona dużo sobie obiecywała, a on nie chciał wyjść na chama, dlatego brał udział bez specjalnego zaangażowania w kolejnych erotycznych ćwiczeniach, z których połowa była tandetna, połowa zwyczajnie głupia, a wszystkie jednakowo wyczerpujące. Opisane byłyby seksprzygodą, o której się opowiada przez lata, przez dekady wspomina. W rzeczywistości Szacki chciał jak najszybciej zapomnieć o tym incydencie. Bardzo potrzebował prysznica.

Otworzył oko, bojąc się, że zobaczy czyhające na jego przytomność sędziowskie ciało i – po raz kolejny w czasie tej wizyty – się zdumiał. Pół metra od nosa miał szybę, metr za szybą mokrą lastrykową płytę, na której napisane było: „Czuwajcie więc, bo nie znacie dnia ani godziny". Szacki zamknął oko, nie chciał myśleć o tym, że obudził się po zwierzęcych perwersjach na nagrobku z ewangelicznym cytatem z przypowieści o pannach roztropnych i nieroztropnych, o ile dobrze pamiętał. Jak bardzo by chciał być wczoraj panną nieroztropną, przed którą zamknięto drzwi, nie wpuszczono jej na imprezę, żeby mu wczoraj sędzia Tatarska powiedziała „zaprawdę nie znam cię" i odprawiła. Odwrócił się tyłem do zwłok pięćdziesięciodwuletniego Mariusza Wypycha i strzegącego go cytatu z Ewangelii świętego Mateusza. Po drugiej stronie, we wnętrzu było niewiele lepiej, sędzia Tatarska pochrapywała na wznak, usta miała otwarte, twarz błyszczącą i spuchniętą, obfite piersi wlały jej się pod pachy. W świetle kwietniowego dnia jej salon nie był już śnieżnobiały, co najwyżej spranoszarawy. Szacki spojrzał na zegar, zaklął i czym prędzej ewakuował się z pogrzebowego domu rozpusty.

Półtorej godziny później, umyty i wykąpany, siedział już w prokuraturze i miał nadzieję, że szczypanie przy sikaniu to po prostu kwestia otarcia, a nie jakiejś tajemniczej infekcji. Dziwnie pewien, że ma na twarzy wypisaną każdą czynność minionej nocy, zamknął drzwi od gabinetu i zagrzebał się w świecie symboli. Po godzinie wiedział już, że z symbolami jest gorzej niż z nożami – liczba znaków graficznych, stowarzyszeń, mnogość logo, poświęconych im stron internetowych – było tego milion. Postanowił usystematyzować poszukiwania.

Zaczął oczywiście od żydowskich i szybko się rozczarował, ponieważ wiele tego nie było. Gwiazda Dawida, menora, zwoje Tory, Tablice Przymierza, zaskakująco – ręka Fatimy. Zawsze kojarzył ten symbol z Arabami, okazało się, że to też żydowski amulet. Widać z kulturami jak z małżonkami, im bardziej podobne, tym bardziej skaczą sobie do gardeł. Szackiemu przypomniało się, jak kiedyś w Warszawie w sklepie halal nazwał przez przypadek jagnięcinę koszerną. Właściciel mało się nie wysadził z wściekłości. Szacki przejrzał dokładnie litery hebrajskiego alfabetu, ale nie znalazł niczego podobnego. Lektura dotycząca Kabały była interesująca, ale na żadnym z rysunków, schematów, w żadnym z mistycznych pism nie znalazł nic, co by w zbliżonej choć formie przypominało leżący przed nim znaczek.

Bezskuteczne badanie żydowskich sekt zaprowadziło go do chrześcijaństwa. Przez chrześcijaństwo doszedł do krzyża we wszystkich jego tysiącach odmian, przez moment sądził, że może to jakaś wariacja na temat krzyża prawosławnego, symbol jego połówki, jakiś zakon – ale nie, nic z tych rzeczy.

Od krzyża doszedł do swastyki. Starożytny znak występował w wielu odmianach, przyjrzał się każdej, jako że znaczek trzymany przez Budnikową wyglądał wypisz, wymaluj jak połowa symbolu nazistowskiego z dzyndzlem na dole. Przy okazji zmarnował kilka minut na oglądanie zdjęć bengalskiej aktorki Swastiki Mukherjee, o wyjątkowo apetycznej urodzie. Co prawda rano ślubował, że już nigdy nie będzie uprawiał seksu, ale dla niej zrobiłby wyjątek. Zdziwił się, jak wiele polskich organizacji korzystało kiedyś z emblematu swastyki, zanim stała się symbolem Hitlera i jego pomysłów na aryjski ład. Zwłaszcza na Podhalu był to popularny talizman, obecnie albo wstydliwie zakrywany, albo – jak w schronisku na Hali Gąsienicowej – opatrywany odpowiednimi wyjaśnieniami, żeby żaden turysta nie omdlał z oburzenia. Tradycyjnie polska, słowiańska swastyka zwana była swargą lub swarzycą. Tym tropem doszedł do symboli słowiańskich, mozolnie przeglądał znaczki, które pojawiały się na przykład na wyrobach garncarskich z czasów przedchrześcijańskich, ryty rzeźby płaskiej, nalepki na ciasta obrzędowe, znaki z pisanek i hafty. I co? I nic.

Serce zadrżało mu żwawiej, kiedy przypomniał sobie o masonach (nic) i kiedy zagłębił się w kipiący od symboli świat okultyzmu, satanizmu oraz tym podobnych bzdur, których adepci lubią sobie wytatuować coś na tyłku albo naszyć na kurtkę. Też nic.

Odchylił się na krześle, bolała go głowa od kaca i ślepienia w komputer. To wyglądało jak żart, jakby ktoś zadał sobie trud przetrząśnięcia wszystkich symboli świata, aby stworzyć logo niepodobne do niczego. Musiał pomyśleć. Gapił się w monitor, na którym w kilku różnych oknach tłoczyły się odwrócone gwiazdy, szatańskie mordy i wykresy zaświadczające, że pentagram jest wpisany w plan ulic miasta Waszyngton. Był też alfabet runiczny, który przykuł uwagę Szackiego. Przeciągnął się i zagłębił w nowe symbole. Poznał runy wymyślone przez Tolkiena dla *Władcy Pierścieni*, poznał różnice między poszczególnymi formami tego starogermańskiego alfabetu i w końcu odniósł – fakt, że połowiczny – sukces. Gdyby w jego symbolu zamazać dzyndzel, wyglądałby on jak runa eiwaz. Runa magnetyczna, oznaczająca cis, będąca symbolem przemiany, odpowiadająca znakowi wodnika, doskonały amulet dla przewodnika duchowego, urzędnika państwowego i strażaka. Nawet katoliccy święci nie mieli tak szerokiego spektrum działania. Tylko co z tego wynika? Absolutnie nic, mielizna, marnacja czasu. No i nie ma dzyndzla.

Wściekły wstał z krzesła. Chciało mu się spać, bolała go głowa i członek, w ustach miał kapeć po winie, w mózgu moralny kapeć po sekswyczynach, na dodatek pogoda była taka, że albo do łóżka, albo do knajpy. Chmury wisiały nisko, siąpiło bez przerwy niemrawym, upierdliwym deszczem, woda zbierała się na szybie i ściekała w dół pojedynczymi strumykami. Pomyślał o Elżbiecie Budnik zawieszonej do góry nogami w jakimś magazynie, mordercy obserwującym, jak krew coraz wolniej wycieka z jej szyi. Podstawił wiadro? Miskę? Pozwolił, żeby spłynęła do kratki kanalizacyjnej? Im szczegółowiej wyobrażał sobie tę scenę, tym bardziej drżała w nim struna takiego zwykłego, ludowego, wcale nie prawniczego poczucia sprawiedliwości. Było coś urokliwego w Elżbiecie Budnik na nagraniu z miejskiej kamery. Ładna kobieta, ale z nutą dziewczęcości, kobieta, która nie zapomniała, co to znaczy podbiec w podskokach, zaśmiać się głośno w kinie i zjeść latem gofra z bitą śmietaną, pozwalając, żeby biała kropka została na nosie. Której chciało się robić warsztaty dla dzieci, przedstawienia, imprezy, większość pewnie za darmo albo za psi grosz. Która pewnie już miała rozpisane wakacje, wiedziała, kiedy kto przyjedzie, kiedy wycieczka, kiedy koncert, kiedy wyjazd do zamku w Ujeździe. Która cieszyła się, kiedy matki jej mówiły, że aż żal, żeby dzieci wyjeżdżały na lato, kiedy tu się tyle dzieje.

Żyła, kiedy powiesił ją do góry nogami, kiedy poderżnął jej gardło. Jasna krew tętnicza najpierw trysnęła mocnym strumieniem, zapieniła się, potem zaczęła płynąć po twarzy w rytm ostatnich uderzeń serca.

Szacki po raz pierwszy poczuł, że bardzo chce zobaczyć sprawcę na sali. Nawet jeśli to oznacza obejrzenie na kacu każdego pieprzonego symbolu, jaki stworzyła ludzkość w swojej historii.

Wrócił do komputera, zapisał, co znalazł o runie eiwaz, i zabrał się do symboli narodowych. Może od tropu żydowskiego właściwszy będzie antysemicki? Lektura portali narodowych była dość zaskakująca, spodziewał się apeli „Jebać Żydów siekierami" i „Pedały do gazu" okraszonych rysunkami w stylu przedwojennych antysemickich paszkwili, a natknął na eleganckie i dobrze zredagowane strony internetowe. Niestety, nigdzie nie było runy z dzyndzlem. Był Szczerbiec, symbol Falangi, krzyż celtycki skinheadów, oczywiście znak „zakazu pedałowania". Miał już dać spokój, z obowiązku kliknął jeszcze na serwis malopolscy--patrioci.pl i głośno westchnął z ulgą. W nagłówku strony oprócz godła Rzeczpospolitej widniała runa z dzyndzlem, czymkolwiek była.

– Alleluja! – krzyknął głośno i w tej samej chwili do środka włożyła swoją rudą głowę Sobieraj.

– Chwalmy Pana – dopowiedziała. – Opisałam rano ten tajemniczy znaczek mężowi i on mówi, że to jest rodło, symbol Związku Polaków w Niemczech. I że musimy wrócić do szkoły chyba, skorośmy go od razu nie rozpoznali. Pogrzebałam trochę i... masz chwilę?

Szacki zminimalizował szybko wszystkie okna w przeglądarce.

– Jasne, porządkowałem papiery. I oczywiście, że rodło, musiałem być wczoraj nieźle padnięty, że na to nie wpadłem.

Sobieraj spojrzała znacząco, ale nie skomentowała. Usiadła obok, razem z otaczającą ją chmurą perfum, dość owocową chmurą, trochę zbyt owocową na wczesną wiosnę, i rozłożyła na biurku zadrukowane kartki. Na jednej ich symbol, rodło, był nałożony na mapę Polski.

– Spójrz, Teodorze – nie pamiętał, kiedy ktoś się do niego zwracał ostatnio w ten sposób, nauczycielki w szkole chyba. – Tajemnicza połówka swastyki z wichajstrem to symbol kształtu Wisły na mapie Polski. W prawo, potem długo na skos do góry, potem w prawo. A wichajster to miejsce, gdzie Wisła przepływa przez Kraków. Symbol powstał w 1933 roku, po przejęciu władzy przez Hitlera. Naziści wprowadzili swastykę, zakazali używania wszelkich innych symboli niż przez nich zaaprobowane, o białym orle w ogóle nie mogło być mowy, zakaz jego używania utrzymywał się jeszcze z czasów pruskich. I teraz spójrz, co robią nasi sprytni krajanie w Niemczech. Tworzą taki znaczek i mówią Niemcom, że to pół swastyki, Niemcy robią mądre miny, kiwają głowami, mówią: no tak, to ma sens. Prawdziwi Niemcy mają całą wspaniałą swastykę, a Polacy w Niemczech tylko pół, *gut, gut, sicher, bachdzo grzetschna polnische schweine, verstehen*?

– Dlaczego nie *verstehen*, ja wszystko *verstehen* – zacytował Szacki *Misia*.

– Oczywiście dla naszych to było absolutne przeciwieństwo swastyki, to znaczy tego, co sobą reprezentowała. Rodło było i jest symbolem więzi niemieckiej polonii z Rzeczpospolitą.

– A ta nazwa? To od radła?

– Neologizm, rebus, coś z rodziny i coś z godła, rozumiesz? Pierwsza sylaba słowa „rodzina" i druga słowa „godło".

Szacki pokiwał głową.

– I co? Istnieje jeszcze ten związek?

– Jak najbardziej, z tego, co mi się udało dowiedzieć, nawet dość prężnie działa, ma siedzibę w Bochum. To taka organizacja, która wspiera polonusów, reprezentuje ich przed urzędami, pomaga w kłopotach, coś w rodzaju pozarządowego konsulatu. Mają też mocną narodową mitologię, powstali w latach dwudziestych, musieli działać za czasów rozwoju nazizmu, domyślasz się, co to oznacza.

– Konfiskata mienia, delegalizacja, aresztowania, rozstrzelania, obozy zagłady.

– Dokładnie tak. Dlatego dziś rodło jest też symbolem męczeństwa, polskości i niezłomności w organizacjach narodowych, na przykład kilka drużyn harcerskich używa tego znaku.

– Narodowych w sensie „chłopak i dziewczyna, normalna rodzina"?

– Nie, raczej takich rozsądnie narodowych, patriotycznych.

– Rozsądnie narodowych? – parsknął Szacki. – Gramy teraz w oksymorony?

Sobieraj wzruszyła ramionami.

– W Warszawie może to niemodne, ale na prowincji niektórzy lubią czuć się dumni z tego, że są Polakami.

– Wczoraj mi tłumaczyłaś, że bycie prawdziwym Polakiem w Sandomierzu może mieć bardzo ciemną podszewkę.

– Może zapomniałam dodać, że między odrzuceniem narodu a paleniem synagog w jego imieniu jest spora przestrzeń do zagospodarowania przez ludzi rozsądnych.

Szacki nie chciał polemizować. Nie lubił ludzi, którzy mieli hobby, więcej – obawiał się ich. Naród to było dla niego hobby. Pasja, która do niczego nie jest potrzebna i w niczym nie pomaga, ale która tak angażuje, że w niesprzyjających okolicznościach może doprowadzić do rzeczy strasznych. Prokurator, jego zdaniem, nie powinien utożsamiać się z narodem, powinien nie wierzyć w nic i nie mieć zasnuwającej umysł mgłą pasji. Kodeks jest precyzyjny, kodeks nie dzieli na lepszych i gorszych, nie patrzy na wiarę i narodową dumę. A prokurator ma być sługą kodeksu, strażnikiem porządku i praworządności.

Sobieraj wstała, oparła się o parapet okna.

– À propos palenia synagog – powiedziała, wskazując głową na coś za oknem.

Szacki wyjrzał, po drugiej stronie ulicy stała furgonetka Polsatu, technicy rozkładali umieszczony na dachu talerz anteny. Cóż, nie jego cyrk, nie jego małpy. Zastanawiał się nad dalszymi ruchami. Elżbieta Budnik miała w dłoni znak Związku Polaków w Niemczech, stosowany też przez niektóre organizacje patriotyczne i narodowe. Trzeba będzie pogadać z tutejszymi narodowcami, o ile w ogóle są tacy, sprawdzić harcerzy, prawicowych działaczy.

– Jurek Szyller jest honorowym członkiem Związku Polaków w Niemczech – powiedziała cicho, jakby do siebie Sobieraj. – Coraz dziwniejsza robi się ta sprawa.

– A kto to jest Jerzy Szyller?

Ruda głowa prokurator Barbary Sobieraj odwróciła się wolno w jego stronę. Były chwile, kiedy wydawała się Szackiemu ładna, w taki fajny, kobiecy, niewulgarny i nienachalny sposób. Na ładnej twarzy malowało się zdumienie i niedowierzanie, jakby spytał, kto był poprzednim papieżem albo jak to możliwe, że ten Kaczyński jest w dwóch miejscach jednocześnie.

– Żartujesz, prawda?

Nie, nie żartował.

2

Wysłuchał tego, co Sobieraj ma do powiedzenia o Jerzym Szyllerze, i zaraz po jej wyjściu z gabinetu zadzwonił do Wilczura, kazał mu natychmiast przyjechać. Potrzebował odtrutki dla kolejnego panegiryku, który wygłosiła jego piegowata koleżanka. Z jej opowieści wyłaniał się przystojny patriota, uczciwy biznesmen, płacący w terminie wysokie podatki obywatel, koneser sztuki, erudyta, człowiek światowy. Słowem, kolejna osoba bez skazy w Sandomierzu, mieście ludzi bez skazy, prawych, uczciwych i szlachetnych, którzy tylko raz na jakiś czas wezmą jakiegoś Żyda na widły albo poderżną komuś gardło i zostawią w krzakach.

Wilczur zagłębił się w fotelu, nie zdejmując płaszcza, przyniósł ze sobą wilgoć, chłód i zaczerwieniony nos pośrodku żółtawej twarzy. W pokoju od razu zrobiło się ciemniej, Szacki włączył lampkę i wyłuszczył, w czym rzecz.

– Nie ma tygodnia, żeby nie przyszedł do nas jakiś donos na Szyllera – zaczął Wilczur, odrywając filtr od papierosa. – Że źle zaparkował pod Bramą Opatowską. Że drzewa przed jego biurem zasłaniają światło. Że jego pies nasrał komuś pod drzwiami. Że ma dwa samochody, w jednym jest kratka, a to przecież limuzyna, a nie dostawczak. Że przeszedł przez Mickiewicza na czerwonym świetle, stwarzając zagrożenie dla ruchu drogowego. Że nie przestrzega ciszy nocnej. Że wysmarkał się pod pomnikiem Jana Pawła II, obrażając uczucia religijne katolickich obywateli Sandomierza i tym samym naruszając artykuł sto dziewięćdziesiąty szósty kodeksu karnego.

– To ostatnie to żart?

– Nie. Wyjątek też nie. Chciałbym dostawać złotówkę miesięcznie od każdego sandomierzanina, który go nienawidzi jak psa. – Wilczur zamyślił się, otoczony chmurą dymu, zapewne wyobrażał sobie, na co by przeznaczył taki majątek.

– Nienawidzą go z jakiegoś konkretnego powodu?

Wilczur zaśmiał się chrapliwie.

– Pan naprawdę nigdy nie mieszkał w małym mieście, prokuratorze. Nienawidzą go, bo jest bogaty, piękny, ma wielki dom i błyszczący samochód. W katolickim świecie może to oznaczać tylko jedno, że jest złodziejem, ciemiężycielem ubogich, który dorobił się kosztem innych.

– A jaka jest prawda?

– Prawda jest taka, że Jerzy Szyller to biznesmen, który ma rękę do nieruchomości, obraca nimi tutaj i w Niemczech, specjalizuje się w miejscach atrakcyjnych turystycznie, słyszałem, że swego czasu skupował od chłopów działki w Kazimierzu Dolnym. Trochę też inwestuje w infrastrukturę, jego jest na przykład ten nowy hotel przy Zawichojskiej. Wiem, że kilka razy go prześwietlała skarbówka i różne urzędy, jest czysty. Dość charakterystyczny typek, ale tego się pan sam dowie.

– Jakie miał stosunki z Budnikami?

– Na pewno nie kochali się z Budnikiem, przez jego przekręty i oddawanie ziemi Kościołowi kilka ładnych działek umknęło Szyllerowi sprzed nosa. Co do Budnikowej, to nie mam pojęcia, facet jest trochę filantropem, na pewno finansował jakieś jej przedsięwzięcia dla dzieci. W ogóle byli z innych bajek. Budnikowie to taka lewicująca inteligencja z „Wyborczej", Szyller raczej spod znaku „Gazety Polskiej" i biało-czerwonej flagi na maszcie przed domem. Oni byli dla niego trochę komunistami, on dla nich trochę faszystą, grilla na pewno razem nie robili.

Wilczur cierpiał na polską przypadłość, że nawet jeśli mówił o kimś dobrze i neutralnie, to brzmiało to jak inwektywy. Zmęczony ton, lekkie skrzywienie ust, podniesiona jedna brew, zaciągnięcie się papierosem w miejscu przecinka, zaciągnięcie i strząśnięcie popiołu w miejscu kropki. Ogólna pogarda do świata brudziła każdego, o kim mówił stary policjant.

– Szyller. Żyd?

Złośliwy uśmieszek przemknął po wargach policjanta.

– Po ostatnich zmianach nie prowadzimy ewidencji wyznania i pochodzenia. Ale jeśli wierzyć donosom, stuprocentowy. Także pederasta, zoofil i czciciel szatana.

Wilczur dla efektu podniósł rękę z wyprostowanymi palcami małym i wskazującym, wyglądał teraz jak brzydszy i bardziej zniszczony brat Keitha Richardsa.

Szacki się nie roześmiał.

3

W telefonie Jerzego Szyllera elegancki niski głos informował po polsku i niemiecku, że właściciel uprzejmie prosi o pozostawienie wiadomości. Szacki nagrał się bez większego przekonania, ale niespełna kwadrans później Szyller oddzwonił, przepraszając, że nie mógł odebrać. Kiedy Szacki zaczął tłumaczyć, w jakiej sprawie dzwoni, przerwał mu uprzejmie, ale stanowczo.

– Oczywiście rozumiem, w pewien sposób spodziewałem się tego telefonu, zarówno państwo Budnikowie, jak i ja jesteśmy w Sandomierzu osobami publicznymi, utrzymywaliśmy – prawie niedostrzegalnie zawiesił głos – chcąc nie chcąc, kontakty. Przyznaję, że specjalnie odwołałem wyjazd do Niemiec, przewidując, że mogę być potrzebny wymiarowi sprawiedliwości.

– W takim razie proszę przyjść na Koseły.

– Cóż, niestety nie jestem aż tak idealnym obywatelem. Odwołałem wyjazd do Niemiec, ale skorzystałem z okazji, żeby pozałatwiać sprawy w Warszawie. Jeszcze jestem w stolicy – Szackiemu spodobało się, że użył tego słowa – zaczyna się piątkowy szczyt, zanim wyjadę... Czy to byłby wielki problem, gdybyśmy się spotkali jutro? Proszę wybaczyć moją bezczelność, oczywiście mogę w każdej chwili wsiąść w samochód, ale boję się, że wtedy i tak nie będę wcześniej jak około dwudziestej.

Doświadczenie uczyło Szackiego, że z każdą godziną mijającą od czasu znalezienia zwłok sprawa się rozmywa, a szanse na znalezienie sprawcy maleją. Już chciał ostro zareagować, ale wytłumaczył sobie, że te parę nocnych godzin nie ma żadnego znaczenia.

– Dobrze, spotkajmy się jutro.

– O której mam pojawić się w prokuraturze?

– Ja pojawię się u pana o piętnastej. – Szacki nie miał pojęcia, dlaczego tak odpowiedział, to był impuls, zadziałał śledczy szósty zmysł.

– Oczywiście. W takim razie do zobaczenia?

– Do zobaczenia – odparł Szacki i odłożył słuchawkę, zastanawiając się, dlaczego Szyller zakończył pytaniem. Kindersztuba nie pozwoliła mu zakończyć rozmowy, której nie zaczął? Czy dopuszczał do siebie myśl, że jednak się nie zobaczą?

Do pokoju zajrzała sekretarka szefowej.

4

Prokurator Teodor Szacki był człowiekiem światłym, znał podstawy psychologii i wiedział, że negatywna identyfikacja to ślepa uliczka. Że człowiek powinien określać siebie przez dobre emocje, przez to, co lubi, co go uszczęśliwia, sprawia mu radość. Że budowanie tożsamości na tym, co go drażni i wkurwia, to wstęp na równię pochyłą zgorzknienia, po której zjeżdża się coraz szybciej, aby na końcu stać się ziejącym nienawiścią frustratem.

Wiedział o tym, starał się z tym walczyć, jak umiał, ale zdarzały się momenty, kiedy zwyczajnie się nie dało. To był jeden z tych momentów. Prokurator Teodor Szacki w swoim nienagannym garniturze i dopasowanym krawacie, wyprostowany, z idealną, szlachetną bielą gęstych włosów i srogim spojrzeniem wyglądał za zaimprowizowanym prezydialnym stołem jak ucieleśnienie wymiaru sprawiedliwości. Patrzył na zgromadzoną po drugiej stronie grupkę kilkunastu dziennikarzy i koncentrował się na swoim oddechu, powstrzymując próbujące pojawiać się na jego twarzy grymasy pogardy, które mogłyby uchwycić kamery.

Tak, białowłosy heros Temidy nienawidził mediów szczerze. Z wielu różnych względów. Na pewno dlatego, że były niemiłosiernie, boleśnie, do krwawych torsji nudne i przewidywalne. Na pewno dlatego, że w żywe oczy kłamały i konfabulowały w zależności od potrzeby chwili, żonglując faktami tak, aby pasowały do z góry założonej tezy. Na pewno dlatego, że wypaczały obraz świata, nadając każdemu marginalnemu ekstremum cechy normy i trendu, bo tylko wtedy margines zyskiwał rangę, która usprawiedliwiała mielenie czegoś nieistotnego dwadzieścia cztery godziny na dobę.

Ale to wszystko byłoby jeszcze do zniesienia, pod warunkiem że włożyło się media do szufladki z rozrywkami dla zaburzonych emocjonalnie. Ktoś lubi oglądać mecze piłki nożnej, ktoś inny pornosy ze zwierzętami, a ktoś TVN24 – ot, różni ludzie, różne pasje. I gdyby Teodor Szacki nie był prokuratorem, pewnie skatalogowałby dziennikarzy obok miłośników dogadzania labradorom i zapomniał o sprawie. Niestety tyle razy w jego śledztwach namieszali debile krzyczący o prawie obywatela do informacji, tyle razy rozdmuchiwanie najbardziej sensacyjnych i krwawych aspektów sprawy mieszało świadkom w głowach, tyle razy mimo próśb i błagań publikowano fakty, które cofały śledztwa o tygodnie lub miesiące – że gdyby dobry Bóg zwrócił się do

Szackiego z pytaniem, która grupa zawodowa ma znienacka wyparować, nie wahałby się ani chwili.

A teraz, proszę, okazało się, że może i cyrk nie jego, ale małpy jak najbardziej.

– Czy wytypowali państwo już jakichś oskarżonych?

– Na razie śledztwo prowadzone jest w sprawie, a nie przeciwko. To oznacza, że badamy różne tropy, przesłuchujemy różne osoby, ale nikomu nie postawiliśmy zarzutów. – Misia odpowiadała gładko, ani na chwilę nie zdejmując z twarzy matczynego uśmiechu. Było to już któreś z rzędu głupie, niekompetentne pytanie i Szacki ze zgrozą skonstatował, że na prowincji pismacy byli głupsi od tych w Warszawie.

– Jak państwo skomentują fakt, że ofiara została brutalnie zamordowana nożem do rytualnego koszernego uboju?

Na sali zapanowała cisza. Po obu stronach stołu. Szacki już otwierał usta, kiedy zabrzmiał dźwięczny, w przyjemny sposób wysoki głos Sobieraj.

– Proszę państwa, niestety mam wrażenie, że ktoś próbuje utrudniać śledztwo, rozpuszczając nieprawdziwe plotki, a państwo podążacie za nimi jak owce na rzeź, niekoniecznie rytualną. Faktem jest, że ofiarę pozbawiono życia poprzez przecięcie tętnicy szyjnej, w bardzo nieprzyjemny sposób. Faktem jest, że posłużyło do tego bardzo ostre narzędzie. Ale nic nam nie wiadomo o rytualnym uboju. Ani koszernym, ani halal, ani żadnym innym.

– Czyli w końcu mówimy o rytuale żydowskim czy arabskim?

– Proszę pana – wtrącił się Szacki – nie mówimy o żadnym rytuale. Powtórzę: żadnym. Skąd państwo w ogóle bierzecie te pomysły? Czy ja coś przegapiłem? Czy teraz u was jest jakaś moda, żeby zabójstwa nazywać mordami rytualnymi? Stała się tragedia, kobieta została pozbawiona życia, wszyscy działamy na pełnych obrotach, żeby wyjaśnić sprawę i doprowadzić do ujęcia sprawcy. Okoliczności zabójstwa nie są w żaden sposób bardziej niezwykłe niż dziesiątki zabójstw, z którymi miałem do czynienia wcześniej, a spędziłem piętnaście lat w śródmiejskiej prokuraturze w Warszawie. I wiele widziałem, proszę mi wierzyć.

Miszczyk spojrzała na niego z uznaniem, wyjątkowo bez matczynej aprobaty. Wstała jakaś brzydka dziennikarka w zielonym golfie, oczywiście się nie przedstawiła, pewnie wszyscy powinni ją znać.

– Czy ofiara była Żydówką?

– To nie ma znaczenia dla śledztwa – odpowiedział Szacki.

– Rozumiem, że gdyby ofiarą był na przykład homoseksualista, też by to dla pana nie miało znaczenia? – Z jakiegoś powodu brzydka dziennikarka sprawiała wrażenie obrażonej.

– Miałoby takie samo jak fakt, że grywała w szachy albo chodziła na ryby...

– Orientacja seksualna to dla pana rodzaj hobby?

Salwa śmiechu. Szacki odczekał.

– Wszystko, co dotyczy ofiary i podejrzanych, ma dla śledztwa znaczenie i wszystko jest sprawdzane. Ale doświadczenie uczy, że rzadko w preferencjach religijnych bądź innych leżą motywy zabójstw.

– A gdzie? – krzyknął ktoś z sali.

– Alkohol. Pieniądze. Stosunki rodzinne.

– Ale taki antysemicki wybryk zasługuje chyba na specjalne traktowanie? – drążyła dziennikarka. – Zwłaszcza w mieście pogromów, w kraju, gdzie ciągle kwitnie antysemityzm i gdzie dochodzi do ksenofobicznych rozruchów?

– Jeśli pani wie o jakichś antysemickich wybrykach, proszę złożyć doniesienie. Mnie nic na ten temat nie wiadomo, na pewno nie ma z tym nic wspólnego śledztwo w sprawie Elżbiety B.

– Ja, proszę pana, ja po prostu chcę napisać prawdę. Polacy zasługują na prawdę o sobie, nie tylko na wypraną i wyprasowaną bohaterszczyznę.

Parę osób zaklaskało, Szackiemu przypomniało się, jak klaskali Lepperowi, gdy ten rechotał, zastanawiając się głośno, czy można zgwałcić prostytutkę. Tak, tamta scena to była esencja prawdy o polskich mediach. Z ostatnią uwagą dziennikarki akurat się zgadzał, niemniej narastało w nim poczucie bezsensu i marnowanego czasu. Spojrzał na Miszczyk i Sobieraj, siedziały przed kamerami bez ruchu, jakby ta heca miała trwać cały dzień.

– Dobrze, proszę pisać prawdę – niestety nie udało mu się ukryć pogardy, widział to na jej twarzy – może przetrze pani szlak kolegom po fachu. Ostatnie pytanie, musimy wracać do pracy.

– Czy jest pan antysemitą, panie prokuratorze?

– Jeśli pani jest Żydówką, to tak, jestem antysemitą.

5

Był wściekły. Po konferencji uciekł do swojego gabinetu, żeby uniknąć rozmowy z Miszczyk. Zamienił parę słów z Sobieraj i zadzwonił do Wilczura, żeby sprawdzić postępy śledztwa, ale żadnych postępów nie było. Świadkowie się nie pojawili, śladów krwi nie znaleziono, przeglądanie nagrań z kolejnych kamer nie przynosiło rezultatu, Budnik siedział w domu. Przesłuchania kolejnych znajomych Elżbiety Budnik potwierdzały jedynie, że była wspaniałą osobą, wesołą i pełną życia społeczniczką. Nie wszyscy oceniali jej małżeństwo wysoko, ale każdy mówił, że „przynajmniej się przyjaźnili". Im bardziej akta pęczniały, tym bardziej Elżbieta Budnik była spiżowa, tym bardziej nie pojawiał się jakikolwiek motyw, tym bardziej prokurator Teodor Szacki był sfrustrowany. Z trudem powstrzymał się, żeby nie wsiąść w samochód i nie wyjechać na spotkanie Szyllerowi, przesłuchać go na Statoilu w Kozienicach, zrobić cokolwiek, czegokolwiek się dowiedzieć, popchnąć sprawę do przodu.

W poszukiwaniu świeżej myśli i świeżego powietrza wyszedł z prokuratury, minął stadion, gdzie ciągle trwała jakaś afera w obronie budek z ziemniakami, i zaczął iść Staromiejską w stronę kościoła Świętego Pawła, mijając wille sandomierskiej elity i nowoczesny park Piszczele, urządzony w wąwozie o tej samej nazwie. Szacki nie widział tego miejsca przed remontem, ale podobno był to typowy zaułek pod wezwaniem Świętego Jabola, gdzie o każdej porze dnia można stracić dziewictwo wbrew swojej woli. Szedł szybko, energicznie. Było na tyle ciepło, że rozpiął płaszcz, mżawka osiadała na tkaninach ubrania, okrywając Szackiego eteryczną lśniącą zbroją.

Doszedł do kościoła i położonego przy nim malowniczo cmentarza, chmury rozwiały się na tyle, że pięknie było widać wzgórze z sandomierską starówką, od którego Szacki oddzielony był teraz łagodnym wąwozem. Miasto wyglądało stąd jak statek dryfujący po zieleniejących już błoniach. Strzelista sygnaturka katedry znaczyła dziób, kamieniczki wyglądały jak poustawiane na pokładzie kontenery, maszt wieży ratuszowej tkwił dokładnie na środku okrętu, na rufie stała zwalista sylwetka Wieży Opatowskiej. Szacki dokładnie widział stąd charakterystyczny, przysadzisty kształt synagogi i rozciągające się pod nią krzaki, w których znaleziono zwłoki.

Zaczął schodzić w dół, w stronę miasta, mnożąc w myślach możliwe scenariusze wydarzeń. Każdy zaczynał się od kluczowego założenia, że albo zabójcą jest Budnik, albo nie jest nim Budnik. Każdy był tak samo bezsensowny i nieprawdopodobny. Czując narastającą frustrację, szedł coraz szybciej, minął zamek i kiedy w końcu zatrzymał się pod katedrą, był mocno zadyszany.

Katedra była taka sobie, ani ładna, ani brzydka, dość duża, ceglana gotycka bryła z doklejonymi barokowymi elementami na fasadzie. Na pewno każdy przewodnik lał na kościół miód i lukier, rozwodząc się nad jego najstarszymi dziejami, na Szackim budowla nie robiła specjalnego wrażenia, zwłaszcza odkąd dowiedział się, że najładniejsza część, czyli strzelista sygnaturka, to efekt neogotyckiej przebudowy pod koniec XIX wieku. Podszedł do bocznego wejścia, wisiała tam świeżutka, zapewne dziś powieszona kartka z napisem „Absolutny zakaz filmowania i fotografowania!!!". Widać media już się dały księżulom we znaki.

Wszedł do środka.

Jak na wielkanocną porę, świątynia była zaskakująco pusta. Jedna osoba o wyglądzie turysty kręciła się po wnętrzu, w ławkach nie było nikogo. Koło chóru mężczyzna i kobieta bliźniaczym gestem zmywali kamienną posadzkę. Szacki odetchnął niepowtarzalnym, nie dającym się z niczym pomylić zapachem starego kościoła, poczekał chwilę, aż oczy przyzwyczają się do półmroku, i rozejrzał się. Był tu pierwszy raz. Spodziewał się gotyckiej monumentalnej surowizny, czegoś w rodzaju katedry Świętego Jana w Warszawie, tymczasem sandomierska bazylika nie przytłaczała kościelnym dostojeństwem. Podobało się Szackiemu, że architektoniczny szkielet – kolumny i żebra sklepienia – wykonany był nie z czerwonej cegły, lecz białego kamienia, który nadawał wnętrzu elegancji. Wolnym krokiem, który włączał mu się zawsze w kościołach, przeszedł między ławkami i stanął pośrodku głównej nawy, pod imponującym kryształowym żyrandolem. Z jednej strony miał chór zwieńczony koroną organów, z drugiej ołtarz główny i prezbiterium – wszystko po barokowemu przepyszne. Marmurowa chrzcielnica na pękatej nóżce, złote ramy w bocznych ołtarzach, każdy powywijany ornament, pulchne aniołki i ciemne olejne obrazy krzyczały do widza: hej, zrobili nas w XVIII wieku.

Przechadzał się slalomem między kolumnami, oglądając bez zainteresowania rzeźby i malowidła świętych, zatrzymał się na chwilę przy prezbiterium, które jakiś sandomierski

Giotto nawet udanie ozdobił scenami z Nowego Testamentu. Szacki patrzył na Ostatnią Wieczerzę, wskrzeszenie Łazarza, na Piłata, Judasza i Tomasza, zestaw nieśmiertelnych motywów, które podobno dwóm miliardom ludzi ofiarowują poczucie pewności, spokój i świadomość, że mogą robić, co chcą, bo w końcu Bóg i tak najbardziej lubi synów marnotrawnych. Kolejne poronione hobby dla zaburzonych, szlag by was wszystkich trafił. Szacki potarł twarz dłońmi, czuł się śmiertelnie znużony.

Odwrócił się gwałtownie od ołtarza, przecież nie po to przyszedł do katedry, żeby podziwiać drugoligową sztukę europejską. Szybkim krokiem zaczął iść główną nawą, między ławkami, w stronę chóru. Pod żyrandolem próbował wyminąć mężczyznę, który jednostajnym gestem robota zamiatał podłogę. Ruch mopa był jak metronom.

– Nie po mokrym – ostrzegł mężczyzna.

Szacki zatrzymał się. Mężczyzna przerwał i spojrzał mu w oczy. Ziemista cera, smutne spojrzenie, czarna koszula zapięta pod szyję. Trochę z zombie, trochę z menela – prawdziwy katolik, radosny i szczęśliwy, że Bóg rozwinął przed nim świetlisty szlak prosto do nieba. Szacki bez słowa cofnął się o krok i skrawkiem suchej podłogi przeszedł do bocznej nawy. Kroki zagłuszały rytmiczne szuranie mopa, który wznowił działalność.

Nie mogło być wątpliwości, gdzie znajduje się słynny obraz. Na zachodniej ścianie, po obu stronach wejścia do kruchty wisiały cztery wielkie płótna. Pierwsze dwa przedstawiały w naturalistyczny sposób dwie rzezie, sądząc po wyglądzie napastników – jakiś najazd tatarski albo mongolski. Niewierni na pierwszym obrazie rozprawiali się z mieszkańcami Sandomierza, na drugim – z łatwo rozpoznawalnymi po białych habitach dominikanami. Po drugiej stronie wejścia znowu rzeź i płonący zamek, tym razem na Tatarów to nie wyglądało, pewnie potop – nikt nie miał takiej tendencji do palenia i wysadzania jak Szwedzi, prawdziwi pasjonaci materiałów wybuchowych, i to na długo przed Noblem. A czwarte płótno? Prokurator Teodor Szacki stanął przed nim, założył ręce na piersiach. Czy to możliwe, żeby miało ono coś wspólnego z morderstwem Budnikowej? Czy naprawdę należy szukać religijnego szaleńca? Odwrócił się w kierunku ołtarza i w myślach poprosił Boga, żeby to nie był religijny szaleniec. Najgorsze są sprawy z szaleńcami. Szaleniec oznacza metry akt, korowody biegłych, spory o możliwość rozpoznania własnych czynów; męka, a jeśli chodzi o wyrok – loteria, niezależnie od materiału dowodowego.

Szacki modlił się i myślał. Z lewej strony systematycznie zbliżało się do niego szur-szur kościelnej toalety. Tym razem kobieta. Przestawiła wiadro, zaczęła zmywać, doszła do nóg Szackiego. Przerwała pracę i spojrzała na niego wyczekująco. Była tak samo promieniejąca i wypełniona radością wiary jak jej partner, sklep z akcesoriami dla samobójców zatrudniłby ją momentalnie. Prokurator cofnął się o krok i zaczął iść w stronę wyjścia wąską alejką suchej posadzki, nie było większego sensu, żeby gapił się na czerwony całun okrywający kontrowersyjny obraz. W ramach nagrody pocieszenia, żeby nie było, że nie ma nic do oglądania, na tkaninie wisiał portret Jana Pawła II.

Szacki wiedział, co jest na obrazie, oglądał go w internecie. Karol de Prevot nie był może dobrym malarzem, ale miał inklinację do makabry i komiksową zdolność obrazkowej narracji, co podobało się ówczesnemu archidiakonowi katedry, który zlecił artyście malarską dekorację świątyni. Jako że archidiakon Żuchowski był prawdziwym chrześcijaninem i zaprzysięgłym żydożercą, de Prevot udokumentował żydowskie zbrodnie na sandomierskich dzieciach. Na obrazie byli Żydzi kupujący dzieci od matek i sprawdzający ich stan jak bydło na targu, byli Żydzi mordujący, byli fachowcy od odzyskiwania krwi dzięki beczce nabitej gwoździami i pies, który zjadał rzucone mu szczątki. Szackiemu najbardziej utkwił w głowie widok porozrzucanych na ziemi niemowlęcych zwłok.

Nie udało mu się dojść do drzwi, pomiędzy nim i wyjściem z bocznej nawy były trzy metry mokrej, świeżo umytej podłogi. Chciał po prostu zrobić trzy duże kroki, ale coś go tknęło. Cisza. Nie było kroków, nie było szurania. Mężczyzna i kobieta stali oparci o swoje mopy w identycznych pozach i patrzyli na niego z oddali. W pierwszej chwili chciał wzruszyć ramionami i wyjść, ale w ich oczach był taki smutek, że westchnął i zaczął szukać drogi po suchym. Ścieżka wiła się; czując się jak szczur w labiryncie, doszedł do przeciwległej strony kościoła – bardzo daleko od wyjścia. Ale wyglądało na to, że teraz ma otwartą drogę do ołtarza i z tamtej strony dojdzie do drzwi. Mężczyzna i kobieta, uspokojeni jego zachowaniem, wrócili do pracy.

Idąc blisko ściany, Szacki patrzył na mijane obrazy, też zresztą dzieła barokowego komiksiarza de Prevota. Patrzył i szedł coraz wolniej, aż w końcu stanął. Katolickie wychowanie nie pozwalało mu użyć słowa „pornografia" w opisie tego, co widział – ale też żadne inne słowo nie oddawało tak dobrze istoty rzeczy. Wielkie obrazy miały jeden temat – śmierć. Śmierć realistyczną, krwawą, męczeńską, na dodatek w setkach odsłon. W pierwszej chwili Szacki nie pojął, dlaczego przy każdym trupie jest numerek, potem spostrzegł, że obrazy opatrzone są łacińską nazwą miesiąca, i zrozumiał, że to rodzaj perwersyjnego kalendarza. Po małej makabrze na każdy dzień roku. Stał właśnie przy marcu, tortury były tak wymyślne, jakby chciały oddać całą beznadzieję zimnego i błotnego polskiego przedwiośnia. 10 marca konał przybity włóczniami do drzewa Aphrodosius, dwa dni później szpadel przecinał szyję Micdoniusa, wzrok przykuwały flaki owijające się krwawą wstęgą wokół zębatego czegoś, co przeszyło 31 marca ich kumpla w męczeństwie Beniamina. W kwietniu było ciut lepiej, zrzucanie ze skarpy do rzeki, obcinanie głów, ciągnięcie za koniem i rozszarpywanie przez dzikie bestie. Jednego chyba gotowano, wyraz twarzy nie wskazywał na ciepłą kąpiel. 12 maja natknął się na Teodora. Akurat jego imiennik mógł mówić o łagodnym wymiarze kary – utopiony z ciężarem u szyi. Szacki poczuł absurdalną ulgę, że to nie jego patron, on sam obchodził imieniny w dniu wspomnienia Teodora z Tarsu, zakonnika i intelektualisty z VII wieku.

Szedł dalej, malarska makabra odrzucała go i przyciągała jednocześnie, jak leżąca na poboczu drogi ofiara wypadku. Podziwiał inwencję de Prevota, jak na 365 dni zadziwiająco mało tortur się powtarzało, choć ukrzyżowania i podrzynania gardeł były zdecydowanie na topie.

Udało mu się w końcu dojść w pobliże drzwi, przyspieszył kroku, bo kościelny w czerni najwyraźniej usiłował zamalować ostatni kawałek suchej posadzki przy wyjściu. Zatrzymał się przy listopadzie, miał urodziny jedenastego. Cóż, akurat ten męczennik naprawdę zasłużył na kanonizację. Nie dość, że w nieprzyjemny sposób powieszono go na haku, to jeszcze dla pewności nogi obciążono odważnikiem, a ciało przeszyto włócznią. Szacki pomyślał ponuro, że to beznadziejna wróżba, jakby ktoś chciał mu powiedzieć, że zawsze znajdzie się miejsce na troszkę dodatkowego męczeństwa.

Kościelny chrząknął znacząco. Szacki oderwał wzrok od wizji barokowego pornografa.

– Znalazłem swoje urodziny – powiedział bez sensu.

– To nie urodziny – odparł sprzątający zaskakująco wesołym tonem – to wróżba, jak pan skończysz.

Na zewnątrz było listopadowo. Mokro, ciemno, zimno. Prokurator Teodor Szacki zapiął płaszcz i wyszedł przez furtę na Kościelną, zaczął iść w stronę rynku. Spojrzał w kamerę, tę samą, która po raz ostatni uchwyciła Elę Budnik, jak poprawiała cholewkę kozaczka, a potem w trzech podskokach doganiała swojego męża. Przez głowę przeleciała mu myśl, żeby zajść do Budnika, ale dał spokój.

Na zewnątrz ciągle pada, zima żegna się z Ziemią Świętokrzyską zmęczonym, słabym płaczem. Tutaj jest sucho i ciepło, gdyby nie rozpalone oczy siedzącego w kącie mężczyzny, byłoby nawet przytulnie. Niewielkiego wzrostu, szczupły, ze spętanymi rękami i nogami, przypomina dziecko, tylko ryża broda wystająca spod knebla zdradza, że ofiara jest dojrzałym człowiekiem. Budzi litość, ale to niczego nie zmienia. W oddali zegar na wieży ratuszowej bije cztery razy na pełną godzinę, potem wybija drugą. Jeszcze doba. Jeszcze tylko doba. Niestety, nie może jej przeczekać tutaj, trzeba jeszcze zajrzeć do psów i wrócić na górę. Na szczęście drugi akt już dobiega końca.

Rozdział czwarty

sobota, 18 kwietnia 2009

Siódmy, przedostatni dzień Oktawy Wielkanocnej dla katolików i Wielka Sobota dla prawosławnych chrześcijan; szabat w całym żydowskim świecie. Tadeusz Mazowiecki świętuje swoje 82. urodziny. Jarosław Kaczyński twierdzi, że tylko PiS może ocalić demokrację w Polsce, a Leszek Miller przekonuje, że nie było afery Rywina ani w ogóle żadnych afer w rządzie SLD. Na świecie parlament Somalii wprowadza szariat w całym kraju, Bułgaria wpada w panikę, bo znany astrolog przepowiada trzęsienie ziemi. A w Usti nad Łabą setki neofaszystów z Czech, Słowacji, Węgier i Niemiec świętują zbliżające się urodziny Hitlera, napadając na romskie osiedle. Łukasz „Flappyhandski" Fabiański w swoje 24. urodziny broni słabo, Arsenal przegrywa z Chelsea i odpada w półfinale z Pucharu Anglii. W Sandomierzu złodzieje wycinają sześć jabłoni i śliwę. Sześćdziesięcioletnie drzewa były warte tysiąc złotych. Wieczorem w klubie w podziemiach ratusza głośna impreza, Soundomierska Strefa Rocka. Pierwszy w miarę wiosenny dzień. Ciepło, słonecznie, nie pada.

Posłuchajcie tego. Rabin i ksiądz jadą w jednym przedziale, czytają, cisza, pełna kultura. Mija chwila, ksiądz odkłada książkę i mówi: „Tak z ciekawości: wiem, że nie wolno wam jeść wieprzowiny. Ale... nie próbował pan nigdy?". Rabin zamyka gazetę, uśmiecha się i mówi: „Szczerze? Zdarzyło mi się". Po chwili dodaje: „I tak z ciekawości: wiem, że obowiązuje was celibat...". Ksiądz mu przerywa: „Wiem, o co panu chodzi, i od razu odpowiem, że tak, uległem raz pokusie". Uśmiechają się, wyrozumiali dla swych niedoskonałości, ksiądz wraca do książki, rabin do gazety, czytają, cisza. Nagle rabin mówi: „Lepsze niż wieprzowina, co nie?".

Szacki znał ten dowcip, ale roześmiał się szczerze, lubił dowcipy o Żydach.

– Dobra, to jeszcze jeden...

– Jędrek...

– Ostatni, obiecuję. Pascha, piękny dzień, Mosze zabiera lunch do parku, siada na ławce i wsuwa. Dosiada się do niego jakiś niewidomy człowiek, a że Mosze w świąteczny czas czuje do ludzi serdeczność, to częstuje go kawałkiem macy. Niewidomy bierze macę, obraca ją w dłoni, mina mu rzednie, w końcu mówi: „Kto napisał to gówno?".

Tym razem Szacki wybuchnął śmiechem już bez żadnych ale, dowcip był przedni, poza tym świetnie opowiedziany.

– Jędrek, proszę cię! Teodor pomyśli, że jesteśmy jakimiś antysemitami.

– Dobra rodzina z Kielecczyzny. Opowiadałaś, jak się poznaliśmy na zlocie ONR? Co to była za noc, w świetle pochodni wyglądałaś jak aryjska królowa... Ała!

Andrzej Sobieraj uchylił się przed rzuconym przez żonę kawałkiem chleba, ale zrobił to tak niezgrabnie, że wyrżnął łokciem o kant stołu. Spojrzał na nią z wyrzutem. Szacki zawsze czuł się niezręcznie, będąc świadkiem bliskości między ludźmi, dlatego tylko uśmiechnął się półgębkiem i suto polał swój kawałek kiełbasy musztardą grillową. Dziwnie się czuł, targały nim emocje, których nie potrafił nazwać.

Mąż piczki-zasadniczki Sobieraj, której Szacki mimo rosnącej sympatii nie potrafił przestać tak nazywać w myślach, był dość typowym misiem. Takim, co to nigdy, nawet za swoich najlepszych lat, nie był amantem, do którego kobiety nie wzdychały i o którym nie śniły, ale wszystkie go lubiły, bo i pogadać można, i się pośmiać, i poczuć bezpiecznie. Potem oczywiście wybierały tajemniczych przystojniaków, alkoholików i dziwkarzy, pewne, że miłość ich zmieni, a ufny misio trafiał się zołzie, która potrzebowała kogoś do pomiatania i wyręki. Sobieraj mimo wszystko na taką nie wyglądała, akurat ten misio trafił dość szczęśliwie. I szczęśliwie też wyglądał, szczęśliwie i sympatycznie. Sympatyczna była jego koszula w kratę, wciśnięta w stare, tanie dżinsy. Sympatyczna była jego krępa, lekko pękata, grillowo-piwna sylwetka. Sympatyczne były spokojne oczy, wąsy wkręcające się do ust i cienkie zakola, dwie przecinki w lesie szpakowatych, falujących włosów.

– Już się tak nie rzucaj – powiedział Sympatyczny Andrzej do żony, obracając kawałki kiełbasy na grillu. – Kto jak kto, ale pan prokurator się chyba z powodu antysemityzmu nie obrazi. Z tego, co piszą w gazetach...

Sobieraj parsknęła, Szacki uśmiechnął się z grzeczności. Niestety, wczorajsza konferencja przewinęła się przez media, niestety, prawie wszystkie pisały o „tajemniczym mordzie", o „antysemickich podtekstach", o „brunatnym podłożu", jedna gazeta ze szczegółami przytoczyła historię miasta i zasugerowała w komentarzu, że „nie jest do końca pewne, czy śledczy zdają sobie sprawę z delikatności materii, z jaką przyszło im się zmierzyć". A to dopiero początek, jeśli szybko nie rozwiążą sprawy albo jeśli szybko nie pojawi się coś nowego, żeby padlinożercy mieli na czym żerować, będzie tylko gorzej.

– Właściwie to czemu w ogóle mówimy o antysemityzmie? – zapytał Sobieraj. – Ela nie była Żydówką, z tego, co wiem, nie miała z nimi nic wspólnego, nie organizowała nawet koncertów klezmerskich, jedyny jej kontakt z judaizmem to recital piosenek ze *Skrzypka na dachu* kilka lat temu. Jej zabójstwo nie jest więc chyba faszystowskim aktem? A samo pojawienie się słowa „żydowskie" w dowolnym kontekście nie musi od razu oznaczać, że kontekst jest antysemicki.

– Mirmiłku, nie filozuj – zbyła jego wywód Sobieraj. – Elcię zabito żydowskim nożem do rytualnego uboju bydła.

– No wiem, ale jeśli odrzucimy histerię, to logiczniej byłoby chyba przesłuchać w takiej sytuacji żydowskich rzeźników niż tych, którzy nienawidzą żydowskich rzeźników? Czy też jesteśmy tak poprawni politycznie, że nawet hipotetycznie nie możemy rozważyć, że sprawca jest Żydem lub ma bliskie związki z tą kulturą? A przez to na przykład dostęp do narzędzi?

Szacki przez moment rozważał słowa dolatujące z chmury dymu nad grillem.

– Nie do końca tak jest – odpowiedział. – Z jednej strony masz rację, ludzie mordują się tym, co jest pod ręką. Rzeźnik tasakiem, wulkanizator łyżką do opon, fryzjer nożyczkami. Ale z drugiej strony zwykle pierwsze, co robią, to starają się zatrzeć ten ślad. A tutaj narzędzie zbrodni leżało obok zwłok, na dodatek umyte, wyjałowione, starannie dla nas przygotowane, żeby nie dać żadnych poszlak poza jedną: że to jakaś brudna żydowsko-antysemicka sprawa. Dlatego uważamy, że to ściema.

– Może i ściema, ale rozumiem, że takiej rytualnej brzytwy nie kupuje się w Biedronce.

– Nie, nie kupuje – przyznał Szacki. – Dlatego staramy się dowiedzieć, skąd pochodzi.

– Z umiarkowanymi sukcesami – dopowiedziała Sobieraj. – Na rękojeści jest lekko zatarty napis „Grünewald", koresponduję z muzeum noży w Solingen, żeby się czegoś dowiedzieć. Twierdzą, że to może być jakaś mała przedwojenna manufaktura z dzielnicy Grünewald, właśnie w Solingen. Tam do dziś się wszędzie produkuje jakieś ostrza, noże i brzytwy, a przed wojną było takich warsztatów i manufaktur dziesiątki. Część na pewno żydowska. Zobaczymy. Jest w idealnym stanie, wygląda bardziej na zabytek, element czyjejś kolekcji, niż faktycznie używany chalef.

Szacki skrzywił się, słowo „kolekcja" skojarzyło mu się ze znienawidzonym słowem „hobby". Ale jednocześnie pchnęło myśli na nowy tor. Nóż to kolekcja, kolekcja to hobby, hobby to antykwariat, a antykwariat to... Wstał, lepiej myślało mu się na chodząco.

– Czyli że gdzie się kupuje takie fanty? – Sobieraj wypowiadał na głos myśli Szackiego. – Na giełdach? W antykwariatach? W tajnych melinach?

– Internet – odpowiedział Szacki. – Allegro, ebay. Nie ma dziś na świecie antykwariatu, który by nie sprzedawał przez internet.

Wymienili z Sobieraj porozumiewawcze spojrzenia, jeśli nóż został kupiony na internetowej aukcji, to po transakcji musiał zostać jakiś ślad. Szacki segregował w głowie czynności, które trzeba będzie wykonać w poniedziałek, żeby to sprawdzić. Zamyślony odchodził w głąb ogrodu, zostawiając z tyłu dom Sobierajów i ich samych. Kiedy zawracał, obchodząc jabłonkę dookoła, miał już gotową listę, ale zamiast satysfakcji z nowego pomysłu czuł niepokój. Dobrze mu znany, uporczywy jak ból zęba niepokój. Coś przeoczył, na coś nie zwrócił uwagi, popełnił błąd. Był tego absolutnie pewien, wałkował w kółko wydarzenia ostatnich dni, żeby dostrzec tę skazę. I nic. To było jak wiszące na końcu języka nazwisko, którego za żadne skarby nie możemy sobie przypomnieć. Nieznośne swędzenie w środku czaszki.

Widział teraz w pełnej krasie willę, domek raczej, Sobierajów. Stał w dzielnicy Kruków, czyli jak na warunki sandomierskie daleko od miasta, blisko obwodnicy, za kominem widać było kościół po drugiej stronie szosy, z charakterystycznym dachem w formie wywróconej do góry nogami łodzi. Szacki z trudem przyzwyczajał się, że posiadanie własnego domu nie oznacza tutaj – jak w Warszawie – luksusu i przynależności do elity, która wyrwała się z blokowisk, że to taki sam średnioklasowy standard jak pięćdziesiąt metrów mieszkania w dużym mieście. Ale o ileż bardziej ludzki. Było coś naturalnego w wyjściu z salonu na taras, w ogrodzie z kilkoma jabłonkami, w leniwej sobocie spędzanej na leżakach przy grillu, w oddychaniu pierwszymi zapachami wiosny.

Nie znał tego świata, ale wydawał mu się bardzo piękny i zazdrościł tym, którzy go nie doceniali i bez końca potrafili narzekać na dom i ogród, na bezmiar pracy przy nich, na to, że zawsze jest coś do zrobienia. Nawet jeśli, to miejskie soboty w mieszkaniach, na basenach, w centrach handlowych, w samochodach i na śmierdzących ulicach były w porównaniu z tym jak wyrok. Czuł się niczym więzień, który po czterdziestu latach odsiadki został wypuszczony na wolność. Nie wiedział, jak się zachować, całym ciałem odczuwał dyskomfort nieprzynależności. Wszystko w nim nie przynależało. Jego samotność do ich przyjaźni – bo miłości nie był pewien – jego zimna wielkomiejskość do ciepłego prowincjonalnego gniazda, cięte riposty do snujących się opowieści bez pointy, wyprasowany garnitur do sportowych ciuchów, w końcu cola do piwa. Tłumaczył sobie, że gdyby nie przesłuchanie, to siedziałby rozwalony w swetrze i kończył drugi browar, ale znał siebie aż za dobrze. Na tym to polegało, że prokurator Teodor Szacki nigdy nie siedział rozwalony w swetrze.

Zrobiło mu się ciężko, wolnym krokiem wrócił do Sobieraj, jej mąż zniknął wewnątrz domu. Trawa tłumiła kroki – albo nie słyszała, jak stanął tuż za nią, albo udawała, że nie słyszy. Wystawiła piegowatą twarz do słońca, sięgające ramion rude włosy założyła za uszy, w przedziałku widział dokładnie krótkie odrosty, typowa mysz polska, już z delikatnymi śladami siwizny. Mały nos, śliczne pełne usta, nawet bez makijażu wyraźnie odcinające się brzoskwiniowym kolorem od bladej cery. Miała na sobie moherowy golf i długą plisowaną spódnicę, bose stopy położyła na taborecie – typowym polskim taborecie z białymi nogami i zielonkawym siedzeniem. Śmiesznie ruszała palcami u stóp, jakby chciała je rozgrzać, lub wybijała rytm nuconej w myślach piosenki. Wydała mu się spokojna i ciepła. Nieskończenie daleka od kobiet, z którymi miał do czynienia ostatnio, właścicielek starannie wygolonych cipek, miłośniczek wulgarnych jęków i ostrego rżnięcia w szpilkach. Szacki pomyślał o czekającej go wieczorem klubowej randce z Klarą i głośno westchnął. Sobieraj leniwie odchyliła głowę i spojrzała na niego.

– Piegi ci wychodzą – powiedział.

– Ja nie mam żadnych piegów.

Uśmiechnął się.

– Wiesz, dlaczego cię zaprosiłam?

– Bo zauważyłaś, jaki jestem przerażająco samotny, i przestraszyłaś się, że jak strzelę samobója, to ten żydowski szajs spadnie na twoją głowę?

– Tak, to powód numer jeden. A powód numer dwa... uśmiechniesz się jeszcze raz?

Uśmiechnął się smutno.

– No właśnie. Nie wiem, jak ci się życie ułożyło, Teodorze, ale mężczyzna z takim uśmiechem zasługuje na coś więcej, niż ci się teraz wydaje. Rozumiesz, o czym mówię?

Złapała go za rękę. Miała suchą, chłodną dłoń osoby z niskim ciśnieniem. Odwzajemnił uścisk, ale co miał powiedzieć? Wzruszył tylko ramionami.

– W Sandomierzu zimy potrafią być po prowincjonalnemu potworne, ale teraz zaczyna się wiosna – powiedziała, nie puszczając jego dłoni. – Nie będę ci opowiadała, co to znaczy, sam zobaczysz. I... – zawahała się – i nie wiem dlaczego, ale pomyślałam, że powinieneś opuścić to ciemne miejsce, w którym siedzisz.

Nie wiedział, co powiedzieć, więc się nie odezwał. Rosnąca pod mostkiem kula emocji wymykała się jego kontroli. Skrępowanie, wzruszenie, zażenowanie, zazdrość, smutek, ból przemijania, zadowolenie z dotyku chłodnej dłoni Barbary Sobieraj, zazdrość raz jeszcze – nie potrafił zapanować nad kulą śniegową emocji. Ale było mu bardzo przykro, że taka zwykła rzecz, jak spędzenie z kimś leniwego wiosennego poranka w przydomowym ogrodzie, nigdy nie stała się jego udziałem. Bez sensu takie życie.

Sobieraj wyszedł na taras z dwoma piwami w ręku, uchwyt jego żony rozluźnił się, Szacki dopiero teraz wyjął rękę z jej dłoni.

– Muszę lecieć na to przesłuchanie – powiedział tylko i skłonił się sztywno.

Prokurator Teodor Szacki odszedł szybkim krokiem, nie oglądając się za siebie, po drodze odruchowo zapiął górny guzik grafitowej marynarki. Kiedy zamykał furtkę, układał już w głowie scenariusze rozmowy z Jerzym Szyllerem. Nic więcej go nie interesowało.

2

Wszystko kryją mogiły, a to co zostało, jakieś bardzo jest dalekie i zawoalowane takimi uczuciami, których nie może pojąć. Taka siła żalu i zawziętości, taka żądza zniszczenia, po prostu chęć zemsty. Żeby zająć myśli, w kółko, do znudzenia, powtarza w głowie wszystkie elementy planu, wydaje się, że nie może być mowy o błędzie, ale strach nie jest przez to mniejszy, napięcie nie znika. Chce uciekać, ale plan nie przewiduje ucieczki, musi czekać. Potworne jest to czekanie, dźwięki są za głośne, światła za jasne, barwy za jaskrawe. Tykanie zegara na ścianie jest dokuczliwe niczym kuranty z ratusza, każda kolejna sekunda doprowadza do pasji. Ma ochotę wyjąć baterie, ale to nie znajduje się w planie, zepsuty zegar może być tropem, poszlaką, wskazówką. Ciężko, bardzo ciężko jest wytrzymać.

3

Szacki już miał wcisnąć guzik dzwonka, ale cofnął rękę i ruszył wolno wzdłuż ogrodzenia posesji. Czy Szyller go obserwuje? Nie widział twarzy w oknie, nie widział ruchu firanki, nie było też kamer. Pije kawę? Ogląda telewizję? Czyta wywiad z Leszkiem Millerem i klnie na czym świat stoi? A może to ten rodzaj patrioty, który nigdy nie sięgnie po „Wyborczą"? Gdyby on czekał na prokuratora prowadzącego śledztwo w sprawie o zabójstwo, raczej nie potrafiłby się skupić na codziennych czynnościach. Sterczałby w oknie albo stał na ganku i przekraczał dzienny limit papierosów.

Dom Jerzego Szyllera stał na zboczach wąwozu Piszczele, bo gdzież miałby stać dom jednego z najznamienitszych i najbogatszych sandomierzan. Sądząc po rozmiarach sąsiednich posesji, właściciel musiał połączyć trzy albo cztery działki, dzięki temu gustowny dworek polski mógł być otoczony zadbanym ogrodem. Żadnych szaleństw, żadnych ścieżek z granitowych płyt, oczek wodnych i świątyń Diany, tylko kilka drzew orzechowych, wiosenna, świeżo wyrośnięta trawa, wino oplatające z jednej strony werandę. Gdyby nie charakterystyczny portyk wsparty na pękatych kolumnach i gdyby nie biało-czerwona flaga zwisająca dość smętnie na maszcie przed wejściem, Szacki pomyślałby: Niemcy. Chociaż nie, w Niemczech byłoby to czuć stylizacją, plastikowe okna byłyby podzielone złotymi szprosami, a w domu Szyllera było coś autentycznego. Kolumny sprawiały wrażenie drewnianych i zmęczonych, dach lekko uginał się pod ciężarem gontu, cały budynek przypominał dostojnego staruszka, który świetnie się trzyma, ale swoje lata ma. Taki Max von Sydow ziemiańskiej architektury. Wcisnął dzwonek, gospodarz odezwał się tak błyskawicznie, że musiał trzymać rękę na domofonie. Czyli jednak.

Jerzy Szyller przynudzał monotonnie, Szacki pozwalał mu gadać. Jego rozmówca był wbrew pozorom otwartości i jowialności niezwykle spięty, zachowywał się trochę jak pacjent u onkologa, który będzie rozmawiał o wszystkim, byleby nie usłyszeć wyroku. Udając życzliwe zainteresowanie, prokurator przyglądał się gospodarzowi i otoczeniu.

– Proszę wybaczyć, że zachowam nazwę miejsca dla siebie, chyba nie było w tym nic nielegalnego, ale nie chciałbym oczywiście, żeby ktokolwiek miał kłopoty.

– Ale przetransportował pan całość, czy tylko część? – zapytał Szacki, myśląc, że Szyller używa zbyt wielu słów. Zagłusza napięcie w sposób, który obserwował setki razy.

– Dwór był dość zniszczony, powstał w połowie XIX wieku, jak pan może przypuszczać, po wojnie nikt się nim oczywiście nie opiekował, popadł w ruinę, ale też miał na tyle szczęścia, że Białorusini nie zamienili go w jakiś sowchoz, myślę, że był zwyczajnie zbyt mały, poza tym ziemie w okolicy nieurodzajne. Moi fachowcy go rozebrali belka po belce, już tutaj trzeba było wymienić i uzupełnić około dwudziestu procent konstrukcji, dach został odtworzony na podstawie kilku przedwojennych zdjęć, które zachowały się w rodzinie Wyczerowskich. Zresztą potomkowie hrabiostwa pojawili się u mnie przed dwoma laty, musi pan wiedzieć, że to bardzo miła...

Szacki wyłączył się. Za chwilę wypchnie Szyllera z tej upierdliwej narracji, ale to za chwilę. Teraz rejestrował. Tembr głosu Szyllera, przy powitaniu niski i aksamitny, wchodził niepostrzeżenie na coraz wyższe tony. Dobrze, niech się podenerwuje. Nie widział obrączki, nie widział nigdzie zdjęć kobiet, nie widział zdjęć dzieci, biorąc pod uwagę fakt, że Szyller był klasycznie przystojnym, dobrze sytuowanym mężczyzną w sile wieku – dziwne. Możliwe, że był gejem. Przemawiałaby też za tym jego staranna garderoba i nienachalna, ale wysmakowana elegancja wnętrz. Zamiast obrazów w złoconych ramach – kilka grafik i rycin, w tym reprodukcje ilustracji Andriollego do *Pana Tadeusza*. Zamiast przodka z szablą – portret gospodarza, w stylu Dudy-Gracza, a może nawet samego Dudy-Gracza, cholera wie.

Szyller skończył nudny wywód o transporcie dworu z Białorusi do Sandomierza i klasnął z emfazą w dłonie. Gejostwo plus jeden, pomyślał Szacki. I dodał za chwilę jeszcze jeden punkt, kiedy gospodarz zerwał się, żeby przynieść czekoladki, przełożone – jeszcze raz plus – na małą kryształową paterę. Minus jeden za ruchy – Szyller ruszał się energicznie i miękko, ale nie było w tym przegięcia, ta miękkość kojarzyła się raczej z ruchami drapieżnika.

Usiadł, zakładając nogę na nogę. Sięgnął do mankietów koszuli typowo męskim gestem człowieka, który wszedł do domu i chce odtrąbić koniec dnia, podwijając rękawy. Jednak cofnął dłoń, zanim dotknęła guzików. Szacki zachował kamienną twarz, ale poczuł gwałtowne uderzenie niepokoju. Coś było nie tak.

– Zacznijmy – powiedział, wyciągając dyktafon z kieszeni marynarki.

Szacki konsekwentnie grał znudzonego i – żeby było jasne – tak naprawdę trochę się nudził, ale chciał uśpić czujność Szyllera i pozwolić mu się wygadać. Odebrał dane osobowe, pouczył o odpowiedzialności za składanie fałszywych zeznań, zdziwił się uprzejmie, że przesłuchiwany ma pięćdziesiąt trzy lata – faktycznie nie wyglądał na więcej niż czterdzieści pięć – i teraz od kwadransa słuchał o relacjach

Szyllera z małżeństwem Budników. Same okrągłe oczywistości. Z nim kontaktował się rzadko, wie pan, kontakty biznesu z politykami nie są dobrze widziane, cha, cha, cha, choć oczywiście znali się i wpadali na siebie w czasie oficjalnych imprez.

Jak by określił charakter tych kontaktów? Sporadyczne, poprawne, może nawet życzliwe.

– A denatka?

– Elżbieta – poprawił go z naciskiem Szyller.

Szacki tylko wskazał ręką dyktafon.

– Z Elą znamy się nieomalże od dnia, kiedy tu wróciła.

Jeszcze nie przywykł do czasu przeszłego, Szacki go nie poprawił.

– Od jej małżeństwa?

– Mniej więcej.

– Jak wyglądały państwa kontakty?

– Wie pan, jeśli się w Sandomierzu szuka sponsora na cokolwiek, to lista jest dość krótka. Huta, ja, kilka zakładów, kilka hoteli, od biedy knajpy. Nieomalże nie ma dnia, żeby ktoś nie prosił. Koncert, biedne dzieci, chorzy staruszkowie, deskorolki dla klubu deskorolkowców, gitary dla nowej kapeli, napoje na wernisaż. Rozwiązałem to tak, że jeden z księgowych dysponuje pewną kwartalną kwotą na cele, nazwijmy to, sandomierskie. On wybiera projekty, ja je zatwierdzam, oczywiście.

– Jak duża jest to kwota?

– Pięćdziesiąt tysięcy kwartalnie.

– Denatka z nim się kontaktowała?

– Elżbieta – znowu podkreślenie – rozmawiała z księgowym albo bezpośrednio ze mną.

Szacki zaczął wypytywać bardziej szczegółowo, jeszcze kilka razy podrażnił Szyllera „denatką", ale żadnych wartościowych informacji nie wyciągnął. Znali się, może nawet przyjaźnili, on fundował (lub nie, ale raczej tak) jej różne wariackie pomysły w rodzaju wystawienia *Shreka* na sandomierskim zamku. Być może, tak się chwilami wydawało Szackiemu, biznesmen z białoruskiego dworku podkochiwał się lekko w Budnikowej.

– W dalszym ciągu będzie pan tak hojnie dotował lokalne życie kulturalne?

– Oczywiście. O ile uznam proponowane projekty za tego warte. Nie jestem instytucją państwową, mam luksus wspierania tego, co mi się podoba.

Szacki zanotował w myślach, żeby sprawdzić, co zyskuje, a co nie akceptację wielmożnego pana.

– Słyszałem, że nie kochał pan – prawie niedostrzegalnie zawiesił głos, aby zobaczyć reakcję rozmówcy – Budnika? Że jego działalność w magistracie nie była na rękę pana interesom.

– Plotki.

– W każdej plotce jest ziarno prawdy. Rozumiem, że prężnemu biznesmenowi, który chce działać w przejrzystych warunkach, nie musi odpowiadać, że miasto oddaje w ramach rekompensaty za wielowiekowe krzywdy nieruchomości Kościołowi, żeby potem obracać nimi poza systemem zamówień publicznych ku wiekuistej chwale wszystkich zainteresowanych. No, nie pana, rzecz jasna.

Szyller spojrzał na niego czujnie.

– Myślałem, że pan jest tu nowy.

– Nowy: tak, ze Szwecji: nie – spokojnie zripostował Szacki. – Wiem, jak ten kraj funkcjonuje.

– Albo nie funkcjonuje.

Szacki gestem dał do zrozumienia, że się zgadza.

– Cieszę się, że jest pan taki zgodny. Jako urzędnik państwowy. To wraca wiarę w Rzeczpospolitą.

No proszę, pan nudzikoń potrafi być błyskotliwy, pomyślał Szacki. Tyle tylko, że nie ma czasu na puste przekomarzanki.

– Jest pan patriotą? – zapytał gospodarza.

– Oczywiście. Pan nie?

– W takim razie nie powinno panu przeszkadzać, że ktoś działa na korzyść Kościoła, jedynie słusznej katolickiej wiary. – Szacki nie uznał za stosowne odpowiedzieć na pytanie, jego poglądy nie miały tu nic do rzeczy.

Szyller wstał gwałtownie. Kiedy nie kulił się na kanapie, sprawiał wrażenie potężnego mężczyzny. Dość wysoki, szeroki w barach, mocnej budowy. Taki typ, na którym nawet garnitur z supermarketu będzie dobrze leżał. Szacki pozazdrościł, jego musiały być szyte na miarę, żeby nie wyglądały jak powieszone na kiju od szczotki. Gospodarz podszedł do barku i Szackiemu przez krótką chwilę wydawało się, że sięgnie po widoczną z daleka metaxę, ale Szyller przyniósł butelkę jakiejś snobistycznej wody mineralnej i nalał im po szklance.

– Nie jestem pewien, czy to temat naszej rozmowy, ale największym i najbardziej szkodliwym idiotyzmem w dziejach Polski jest utożsamienie patriotyzmu z tą pedofilską sektą. Przepraszam za mocne słowa, ale wystarczy mieć trochę rozumu, żeby zobaczyć, że Kościół stoi nie za największymi naszymi osiągnięciami, tylko za klęskami. Za krwiożerczym mitem o przedmurzu chrześcijaństwa, za pornograficzną żądzą męczeństwa, za podejrzliwością wobec bogatych...

Tu cię boli, pomyślał Szacki.

– ...za lenistwem, zabobonem, biernym czekaniem na boską pomoc, w końcu za nerwicą seksualną i za bólem tych wszystkich biednych par, których nie stać na in vitro i którym nie będzie dane cieszyć się potomstwem, bo państwo boi się mafii onanistów w czarnych kieckach. – Szyller spostrzegł, że ponoszą go emocje, i opanował się. – Dlatego tak, jestem patriotą, staram się być dobrym patriotą, chcę, żeby moje czyny świadczyły o mnie i chcę być dumny z mojego kraju. Ale proszę mnie nie obrażać posądzeniami, że jakąś żydowską sektę stawiam ponad inne zabobony i nazywam to patriotyzmem.

Szacki poczuł odrobinę sympatii do tego faceta, nikt jeszcze nigdy nie wyraził tak celnie jego własnych poglądów. Zachował tę myśl dla siebie.

– Patriotyzm bez katolicyzmu i antysemityzmu, naprawdę, tworzy pan nową jakość – po raz kolejny skierował rozmowę na interesujące go tematy. Widział, że są one też bliskie gospodarzowi, wyraźnie się rozkręcał, rozluźniał, znać było, że takie rozmowy wielokrotnie toczyły się w tym domu.

– Proszę się nie obrazić, ale myśli pan poprawnymi stereotypami, wdrukowano panu, że najlepszy obywatel to lewicowy kosmopolita o krótkiej pamięci. A patriotyzm to rodzaj wstydliwego hobby, które idzie w parze z ludowym katolicyzmem, ksenofobią i oczywiście antysemityzmem.

– Czyli jest pan niewierzącym, kochającym Żydów patriotą?

– Powiedzmy, że jestem niewierzącym polskim patriotą i antysemitą.

Szacki podniósł brew. Albo gość nie czytał gazet, albo jest pieprznięty, albo pogrywa z nim w jakiś pokrętny sposób. Intuicja mówiła mu, że raczej to ostatnie. Niedobrze.

– Zdziwiony? – Szyller rozsiadł się wygodniej na kanapie, wyglądało to, jakby mościł się w swoich poglądach. – Nie wyciąga pan kodeksu, nie stawia mi zarzutów o nawoływanie do nienawiści na tle rasowym?

Szacki nie skomentował. Miał ważniejsze rzeczy na głowie. Poza tym wiedział, że Szyller i tak powie swoje. To ten typ.

– Widzi pan, żyjemy w dziwnych czasach. Po Zagładzie każdy, kto odważy się przyznać do antysemityzmu, staje ramię w ramię z Eichmannem i salutuje Hitlerowi, patrzą na niego jak na zboczeńca, który marzy o tym, żeby rozdzielać rodziny na rampie. Tymczasem między pewną rezerwą wobec Żydów, ich roli w historii Polski i ich obecnej polityki, a nawoływaniem do pogromów i ostatecznego rozwiązania jest pewna różnica, zgodzi się pan ze mną?

– Proszę mówić dalej, to bardzo ciekawe – zachęcił go Szacki, nie chcąc wdawać się w otwartą kłótnię. Szczerze musiałby odpowiedzieć, że każda próba oceny ludzi poprzez przynależność do grupy narodowej, etnicznej, religijnej czy jakkolwiek innej jest dla niego obrzydliwa. I że jest pewien: każdy pogrom miał swoje źródła w kulturalnej dyskusji o „pewnej rezerwie".

– Niech pan spojrzy na Francję i Niemcy. Czy okazując rezerwę wobec przybyszów z Algierii i Turcji, stają się od razu faszystami i mordercami? Czy może to po prostu obywatele zaniepokojeni przyszłością swojego kraju, zaniepokojeni rozrastającymi się gettami, brakiem asymilacji, agresją, obcym elementem, który rozsadza ich kulturę?

– Nie przypominam sobie, żeby Żydzi w przedwojennej Polsce palili dorożki, organizowali się w mafie i żyli z przemytu narkotyków. – Szacki opieprzył się w myślach za to, że nie powstrzymał riposty. Daj mu mówić, człowieku, daj mu mówić.

– Tak pan mówi, bo nie żył pan w tamtych czasach...

– Faktycznie, jestem trochę młodszy od pana.

Szyller tylko parsknął.

– Nie wie pan, jak to wyglądało. Że Polak z Żydem z sąsiedniej dzielnicy nie mogli się dogadać, bo mówili różnymi językami. Że żydowskie dzielnice niekoniecznie były zadbanymi skansenami interesującej kultury. Brud, nędza, prostytucja. Zazwyczaj czarna dziura na mapie miasta. Ludzie, którzy bardzo chcieli żyć w rozwijającej się Polsce, ale nie chcieli dla niej pracować i walczyć dla jej dobra. Słyszał pan o batalionach żydowskich w powstaniach narodowych? O starozakonnych oddziałach w legionach? Ja nie. Siedzieć cicho i czekać, aż Polacy się wykrwawią, żeby móc potem zająć jeszcze kilka ulic w wyludnionym mieście. Tak, sądzę, że gdybym żył w tamtych czasach, nie byłbym ich fanem, niezależnie od szacunku dla Tuwima i Leśmiana. Tak samo jak dziś nie zgadzam się z tym, żeby każdy pełen agresji i ksenofobii ruch Izraela na Bliskim Wschodzie był momentalnie rozgrzeszany, bo przecież Zagłada. Wyobraża pan sobie, co by było, gdyby Niemcy zaczęli się odgradzać kilkumetrowym murem od tureckich osiedli?

Szacki sobie nie wyobrażał. Więcej: nie chciał sobie wyobrażać. Nie chciał też opowiadać o Berku Joselewiczu. Chciał znaleźć mordercę Elżbiety Budnik, najlepiej razem z niepodważalnymi dowodami, postawić zarzuty, napisać akt oskarżenia i wygrać w sądzie. Tymczasem siedział w tym irytująco doskonałym salonie, w którym poza tandetnym porożem nad lustrem nie było się do czego przyczepić, słuchał mętnych światopoglądowych wynurzeń i trafiał go szlag. Czuł, że zaangażowanie Szyllera podszyte jest rutyną, wyobrażał sobie gości przy stole, rozlewanie wina minimum pięć dych za butelkę, zapach perfum minimum dwie stówy za trzydzieści mililitrów, polędwicę wołową minimum siedem dych za kilogram. Szyller w swojej koszuli za minimum trzysta bawi się spinką za Bóg wie ile i pyta, co by było, gdyby Niemcy. Goście potakują, uśmiechają się ze zrozumieniem: ależ on to potrafi ująć w słowa, co za mówca ten nasz Jurek.

– Tamtych czasów nie ma, Żydów nie ma, może pan dziękować komu trzeba.

– Błagam, stać pana na więcej. – Szyller wydawał się autentycznie zdruzgotany odzywką Szackiego. – Jestem antysemitą, ale nie zboczonym faszystą. Gdybym miał boski wybór i mógł cofnąć Zagładę, świadom, że Polska zostaje ze swoimi przedwojennymi problemami, cofnąłbym, nie wahałbym się ani ułamka sekundy. Ale teraz, kiedy to się stało i nie odstanie, jest smutnym faktem historii, blizną na dziejach świata, gdyby pan się teraz spytał, czy zniknięcie Żydów z Polski było dla niej dobre, to odpowiadam: tak, dobre. Tak samo jak dziś zniknięcie Turków z Niemiec byłoby dobre dla naszych sąsiadów.

– Tak, polskie dzieci w końcu są bezpieczne.

– Mówi pan o mordzie rytualnym? Ma mnie pan za idiotę? Myśli pan, że ktokolwiek rozsądny może brać na poważnie tę bzdurę, tę miejską legendę o straszliwych, rzeczywistych konsekwencjach?

– Podobno w każdej legendzie jest ziarno prawdy – prowokował dalej Szacki.

– Widzi pan, właśnie o tym mówię. Wystarczy słowo krytyki i już jestem oczywiście faszystą, gotowym maszerować z pochodniami przez miasto, krzyczeć, że polskie dziecko na macę porwali. Kraj przesądów, przekłamań, uprzedzeń i histerii. Ciężko jest być tutaj patriotą.

Nowoczesny antysemita przerwał, zadumał się nad swoimi słowami, zapewne dostrzegł w nich zaskakującą nawet dla siebie głębię.

– Szyller – powiedział z namaszczeniem Szacki. – Prawdziwie polskie nazwisko.

– Niech pan nie kpi, to nazwisko starej polskiej arystokracji z Ukrainy, proszę przeczytać *Sławę i chwałę*.

– Nie przepadam za Andrzejewskim.

– Iwaszkiewiczem.

– Zawsze mi się mylą te socrealistyczne pedały. – Szacki uśmiechnął się głupkowato.

Jerzy Szyller obdarzył go spojrzeniem pełnym pogardy, rozlał resztkę wody i poszedł do kuchni, pewnie po nową butelkę. Szacki myślał. Rozmawiał już wystarczająco długo, żeby poznać reakcję rozmówcy, uważał swój wewnętrzny wykrywacz kłamstw za nastrojony. Na dodatek dał się poznać jako idiota, co zawsze pomaga. Pora przejść do rzeczy naprawdę istotnych. Czuł spokój, ponieważ był pewien, że nie wyjdzie od Szyllera z pustymi rękami. Czegoś się dowie. Nie wie jeszcze czego, ale czegoś na pewno. I to coś będzie ważne.

4

Prowadzący długą Polaków rozmowę Jerzy Szyller i prokurator Teodor Szacki z kilku rzeczy nie zdawali sobie sprawy. Szacki – że wbrew intuicji i oczekiwaniom wcale nie zbliża się do szybkiego rozwiązania sprawy, przeciwnie, każda minuta spędzona na dyskusji go od tego finału oddala. Szyller – że znudzona mina prokuratora to maska i że jego rosnące przeświadczenie, jakoby śledczy był typowym niekompetentnym urzędnikiem, jest boleśnie błędne. Obaj – że należą do bardzo nielicznej grupy sandomierzan, którzy mogą, a mimo to nie oglądają siódmego odcinka przygód ojca Mateusza.

Irena i Janusz Rojscy mniejszością żadną nie byli, siedzieli obok siebie na kanapie, żałując, że to nie Polsat, gdzie w przerwie na reklamę można się wysikać, zrobić herbatę i obgadać, co się wydarzyło do tej pory. Artur Żmijewski właśnie przeprowadzał wizję lokalną w zaniedbanym domu opieki, której pensjonariusz z cudzą pomocą przeniósł się na tamten świat.

– Gdzie oni to kręcili? Bo na pewno nie u nas. Robią tyle zamieszania, a potem jeździ tylko rowerem po rynku w te i we wte. Nie zazdroszczę, po tych kocich łbach.

Rojska nie wdawała się w dyskusję, zrzędzenie męża przestała zauważać jakieś dwadzieścia lat temu, na półmetku ich wspólnej przygody. Dziś jej mózg do tego stopnia zamieniał je w szum tła, że nawet nie zagłuszało serialowych dialogów.

– Albo początek? Widziałaś to, jak ojciec Mateusz nowe kino otwiera? Ksiądz! Kino! W Sandomierzu! Przecież ta czarna mafia zabrała nam kino koło katedry. Bo się okazało, że to wszystko kościelne, a jakże, to dostali i zrobili tam dom kultury, w którym się gówno dzieje, żeby biskup z okien nie patrzył, jak młodzież na amerykańskie filmy chodzi, i się nie gorszył. I co? I nie ma w Sandomierzu kina. No, chyba że w *Ojcu Mateuszu*.

– Nie bluźnij.

– Nie bluźnię. Na Boga złego słowa nie powiedziałem, a na czarnych i na scenarzystów mogę gadać, ile chcę. Polski kryminał, jak Boga kocham, takie kryminały jak wszystko inne. Co to za kryminał, w którym się gówno dzieje, na dodatek od początku wiadomo, o co chodzi. O, spójrz, Maliniak. Jak on się nazywa?

– Kłosowski. To po co oglądasz?

– Oglądam, bo chcę zobaczyć swoje miasto w telewizji. I oczywiście nie mogę, bo oni to podobno gdzieś pod Warszawą kręcą, tutaj ani kościoła, ani zakrystii, tylko rynek i rower. A komenda w urzędzie skarbowym, to akurat dobre. Poza tym pamiętasz, jak byliśmy na kawie i akurat kręcili? Trzeba oglądać, nie wiadomo, w którym odcinku będziemy, wszystkie nagrywam na wszelki wypadek. O, spójrz, Turecki.

– Turecki to był Gajos, a to jest Siudym.

– Nawet nieźle się trzyma, nie rozumiem, czemu go ci grafomani wsadzili do domu starców.

– Jest dyrektorem.

– Aha. Myślisz, że nas dzieci też oddadzą do domu starców? Ja wiem, to nie jest przyjemny temat, ale może sami powinniśmy zaproponować? Ja wiem, że czujemy się młodo, ale ja już mam siedemdziesiątkę, ty sześćdziesiąt siedem, nie wolno uciekać od takich tematów. Dla mnie codzienne wchodzenie na nasze drugie piętro to jest wyzwanie. A i im by pewnie łatwiej było, ktoś by się opiekował nami, byliby spokojni. A tak naprawdę ten dom starców mi niestraszny, bylebyśmy razem byli.

Rojska złapała męża za rękę, poczuli to samo wzruszenie. Na ekranie Artur Żmijewski w swoim sandomierskim kościele pod Warszawą prosił wiernych, żeby modlić się o samotnych i cierpiących, żeby zaznali miłości, że nigdy nie jest za późno, aby kochać i być kochanym. Rojski pogłaskał żonę po przedramieniu, czasami zastanawiała się, dlaczego mąż bez przerwy do niej gada, skoro potrafią się idealnie porozumieć bez słów. Ot, zagadka.

– Wiesz, pomyślałam o Zygmuncie.

– Tym z serialu? – Tamten denat miał na imię Zygmunt.

– Nie, naszym Zygmuncie...

– Swoją drogą, to dziwne, że wszyscy o tym imieniu mają minimum siedemdziesiątkę. Nawet w serialach. Wyobrażasz sobie w ogóle Zygmunta niemowlaka? Nie, zawsze jakieś zgrzybiałe dziadki.

– Pomyślałam, że może byśmy poszli się pomodlić za samotnych, żeby jeszcze kogoś pokochali. Zygmunt jest taki dziwny, jak mu Ania odumarła, to się postarzał chyba z piętnaście lat, martwię się o niego. I pomyślałam, że wielu jest takich ludzi.

Przez chwilę oglądali w milczeniu serial. Rojska myślała o wszystkich samotnych przyjaciołach, Rojski, że dobre serce jego żony nigdy nie przestanie go zaskakiwać i że jest największym szczęściarzem na świecie, bo go kiedyś zechciała ta córka piekarza z warkoczem do pasa.

– To może dziś pójdziemy? Pomodlimy się i będziemy mieli mszę z głowy, jutro nie będziemy musieli iść.

– Nie, dziś chyba nie. Chciałam jeszcze zrobić roladę na jutro, może Krysia wpadnie, poza tym wiesz, co o tym sądzę, do kościoła trzeba chodzić w niedzielę. Nie jesteśmy jakimiś Żydami, żeby szabas święcić.

Pokiwał głową, co prawda, to prawda. Najbardziej przekonała go jednak rolada, jego żona potrafiła wyczarować z wołowiny prawdziwe dzieła sztuki, gdyby krowa je zobaczyła, byłaby dumna, że oddała życie dla czegoś tak cudownego. Rojski przy każdej sposobności powtarzał wyświechtany bon mot, że jeśli zabije go cholesterol, to będzie odchodził z uśmiechem na ustach. Bo było warto.

– Pozornie uśpione sumienie nagle budzi się – mówił na ekranie sandomierski biskup głosem Sławomira Orzechow-

skiego. – Nie jest to przyjemne, bo prowadzi do uczucia bezradności, rozgoryczenia, bólu. I wtedy On pomaga nam się
podnieść z kolan.

Irena i Janusz Rojscy nie poszli dziś do kościoła, u niej
zadecydowały względy światopoglądowe, u niego – rolada.
Przytuleni do siebie oglądali piękne ujęcie Sandomierza
z lotu ptaka w ostatniej scenie odcinka, myśląc, jak spokojne, niewinne jest ich miasto.

5

Pod pozorem odważnych i kontrowersyjnych poglądów
Szyller był niesłychanie płytki, a jego erudycja okazała się
zręcznym żonglowaniem stereotypami, niczym więcej. Do
takich wniosków doszedł prokurator Teodor Szacki, wy-
słuchując wywodów przesłuchiwanego o Niemczech. Jako
honorowy członek Związku Polaków w Niemczech miał
mnóstwo do powiedzenia na ten temat, nic z tego nie było interesujące – nie było też zbyt pozytywne, sugerował, że Polacy to prześladowana mniejszość. Na dodatek Szyller miał
specyficzny sposób mówienia, który zapewne podobał się
kobietom, ale niezmiernie drażnił prokuratora. Niezależnie
od rangi sprawy, wszystko wypowiadał z zaangażowaniem
i staranną emfazą, dość podniesionym tonem, co mogło
sprawiać wrażenie, że to człowiek męski, pewny siebie i swoich poglądów, który wie, czego chce, i zazwyczaj to dostaje.
A tak naprawdę Jerzy Szyller był po prostu skoncentrowa-
nym na sobie egotykiem, uwielbiającym brzmienie własnego głosu, dlatego tyle staranności wkładał w wypowiadane
kwestie.

Werbalny onanizm, skomentował w myślach Szacki, słuchając historii rodzinnej Szyllera. Był potomkiem jednego

z pierwszych członków Związku, stąd jego wysoka pozycja i honorowe członkostwo. Urodził się w Niemczech, miał mały dom w Nadrenii Północnej-Westfalii, niedaleko Bochum, gdzie mieściły się władze – jak mówił – Bundu. Ale więcej bywał w Sandomierzu lub mieszkaniu w Warszawie, które nazywał w kółko służbówką, jakby to miało być zabawne.

– Czy zna pan ten symbol? – prokurator wyciągnął z teczki wydruk rodła, niechętnie, bał się, że skrzywi się na kolejne emfatyczne „oczywiście".

– Oczywiście! Przecież to rodło, właśnie symbol Bundu, dla nas nieomalże święty znak. Nie wiem, czy zna pan historię jego powstania, akurat miałem honor usłyszeć ją od samej autorki, Janiny Kłopockiej...

– Znam – przerwał Szacki. – Przepraszam, jeśli moje pytanie wyda się panu głupie, ale w jakiej formie używacie rodła? Sztandary, herby, papier firmowy, koszulki, jakieś znaczki w klapie marynarki?

– Wie pan, nie jesteśmy sektą, oczywiście rodło pojawia się wszędzie tam, gdzie oficjalnie występuje Związek, ale nie wieszamy go obok Orła Białego. Ostentacja nigdy nie jest wskazana.

Szacki wyciągnął zdjęcie znaczka, który trzymała denatka. Specjalnie przygotował dość zwyczajne, które nie sugerowało, że to ważny dowód w sprawie. Podsunął Szyllerowi.

– Czy członkowie Związku często noszą coś takiego?

Szyller oglądał zdjęcie.

– Jedynie działacze, ewentualnie zasłużeni członkowie. Nie kupi pan tego od Turka, można to dostać jedynie od przewodniczącego Bundu.

– Pan oczywiście ma taki?

– Oczywiście.

– Mógłbym go zobaczyć?

– Oczywiście.

Gospodarz wstał i zniknął w głębi domu. Szacki czekał, z trwogą myślał o papierkowej robocie, jaka go czeka po tej rozmowie. Przesłuchać nagranie, wydobyć istotne fragmenty, spisać, dać do podpisania. Osobno protokół okazania. Chryste, dlaczego nie ma asystentki.

– Dziwna sprawa... – Gospodarz stanął w drzwiach, w ciepłym świetle popołudnia jego śnieżnobiała koszula wydawała się brzoskwiniowa.

– Ale nie może pan go znaleźć – dopowiedział prokurator.

– Nie mogę.

– Gdzie go pan trzyma?

– W pudełku ze spinkami, wpinam go tylko na specjalne okazje.

– Ktoś o tym wie? Kochanka? Przyjaciele?

Szyller przecząco pokręcił głową. Wyglądał na autentycznie zdziwionego. To nie był dobry znak, Szacki wolałby, żeby zaczął motać, opowiadać, że jest w marynarce w Warszawie, cokolwiek.

– A mogę spytać, skąd pan go ma? – zapytał w końcu prokuratora.

– Wyjęliśmy go z dłoni denatki.

– Elżbiety – Szyller poprawił automatycznie, ale z jego głosu zniknęła staranna emfaza.

– Denatki Elżbiety.

Szyller ciężkim krokiem podszedł do kanapy, bez słowa usiadł naprzeciwko prokuratora. Spojrzał na niego pytająco, jakby czekał, aż Szacki poradzi mu, co ma powiedzieć.

– Gdzie pan spędzał święta?

– W niedzielę byłem u siostry w Berlinie, przyleciałem w poniedziałek rano, o trzynastej byłem już tutaj.

– Gdzie pan był w poniedziałek i wtorek?

– W domu.

– Ktoś pana odwiedzał? Znajomi, przyjaciele?

Zaprzeczenie. Szacki tylko spojrzał przeciągle, milczał, planując dalszy ciąg rozmowy, i nagle w jego głowie pojawiła się zaskakująca myśl. Myśl głupia, pozbawiona podstaw, mająca źródło tylko i wyłącznie w intuicji. Na tyle jednak niepokojąca, że prokurator wstał i zaczął wolno chodzić po pomieszczeniu, uważnie mu się przyglądając. Szukał w tym gustownym muzeum ziemiaństwa znaków, że mieszka tu człowiek z krwi i kości. Plamy po winie, zdjęcia na ścianie, okruszków po śniadaniu, brudnego kubka po kawie. Upchniętych zabłoconych butów, koca, którym można owinąć się wieczorami, rzuconej na parapet czapki. Niczego nie znalazł. Dom był albo nieużywany, albo wyjątkowo dokładnie wysprzątany. Z brudu? Z czyjejś obecności? Ze śladów niewygodnych wydarzeń? Żeby nie powiedzieć nic więcej ponad to, co gospodarz miał o sobie do powiedzenia? Myśli w histerycznym tempie przelatywały przez umysł Szackiego. Jeśli ma przycisnąć Szyllera, musi przyjąć jakąś hipotezę, założyć, że kłamie w konkretnej sprawie, i w tej sprawie zaatakować. Niestety, chwilowo najmocniej rozpychała się w jego głowie hipoteza najbardziej absurdalna.

– Często w ogóle ktoś pana odwiedza?

– Nie jestem specjalnie towarzyski. Jak pan słyszy, spędziłem sam pół Wielkiejnocy. A to miejsce jest dla mnie szczególne, taki azyl. Lubię tu być sam, nie chcę imprez, głośnych rozmów, cudzych zapachów.

Parapet nad kominkiem, miejsce, gdzie kurz i brud zalegają już pół minuty po wysprzątaniu, też był sterylny. Szacki przesunął palcem po dębowej, polakierowanej desce – nic. Półka z książkami – tak samo. Telewizora nie było. Żaden z mężczyzn nic nie mówił od dłuższej chwili i Szacki poczuł się nieswojo. Był sam w pustym domu razem z dwa razy większym od niego facetem, który być może jest mordercą. Zerknął na Szyllera. Biznesmen patrzył na niego czujnie. Gdyby Szacki był paranoikiem, mógłby pomyśleć, że śledzi jego ruchy, przygotowując się do ataku. Gospodarz zauważył wzrok prokuratora i na wszelki wypadek przybrał lekko przestraszony wyraz twarzy.

– Rozumiem, że nie najlepiej to wygląda? – zapytał.

– Kiedy pan widział denatkę ostatni raz?

– Z Elżbietą spotkałem się jakieś dwa tygodnie przed świętami. Rozmawialiśmy o wakacjach, chciała zrobić kino letnie na Małym Rynku, gadaliśmy, jak przekonać do tego mieszkańców. Wie pan, jak to jest, ludzie zawsze są przeciw. Chcieliby, żeby dużo się działo, ale nie pod ich oknami.

Szacki podjął decyzję. Raz się żyje, najwyżej przestrzeli i Szyller napisze na niego skargę. Nie pierwszą i nie ostatnią zapewne w karierze białowłosego prokuratora.

– Mógłbym zobaczyć zdjęcie, które stało na kominku?

– Słucham?

– Chciałbym zobaczyć zdjęcie, które stało na kominku.

– Tam nie stało...

– Pokaże mi je pan czy nie?

Szyller nie odpowiedział. Ale jego twarz spoważniała. Cóż, koniec anegdotek dla pana prokuratora, już się chyba nie przyjaźnimy, pomyślał Szacki.

– Rozmawiałem o panu z ludźmi. Same superlatywy. Wzorowy obywatel. Filantrop. Biznesmen z ludzką twarzą.

Szyller wzruszył ramionami. Jeśli chciał grać zaaferowanego, lekko przestraszonego obywatela, to teraz właśnie porzucał tę pozę. Podwinął w końcu rękawy koszuli, mięśnie na opalonych przedramionach zagrały groźnie. Sandomierski filantrop dbał o swoje patriotyczne ciało, bez dwóch zdań.

– Duża kultura. Duża inteligencja. Wydawałoby się, że powinien pan rozumieć swoje położenie. Brutalnie zamordowana kobieta ściskała w kurczowo zaciśniętej dłoni rzadki znaczek, którego pan nie może znaleźć. I nie potrafi wytłumaczyć, co się mogło z nim stać. Nie może pan też w żaden sposób udowodnić, gdzie był w czasie, kiedy popełniono zabójstwo. A mimo to pan kłamie. Bardzo mnie to dziwi.

– Pan się łatwo dziwi, panie prokuratorze. Taka dziecięca cecha się przydaje w pańskim zawodzie?

Szacki pokręcił z niedowierzaniem głową. Co za tania odzywka, chyba przecenił Szyllera.

142

– Powinienem pana zamknąć, przedstawić zarzuty, potem zastanawiać się, co dalej – prawie się roześmiał, mówił to już drugi raz w ciągu kilku dni, co za pieprzone miasto krętaczy, czy ktoś tu w ogóle mówi prawdę, do jasnej cholery?

– Co pana powstrzymuje?

– Nie widzę powodu, dla którego miałby pan zabić swoją kochankę. Zwłaszcza w ten sposób.

– Niech pan się nie wygłupia.

– Po kolei. Chcę usłyszeć wszystko po kolei. Może pan zacząć od zdjęcia.

Jerzy Szyller siedział bez ruchu, powietrze było gęste od jego emocji, jego wahania, jego panicznych rozważań, co zrobić.

– Pan nic nie rozumie. To małe miasto. Już zawsze będą mówili, że kurwa, że się puszczała.

– Zdjęcie. Już.

Jerzy Szyller szybko doszedł do wniosku, że przylepienie miłości swego życia łatki kurwy to rzecz przykra, ale nie tak przykra jak areszt śledczy w Tarnobrzegu. Przyniósł wszystkie rzeczy, które wcześniej pieczołowicie wysprzątał. Jej koc, którym owijała się na kanapie, jej szlafrok w śmiesznym lazurowym kolorze, album ze wspólnymi zdjęciami i w końcu oprawioną w gustowną – jakżeby inaczej – drewnianą ramkę fotografię z kominka. Szacki go rozumiał, gdyby miał z kimkolwiek takie zdjęcie, traktowałby je jak relikwię. Zrobione na Błoniach w Krakowie, siedzieli razem na ławce, w tle widać było kawałek Wawelu. Szyller wyglądał jak Pierce Brosnan na wakacjach, Ela Budnik uwiesiła się jego szyi w wariackiej, pełnej zgrywy pozie, teatralnie zginając jedną nogę gestem Audrey Hepburn i układając usta do całusa. On był po pięćdziesiątce, ona po czterdziestce, a wyglądali jak para nastolatków, szczęście wypływało każdym porem skóry, prześwietlało kliszę, tyle było miłości w tym małym obrazku, że Szackiemu zrobiło się żal Szyllera. Być może był zabójcą, być może nie, ale jego strata musiała być niewyobrażalna.

Prokurator poznał dzieje romansu ze szczegółami i choć znać było, jak ważne to są dla Szyllera wydarzenia, jak przełomowe i głębokie, w gruncie rzeczy była to historia banalna. Kobieta, której wydaje się, że jest kimś więcej, niż jest w istocie, i która syndrom zamykających się drzwi błędnie interpretuje jako uwięzienie w klatce, w której nie może rozwinąć skrzydeł. Wieloletnie małżeństwo, cicha stabilizacja, małomiasteczkowa nuda. I facet, drobny biznesmen i drobny antysemita, do tego stopnia przekonany o swojej wyjątkowości i erudycji, że udaje mu się przekonać także ją, i razem wmawiają sobie, że oni sami i ich grafomański romans to tak naprawdę wielka literatura. Norma, standard, nuda. Szacki z zadziwiającym nawet jego samego cynizmem pomyślał, że tak naprawdę dopiero gipsowo blady trup przydał tej historii wielkości.

– Czy przez te półtora roku mąż denatki nabrał jakichś podejrzeń, mówiła coś panu?

– Nie, nic nie mówiła. Ale też w tym związku łatwo było coś ukryć. On siedział w urzędzie w bardzo nietypowych godzinach, sporo jeździł. Ona też miała spotkania z artystami w najróżniejszych porach w najróżniejszych miejscach. Dzięki temu spędziliśmy kilka razy wspaniałe dni w Bochum.

– Czy planowała zostawić męża?

Cisza.

– Rozmawialiście o tym? To nie mogło być dla pana przyjemne. Świadomość, że codziennie kładzie się obok niego, całuje na dobranoc, robi to, co zwykle robią małżonkowie.

Cisza.

– Panie Szyller, rozumiem, że Sandomierz to małe miasto, ale nie aż tak małe. Tu chyba zdarzają się rozwody, zejścia, ludzie rozpoczynają nowe życie. Rozumiem, że w waszej sytuacji nie byłoby to trudne. Bezdzietni, o wolnych zawodach. Tak naprawdę mogła mu przysłać papiery pocztą.

Przesłuchiwany wykonał ręką nieokreślony gest, dając do zrozumienia, że ta kwestia ma tyle skomplikowanych niuansów, że nie da się jej ująć w słowa. Szackiemu przypomniał się Budnik, to, że sprawił na nim wrażenie Golluma, dla którego nic nie miało znaczenia – tylko jego skarb. Co by zrobił, gdyby się dowiedział, że jego skarb ktoś mu zabiera? I to nie ktoś, tylko znany adwersarz, człowiek, z którego poglądów być może razem z Elą śmiali się w łóżku, którego emfazę przedrzeźniali. Być może ona dla niepoznaki skarżyła się, że musi do niego chodzić, że to taki dziwny typ, wiesz, taki aż nadto samczy, wbrew pozorom prostak, ale co poradzić, dzięki niemu zrobimy coś dla dzieci. I nagle dowiaduje się, że nie wysiadywała u niego z męczeńską miną, opowiadając o biednych dzieciach, tylko spocona ujeżdżała go, wiła się pod nim, błagała, żeby rżnął ją mocniej, i oblizywała wargi z jego spermy.

Odchodzę. Żegnaj. Miałeś rację, słusznie przez całą naszą znajomość przeczuwałeś, że nigdy nie będziesz mnie miał do końca. Jestem dla ciebie za dobra, zawsze byłam.

Wystarczy do zabójstwa? Oczywiście.

– W poniedziałek czekałem na nią.

– Słucham?

– W poniedziałek wielkanocny miała przyjść do mnie i już zostać, we wtorek mieliśmy wyjechać i nigdy nie wrócić.

– Czy to oznacza, że miała powiedzieć o was mężowi?

– Nie wiem.

Ożeż do kurwy nędzy! Szacki wyciągnął telefon i zadzwonił do Wilczura, stary policjant odebrał od razu.

– Zgarnijcie Budnika błyskawicznie, potrzebuję też kogoś do zabezpieczenia na Słoneczną, do Jerzego Szyllera. Będziemy robili przeszukanie, a potem konfrontację. Raz, raz.

Wilczur był zawodowcem. Powiedział tylko „jasne" i odłożył słuchawkę. Biznesmen patrzył zaskoczony.

– Jak to „przeszukanie"? Przecież wszystko panu opowiedziałem, wszystko pokazałem.

– Niech pan nie będzie naiwny, ludzie codziennie mi pokazują i opowiadają. Co najmniej połowa to ściemy, półprawdy i ordynarne kłamstwa. Biorąc pod uwagę pański stopień zażyłości z denatką...

– Elżbietą.

– ...powinienem oprócz przeszukania kazać przekopać ogródek i zamknąć pana do czasu wyjaśnienia wszystkich kwestii. Co może zresztą zrobię.

– Mój prawnik...

– Pański prawnik będzie mógł napisać zażalenie – warknął Szacki, rosła w nim wściekłość, której nie potrafił powstrzymać. – Zdaje sobie pan w ogóle sprawę, jak ważne dla śledztwa fakty zataił? Zamordowano pańską kochankę, a pan, mając informacje, które mogą być kluczowe, siedzi cicho, bo jeszcze ktoś o niej złe słowo powie? Co z pana za obywatel i patriota, skoro ma pan w dupie sprawiedliwość, przypomnę: ostoję mocy i trwałości Rzeczpospolitej! Zwykły małomiasteczkowy antysemita i tyle, rzygać się chce.

Jerzy Szyller zerwał się na równe nogi, na przystojną twarz wystąpiły mu czerwone plamy, ruszył w stronę Szackiego szybkim krokiem i kiedy prokurator był pewien, że dojdzie do bójki, zadzwonił telefon. Wilczur. Załatwione, dobrze.

– Tak?

Szacki przez chwilę słuchał.

– Zaraz będę.

Wybiegł, w furtce zderzył się z mundurowymi, kazał im pilnować Szyllera.

6

Prokurator Teodor Szacki usiadł na kanapie w salonie Budników, ponieważ zrobiło mu się autentycznie słabo. Krew pulsowała w skroniach, nie mógł skoncentrować wzroku na jednym punkcie, czuł dziwne mrowienie w palcach rąk i nieprzyjemny, metaliczny posmak w ustach. Gwałtownie nabrał powietrza, ale to nie przyniosło mu ulgi, wręcz przeciwnie, poczuł ukłucie w płucach, jakby powietrze pełne było małych igiełek.

A może to nie płuca, tylko serce? Zamknął oczy, policzył do dziesięciu i z powrotem.

– Wszystko w porządku? – spytała Sobieraj.

Wszyscy byli wyrwani z domowych pieleszy. Sobieraj miała na sobie dżinsy i czerwony polar, Wilczur dziwne brązowe spodnie – które sprawiały wrażenie, jakby wewnątrz nie było nóg – i ciężki golf, dwóch policjantów przyozdabiały bazarowe wiatrówki, tak brzydkie, że nie było wątpliwości, że są policjantami. Szacki w swoim garniturze po raz kolejny tego dnia czuł się jak kretyn. A to był tylko jeden z powodów.

– Nie, Basiu – odpowiedział spokojnie. – Nic nie jest w porządku. Ponieważ bardzo ważny świadek, a od niedawna główny podejrzany w sprawie o bardzo głośne i bulwersujące zabójstwo, pilnowany bez przerwy przez dwójkę policjantów, zniknął. I choć oczywiście nie ma to teraz żadnego praktycznego znaczenia, to błagam, zaspokójcie moją ciekawość i powiedzcie: jak to jest, kurwa, możliwe?

Policjanci jednocześnie wzruszyli ramionami.

– Panie prokuratorze, nie ruszyliśmy się ani na krok, przysięgamy. Jak wcześniej byliśmy głodni, to zadzwoniliśmy do kolegów, żeby coś przywieźli, mogą zaświadczyć. Siedzieliśmy przed tą chałupą bez przerwy.

– Wychodził?

– Koło południa do ogrodu kilka razy. Coś przyciął, włączył spryskiwacz, dokręcił skrzynkę na listy. Wszystko zanotowane.

– A potem?

– Kręcił się po domu, jak się zrobiło ciemniej, widzieliśmy, jak się zapalały i gasły światła.

– Ktoś obserwował dom od strony skarpy?

– Ale tam jest dwumetrowy mur, panie prokuratorze, no.

Szacki spojrzał na Wilczura. Inspektor strząsnął popiół do doniczki z fikusem, odchrząknął.

– Obstawiliśmy trasy wylotowe, sprawdzamy samochody i autobusy. Ale jeśli puścił się gdzieś piechotą przez krzaki, to czarno to widzę.

Cóż, nie było żadnej możliwości, żeby to zrobić po cichu.

– Zawiadomcie okoliczne komendy rejonowe, ja wystawię nakaz aresztowania i list gończy, zróbcie notatkę i załatwcie przez Kielce, żeby to jak najszybciej trafiło do mediów. Sprawa jest świeża, facet to nie zawodowiec, tylko podstarzały radny, zbierzemy co prawda od wszystkich zjebkę, ale powinno się udać. Przynajmniej mamy podejrzanego, zawsze jakiś konkret, spróbujemy to przedstawić jako sukces organów ścigania.

– Nie będzie łatwo – mruknęła Sobieraj. – Media się rzucą.

– Tym lepiej. Będą o tym trąbili na okrągło, każda ekspedientka będzie znała Budnika, zanim zgłodnieje na tyle, żeby gdzieś wejść po bułkę.

Szacki wstał gwałtownie, zakręciło mu się w głowie. Odruchowo złapał się ramienia Sobieraj, kobieta spojrzała na niego podejrzliwie.

– Luz, nic mi nie jest. Do roboty, my wypełnimy kwity w prokuraturze, wy przygotujcie komunikat, za pół godziny się zdzwonimy, za godzinę chcę to widzieć na pasku w telewizji.

Przed wyjściem omiótł wzrokiem mieszczański salon Budników. Znowu zabrzęczał mu jakiś dzwoneczek alarmowy. Czuł się jak człowiek patrzący na dwa obrazki różniące się dziesięcioma szczegółami. Miał pewność, że coś było nie tak, ale nie wiedział co. Cofnął się na środek pomieszczenia, policjanci minęli go i wyszli, Sobieraj zatrzymała się w drzwiach.

– Dawno tu byłaś? – spytał.

– Ja wiem? Jakiś miesiąc temu, przez chwilę, na kawie.

– Coś się zmieniło?

– Tu się ciągle coś zmienia, zmieniało raczej. Ela co kilka miesięcy przestawiała meble, zmieniała oświetlenie, dodawała kwiaty i tkaniny, z tych samych klocków tworzyła zupełnie nowe mieszkanie. Twierdziła, że woli wprowadzać kontrolowane zmiany, niż czekać, aż jej dusza się zbuntuje i poszuka sobie zmiany wbrew niej.

Spojrzał na nią przeciągle.

– Tak, wiem, jak to teraz brzmi.

– Ale poza tym, że pomieszczenie wygląda inaczej, ma inny wystrój, niczego ci nie brakuje? Czegoś, co tutaj zawsze było?

Basia Sobieraj rozglądała się przez chwilę uważnie.

– We framudze drzwi do kuchni zawsze wisiał taki drążek do podciągania, Grzesiek na nim ćwiczył. Ale ciągle im odpadał, pewnie w końcu go wyrzucili.

– Coś jeszcze?

– Nie, raczej nie. Dlaczego?

Machnął ręką, że to nieważne, i razem wyszli z małego domku przy Katedralnej, prosto w cień ogromnego z tej perspektywy kościoła, ostre gotyckie kształty odcinały się wyraźnie na tle rozgwieżdżonego nieba. W sieni wisiało zdjęcie Eli Budnik sprzed dziesięciu, piętnastu lat. Była bardzo piękna, bardzo dziewczęca, jak to się mówi – tryskająca życiem. I bardzo fotogeniczna, dopowiedział sobie Szacki, myśląc o zdjęciu na kominku Szyllera.

Dochodziła dziewiąta wieczorem. Baśka Sobieraj poszła w końcu do domu, wcześniej opuściła ich szefowa, prokurator Teodor Szacki siedział zgnębiony w biurze, wsłuchany w młodzieżowy harmider i stłumione dźwięki dyskotekowej muzyki, w klubie po drugiej stronie ulicy zaczynała się impreza. Czuł się nieswojo, od paru godzin w fizyczny sposób odczuwał niepokój, fizjologiczny lęk, który nie miał źródła w żadnym realnym zagrożeniu, po prostu był, rozlewał się po całym ciele – bały się jego ramiona, jego szyja, bały się narządy wewnętrzne. Byłoby to nawet śmieszne, gdyby nie było męczące i przewlekłe, jakby znane wszystkim krótkie ukłucie strachu rozciągnęło się na godziny. Im bardziej o tym myślał, tym czuł się gorzej.

Zaczął chodzić po gabinecie.

Spisana pokrótce, przedstawiona Misi – która przyszła z domu z kanapkami i termosem herbaty z sokiem malinowym – i wpięta do akt wersja śledcza wydawała się prawie stuprocentowo pewna. Grzegorz Budnik zostaje porzucony lub dowiaduje się o romansie żony z Jerzym Szyllerem. Wściekłość porzuconego, żal, ból, do tego świadomość, że może to być złamanie jego budowanej przez lata kariery politycznej, zapewne dochodzi do kłótni. W czasie kłótni ściska jej szyję trochę za mocno, Elżbieta Budnik traci przytomność, Budnik wpada w panikę – zabił żonę. Ogląda *CSI*, wie, że na szyi zostały jego odciski, dlatego decyduje się na upozorowanie poderżnięcia gardła, przy okazji postanawia wzbudzić histerię na tle stosunków polsko-żydowskich, jest z Sandomierza, zna temat. Być może nawet dziwi się, kiedy z jego żony wypływają litry krwi, być może za późno zdaje sobie sprawę z tego, że jeszcze żyła. Zna miasto, każde przejście podwórkami, wie, gdzie wisi każda kamera. Wykorzystuje to, żeby niepostrzeżenie podrzucić zwłoki pod starą synagogą. Jednak kiedy do Sandomierza wraca Szyller – pęka. Wie, że jeśli śledczy dowiedzą się o romansie, stanie się głównym podejrzanym. Jeszcze raz wykorzystuje znajomość miasta, tym razem, żeby z niego uciec pod bokiem pilnujących go policjantów.

Historia miała słabe strony, zagadką było miejsce zabójstwa, sposób przeniesienia zwłok, samo narzędzie zbrodni też nie należało do rzeczy, które trzyma się w kredensie obok widelczyków do tortu. Szackiemu nie dawała spokoju także sprawa znaczka znalezionego w dłoni denatki. Od początku nie sądził, żeby to obciążało Szyllera – takie rzeczy się nie zdarzają w rzeczywistości i prokurator był przekonany, że sprawca z jakichś powodów chciał koniecznie pogrążyć biznesmena. Ale Budnik? Przecież musiał przewidzieć, że skierowanie śledztwa na Szyllera momentalnie rykoszetem trafi w niego.

Jednak mimo luk brzmiało to wiarygodnie, mimo fizycznego braku podejrzanego wyglądało o niebo lepiej niż jeszcze dwanaście godzin wcześniej, kiedy nie było nic wiadomo i rozważano opcję poszukiwania jakiegoś świra z religijno-narodową obsesją. Jest konkret, mediom można mówić, że poszukują podejrzanego, człowieka z imieniem i nazwiskiem. Można się też spodziewać, że Budnik wpadnie lada dzień, lada godzina.

Tak, tyle teorii. W praktyce Szackiego roznosiło. Próbował siebie przekonać, że miesza dwa porządki, że jego niepokój jest czysto prywatny, że ciało się upomina, aby zapłacił cenę za przeprowadzkę, za rozstanie, za samotność, za wszystkie zmiany – wszystkie na gorsze zresztą – ostatnich miesięcy. Próbował, ale wewnątrz aż skomlił jak gończy pies. Coś było nie tak.

Bardzo nie chciał być tego wieczoru sam. Spławił wcześniej Klarę, która ciągnęła go na jakiś wioskowy dyskotekowy koncert do ratusza, ale teraz zadzwonił do niej i powiedział, że dojdzie. Trzeba jej powiedzieć, że nie będą kontynuować tej znajomości, trzeba trochę uporządkować swoje życie.

8

Wpadł jeszcze do domu, żeby założyć dżinsy i sportową koszulę, ale i tak czuł się jak stary dziad, wchodząc razem z Klarą do podziemi sandomierskiego ratusza, jakby przyprowadził starszą córkę na imprezę. Znał z prokuratorskiej praktyki zagadnienia tabletek gwałtu i crystal meth, ale nigdy nie miał do czynienia z klubowym podziemiem w praktyce. Czy obowiązuje tu jakiś kodeks, niepisane zasady? Co ma zrobić, jeśli jakieś umalowane dziecko zaproponuje, że mu obciągnie? Podziękować grzecznie? Zadzwonić na policję? Odprowadzić do rodziców? A jeśli będą chcieli mu wcisnąć narkotyki? Przedstawić od razu zarzuty? Głowę miał pełną pytań, kiedy znalazł się w niewielkiej nisko sklepionej ceglanej piwnicy.

Miejsce było ciasne, ale malownicze, na suficie wisiała obwieszona jakimiś łańcuchami krata, w kącie kawałek kamiennej rzeźby jakiegoś świątka – stąd pewnie nazwa klubu, Lapidarium – nie mogło być wątpliwości, że to podziemia starego i zacnego budynku. Ludzi było sporo, ale nie tyle, żeby nie móc dopchać się do baru, Szacki wziął piwo dla siebie i dla Klary, jednocześnie oglądając towarzystwo. Cóż, było to towarzystwo zaskakujące. Żadnych plastikowych panien, małolat ze świecącymi od błyszczyka ustami i cyckami na wierzchu, żadnych żelbojów w opalizujących koszulach, żadnych białych stringów połyskujących trupio w ultrafioletowym stroboskopie. Stroboskopu zresztą nie było, ultrafioletu też nie. Mało tego, nawet grupa wiekowa Szackiego była dość licznie reprezentowana, kilka par typu zakola-i-odrosty mogło już mieć dzieci w wieku najmłodszych uczestników imprezy.

Obserwował Klarę, która dołączyła do grupki znajomych. Wszyscy mieli tyle lat, co ona, jakieś dwadzieścia sześć, dwadzieścia siedem. Ktoś opowiedział dowcip, reszta wybuchnęła śmiechem. Wyglądali sympatycznie: gość o wyglądzie administratora sieci w okrągłych okularkach i z przerzedzonymi blond włosami, dwie panny w dżinsach, jedna płaska i szeroka w biodrach, druga cycata i szczupła, śmiesznie wyglądały obok siebie. No i Klara. W dżinsach, bordowej bluzce z dekoltem w serek, z włosami spiętymi w koński ogon. Młoda, śliczna, może nawet najładniejsza na tej sali. Dlaczego miał ją za głupią tipsiarę? Tylko dlatego, że jest bardziej kobieca od jego wymiętej byłej żony, z którą spędził ostatnie półtorej dekady? Czy teraz każdy przejaw kobiecości, każdy but na obcasie i pomalowany paznokieć będą mu się wydawały wulgarne, czy aż tak ma przeoraną psychikę po etapie koszmarnych ikeowskich kapci za 4,99, które walały się koło jego łóżka, odkąd w ogóle Ikea pojawiła się w Polsce?

Podszedł do towarzystwa, patrzyli na niego z życzliwą ciekawością w czasie prezentacji. Klara, dziwna rzecz, wydawała się dumna, że taki dziadek znalazł się w ich gronie.

– Boże, prawdziwy prokurator, nie będziemy teraz mogli palić trawki – zażartowała płaska z biodrami, Justyna.

Twarz Szackiego zamieniła się w kamienną maskę.

– Nie będziecie mogli palić trawki, ponieważ nie możecie posiadać trawki. Ustawa o przeciwdziałaniu narkomanii, paragraf sześćdziesiąty drugi, ustęp pierwszy, przewiduje karę pozbawienia wolności do lat trzech dla posiadacza środków odurzających lub substancji psychotropowych.

Towarzystwo zamilkło i patrzyło niepewnie, Szacki upił spory łyk piwa. Szczyny, jak zawsze z nalewaka.

– Ale nie martw się, znam paru dobrych adwokatów, może nawet załatwią ci osobną celę na drugą połowę odsiadki.

Wybuchnęli śmiechem i zaczęła się luźna rozmowa, Klara zaczęła coś opowiadać o otwarciu przewodu doktorskiego – był wstrząśnięty, nie wiedział nawet, że skończyła jakieś studia – ale w pół zdania przerwało jej głośne wejście supportu. Szacki mało nie wypuścił ze zdumienia piwa z ręki i to zdumienie nie opuściło go już do końca imprezy, najlepszej, na jakiej był od lat. Okazało się, że na tej wiosce słuchali i grali zajebistą muzykę. Support zaczął mocno punkrockowo, żeby potem zejść w stronę melodyjnej stylistyki Iron Maiden, następne dwie kapele – z tego, co zrozumiał, obie miały korzenie w Corruption, które jak się okazało, było z Sandomierza – także jechały rockowo, bez żadnych zaśpiewajek, rapowanych wstawek i jęczenia o tym, że ona i on, *yeah, baby.*

Z każdym kawałkiem ludzi jakby było więcej, wszyscy darli się głośniej i skakali wyżej, pod sklepieniem coraz gęściej zbierały się endorfiny, pot zaczął skraplać się na metalowej kracie, było w tym coś z plemiennego doświadczenia, które przywodziło mu na myśl stare warszawskie kluby, do których chodził przed wiekami na koncerty Kultu. Pierwsza kapela była zdecydowanie lepsza muzycznie, miejscami podchodziła pod Soundgarden, miejscami było to takie megadeathowate, ale bardziej płaskie, bez zaskoczeń. Szackiemu do gustu przypadła druga, emanująca szybką, świeżą energią w stylu *Load/Reload* Metalliki. Śpiewali po polsku, mieli fajne teksty, wszystko w nich było milion razy ciekawsze i trylion razy prawdziwsze od wypełniających ramówkę Zetki plastikowych gwiazd.

Gdzieś tam na górze kręci się świat. Drogówka sprawdza na moście wyjeżdżające z miasta samochody, patrole pilnie kręcą się po bocznych uliczkach z wygaszonymi kogutami, wypatrując drobnej sylwetki i rudych włosów. Jerzy Szyller stoi w ciemnej kuchni, obserwując mężczyzn czuwających w granatowym oplu vectrze przed jego furtką. Ma na sobie tę samą koszulę z podwiniętymi rękawami i w ogóle nie chce mu się spać. Leon Wilczur ogląda na Polsacie trzecią część *Obcego* i nie pali, inspektor nigdy nie pali u siebie w domu. Barbara Sobieraj odbywa z mężem zmęczoną rozmowę doświadczonego małżeństwa i choć dotyczy ona emocjonującej sprawy adopcji, to i tak śmierdzi rutyną i przekonaniem, że jak zwykle do niczego nie doprowadzi. Sędzia Maria Tatarska czyta w oryginale *Tajemniczy ogród*, wmawia sobie, że ćwiczy język, ale tak naprawdę chce to jeszcze raz przeczytać i jeszcze raz popłakać się ze wzruszenia. Maria „Misia" Miszczyk je kabanosa – rzygać już jej się chce od tych ciast, z których zrobiła swój znak rozpoznawczy – i ogląda zdjęcie Budnika w Polsat News. Zdjęcie zrobione przez policję w czasie ostatniego przesłuchania, Miszczyk myśli, że do dupy musi być praca polityka, skoro Budnik wygląda tak mizernie, połowa człowieka, jakiego pamięta z dawnych lat. I jeszcze ten plaster. Małżeństwo Rojskich śpi spokojnie, nie zdając sobie sprawy z tego, jak niewiele jest par, które po czterdziestu latach małżeństwa ciągle śpią pod jedną kołdrą. Dwieście dwadzieścia kilometrów dalej, na warszawskim Grochowie, Marcin Ładoń – w tej samej chwili, co miliony innych czternastolatków – onanizuje się zapamiętale, myśląc o wszystkim, tylko nie o czekającej go w przyszłym tygodniu wycieczce do Sandomierza. A Romanowi Myszyńskiemu znowu się śni, że porcelanowo białe zwłoki sztywnym krokiem manekina chodzą za nim wewnątrz synagogi, a on nie może uciec, ponieważ potyka się o sterty wypisanych cyrylicą akt.

Gdzieś tam na dole prokurator Teodor Szacki kręcił się zapamiętale w plemiennym rytmie metalowego rock'n'rolla. Sczepieni pod rękę, wirowali razem z Klarą aż do utraty równowagi, pijani piwem i endorfinami, kasztanowe włosy przyklejały się jej do spoconego czoła, twarz błyszczała, bluzka pod pachami była mokra od potu. Zadyszani, znaleźli w sobie resztkę oddechu, żeby wykrzyczeć refren.

– Nie mogę, drogi Boże, czuć się jeszcze gorzej! – darł się zgodnie z prawdą Szacki. – Nie mogę, mój Boże, pamiętać upokorzeń!

Nie czekał na bisy, zarzucił na Klarę swoją kurtkę i zaciągnął do mieszkania na Długosza niczym zdobycz do jaskini.

Pachniała potem, piwem i papierosami, każdy zakamarek jej ciała był rozgrzany, wilgotny i słony, a Szacki po raz pierwszy pomyślał, że jej jęki i krzyki wcale nie są wulgarne.

To był wspaniały wieczór, Szacki, nawet jeśli nie zasypiał szczęśliwy, to zasypiał spokojny, ostatnia jego myśl była taka, że zostawi małolatę rano, po co psuć sobie i jej taki wspaniały wieczór.

Rozdział piąty

niedziela, 19 kwietnia 2009

Joseph Ratzinger obchodzi czwartą rocznicę zostania Benedyktem XVI, on i inni katolicy zamykają obchody Oktawy Wielkanocnej, świętując Niedzielę Miłosierdzia Bożego, w Łagiewnikach kardynał Dziwisz komentuje sytuację polityczną, mówiąc, że warunkiem życia społecznego jest opanowanie sztuki przebaczającej miłości. W tym samym czasie poseł Palikot oskarża Lecha Kaczyńskiego o alkoholizm na podstawie liczby „małpek" zamawianych przez kancelarię. Marek Edelman w milczeniu składa bukiet żonkili przed pomnikiem Bohaterów Getta w 66. rocznicę wybuchu powstania. Zawsze robił to w samo południe, dziś musi czekać, aż skończą oficjalne delegacje. Tymczasem w Czechach przygotowań do urodzin Führera ciąg dalszy, w wyniku podpalenia romskiego domu dwuletnia dziewczynka trafia do szpitala w stanie krytycznym. Policja inauguruje sezon motocyklowy, ostrzegając przed brawurą zgrabnym hasłem: „Idzie wiosna – będą warzywa". Pod Sandomierzem wypadek samochodowy, auto ścina słup energetyczny i staje w płomieniach, ginie siedemnastoletni chłopak. Słonecznie, ale zimno jak diabli, temperatura nie przekracza 12 stopni, w nocy spada do 0.

1

Prokurator Teodor Szacki nie mógł znaleźć prezerwatywy. Ani opakowania po prezerwatywie. Ani otwartego pudełka po prezerwatywach. Ani w ogóle żadnego śladu po tym, że wczorajszej upojnej nocy użyli zabezpieczenia. A wcześniej używali. Czyli że nie ma spirali. Nie ma pigułek. Są dni płodne i niepłodne, jest uważanie i przede wszystkim pieprzone antykoncepcyjne małomiasteczkowe średniowiecze, opresyjne zakładanie gumy. O ile w ogóle była guma. A to nie jest pewne.

Szacki miotał się po pokoju niczym pan Hilary w wersji dla dorosłych, czując narastającą panikę, chcąc za wszelką cenę upewnić siebie, że nie, nie ma takiej szansy, żeby zapłodnił tę uroczą, młodszą o piętnaście lat sandomierzankę. Którą na dodatek przed zdaniem sobie sprawy z antykoncepcyjnej katastrofy oddalił, przez co zamknęła się w łazience i tam szlochała.

Trzasnęły drzwi. Szacki błyskawicznie wstał z kolan i założył na twarz minę pełną współczucia i empatii. Klara bez słowa zaczęła zbierać swoje ciuchy i przez chwilę nawet miał nadzieję, że obędzie się bez rozmowy.

– Studiowałam w Warszawie, studiowałam w Getyndze, sporo podróżowałam po świecie, mieszkałam w trzech stolicach. Miałam też, nie ukrywam, różnych mężczyzn. Niektórych na dłużej, niektórych na krócej. Wszyscy mieli tę wspólną cechę, że byli fajni. Nawet jak dochodziliśmy do wniosku, że może jednak niekoniecznie, to i tak byli fajni. Jesteś pierwszym prawdziwym chujem, jaki stanął na mojej drodze.

– Klara, proszę cię, po co od razu takie słowa – powiedział spokojnie Szacki, starając się nie myśleć o dwuznaczności jej ostatniego zdania. – Wiesz przecież, kim jestem. Starszy o półtorej dekady urzędnik państwowy, z przeszłością i po przejściach. Co chcesz ze mną budować?

Podeszła i stanęła tak blisko, że prawie stykali się nosami. Poczuł, że ma na nią straszną ochotę.

– Teraz już nic, ale jeszcze wczoraj nie byłam pewna. Masz w sobie coś, co mnie ujmowało. Jesteś bystry, dowcipny, trochę tajemniczy, w nieoczywisty sposób przystojny, masz jakiś rodzaj męskości, który mi się podobał. I te garnitury są naprawdę fajne, uroczo sztywniackie. – Uśmiechnęła się, ale momentalnie spoważniała. – To zobaczyłam w tobie. I dopóki myślałam, że ty coś zobaczyłeś we mnie, z dnia na dzień nabierałam ochoty, żeby dać ci więcej. Ale ty zobaczyłeś we mnie tipsiarę, wiejską dupę do dymania, lachociąga z prowincji. Aż dziw, że mnie nie zabrałeś do macdonalda. Nie powiedzieli ci, że wsiowe pokrowce na kutasa najbardziej lubią do maca?

– Nie ma chyba potrzeby, żebyś była ordynarna.

– To ty jesteś ordynarny, Teo. W każdej swojej myśli o mnie jesteś wulgarnym, ordynarnym, chamskim i prostackim mizoginem i seksistą. Smutnym urzędniczyną też, przyznaję, ale to dopiero potem.

Wypunktowała go tymi słowami, po czym odwróciła się gwałtownie, podeszła do łóżka i zrzuciła ręcznik. Ostentacyjnie zaczęła się przy nim ubierać. Dochodziła dziesiąta, słońce stało wysoko, na tyle wysoko, żeby dokładnie oświetlić jej posągową figurę. Była prześliczna. Smukła, po kobiecemu pozaokrąglana, z piersiami na tyle młodymi, żeby mimo swoich rozmiarów zadziornie sterczały. Potargane po nocy długie włosy, gęste, pofalowane, nie potrzebujące żadnych sztuczek, zawijały się na jej dekolcie, pod słońce widział delikatny meszek na brzoskwiniowej skórze ud i ramion. Zakładała bieliznę, nie spuszczając z niego wzroku, a on odchodził od zmysłów z pożądania. Naprawdę nie robiła na nim kiedyś wrażenia?

– Odwróć się – poleciła zimno.

Odwrócił się posłusznie, śmieszny w swoich paroletnich, wyblakłych od częstego prania bokserkach, jedynej ozdobie białego, zaniedbanego ciała. Było zimno, widział, jak dostaje gęsiej skórki na chudych udach, i zrozumiał, że bez garnituru lub togi jest absolutnie bezbronny, żółw wyjęty ze skorupy. Czuł się śmiesznie. Z tyłu doleciał go cichy szloch. Zerknął przez ramię, Klara siedziała na łóżku ze spuszczoną głową.

– No i co ja im wszystkim powiem? – szeptała. – Tak o tobie opowiadałam. Mówili, żebym się opanowała, a ja się kłóciłam, głupia.

Zrobił parę kroków w jej kierunku, na co ona wstała, pociągnęła nosem, zarzuciła torebkę na ramię i wyszła, nie obdarzając go spojrzeniem.

– Aha, jeszcze jedno – odwróciła się w drzwiach. – Wczoraj byłeś uroczo natarczywy i rozkosznie nieuważny. A mówiąc oględnie, to był bardzo, bardzo niedobry dzień na nieuwagę.

Uśmiechnęła się smutno i wyszła. Wyglądała przepięknie, Szackiemu przypomniała się scena z *Amatora*.

2

Bazylika katedralna Narodzenia Najświętszej Maryi Panny w Sandomierzu była pełna. Jeden duch i jedno serce ożywiało wszystkich wierzących – jeśli wierzyć odbijającym się od kamiennych ścian słowom czytania z Dziejów Apostolskich. Ale – jak to zwykle w kościele bywa – nikt nie słuchał, każdy patrzył, pogrążony w swoich myślach.

Irena Rojska spoglądała na siedzącego w fotelu biskupa Frankowskiego i zastanawiała się, jaki będzie nowy biskup, bo ten był tylko na chwilę, po tym jak starego zabrali do Szczecina. Mógłby być i Frankowski, ale to niepewne. Ludzie gadali, że za dużo się udziela w Radiu Maryja. Może i tak, ale Rojska pamiętała, jak w Stalowej Woli robotników bronił, jak strajkujących tajnym tunelem do kościoła wyprowadzał, jak go komuna dręczyła. Nie dziwne, że jest cięty na czerwonych, że go boli, jak widzi, że teraz to tacy sami dobrzy Polacy jak ci, co w więzieniach siedzieli. A gdzie ma o tym mówić, jak nie w Radiu Maryja? Nie w TVN przecież.

Janusz Rojski oderwał w końcu tęskny wzrok od ławki, na której siedziała jego żona. Potwornie rwała go noga od stania, gdzieś tak aż od kręgosłupa, od nerek szło do pięty. Ale co miał zrobić, wszystkie ciężarne i wszystkie zgrzybiałe staruszki z diecezji przyjechały dziś do katedry, a żonę prosić o miejsce było głupio. Spojrzał w górę na obrazy, na jakiegoś biedaka pożeranego przez smoka i na drugiego tak skutecznie wbitego na pal, że końcówka wychodziła mu przez łopatkę. Ci musieli swoje wycierpieć za wiarę, to i ja godzinę mogę odstać, pomyślał. Nudziło mu się, chciał już iść na świąteczną kawę do kawiarni, usiąść w miękkim cieple, porozmawiać. Chuchnął w dłonie. Znowu pieruńsko zimny dzień, nigdy ta wiosna nie przyjdzie.

Maria Miszczyk nie była wierząca, a nawet gdyby była, to jej parafia mieściła się dwadzieścia kilometrów dalej. Coś ją jednak rano podkusiło, żeby tu przyjechać. Nie dawała jej spokoju sprawa Budnika, jedną rękę cały czas trzymała na wyciszonej komorce, zeby nie przegapić wibracji, kiedy będą dzwonić, że go złapali i że skończy się ten koszmar. A Budnik mieszkał obok katedry, tu była jego parafia, tu wisiał ten cholerny obraz, przez który jej ukochane miasto raz po raz stawało się antysemicką stolicą Polski. Prokurator Miszczyk stała w lewej nawie pomiędzy ludźmi, czuła wbity w siebie wzrok Jana Pawła II, którego portret ozdabiał skrywającą obraz tkaninę. I zastanawiała się, czy on czuje wbite w siebie spojrzenia Żydów upuszczających krew z chrześcijańskich dzieci i wsadzających niemowlęta do beczek nabitych gwoździami. I co miałby na ten temat do powiedzenia.

Nikt o tym nie wiedział, ale niewierząca prokurator Miszczyk była kiedyś bardzo wierząca, tak wierząca, że zanim zrobiła fakultet z prawa, studiowała na KUL-u, chciała się jak najwięcej dowiedzieć o swoim Bogu i swojej religii. A im więcej wiedziała, tym mniej stawała się wierząca. Słuchała teraz ze wszystkimi psalmu sto osiemnastego, słuchała, żeby dziękować Panu, bo jest dobry, bo łaska jego trwa na wieki. I pamiętała, jak kiedyś uwielbiała ten psalm. Dopóki się nie dowiedziała, że w katolickiej liturgii zostało z niego kilka wersów. Że w całości to opowieść o boskiej pomocy w walce i zemście, o ścieraniu z powierzchni ziemi innych narodów w Imię Pańskie. „Prawica Pańska moc okazuje, prawica Pańska wysoko uniesiona". Uśmiechnęła się blado. Dziwnie to się układa, katoliccy wierni w kościele z żydożerczym bohomazem wysławiają zapamiętale swojego Boga słowami psalmu, który w istocie jest dziękczynieniem za zwycięstwo Izraela nad jego sąsiadami. Tak, wiedza była najbardziej zajadłym mordercą wiary i czasami żałowała, że ją zdobyła. Zaśpiewała na koniec ze wszystkimi refren: „Dziękujcie Panu, bo jest miłosierny".

Przygnębiona swoimi religioznawczymi rozważaniami, wspomnieniem utraconej wiary i wszystkiego, co w jej życiu niegdyś było, a pozostawiło po sobie jedynie pustkę, Maria Miszczyk wyszła z kościoła jako jedna z pierwszych, wsiadła w samochód i szybko odjechała. Właśnie dlatego prokurator Teodor Szacki pojawił się przed nią na miejscu zbrodni.

3

Janusz Rojski musiał chyba nadrobić ponadgodzinne, nie licząc aklamacji, milczenie, dlatego jeszcze w kruchcie zaczął mówić i nie zamknął się od tej pory ani na chwilę.

Rojska pomyślała, że w kawiarni wciśnie mu do rąk gazetę, może to go uciszy.

– Myślisz, że on naprawdę mu grzebał?

– Słucham? Kto? Komu?

– Święty Tomasz. Jezusowi. Nie słuchałaś czytania?

– Boże, Janku, skąd mam wiedzieć. W Ewangelii tak pisze, to chyba tak.

– Bo się zastanawiałem, że to trochę obrzydliwe. Jeszcze w ręce, to palec, ale do brzucha musiał mu włożyć całą rękę. Myślisz, że tam było pusto, czy coś poczuł? Trzustkę na przykład albo śledzionę? Czy po zmartwychwstaniu ma się trzustkę?

– Jak się umarło w wieku trzydziestu trzech lat, to nie, dopiero po pięćdziesiątce dowiadujesz się, że masz jakieś narządy. Jak twoja noga?

– Lepiej – skłamał.

– Przepraszam, że cię nie puściłam, widziałam, że boli, ale kołacze mi się strasznie...

Rojski w odpowiedzi przytulił do siebie żonę i pocałował ją w wełniany beret.

– Już nie wiem zupełnie, co z tym zrobić, może powinnam się zdecydować na tę operację.

– Po co się kroić niepotrzebnie? Doktor Fibich przecież mówił, że niegroźne, tylko nieprzyjemne. A nawet jak cię pokroją, to nie wiadomo, czy minie, nerwowe może być.

– No wiem, wiem, zmieńmy już temat lepiej. Pamiętasz, śmialiśmy się kiedyś, że starzy ludzie tylko o chorobach i dolegliwościach. A teraz tak samo, czasami sama siebie nudzę.

– A nie, to ja raczej nie.

Rojska spojrzała na męża z ukosa, czy żartuje, ale nie, tak się wyrwało staruszkowi ze szczerego serca. Nie skomentowała, żeby nie sprawić mu przykrości. Zamiast tego wzięła go pod rękę, było jej zimno, zastanawiała się, czy to starość, czy też wiosna w tym roku taka słaba, koniec kwietnia, a jabłonki w katedralnym ogródku szare, ani jednego kwiatka, jak tak dalej pójdzie, to jej bez chyba w lipcu zakwitnie. Stali pomiędzy katedrą a zamkiem, koło pomnika ofiar drugiej wojny światowej, wyglądającego jak reklama gry w domino. Rano rozważali, czy nie pójść po mszy na spacer nad Wisłę, ale teraz jednomyślnie skręcili w kierunku miasta i zaczęli się piąć Zamkową w stronę rynku, nie musieli uzgadniać, gdzie idą, zawsze szli do Małej. Było tam może trochę drożej, ale jakoś tak inaczej, ładniej. I posypywali piankę na kawie cukrem pudrem. Rojska raz naprawdę długo się zastanawiała, czy nie wyspowiadać się z tego, że przez całą mszę myślała tylko o tym, kiedy ta męka się skończy i będzie mogła dostać swoją słodką piankę.

– Naprawdę rozmawiamy ciągle o chorobach? – włączył swoją narrację Rojski. – Chyba nie, to ten Tomasz tak mnie nastroił, jakoś to mi stanęło przed oczami, jak grzebie Jezusowi, może przez te obrazy, sam nie wiem, nie lubię stać pod kwietniem, tam chyba najgorsze męczarnie, ten na pal wbity zawsze tak mi wzrok ciągnie, jeszcze tam mu coś cieknie po tym palu...

– Janek! – Irena Rojska aż się zatrzymała. – Ty weź się uspokój z tymi okropieństwami.

Jakby na podkreślenie oburzenia tuż obok jej głowy, na murze okalającym opuszczony, niszczejący dworek, usiadł granatowoczarny kruk, naprawdę wielkie ptaszysko, i przekrzywiał głowę, patrząc na staruszków. Spojrzeli zaskoczeni, mieli go na wyciągnięcie ręki. Ptak chyba zrozumiał, że popełnił faux pas, bo szybko zeskoczył na drugą stronę muru. Rojska zrobiła znak krzyża, na co jej mąż popukał się znacząco w czoło. Bez słowa kontynuowali spacer pod górę i wtedy kruk wrócił. Tym razem zeskoczył na ich stronę, przedefilował pod nogami i schował się w bramie opuszczonej posesji. Zachowywał się jak pies, który chce coś pokazać panu.

Rojska poczuła niepokój i przyspieszyła kroku, jej mąż jednak, którego wzrok starzał się wolniej niż jej, został w miejscu, wpatrzony w granitowe płyty chodnika. Ptak pozostawił po sobie małe, charakterystyczne potrójne ślady, jakby wcześniej specjalnie umoczył pazury w ciemnej farbie.

– Idziesz czy nie?

– Zaczekaj, coś się stało chyba.

Zatrzepotały skrzydła, na wyszczerbionym murze usiadło już kilka kruków. Rojski jak zahipnotyzowany przeszedł nad deską z tabliczką ostrzegającą o możliwości zawalenia się budynku i wszedł do zarośniętego ogrodu. Stojący pośrodku krzaków piętrowy dworek też był częściowo zarośnięty zielskiem, niszczał tutaj od dekad, aż zyskał tak charakterystyczny dla opuszczonych budynków trupi wygląd. Zzieleniały, z częściowo zawalonym dachem, z pustymi oczodołami okien, wyglądał jak pysk utopca, który wychylił się na chwilę z rzęsy, żeby upolować kolejną ofiarę.

– Czyś ty zwariował już doszczętnie?! Janek!

Rojski nie odpowiedział, rozgarniając szare gałęzie krzaków, szedł wolno w stronę domu, noga bolała go jak diabli, mógł nią tylko bezwładnie szurać. Na podwórku było pełno kruków, nie latały, nie krakały, chodziły tylko w milczeniu i patrzyły wyczekująco. Puste okna dworu przywodziły na myśl torturowanych męczenników z katedry, ich wypalone oczy, grymas cierpienia, usta otwarte do krzyku. Z tyłu Irena Rojska awanturowała się, straszyła swoim kołataniem i tym, że nigdy już nie zrobi rolady, jeśli natychmiast nie wróci. Słyszał, rozumiał, ale zatrzymać się nie mógł. Wszedł do środka, zbutwiałe deski podłogi nie tyle skrzypnęły, co zamlaskały nieprzyjemnie.

Jego wzrok chwilę przyzwyczajał się do półmroku, okna były niewielkie, częściowo zabite deskami, mimo słońca niewiele światła przedostawało się do wewnątrz, a przynajmniej na parter, bo z piętra biła jasna łuna i tam skierował swoje kroki Rojski. Kruki zostały na zewnątrz, jeden, największy, stał na progu, odcinając drogę odwrotu. Starszy pan stanął u podnóża schodów i pomyślał, że to nie jest dobry pomysł, że stopni nie zostało wiele, a te, co zostały, nie budzą zaufania. Nawet gdyby był wyjątkowo lekkim i wyjątkowo odważnym kotem, powinien zrezygnować. Mimo to ruszył do góry, wyrzucając sobie cały czas w myślach, że jest głupim starym dziadem i że już dawno minęły czasy, kiedy po każdej przygodzie, doszedłszy do siebie, mógł powiedzieć „ech, zawsze się udaje".

Poręcz była śliska od wilgoci i pleśni, nie sposób było jej uchwycić gołą dłonią. Owinął więc rękę szalikiem. Pierwszy stopień załamał się, jak tylko postawił na nim stopę, na szczęście był na to przygotowany. Drugi był solidny, trzeci tak samo, do ósmego jakoś to wyglądało, na wszelki wypadek ominął dziwnie wybrzuszony siódmy. Potem było gorzej. Dziewiątego nie było, jedenastego i dwunastego też nie. A dziesiąty, cóż, zresztą za daleko zaszedł, żeby dywagować, stanął na nim i szybko podciągnął rwącą nogę. Stopień zajęczał ostrzegawczo i zatrzeszczał, zaczął lekko się przechylać i Rojski poczuł, że zsuwa się po zbutwiałym drewnie. Bojąc się upadku, szybko jak na swoje lata przeskoczył przez dziurę i to był moment, kiedy powinien się uspokoić, ale podłoga piętra znalazła się na wysokości jego oczu i to go zgubiło. Chcąc jak najszybciej minąć linię mety, prędko pokonał jeszcze dwa stopnie, ale zawiodła chora noga, stracił równowagę i bojąc się upadku na dół, rzucił się szczupakiem w smugę wpadającego przez dziury w dachu i wielkie balkonowe okno słonecznego światła. Coś trzasnęło i niestety nie była to deska, ból ze złamanego nadgarstka rozlał się po ciele Rojskiego gorącą, mdlącą falą. Jęcząc, przewrócił się na plecy, słońce oślepiło go mocno, odruchowo zasłonił oczy złamaną ręką, ból szarpnął, uczucie było straszne, jakby obcęgami wyrywano mu kości przedramienia. Krzyknął głośno i przycisnął rękę do piersi, oddychał szybko i gwałtownie przez zaciśnięte zęby, zrobiło mu się słabo, pod zaciśniętymi powiekami słoneczne powidoki walczyły o miejsce ze szkarłatnymi płatkami. Mimo to udało mu się dźwignąć na kolana i otworzyć oczy, pierwsze, co zobaczył, to rodzina malutkich grzybków wyrastająca ze szpary w czerwonej podłodze. Widok był tak absurdalny, że musiał się roześmiać. Co za głupi stary dziad, po co on tu w ogóle lazł – i jak teraz zejdzie. Straż pożarna będzie go musiała ściągać jak kotka z drzewa. W plecy uderzył go delikatnie jakiś kawałek papy. Rojski uspokoił oddech i wstał, uderzając głową o wiszący kawałek dachu. Zaklął i odwrócił się, żeby stwierdzić, że niestety ani papa nie była papą, ani kawałek dachu kawałkiem dachu. Zwłoki powieszono na haku pod powałą jak półtuszę, tułów zamknięto w ocembrowanej, ponabijanej bretnalami beczce. Powyżej beczki ciało było gipsowo białe, poniżej pokryte warstwą zaschniętej krwi, słońce blikowało radośnie na amarantowej politurze. Na ryżej czuprynie trupa siedział kruk i patrzył jednym okiem na Rojskiego. Bez przekonania dziobnął zwisający smętnie z czoła zwłok plaster.

Rojski zamknął oczy. Widok zniknął, powidok został pod powiekami na zawsze.

4

Zastanawia się, czy już znaleźli trupa. Nie ma to żadnego znaczenia, po prostu się zastanawia. Czy znajdą dziś, czy – wątpliwe – za tydzień, to bez znaczenia. Włącza telewizor, nastawia kanał informacyjny, wycisza dźwięk. Palikot wypija „małpkę" whisky, Edelman składa kwiaty pod pomnikiem Bohaterów Getta. Te same dwa obrazy na przemian. Jeśli znajdą trupa, wszystko to stanie się drugorzędne.

Prokurator Teodor Szacki dobiegł na miejsce jeszcze przed Wilczurem, wszedł po drabinie na piętro opuszczonego dworku zaraz po mundurowych. Wieści rozchodziły się szybko, na Zamkowej stał już tłum ludzi, a kolejni schodzili się ze wszystkich stron. Za nim wgramolił się po drabinie Marszałek, gruby policjant z sumiastymi wąsami. Zanim Szacki zdążył wydać jakiekolwiek polecenie, Marszałkiem wstrząsnęły torsje, chwilę z nimi walczył, a potem obrzygał siebie i swoje wąsy. Niewiarygodne, pomyślał Szacki, ale w gruncie rzeczy nie miał do niego pretensji. Widok był straszny, chyba najgorszy, jaki widział w swojej karierze. Rozkładające się zwłoki, topielcy, pogorzelcy, ofiary meliniarskich mordów i bójek z roztrzaskanymi czaszkami – wszystko to blakło przy wiszącym na haku trupie Grzegorza Budnika, jeszcze do niedawna poszukiwanego listem gończym jedynego podejrzanego w sprawie o zabójstwo swojej żony.

Szacki patrzył na surrealistyczny w swym okropieństwie obraz, zaatakowany przez nadmiar bodźców mózg z pewnym oporem, jakby na zwolnionych obrotach, przetwarzał informację. Co najbardziej rzucało się w oczy?

Na pewno beczka, upiorny rekwizyt, który nadawał scenie cechy teatralnej nierealności, sprawiając, że jakaś część Szackiego czekała na oklaski, po których trup otworzy oczy i uśmiechnie się do widowni.

Na pewno przykuwała wzrok twarz. Szacki uczył się na jakimś szkoleniu z kryminalistyki, że ludzki mózg jest zaprogramowany na rozpoznawanie twarzy, na niuanse ich wyrazu, na rysujące się na nich emocje, na wszelkie zmiany, które informują o tym, czy do innego człowieka trzeba się raczej uśmiechnąć, czy raczej szykować się do ucieczki. Dlatego czasami widzimy Matkę Boską na szybie albo upiorny grymas na pniu drzewa – to mózg wszędzie, cały czas, poszukuje ludzkich twarzy, stara się je wyłowić, posegregować na znane i nieznane, rozpoznać emocje. Mózg Szackiego cierpiał od widoku twarzy Budnika. Znaki szczególne wiceprzewodniczącego Rady Miejskiej – chorobliwe wychudzenie, zapadnięte oczy, ryża czupryna i broda, to nieszczęsne skaleczenie na czole – były zniekształcone przez wbity w podbródek i wychodzący policzkiem hak. Zmasakrowane mięśnie nadawały twarzy obcy, niepokojący wyraz, jakby Budnik zajrzał na chwilę do piekła i widziane tam obrazy zmieniły go na zawsze. Szacki pomyślał, że w zależności od stopnia sadyzmu zabójcy ta metafora nie musiała być daleka od prawdy.

Najgorsze jednak były barwy, bezlitośnie wydobyte przez ostre już o tej porze roku słońce. Ciało Budnika, u góry śnieżnobiałe, pozbawione krwi jak ciało jego żony kilka dni wcześniej, u dołu było błyszcząco krwiste – wyglądało to jak perwersyjna instalacja sztuki nowoczesnej, głos obrazoburczego artysty o współczesnej Polsce. Spójrzcie, oto wasze barwy narodowe. Goły polski trup, zamordowany wedle legendy, którą wymyślili jego przodkowie, aby móc bezkarnie mordować innych.

Cała podłoga także pokryta była krwią zmieszaną z brudem, zaschnięta kałuża o brunatnym kolorze miała trzy metry średnicy i środek dokładnie pod sękatymi stopami Budnika. W miejscu koło schodów była rozmazana, zapewne przez osobę, która znalazła zwłoki.

– Odczepić go? – zapytał Marszałek, kiedy doszedł do siebie.

Szacki pokręcił przecząco głową.

– Najpierw zdjęcia, technicy muszą zebrać wszystkie ślady. Tym razem zwłoki są w miejscu popełnienia przestępstwa, musiało coś zostać.

Ostrożnie, uważając na najbardziej zmurszałe deski podłogi, prokurator podszedł do środka pomieszczenia. Dobrze mu się wydawało, na krawędzi okrągłej kałuży, niczym na rancie monety, widniał jakiś napis, zrobiony zapewne palcem. Szybko pomodlił się w duchu, żeby to był palec bez rękawiczki i żeby wariat, który to zrobił, był notowany. Pochylił się nad kałużą i przeczytał. Błagam, tylko nie to, pomyślał. Błagam, niech to nie będzie jakiś świr, który naoglądał się amerykańskich filmów i teraz bawi się z nami w kotka i myszkę. Na brzegu kałuży były wyżłobione w zaschniętej krwi litery KWP, a zaraz za nimi trzy sześciocyfrowe numery: 241921, 212225, 191621. Szackiemu niewiele to mówiło, na wszelki wypadek zrobił zdjęcie komórką.

Zmusił się, żeby spojrzeć do góry, na twarz Budnika. Zmieniony nie do poznania mężczyzna wyglądał jeszcze mizerniej niż przed paroma dniami w jego gabinecie, śmierć pozbawiła go resztek sportowej drapieżności. Najgorszy był ten plaster, żałosny nawet wtedy, kiedy trzymał się czoła, a teraz zwisał smętnie, odsłaniając ledwo zagojone skaleczenie – wisienka na torcie pośmiertnego upokorzenia.

Kiedy na miejsce dotarły jednocześnie Basia Sobieraj i Maria Miszczyk, zwłoki były już zdjęte i nakryte czarną folią. Szacki w jednorazowych rękawiczkach przeglądał portfel zmarłego, Wilczur stał oparty o pustą ramę okienną i palił.

Sobieraj rozejrzała się po pomieszczeniu i wybuchnęła płaczem. Kiedy Szacki podszedł, żeby ją pocieszyć, i przyjacielskim gestem położył jej rękę na ramieniu, rzuciła mu się na szyję i objęła go kurczowo. Czuł, jak jej ciałem wstrząsa szloch. Ponad ramieniem koleżanki obserwował Miszczyk, mając nadzieję, że nie zemdleje, po pierwsze, nie chciał łapać jej stukilogramowego ciała, po drugie, bał się, że przeleci przez zmurszały strop. Jednak na twarzy jego zbyt obfitej szefowej nie drgnął ani jeden matczyny mięsień, rzuciła okiem na miejsce zbrodni i utkwiła wzrok w Szackim. Pytająco podniosła brew.

– Oględziny zwłok będą dzisiaj, tak samo jak oględziny miejsca zbrodni i wyniki, czy w tej krwi jest też krew Budnikowej – odpowiedział na jej nieme pytanie. – Jak najszybciej przygotujemy nowe wersje śledcze, przedstawimy plan postępowania. To niestety wygląda na jakiegoś szaleńca, trzeba będzie zrobić portret psychologiczny, przejrzeć bazy danych pod kątem przestępstw na tle religijnym. Konferencję możemy zrobić jutro w południe.

– I co im powiemy?

– Prawdę. Jakie mamy inne wyjście? Jeśli to szaleniec, szum może nam pomóc. Może się komuś pochwali, może powie przypadkiem coś, co go zdradzi.

– Chce pan ściągać rodzinę do identyfikacji?

Szacki zaprzeczył, nie było sensu obarczać innych tym koszmarem. W dokumentach miał wszystkie potrzebne dane.

– Mówi pani coś skrót KWP?

– Komenda Wojewódzka Policji. Dlaczego?

6

Prokurator Teodor Szacki nie cierpiał chaosu. Uczucia zagubienia w wydarzeniach i w swojej ocenie wydarzeń, uczucia niemożności utrzymania myśli na jednym wątku, gubienia ciągu logicznego, bezradnego i nieefektywnego miotania się od myśli do myśli. Rezultat przynosiło wysnuwanie jednej myśli z drugiej, zazębianie ich ze sobą, tworzenie skomplikowanych precyzyjnych mechanizmów logicznych, które na końcu produkowały piękne i estetyczne rozwiązanie. Tym razem nie było o tym mowy, myśli szalały w jego głowie jak stado przedszkolaków na placu zabaw, śmierć Budnika rozmontowała wszystkie poprzednie założenia, do których zdążył się już przyzwyczaić. W pewien sposób od pierwszej chwili śledztwa gdzieś głęboko był przekonany, że winien śmierci żony jest Budnik, dawało mu to spokój, pozwalało szukać dowodów. Jeszcze nigdy intuicja tak bardzo go nie zawiodła.

Boże, jaki był wściekły. Ze złością kopnął leżącą na ulicy puszkę, idąca z naprzeciwka ciężarna piękność spojrzała na niego z naganą. Oczywiście ciężarna, oczywiście piękność, jak na złość. Był zmęczony, bo za każdym razem, kiedy próbował ustawić jedną myśl na drugiej, pojawiała się Klara, burzyła konstrukcję i wciskała się do jego jaźni. Co, jeśli jest w ciąży? Może to i dobrze, w końcu wczorajszy wieczór był wspaniały, może to by oznaczało, że ustatkuje się u boku młodej i pięknej żony? A jeśli uległ nastrojowi chwili? Jeśli to tak naprawdę głupia plastikowa lala, która nigdy go nie pociągała i której raz udało się jakimś cudem wywrzeć pozytywne wrażenie? I czy to dobrze, że ją spławił? I czy w ciąży dałaby mu drugą szansę, czy wręcz przeciwnie, zamieniłaby się w roszczeniową zołzę, czerpiącą z niego alimenty wiadrem, niczym wodę ze studni? A jeśli nie jest w ciąży, to powinien się cieszyć czy żałować?

Myślał, że długi spacer ze szpitala do prokuratury go otrzeźwi, chłodne powietrze pomoże zebrać myśli. A było tylko gorzej. Skręcił z Mickiewicza w Koseły, za chwilę dotrze na miejsce, usiądzie w gabinecie Miszczyk, przedstawi jej plan śledztwa. Plan śledztwa! W głos się zaśmiał. Dobre sobie, plan śledztwa.

Przed schodami do prokuratury stała grupka dziennikarzy, ktoś coś powiedział i wszyscy ruszyli w jego stronę. Po tym, jak telewizje pokazały wymianę zdań z upierdliwą małpą w zielonym, stał się rozpoznawalny. Wyprostował się, przykleił kamienną maskę na twarz.

– Panie prokuratorze, można słowo komentarza?

– Jutro będzie konferencja, o wszystkim państwa poinformujemy.

– Czy to seryjny zabójca?

– Jutro. Dziś miałbym dla państwa tylko plotki, jutro będziemy mieli informacje.

– Mogą być plotki.

– Nie mogą.

– Zabito podejrzanego o poprzednie morderstwo. Czy to znaczy, że śledztwo stanęło w miejscu?

– W żadnym wypadku.

– Czy powinno się zamknąć szkoły?

Szacki zdębiał. Przeciskał się systematycznie w kierunku wejścia, ale pytanie było tak głupie, że stanął.

– Dlaczego szkoły?

– Żeby chronić dzieci.

– Przepraszam, przed czym?

– Przed misterium krwi.

– Oszalał pan?

Prokurator Teodor Szacki miał wrażenie, że uchylił drzwi do alternatywnej rzeczywistości. Rzeczywistości, jak sądził, dawnej, zapomnianej i nieprawdziwej, zasłanej trupami starych demonów. Cóż, wystarczyło zerknąć przez szparę, żeby dowiedzieć się, że żadne demony nie umarły, poszły jedynie spać, na dodatek była to drzemka nad wyraz lekka. I teraz z radości merdają wszystkimi swoimi demonicznymi ogonami, że mogą wyjść przez uchylone w Sandomierzu drzwi i pobawić się z prokuratorem Szackim. Niewiarygodne. Jak głęboko wyryte w narodowej świadomości muszą być zastępujące myślenie stereotypy, skoro sześćdziesiąt pięć lat po Zagładzie, sześćdziesiąt trzy po ostatnim pogromie i czterdzieści po wygonieniu żydowskich niedobitków w 1968 roku przychodzi jakiś szaleniec urodzony na oko już w latach siedemdziesiątych i wierzy w misterium krwi.

– Nie oszalałem i nie żartuję – kontynuował mężczyzna, który ze swoją drobną posturą i kręconymi czarnymi włosami sam przypominał Szackiemu Żyda z karykatury. Ubrany był w pulowerek. – I nie rozumiem, dlaczego nie mamy odwagi zastanawiać się głośno, czy przypadkiem po latach nie wróciły do Polski mordy rytualne. Ja nie mówię, że tak jest. Ja tylko pytam.

Szacki czekał, aż ktoś go wyręczy i uciszy pajaca, ale nikt się nie kwapił, kamery i mikrofony czekały, co zrobi.

– Pan jest wariatem. Mord rytualny to antysemicka legenda, nic więcej.

– W każdej legendzie jest ziarno prawdy. Przypominam, że wielu Żydów zostało skazanych w prawomocnych procesach za porwania i zabójstwa dzieci.

– Tak samo jak wiele czarownic. Myśli pan, że czarownice też wróciły do Najjaśniejszej? Pieprzą się z diabłem, wyciskają sok z czarnych kotów i knują, jak zdetronizować Chrystusa Króla?

Gromadka dziennikarzy wybuchła służalczym śmiechem. Wariat nie miał notesu ani dyktafonu i Szacki zrozumiał, że oprócz dziennikarzy byli tu też wielbiciele wszelkiego rodzaju spisków.

– Polityczna poprawność nie zmieni faktów, panie prokuratorze. A fakty to są dwa trupy zabite według starego żydowskiego rytuału, misterium krwi, praktykowanego od wieków w wielu miejscach świata. Może pan zaklinać rzeczywistość, ale ciągle ma pan w kostnicy dwa ciała. I żydowski obrządek, którego istnienie jest poza wszelką dyskusją. Istnieją dokumenty, istnieją zeznania świadków i nie mówimy tu o średniowiecznych podaniach, jeszcze w XX wieku niezawisłe sądy potwierdzały istnienie tego procederu.

– Nie zapominajmy o Piaseckim – dorzucił niemłody mężczyzna, który stał z tyłu, płaszcz i kapelusz nadawały mu wygląd amerykańskiego reportera z lat pięćdziesiątych.

– Święte słowa – ożywił się czarniawy. – Straszna, do dziś niewyjaśniona żydowska zbrodnia. Tym bardziej obrzydliwa, że ofiarą padł niewinny syn Piaseckiego. Wiedzieli, że dla niego to będzie gorsze niż jego własna śmierć.

– Skąd pan wie, że to żydowska zbrodnia, skoro jest niewyjaśniona? – zapytał odruchowo Szacki.

– Przepraszam, gdyby panowie mogli wytłumaczyć... –
Jakiś pismak poczuł się zagubiony.

– Bolesław Piasecki – zaczął szybko wyjaśniać czarniawy –
proszę poszukać, wielki Polak, działacz ruchu narodowego
przed wojną, po wojnie szef PAX-u...

– Antysemita i żydożerca – burknął jeden z telewizyjnych
operatorów, nie odrywając oka od wizjera.

Czarniawy zaczął opowiadać o Piaseckim, a Szacki myślał, że po czterdziestu latach niewiary w cuda i dziwy przyjdzie mu uwierzyć w pamięć genetyczną. O co, cholera, im
wszystkim chodzi. Jak nie obrazy w katedrze to getta ławko-
we, jak nie getta to pogromy, jak nie pogromy to Piasecki, jak
nie Piasecki to sześćdziesiąty ósmy, jak nie sześćdziesiąty
ósmy to – Szacki zawiesił na chwilę myśl – to pewnie Michnik i Balcerowicz, nie może być inaczej. Założył się ze sobą
o butelkę dobrego wina, że nie minie pięć minut, a tropiciele
pejsatej mafii dojdą do Michnika.

– ...w pięćdziesiątym siódmym roku Żydzi z SB porwali
i zamordowali mu syna. Pan prokurator dziwi się, że zbrodnia jest niewyjaśniona, oficjalnie oczywiście nie jest, oficjalnie żadna komunistyczna zbrodnia nie jest wyjaśniona. Czy
to oznacza, że ksiądz Popiełuszko żyje i dobrze się miewa,
a w kopalni Wujek nikomu nie stała się krzywda? Zabójstwo młodego Piaseckiego może i nie jest wyjaśnione, tylko
tak się dziwnie składa, że nazwiska, jakie wypłynęły w tej
sprawie, to funkcjonariusze SB żydowskiego pochodzenia.
Zwracam też uwagę, że w polskiej tradycji nie ma zwyczaju
mordowania dzieci, aby ukarać rodziców.

– W żadnej kulturze nie ma takiej tradycji – warknął Szacki,
znajoma czerwona zasłona opadała mu powoli na oczy. Nienawidził głupoty, którą uważał za jedyną naprawdę szkodliwą cechę, gorszą od nienawiści. – Proszę nie opowiadać
bzdur. Pan chyba nie wie, że za to są paragrafy.

– Nie sprowokuje mnie pan. – Tamten dumnie wypiął cherlawą pierś pod pulowerkiem. – Ja wiem, że władza lubi, kiedy tylko jeden sposób myślenia jest właściwy. A teraz sposób myślenia panów Szechtera i świętej, w cudzysłowie świętej, pamięci Lewertowa jest jedynie słuszny. Ale na szczęście można dziś mówić prawdę. Można mówić prawdę, jeśli wraca misterium krwi i jeśli polska krew wsiąka w sandomierską ziemię. I można mówić, jeśli się komuś nie podoba, że Polacy są spychani do roli mniejszości we własnym kraju.

Szacki poczuł się zmęczony. Bardzo, bardzo zmęczony. Tak bardzo, że nawet nie chciało mu się zastanawiać, jakie wino dla siebie wygrał. Odpowiedział tylko z przyzwyczajenia, z wieloletniego ojcowskiego nawyku, który każe tłumaczyć rzeczy oczywiste i powtarzać, że nie, słońce nie kręci się wokół ziemi, i nie, nie możesz mieć, drogie dziecko, własnego zdania na ten temat.

– To między innymi dzięki panom Michnikowi i Geremkowi może pan dziś mówić, co pan chce. Niestety.

Czarniawy pokraśniał.

– Nooo, widzę, że pan prokurator jednak się orientuje, co w trawie piszczy.

Pan prokurator poczuł się zbrukany sympatią wariata. Poczuł, że tonie. Tonie w rzece pieprzonej polskiej ksenofobii, która cały czas płynie pod powierzchnią, bez względu na moment dziejów, tylko czekając na sposobność, żeby wypłynąć na wierzch i zalać okolicę. Mentalna Wisła, niebezpieczny i nieuregulowany ściek przesądów i uprzedzeń, zupełnie jak w tej piosence biesiadnej, co to Wisła płynie po polskiej krainie. „Bo ten naród polski ma ten urok w sobie, kto go raz pokochał, nie zapomni w grobie". Urok, na psa urok, szlag by to trafił, hobbyści patriotyczni, kolekcjonerzy pogardy.

Szacki nakręcał się wewnątrz coraz bardziej, a właściciel pulowerka patrzył na niego z sympatycznym uśmiechem człowieka, który odnalazł zaginionego brata. Im bardziej się uśmiechał, tym bardziej Szacki się nakręcał, aż w końcu wściekły wyrzucił z siebie słowa, których żałował, jeszcze zanim przecisnęły się przez krtań, ale było już za późno, żeby je powstrzymać.

– Tak, jasne, orientuję się, że Michnik z Geremkiem sprzedali Polskę razem ze swoją żydowską bandą, a Okrągły Stół to było tak naprawdę święto Chanuka. Proszę mnie posłuchać, bo nie będę tego więcej powtarzał. Jestem urzędnikiem Rzeczypospolitej Polskiej i interesuje mnie tylko i wyłącznie jedno: znaleźć i postawić przed sądem sprawcę tych zbrodni. Jest mi obojętne, czy to będzie wskrzeszony z martwych Karol Wojtyła, Ahmed z budki z kebabami, czy jakiś chudy Żyd w pana typie, wypiekający macę w piwnicy. Ktokolwiek to jest, zostanie wyciągnięty za swoje zawszone pejsy z tej wilgotnej nory, w której się schował, i odpowie za to, co zrobił. Gwarantuję to państwu.

Czarniawemu cała krew odpłynęła z twarzy, wściekły Szacki już tego nie widział, bo odwrócił się na pięcie i czując, jak mu drętwieją ręce z wściekłości, wszedł do budynku prokuratury. Drzwi zamknęły się z trzaskiem. Nie wiedział, że na podglądach wycelowanych w niego kamer wyglądało to zupełnie jak słynna scena z *Amatora*, którą wspominał przed południem.

7

Ptysiulka? – Maria Miszczyk podsunęła mu srebrną tackę, małe ptysie były ułożone na niej w zgrabną piramidę.

Szacki miał ochotę powiedzieć, że na chuj mu te ptysie, ale wyglądały tak apetycznie, że sięgnął i włożył jednego do ust. A potem od razu następnego, ciastka były nieprzyzwoicie, niewyobrażalnie pyszne. Biorąc pod uwagę fakt, że w Sandomierzu nie było ani jednego miejsca z dobrymi słodyczami – nie licząc bombonierek na stacji Orlenu – i że Szacki od tygodni czuł się jak narkoman na odwyku, miał ochotę podskoczyć z radości i krzyknąć: „Alleluja".

– Smaczne – docenił oszczędnie.

Miszczyk uśmiechnęła się ciepło, jakby doskonale wiedziała, że ptysie są doskonałe, ale rozumiała, że nie wypada mu popadać w pretensjonalną egzaltację. Spojrzała pytająco.

– Dobra wiadomość jest taka, że mamy więcej, znacznie więcej – zaczął Szacki swoją relację. – Przede wszystkim wiemy, że Elżbieta Budnik została zamordowana w tym samym budynku, jest tam pełno jej krwi. Mamy też materiał do badań daktyloskopijnych i traseologicznych, gorzej jest ze śladami biologicznymi i materiałem DNA, budynek jest brudny, usyfiony, na skraju katastrofy budowlanej i od wielu lat zamieszkiwany przez najróżniejsze zwierzęta. Nic z tego nie będzie. Z tego samego powodu odpadają próbki zapachowe. Policja wstępnie przepuściła odciski przez bazę danych, niestety nic nie wyskoczyło.

– Mężczyzna?

– Nie da się tego stwierdzić na podstawie linii papilarnych. Odcisk sportowego buta ma rozmiar 39,5, też nam to nic nie mówi.

– Ale trzeba konkretnej siły, żeby wciągnąć kogoś na piętro.

– Niekoniecznie. – Szacki rozłożył przed szefową wykonane na miejscu zbrodni fotografie. – Strop między kondygnacjami istnieje tylko częściowo, tam gdzie go nie ma, znaleziono system bloczków, biorąc pod uwagę pozostawione w brudzie ślady, raczej pewne jest, że bloczków użyto do wciągnięcia ofiar. Budnikowa i jej mąż byli drobnej postury, mogła to zrobić kobieta. Niezbyt cherlawa, fakt, ale to możliwe.

– Jaka była bezpośrednia przyczyna śmierci Budnika? – Miszczyk zadała pytanie i sięgnęła po ptysiulka, zbyt szybko go rozgryzła, bita śmietana zakwitła jej na dolnej wardze na kształt kwiatu bawełny. Prokurator bardzo powoli i bardzo dokładnie oblizała wargi, ruch był tak zmysłowy, że Szacki się podniecił, choć nigdy dotąd nie myślał o swojej macierzyńskiej szefowej w kategoriach seksualnych. Nagle zobaczył, jak go gwałtownie ujeżdża, fałdy obfitego ciała radośnie mlaskają, piersi majtają się na wszystkie strony, skacząc i odbijając się od siebie jak pogrążone w zabawie szczeniaki.

– Przyczyna śmierci, panie prokuratorze.

– Wykrwawienie. Wcześniej wstrzyknięto mu silny środek uspokajający, trankiloxil.

– Jak to... – Miszczyk zawahała się – jak to wyglądało, wie pan, pod beczką.

– Lepiej, niż się spodziewałem – odparł zgodnie z prawdą Szacki. – Budnik wykrwawił się przez przecięte w pachwinie tętnice, beczka była dla hecy i dla efektu, dekoracja teatralna. Oczywiście gwoździe pokaleczyły go i podrapały w kilku miejscach, ale nie były przyczyną śmierci.

– A te numery namazane we krwi?

– Wieczorem się tym zajmę razem z Basią.

Nawet jeśli Miszczyk zdumiała ciepło wypowiedziana „Basia", nie dała tego po sobie poznać.

– Dobrze, to teraz złe wiadomości. Ale najpierw ptysiulka na poprawę nastroju.

Szacki bez ponaglania sięgnął po ciastka. Mały ptyś był idealny. Świeżutka, chłodna, lekko kwaśna bita śmietana rozpływała się w ustach i łączyła z pachnącym jajkami ciastem, rozlewając się po kubkach smakowych w sposób ekstatyczny, ptyś Miszczyk był skończonym dziełem sztuki, platońską ideą wszystkich ptysiów.

– Po pierwsze, nasz podejrzany wykrwawił się na biało-
-czerwono, ku chwale antysemickiej legendy o krwi. Co oznacza, że histeria mediów za chwilę będzie nie do opanowania i że z całego świata zjadą tu zarówno faszystowskie

świry i tropiciele żydowskiego spisku, jak i fanatyczni obrońcy politycznej poprawności. Przed chwilą miałem próbkę na dole.

Zjadł następnego ptysia, postanowił w ten sposób rozdzielać złe wiadomości.

– Po drugie, był to nasz jedyny podejrzany. Nie wiemy o nikim, kto miałby motyw, aby zabić małżeństwo Budników. Rozważałem przez chwilę wersję, czy Budnik nie zabił żony, a następnie nie został w zemście zamordowany przez jej kochanka, Jerzego Szyllera. To jednak nieprawdopodobne, Szyller nie miałby żadnego powodu, aby powielać *modus operandi* Budnika. Prędzej uwierzę w to, że Szyller zamordował oboje. Między tą trójką działo się coś dziwnego i brudnego.

– A obecnie pan Szyller...

– Pozostaje na wolności, ale jest pod stałą obserwacją policji. – Szacki wyczuł ciężkie spojrzenie szefowej i dodał, że tym razem obserwacja oznacza, że aby zniknąć, musiałby wyparować lub przecisnąć się przez rurę kanalizacyjną.

Ptysiulek.

– Po trzecie, nie bardzo na razie wiadomo, jak ofiary znalazły się na miejscu zbrodni. Na pewno na posesję nie wjeżdżał żaden samochód, nie znaleźliśmy też śladów ciągnięcia przez krzaki, śladów po wózku albo taczce, ba, nie ma nawet śladów stóp, nie licząc tych pozostawionych przez staruszka, który znalazł zwłoki Budnika.

– To skąd to 39,5?

– Odciśnięte we krwi na górze.

I następny. Ptyś był jak heroina, z każdym kolejnym Szacki coraz szybciej potrzebował następnego.

– Po czwarte, numery wymazane we krwi mogą wskazywać, że mamy do czynienia z wariatem, który chce się bawić w zagadki, amerykańskie filmy, dyszenie do telefonu i szycie sobie chałata z ludzkiej skóry.

– Co pan o tym sądzi?

Szacki się skrzywił.

– Studiowałem przypadki seryjnych zabójstw, mordercy tylko w Hollywood są geniuszami zbrodni. W rzeczywistości to zaburzone jednostki, uzależnione od zabijania. Mordowanie za bardzo ich podnieca, żeby bawili się w teatralne stylizacje, gierki ze śledczymi, a przede wszystkim przykładali się do zaplanowania zbrodni i późniejszego zatarcia śladów. Oczywiście próbują, ale sadzą błąd na błędzie, a problem z ich schwytaniem bierze się stąd, że nie wywodzą się ze środowisk przestępczych, nie są notowani, ciężko ich namierzyć.

– W takim razie, o co tu może chodzić?

– Szczerze? Nie mam najmniejszego pojęcia. Na pewno o coś innego niż mordowanie dla mordowania. Budnikowa była lokalną społeczniczką, Budnik powszechnie znanym politykiem samorządowym, oboje byli mocno związani z miastem. Miejsce zbrodni leży dokładnie między największymi lokalnymi zabytkami: zamkiem, katedrą i ratuszem. Oba ciała znaleziono na Starym Mieście. Gdybym miał się zakładać, tobym postawił na to, że rozwiązanie zagadki prędzej znajdziemy w tych starych murach niż w umyśle jakiegoś szaleńca.

– Dużo by pan postawił? – spytała Miszczyk, sięgając po jednego z trzech ostatnich ptysiów.

– Raczej niewielką kwotę.

Roześmiała się, chmurka śmietany sfrunęła na uwięzioną w nieapetycznym czółenku nieapetyczną stopę. Miszczyk wyjęła ją z buta i zaczęła wycierać chusteczką jednorazową, stopa była duża i nieforemna, przy palcach rajstopy były mokre od potu. Niestety od czasu wizji odbijających się od siebie wielkich, obwisłych piersi w Szackim coś pękło i teraz uznał ten widok za perwersyjnie atrakcyjny.

– Musimy sprawdzić trop żydowski.

Miszczyk westchnęła głośno, ale pokiwała ze zrozumieniem głową.

– Czy nam się to podoba, czy nie, trzeba poszukać w środowisku, sprawdzić potomków starej gminy.

– Zajebią nas – powiedziała cicho Miszczyk. W połączeniu z jej aparycją królowej niań zabrzmiało to dziwnie. – Zajebią nas, jak się wyda, że penetrujemy środowisko żydowskie w poszukiwaniu zabójcy. Obwołają faszystami, nazistami, uprzedzonymi, ziejącymi nienawiścią Polakami, którzy wierzą w legendę o krwi. Wszystkie media nawijają już o antysemickiej prowokacji, a jest niedziela. Jutro ruszą na dobre.

Szacki wiedział, że to prawda, ale przypomniała mu się wczorajsza rozmowa z Sobierajem przy grillu.

– Nie mamy wyjścia, nie możemy zignorować tezy, że to jednak jest sprawka jakiegoś żydowskiego świra. Tezy, która się mimo wszystko narzuca. Ofiary są Polakami, katolikami, patriotami. Zabójstwa są stylizowane na żydowski rytuał, legendarny, fakt, ale legenda jest rozpoznawalna. Miasto słynie z napięć na tle stosunków polsko-żydowskich. A lud Izraela przeszedł długą drogę od postawy biernej ofiary historii do walczącego brutalnie o swoje i mszczącego się za krzywdy agresora.

Miszczyk patrzyła na niego, zastygła w idealnym bezruchu, z każdym zdaniem jej oczy rozszerzały się coraz bardziej.

– Ale może pani być spokojna, nie będę cytował tej reasumpcji na konferencji prasowej.

Dopiero teraz wypuściła powietrze.

Chwilę jeszcze rozmawiali o planach poczynań na najbliższe dni, układali listę spraw do załatwienia, czynności, które mogą uwiarygodnić lub wykluczyć niektóre założenia śledztwa. Był to żmudny proces eliminacji, ale Szacki nie czuł się przytłoczony, na tym etapie każda chwila mogła przynieść przełom, ważną informację, rewolucyjny zwrot akcji. Rzucili monetą, kto zje ostatniego ptysiulka. Szacki wygrał, rozsmarowywał resztki ciastka na podniebieniu, myśląc już o na-parze z mięty, kiedy Miszczyk wystrzeliła swoje ostatnie pytanie.

– Podobno rzucił pan Klarę Dybusównę?

Atak na jego prywatność był bardzo niespodziewany i Szacki zapomniał języka w gębie. Nie był przyzwyczajony do małomiasteczkowego obiegu informacji.

– Chodzą słuchy na mieście, że od rana płacze i pomstuje, a jej bracia nabijają muszkiety.

Kurwa mać, nawet nie wiedział, że ma jakichś braci.

– To nie był rokujący związek – powiedział, żeby powiedzieć cokolwiek.

Parsknęła śmiechem.

– Związek z najlepszą partią w Sandomierzu nie był dla pana rokujący? Tutaj już wszyscy rycerze bez skazy połamali koniom nogi, próbując się wdrapać na jej szklaną górę. Jak pana wybrała, to nawet głuchy słyszał dobiegające z setek domów myśli samobójcze. Piękna, mądra, bogata, jak Boga kocham, połowa tutejszych kobiet zostałaby dla niej lesbijką. A dla pana to nie był rokujący związek?

Szacki wzruszył ramionami i wykonał jakiś idiotyczny grymas. Co innego mu zostało?

8

„Miasteczko samo napełnia mnie smutkiem, ubóstwo i prymitywizm żałosne, nie ma co pić i nie ma gdzie co jeść, bo wszystkie restauracje zamknięte. W Gospodzie Ludowej zaczęło się od konfliktu, ale na szczęście schowałem swoje ambicje do kieszeni i przeprosiłem się. Toteż dostaję tam trochę jadła. Gorsza rzecz jest z kakaniem. Komórki dwie zamknęli na kluczyk, brudne i cuchnące. O siadaniu mowy nie ma. To jest dla mnie potworna strona mojego

183

mieszkania tutaj i chyba już w przyszłości przestanę tu przyjeżdżać".

Prokurator Teodor Szacki był zadowolony, że to wynotowane z *Dzienników* Iwaszkiewicza zdanie nie ma już zastosowania. Nabrał na łyżeczkę trochę zdobiącej jego kawę mlecznej pianki i wciągnął łapczywie, drobinki cukru pudru połaskotały go w podniebienie. Albo jakiś bezimienny sandomierski geniusz wpadł na pomysł, żeby posypywać kawę cukrem zamiast czekolady, albo właściciele kafejki gdzieś to podpatrzyli, nieważne – pierwszy łyk kawy w Małej był dzięki temu tak niezmiennie pyszny, że Szacki nie miał ochoty chodzić nigdzie indziej. W ogóle lokal należał do jego ulubionych, był spełnieniem mieszczańskich marzeń o „bezpretensjonalnej małej kafejce na dole". Krótka karta z tostami i naleśnikami, kawa, herbata, domowe ciasto. Kanapa, kilka krzeseł, cztery stoliki na krzyż. Miejscowi narzekali na warszawskie ceny, co Szackiego niezmiennie śmieszyło, kiedy płacił siedem złotych za mistrzowską latte. Ostatnio mniej, kiedy z jakichś powodów zyskał miano stałego klienta, co było tyleż miłe, co zaskakujące – nigdy nie zamienił tu z nikim jednego słowa poza złożeniem zamówienia, siedział w kącie, pił kawę, milczał i czytał Iwaszkiewicza, taki sandomierski snobizm.

Iwaszkiewicza albo coś innego, wygrzebanego z księgarenki vis-à-vis. Która z kolei była ziszczeniem marzeń o „bezpretensjonalnej małej księgarence na dole", odtrutką na empiki, które Szackiemu zawsze kojarzyły się z przepełnionym więzieniem o zaostrzonym rygorze. Jakby książki odbywały tam jakiś wyrok, a nie mieszkały, spokojnie czekając na czytelnika. Tutejsza księgarenka była może ciut zapyziała, ale przynajmniej nie czuł się w niej jak ofiara więziennego gwałtu zbiorowego, z którą jeszcze nie skończyły wszystkie nowości, a już dobierają się do niej promocje i bestsellery.

Teraz nie miał książki, siedział z zamkniętymi oczami i grzał dłonie o ciepły kubek. Za oknem było już ciemno, dochodziła dziewiąta, za chwilę będą zamykać. Trzeba odgwizdać koniec przerwy i wrócić do ślepienia w ekran komputera. Basia Sobieraj siedziała obok na kanapie, ze skrzyżowanymi po turecku nogami, kartkowała wyciągniętego ze sterty gazet i komiksów Tytusa, Romka i A'Tomka.

Dwie godziny siedzieli u niego w mieszkaniu, starając się znaleźć cywilnymi metodami jakiekolwiek powiązania pomiędzy pozostawionymi na miejscu zbrodni numerami: 241921, 212225, 191621. Boh trojcu lubit, wszystkie trzy naraz występowały na dokładnie trzech internetowych stronach. Jednej arabskiej, służącej – o ile dobrze wykoncypowali z rozsianych między robaczkami łacińskich nazw – do pokątnej sprzedaży środków na potencję. Jednej islandzkiej, która składała się z dziesiątek stron liczb opublikowanych w celach informatycznych. I jednej niemieckiej, będącej spisem bibliograficznym, liczby pojawiały się w numerach indeksów. I tyle. Wobec skali porażki zaczęli studiować pojedyncze numery, przerzucając się dowcipami i spostrzeżeniami. Próbowali znaleźć numery telefonów, przerabiali liczby na daty – dzięki czemu Szacki dowiedział się, że 2 kwietnia 1921 roku otwarto po raz pierwszy Targi Poznańskie, Albert Einstein miał w Nowym Jorku wykład o teorii względności, a 4 lutego 1921 roku urodził się indyjski polityk Kocheril Raman Narayanan, żył osiemdziesiąt cztery lata – mimo to nie znaleźli żadnego punktu zaczepienia. Poza tym sam pomysł był rozpaczliwy, tylko pierwsza z liczb dawała się przerobić na w miarę współczesną datę.

Sobieraj zamknęła Tytusa i odłożyła na stertę.

– Zestarzałam się chyba, nie śmieszy mnie już prawie wcale – powiedziała i wyjęła z kieszeni polaru złożoną kartkę. – To co, jeszcze raz?

– Myślałem, że mamy przerwę – jęknął, ale wziął kartkę do ręki. Sobieraj wypisała na niej te interpretacje liczb, które wydawały się najrozsądniejsze. Sama śmietanka, już po odrzuceniu numerologii, identyfikatorów na serwisach randkowych i numerów aukcji internetowych. Na kartce stało:

241921 – symbol Animatora gospodarczego ds. rozwoju technologicznego w klasyfikacji zawodów Ministerstwa Pracy i Polityki Społecznej; numer, pod którym wpisana jest do KRS spółka Goldenline, prowadząca biznesowy serwis społecznościowy.

212225 – symbol modnych, wsuwanych butów Gucciego.

191621 – numer polskiego patentu dla korytka kablowego do światłowodów; asteroida z pasu asteroidów rozciągającego się pomiędzy wewnętrznymi i zewnętrznymi planetami Układu Słonecznego.

Masakra. Szacki spojrzał na to i od razu ponownie zamknął oczy.

– Źle kombinujemy – powiedział.

– Hmm? – mruknęła Sobieraj, Szacki nauczył się już, że uprzejme „hmm" to jej sposób na aktywne słuchanie.

– Zamiast myśleć, wrzucamy to bez sensu w Google'a, jakbyśmy naprawdę wierzyli, że cały świat jest już w internecie. A nie ścigamy kogoś, kto morduje informatyków, wieszając ich na kablach sieciowych. Wszystko ociera się o starą tradycję, zabobony, zabytki. Google nam nie pomoże. Musimy pomyśleć. Trzy sześciocyfrowe numery, stosunkowo blisko siebie, ale nie ułożone w kolejności. Ustaliliśmy, że sześciocyfrowe były kiedyś numery telefonów, sprawdzimy je w starych książkach adresowych województwa. Co jeszcze?

– Legitymacje policyjne!

Szacki otworzył oczy. To było to. To musiało być to. Skrót oznaczający Komendę Wojewódzką Policji i trzy sześciocyfrowe numery. Odstawił kawę i od razu zadzwonił do Wilczura, który na szczęście był jeszcze na komendzie. Kazał mu wrzucić w system trzy numery i oddzwonić. Sobieraj słuchała z wypiekami, jak wydaje chłodnym głosem polecenia służbowe, wyglądała jak mała ruda dziewczynka na tropie wakacyjnej tajemnicy.

– Co jeszcze? – zapytał Szacki. – Co jeszcze jest oznaczane sześciocyfrowymi numerami? Mów wszystko, co ci przyjdzie do głowy, najodleglejsze skojarzenia, rzeczy w ogóle nie na temat.

Sobieraj spojrzała na niego. Jeśli chciała o coś spytać, to zrezygnowała, przygryzła dolną wargę w zamyśleniu.

– Numery obozowe. Niemcy, Żydzi, antysemityzm. KWP to może być oznaczenie jakiejś kategorii.

– Dobrze. Do sprawdzenia. Co jeszcze?

– Numery na gadu są chyba sześciocyfrowe. Nie jestem pewna.

– Do sprawdzenia. Co jeszcze?

Sobieraj zagryzła mocniej wargę, zmarszczyła brwi i nachyliła się do niego.

– Mam! Liczba szarych komórek.

– Że jak?

– Liczba szarych komórek, które obumierają za każdym razem, kiedy zamiast myśleć, wydajesz polecenia.

– Ktoś musi zorganizować robotę.

– No, słucham. – Sobieraj zaplotła dłonie, odchyliła się w stronę oparcia kanapy i zaczęła kręcić młynka kciukami. Wyglądała słodko i Szacki poczuł, że lubi ją coraz bardziej. Trochę to był typ koleżanki z harcerstwa, dziewczyny, z którą można przesiedzieć całą noc na warcie i cały obóz przegadać, a jak w końcu dociera, że to była nie tylko przyjaźń, to ona już dawno jest czyjąś żoną. Zamknął oczy i zaczął wyobrażać sobie cyfry. Zobaczył teczkę na akta, ale odepchnął obraz od siebie, wszystkie sygnatury świata zawsze są łamane przez rok, to nie może być to. Z tego samego powodu odpadali więźniowie i aresztanci, poza tym ich numery nie były sześciocyfrowe. Opieprzył się za zbyt klasyczne myślenie. Trzeba coś zakręcić, pomyśleć odwrotnie. Może to rozbić? Nie numery sześciocyfrowe, tylko zbitki trzycyfrowych? 241 921 – 212 225 – 191 621. Trochę jak część numerów IP. Trochę jak numery telefonów komórkowych bez oznaczenia

operatora. A zbitki dwucyfrowych? 24 19 21 – 21 22 25 – 19 16 21.
Wyświetlał je w pamięci, obracał na wszystkie strony.
– Dziwna prawidłowość... – powiedział cicho.
– Hmm?
– Dziwna prawidłowość – powtórzył. – Jeśli rozbijemy nu-
mery na liczby dwucyfrowe, to żadna z nich nie jest wyższa
niż dwadzieścia pięć. Spójrz.

Wyjął pióro z wewnętrznej kieszeni marynarki, zapisał
cyfry na serwetce w następujący sposób:

24 19 21
21 22 25
19 16 21

Sobieraj obróciła do siebie serwetkę.
– Kwadrat magiczny? Rebus matematyczny? Jakiś szyfr?
Łaciński alfabet ma dwadzieścia sześć znaków.

Szacki szybko przepisał:

X S U
U V Y
S P U

Spojrzeli na siebie z Sobieraj. Nie wyglądało to sensow-
nie. Ale Szacki poczuł niepokój. Uciekła mu jakaś myśl. Coś
przemknęło w tyle głowy. Kiedy zamieniał cyfry na litery?
Nie, wcześniej. Kiedy patrzył na rozpisane w kwadrat liczby.
A Sobieraj powiedziała o rebusie? Nie, najpierw wspomniała
o kwadracie magicznym. Nie wiedzieć czemu, kwadrat magiczny zapachniał mu papierem, tajemnicą, czytaną pod kołdrą przy świetle latarki książką. Co to było? Jakaś młodzieżo-
wa lektura, żydowski alchemik wskrzesza w Pradze Golema,
wkładając mu w usta kartkę z kwadratem magicznym. Mój
Boże, czy naprawdę do jego śledztwa wkracza właśnie Kabała? To był jakiś trop, ale to jeszcze nie to, jakaś inna myśl
przeleciała, kiedy patrzył na te cyfry, jakieś odległe skoja-
rzenie. Pary liczb. Kwadrat magiczny. Kabała. Przesądy. Zabobony. Ezoteryka. Wiara. Złapał Sobieraj za rękę, nakazał
palcem, żeby się nie odzywała, wyciągnięta myśl była coraz

bliżej, nie chciał jej stracić. Liczby. Kabała. Wiara. No, jeszcze trochę. Wstrzymał oddech, zamknął oczy, widział, jak z neuronowej mgły wyłania się odpowiedź.

I wtedy zadzwonił telefon. Wilczur. Myśl przepadła, Szacki odebrał i wysłuchał, co ma do powiedzenia stary policjant.

Sobieraj patrzyła wyczekująco, położyła dłoń na jego dłoni, Szacki pomyślał, że widok dwóch trzymających się kurczowo za ręce prokuratorów jest cokolwiek surrealistyczny, ale nie cofnął swojej.

– No i? – spytała, kiedy prokurator zakończył rozmowę.

– No i nic – odparł Szacki. – Pani nadkomisarz z dochodzeniówki w Brzegu Dolnym, aspirant drogówki z Barczewa i dzielnicowy z Gorzowa Wielkopolskiego. Różne miejsca urodzenia, różne nazwiska, żadnych punktów stycznych ani ze sobą, ani z naszą sprawą. Wilczur obiecał, że jego kumpel w Tarnobrzegu sprawdzi jeszcze w archiwum legitymacje milicyjne. Może tam coś będzie.

Chciało mu się płakać. W zaginionej myśli mogło być rozwiązanie zagadki.

– Hmm – mruknęła Sobieraj. – Tak cię słucham, że Brzeg, Barczewo, Gorzów, miejsca na mapie. Myślisz, że to mogą być współrzędne geograficzne? Wiesz, stopnie, minuty, sekundy?

Szacki szybko dopił resztkę kawy, prawie pobiegli z powrotem do jego kawalerskiej nory, w której wyczuwał ciągle perfumy Klary. Klary – najlepszej partii w Sandomierzu.

Wykorzystując różne kombinacje, na naszej ćwiartce globu (szerokość północna, długość wschodnia) udało im się oznaczyć kilka pustynnych miejsc w Libii i Czadzie. Inne eksperymenty prowadziły na bezdroża Namibii i fale Oceanu Atlantyckiego.

– Spróbujmy oznaczyć to w Polsce – powiedziała Sobieraj, nachylając się nad jego ramieniem. Rude włosy łaskotały go w ucho.

– Libię w Polsce?

– To znaczy gdzie te południki przecinają Polskę. Kojarzysz, jak w *Dzieciach kapitana Granta*.

Tam, co prawda, chodziło o równoleżnik, ale Szacki szybko zrozumiał. Faktycznie, gdyby wszystkie numery były oznaczeniem szerokości geograficznej, to wszystkie przecinałyby nasz rejon świata. 19°16'21" od Bielska-Białej, przez Dąbrowę Górniczą i zachodnie przedmieścia Łodzi po Mierzeję Wiślaną w okolicach Krynicy Morskiej. 21°22'25" startowało z kolei niedaleko Krynicy Zdroju, aby przelecieć przez sam środek Ostrowca Świętokrzyskiego – tutaj spojrzeli na siebie znacząco – przeciąć wschodnie dzielnice stolicy i przez Mrągowo dotrzeć do granicy z Rosją. 24°19'21" było w całości poza Polską, ale ciągle w jej przedwojennych granicach, delikatnie omijało od wschodniej strony Lwów, Grodno i Kowno.

– Ten Ostrowiec to już coś – wymruczała mu do ucha Sobieraj, za wszelką cenę próbując udowodnić, że dla prawdziwego optymisty i stłuczona szklanka może być do połowy pełna.

– Nawet wiem co – powiedział Szacki, wstając gwałtownie.

– Hmm?

– Gówno. Ściema. Kłamstwo. Wielkie gówno wielkości Australii, monstrualna kupa rzadkiej kupy!

Sobieraj założyła włosy za uszy i patrzyła na niego cierpliwie, czekając, aż się uspokoi. Szacki chodził po pokoju od ściany do ściany.

– Na amerykańskich filmach zawsze pojawia się geniusz, który usiłuje myśleć jak morderca, tak? Marszczy czoło, chodzi po miejscu zbrodni i w gwałtownych czarno-białych retrospekcjach widzimy, jak jego umysł się dostraja, jak rozumie, co dokładnie się wydarzyło. – Coś błysnęło między szafą a ścianą, coś, co wyglądało jak srebrne opakowanie, Szacki z trudem oparł się pokusie sprawdzenia, czy to opakowanie prezerwatywy, czy opakowanie po prezerwatywie.

– Hmm? – tym razem Sobieraj wzbogaciła swoje mruknięcie o zachęcający gest. Jedną ręką wystukiwała coś na klawiaturze.

– Tylko że filmy mają inną logikę niż życie. Mają logikę, która w półtorej godziny musi doprowadzić do rozwiązania, zamknięcia akcji, pojmania sprawcy. A teraz wczujmy się w logikę prawdziwej sprawy i naszego mordercy. Zapewne nie chce, żebyśmy go złapali w półtorej godziny, więc jeśli nie jest absolutnie i do końca popieprzony, nie będzie zostawiał szarad, których rozwiązanie doprowadzi nas do niego.

– Czyli?

– Czyli albo zostawi szaradę, która skieruje nas na zupełnie fałszywy trop. Albo, co z jego, lub jej, punktu widzenia musi być zabawniejszym rozwiązaniem, zostawi nonsensowną szaradę. Taką, która nie ma rozwiązania i donikąd nie prowadzi, sprawia jedynie, że marnujemy czas, oglądając satelitarne zdjęcia pustyni w Libii. A z każdą minutą on, lub ona, jest zapewne coraz dalej, coraz bardziej bezpieczny.

– Okej – powiedziała wolno Sobieraj, bujając się na krześle, ręce miała splecione pod brodą. – I co proponujesz?

– Idziemy do łóżka.

Sobieraj wolno podniosła jedną brew do góry.

– Nie wzięłam swojej koronkowej bielizny, więc jeśli zgodziłbyś się przełożyć to na inny termin...

Szacki parsknął śmiechem. Naprawdę lubił ją coraz bardziej.

– Wy strasznie jesteście lubieżni na tej prowincji.

– Długie zimy, długie noce, kina nie ma, w telewizji nudy. Co robić?

– Spać. Idziemy spać, wypocząć. Jutro mamy profilera, spłyną dane z laboratorium, nagrania z miejskiego monitoringu, może będziemy mieli coś więcej.

Sobieraj odwróciła do niego laptopa.

– Najpierw spójrz na to.

Podszedł, wzmianka o bieliźnie sprawiła, że najpierw spojrzał na nią, inaczej, ale zobaczył to samo, co zwykle. Dżinsy, grube trekkingowe skarpety, czerwony polar, zero makijażu. Podręcznikowy przypadek stuprocentowej oazowej harcerki. Jedyna koronka, jaką sobie wyobrażał w jej kontekście, to koronka do Miłosierdzia Bożego. Ale pachniała ładnie, pomyślał, pochylając się nad nią – bardziej szamponem niż perfumami, ale ładnie.

W oknie przeglądarki otwarte było hasło Konspiracyjne Wojsko Polskie. No tak, KWP. W głowie pojawiły się odpryski powierzchownej historycznej wiedzy. Żołnierze wyklęci, walcząca z komunistami powojenna partyzantka, wyroki sądu podziemnego, antysemickie wybryki. Szyller?

– Zostawiam cię z problemem, czy to może być ściema, czy nie, i faktycznie idę spać. Odezwę się, jak wskoczę w coś bardziej sexy. Buziak.

Cmoknęła go po koleżeńsku w policzek i wyszła. Pomachał jej, nie odrywając wzroku od komputera.

Kilka godzin później, kiedy wypalał swojego pierwszego papierosa przy uchylonym oknie w kuchni, a dym razem z piaskiem w jego oczach tworzył bolesną mieszankę, wiedział już znacznie więcej o Konspiracyjnym Wojsku Polskim. O tyle więcej, żeby wpiąć do akt jeszcze jedną wersję śledztwa, wersję złowieszczą, która najbardziej ze wszystkich zakładała, że cała sprawa to krwawa żydowska dintojra. I która niestety przewidywała, że nie musi się skończyć na dwóch trupach, wręcz przeciwnie.

Świt zapowiedział się tym, że w czerni podwórka pojawiły się pierwsze niewyraźne kształty, ciemne plamy na tle bardzo ciemnych plam. Szackiemu przypomniała się noc sprzed kilku dni, palił w tym samym miejscu, kiedy ku jego utrapieniu na polarze pojawiły się czerwone paznokcie Klary. Myślał o tamtej nocy, myślał o niej, jak rano kazała mu się odwrócić, ubierając swoje posągowe ciało. Do wyciskanych przez zmęczenie i dym łez dołączyło trochę smutnej wilgoci. Prokurator Teodor Szacki znowu coś spierdolił, znowu został sam, bez nikogo i bez niczego.

Ale może tak było najlepiej.

Rozdział szósty

poniedziałek, 20 kwietnia 2009

Prawosławni chrześcijanie świętują Wielki Poniedziałek, katolicy w końcu mają wolne, nie licząc tych o skrajnie prawicowych poglądach, którzy świętują okrągłe, 120. urodziny Adolfa Hitlera. Pozostałe Ludy Księgi też nie próżnują: muzułmanie obchodzą 1442. urodziny Mahometa, a Żydzi słuchają, jak prezydent Iranu na konferencji ONZ na temat walki z rasizmem wygłasza antysemickie przemówienie. W Polsce 48 procent Polaków twierdzi, że w Sejmie nie ma partii, która reprezentowałaby ich interesy, a 31 procent – że żadna nie prezentuje ich poglądów politycznych. Indie wystrzeliwują na orbitę szpiegowskiego satelitę produkcji izraelskiej, Rosja ostrzega NATO, że manewry wojskowe w Gruzji to niepotrzebna prowokacja, a we Włoszech Juventus zostaje ukarany za rasistowskie okrzyki kiboli, najbliższy mecz zagra bez publiczności. W Sandomierzu 37-latek parkuje swoją fiestę w sklepie hydraulicznym na Mickiewicza, nieopodal rozpoczyna się etap diecezjalny XIII Konkursu Wiedzy Biblijnej. Wszyscy 44 finaliści już wygrali jednodniowy pobyt formacyjno-wypoczynkowy w pustelni w Rytwianach. Trochę cieplej, ale bez ekscytacji, temperatura w dzień to około 13 stopni, jak na złość pięknie i słonecznie.

Śniły mu się jakieś bzdury. Koszmarne bzdury. Znowu był w Lapidarium, zamiast rocka leciały w kółko przeboje z lat osiemdziesiątych. Ciągle brzmiało mu w uszach *Wake Me Up Before You Go Go*, kiedy sięgał po stojącą zawsze obok łóżka butelkę wody. W miarę odzyskiwania świadomości wspomnienia snu blakły w szybkim tempie, ale nie na tyle szybkim, żeby zmyć zdziwienie z zaspanej twarzy. Leciał Wham!, on tańczył z różnymi kobietami, na pewno były tam Tatarska, Klara, Weronika i Sobieraj. Baśka miała na sobie tylko czerwoną koronkową bieliznę, byłoby to wszystko bardzo erotyczne, gdyby nie pojawił się Hitler – dokładnie przy słowach *you put the boom boom into my heart*. Prawdziwy Adolf Hitler, z małym wąsikiem i w nazistowskim mundurze, niski, śmieszny facecik. Może niski, może śmieszny, ale tańczył zajebiście, naśladował ruchy George'a Michaela jak bóg tańca, dziewczyny zrobiły mu miejsce na parkiecie, wszyscy klaskali w kółeczku, a w środku tańczył Hitler. Nagle złapał Szackiego za rękę i zaczęli tańczyć razem, pamiętał ze snu, że uczucie niestosowności tańca z Hitlerem walczyło z uczuciem przyjemności, Hitler tańczył świetnie, zmysłowo, dawał się lekko prowadzić, pomysłowo reagował na każdy ruch. Ostatni blaknący obraz to roześmiany Hitler, wyrzucający na zmianę ramiona nad głowę, patrzący zalotnie na niego i piszczący *come on baby, let's not fight, we'll go dancing and everything will be all right*. Czy jakoś tak. Co za bzdura, Szacki kręcił głową z niedowierzaniem, ciągnąc swoje wymięte czterdziestoletnie ciało do łazienki. Sikając, w końcu poddał się narastającej w krtani potrzebie i wychrypiał do lustra słowa refrenu.

Wieczny dylemat, czy najpierw wziąć prysznic, czy najpierw zjeść śniadanie, rozstrzygnął w salomonowy sposób, narzucając cokolwiek i wychodząc na zakupy, żeby złapać trochę powietrza i zebrać myśli przed spotkaniem z profilerem. Basia z nim raz pracowała, Szacki tylko o nim słyszał, gość pochodził z Krakowa i w południowej Polsce był legendą, legendą o opinii tyleż geniusza, co ekscentryka. Nie podobało mu się to, nie lubił gwiazd, zawsze wolał tych nierzucających się w oczy, precyzyjnie wykonujących swoją robotę. Dobry śledczy musiał być jak równy bramkarz, który może nie obroni strzału nie do obrony, ale też nie puści szmaty. Nie ma miejsca w wymiarze sprawiedliwości dla Bartheza czy Boruca.

Stał w społemowskim sklepie w kolejce do kasy, ręka cały czas bezwiednie wystukiwała o udo początek przeboju Wham! – pa, pa, pa, pam, pam – oczy błądziły po poukładanych w chłodniczej ladzie wędlinach. Jakże one były smutne. Naprawdę, nigdzie nie widział tak smutnych wędlin jak w tym sklepie. Większość wyglądała, jakby nie była prawdziwa – plastikowa podróbka wykonana na zepsutej wtryskarce. A te, które wyglądały na prawdziwe, były z kolei zbyt prawdziwe, mieniące się różnymi kolorami, zeschnięte lub zwilgotniałe. Na dodatek miały jakieś dziwnie niskie ceny. Dlatego, choć wzięła go ochota na kawałek kabanosa do kawy, stał w kolejce, trzymając w objęciach serek wiejski, opakowanie paczkowanego sera, sok pomidorowy i dwie bułki i przysłuchując się toczonej za jego plecami dyskusji dwóch kobiet.

– Dobry dzieciak, tylko najchętniej by czytał Ewangelię Jana, te wszystkie sądy ostateczne i okropieństwa, dla niego to jak Sapkowski. A konkurs jest właśnie bez Jana.

– A to dziś ten konkurs?

– Tak, w instytucie. Właśnie się zaczyna, nawet denerwuję się trochę. Wczoraj jeszcze żeśmy powtarzali, spytał się, czy Maria Magdalena była żoną Jezusa. Skąd oni to biorą?

– Z Dana Browna. Magdalena to się chyba w Biłgoraju objawiała, prawda?

– U Palikota?

Kobiety zachichotały, Szacki też się uśmiechnął. Jednocześnie ta rozmowa coś w nim poruszyła, znajomo zaswędziała w głowie. Dan Brown, wczorajsze zagadki, kamień magiczny, Kabała. Znowu coś umyka, powinien albo więcej spać, albo łykać jakiś magnez.

– A może wędlinki pan spróbuje? – kasjerka uśmiechnęła się tak promiennie, jakby po latach odnalazła syna. – Żywiecką pyszną przywieźli, zresztą co ja będę gadała – wstała od kasy i ukroiła pokaźny plasterek – pan sam spróbuje. Chłop musi mieć siłę, a nie tak na jakimś nabiale jak modelka.

Szacki podziękował grzecznie i pogryzł kiełbasę, choć nienawidził jeść czegokolwiek przed pierwszym łykiem kawy. Żywiecka była podła i rosła mu w ustach, mimo to uśmiechnął się miło i wziął dziesięć deka. Rozejrzał się dyskretnie, czy przypadkiem nie ma tu jakiejś telewizji, nigdy w żadnym sklepie przez czterdzieści lat nikt nie był wobec niego tak uprzedzająco grzeczny. Ale nie, nie było kamer, tylko on, rozanielona kasjerka i dwie gimnazjalne mamy. Jedna uśmiechała się do niego, druga przymknęła oczy i z aprobatą pokiwała głową. Absolutnie surrealistyczne. Jak tańczył z Hitlerem, przynajmniej był pewien, że to sen, teraz bał się, że wariuje. Czym prędzej zapłacił.

Znowu było lodowato, Szacki zwabiony słońcem zarzucił tylko lekką bluzę i teraz trząsł się z zimna, mimo to podskoczył jeszcze do szwajcarskiej piekarenki. Musiał zjeść pączka, chociaż wiedział, że będzie niesmaczny.

– Uszanowanie – starszy pan, mijając go, uchylił dworsko kapelusza i ukłonił się Szackiemu.

Szacki odkłonił się automatycznie, myśląc, że to się robi naprawdę dziwne, i wszedł do piekarni. Przy kasie stała starsza pani, cała w pogrzebowej czerni, widząc Szackiego, odsunęła się od lady.

– Ależ proszę, proszę, ja się muszę zastanowić jeszcze.

Nic nie powiedział, wziął dziwnie rozdęty wielki pączek i wyjął z kieszeni garść drobnych.

– Nie trzeba – uśmiechnęła się panienka. – Dziś promocja.

– Jaka promocja? – nie wytrzymał. – Weź jednego, dostaniesz go gratis?

– Promocja dla naszego pana prokuratora – dopowiedziała z tyłu starsza pani. – A dla mnie, Nataszko, ta paróweczka w cieście, ta taka bardziej przypieczona taka.

Szacki wyszedł bez słowa, czuł, że go dławi w gardle, że tężeją mu mięśnie karku. Śni mu się *Truman Show*, a on nie potrafi odróżnić snu od jawy, nie potrafi się obudzić. Zwariował.

Szybkim krokiem wracał do siebie na Długosza, mijając sklep, w którym wcześniej robił zakupy, zderzył się z wychodzącym mężczyzną o wyglądzie wulkanizatora w garniturze. Mężczyzna wyraźnie był pogrążony w swoich myślach, ale kiedy zobaczył Szackiego, cały się – ku rozpaczy prokuratora – rozpromienił.

– Gratuluję – wyszeptał konspiracyjnie. – W naszych czasach potrzeba odwagi, żeby mówić takie rzeczy wprost. Niech pan pamięta, że jesteśmy z panem.

– Jacy my, na Boga?

– My, zwyczajni, prawdziwi Polacy. Powodzenia! – mężczyzna konfidencjonalnie uścisnął go za ramię i odszedł w stronę ratusza, a Szackiemu dopiero teraz uchyliły się właściwe klapki w mózgu. Błagam, pomyślał, niech to nie będzie prawda. Wskoczył do sklepu, potrącił jakiegoś chłopaczka, który mówił do kolegi: „Ty, weź no, kurwa, ale żeby ice tea nie było, co to w ogóle za wioska jest", i dopadł stojaka z gazetami. Zagadka momentalnie się rozwiązała, ani nie śnił, ani nie zwariował, ani nie był bohaterem *Truman Show*.

Na okładce „Faktu" zobaczył siebie w ulubionym grafitowym garniturze, stojącego na schodach sandomierskiej prokuratury. Obie ręce miał uniesione w geście, który wczoraj oznaczał „koniec pytań", ale na zdjęciu wyglądało to, jakby stawiał mur jakiemuś niewidocznemu zagrożeniu, stanowcze *non possumus* rysowało się na jego wychudzonej – teraz widział to wyraźnie – twarzy. Tytuł *Tajemniczy żydowski mord?* i krótki tekst nie pozostawiały wątpliwości, czemu stawia tamę prokurator.

„Prokurator Teodor Szacki (40 l.) z całą stanowczością zapowiedział wczoraj, że dorwie zwyrodnialca, który zamordował już dwie osoby w Sandomierzu. Mieszkańcy mogą spać spokojnie, pod nieobecność księdza Mateusza to on rozwiąże zagadkę żydowskiego być może mordu. Szeryf w garniturze zagwarantował wczoraj osobiście reporterowi «Faktu», że złapie złoczyńcę, nie patrząc, czy to Żyd, czy Arab, nawet gdyby musiał «wyciągać go za pejsy z najbardziej zapluskwionej dziury». Brawo, panie prokuratorze! Na stronach 4–5 przedstawiamy szczegóły obu bestialskich mordów, wypowiedzi świadków i graficzną rekonstrukcję wydarzeń".

Prokurator Teodor Szacki zamknął oczy. Świadomość, że właśnie został bohaterem małomiasteczkowej Polski, była przerażająca.

2

Tak naprawdę nie przeszkadzało mu, że w sklepie nie było ice tea, w ogóle nie miał ochoty ani na nią, ani na nic innego, po prostu chciał głośno dać upust swojemu rozczarowaniu i użyć słowa „kurwa". Ten wyjazd od początku nie układał się po jego myśli. O świcie dowiedział się, że matka wyprała mu wczoraj ulubioną bluzę z Abercrombie, którą wujek Wojtek przywiózł z Mediolanu, i że musi jechać w fajansiarskim polarze, którego używał tylko na nartach, a i tak wtedy zapinał kurtkę pod szyję. Niestety, już pod szkołą okazało się, że to i tak nie ma wielkiego znaczenia, bo Ola zachorowała i w ogóle nie jedzie na wycieczkę. Zadzwonił do niej, Ola się popłakała i musiał ją pocieszać, przez ten czas wszyscy weszli do autokaru i zamiast siedzieć na końcu i pić rozrobioną przez Waltera wódkę z colą, wylądował w trzecim rzędzie obok Maćka, który patrzył na jego PSP tak długo, że musiał je schować do plecaka, zanim Kratos doszedł do końca etapu. Potem zrobiło mu się wstyd, bo co mu zależało, mógł na trochę dać Maćkowi to PSP, przecież mu nie ubędzie. I kiedy myślał, że nie może być gorzej, zawisła nad nim Gołąbkowa, żeby głośno chwalić jego opowiadanie o samotności i rozmaślać się, jaki z niego wrażliwy chłopiec. Potem poszła. Niestety, nie zabrała ze sobą siedzących z tyłu i jęczących Marysi i Stefci, które przez resztę drogi chichotały w przerwę między siedzeniami, że jest wrażliwy jak chomiczek. Nie no, poważnie, jeśli dziewczynki naprawdę dojrzewały szybciej od chłopców, to te musiały mieć jakąś wadę genetyczną. Dał Maćkowi PSP i przez resztę drogi udawał, że śpi.

Sam Sandomierz nie stanowił dla niego wielkiej atrakcji, odwiedził miasto jesienią, kiedy jeszcze było ciepło. Ojciec go zabrał, jego ojcostwo od czasu rozstania z matką to były na zmianę seanse nieobecności i seanse egzaltowanego podlizywania się. Marcin chciał, żeby stary choć raz przestał się starać, ale nie wiedział, jak mu to powiedzieć. Chciał przyjść do niego i nie trafić na zajebisty obiad, nie zobaczyć wypożyczonego filmu i nowej książki w swoim pokoju. Chciał przyjść i zobaczyć go w gaciach, jak nieogolony pije browara i mówi, że sorry, jakiś ten dzień do dupy, weź sobie, synu, zamów pizzę i pooglądaj telewizję czy coś. W końcu byłaby to jakaś normalna sytuacja, dowiedziałby się, że ma ojca, a nie jakąś plastikową lalę, która realizuje program z podręcznika rodzicielstwa po rozstaniu. Oczywiście, wiedział, że inni trafiali gorzej, stary dematerializował się w ogóle albo przysyłał esemes raz na dwa tygodnie. Ale co z tego, i tak wszystko to było chujowe, nawet nie ich rozstanie, bo to go nie zaskoczyło, tylko jak się teraz starali, matka tak samo, wystarczyło, że krzywo spojrzał, i już sięgała do portmonetki, żeby pocieszyć swoje biedne dziecko z rozbitego domu, nawet jak nie miała na rachunki. Wstyd mu było, że są tacy słabi, że tak łatwo nimi sterować, tak łatwo, że nie przynosiło to żadnej satysfakcji, jak przejście zbyt prostej gry. Dobrze, że miał skrzypce, skrzypce były uczciwe, nie oszukiwały, nie obiecywały, nie podlizywały się. Potrafiły się odwdzięczyć, ale potrafiły też być bezlitosne, wszystko zależało od niego – tak, związek ze skrzypcami to był najbardziej uczciwy układ w dotychczasowym, niedługim przecież, życiu Marcina Ładonia.

Pogrążony w niewesołych myślach i pozbawiony ice tea, na którą nie miał ochoty, stanął z boku grupy i czekał na wejście do sandomierskich podziemi. Gołąbkowa patrzyła na niego mokrymi oczami, pewnie myślała, że znowu się alienuje, pogrąża w samotności, biedny chłopiec, zbyt wrażliwy na współczesny świat. No naprawdę, lubił ją, ale czasami była tak odrealnioną kretynką, że wzbudzała litość. Co się dzieje z nimi wszystkimi, miękcy są i rozmemłani, rozłażą się w oczach jak bibuła na deszczu, a potem wielkie zdziwienie, że dzieci ich nie szanują. Dzieci, dobre, na jednej ręce potrafił policzyć dziewice wśród swoich koleżanek. W tym Ryśka, zbyt głupia, żeby rozłożyć nogi, i Faustyna z katolickiej rodziny, pewnie zatknięta poświęconym kołkiem i zaszyta, tę to dopiero nieszczęście spotkało. No i Ola, ale Ola jest inna, wiadomo.

– Mario, łyka? – Walterowi błyszczały już trochę oczy i Marcin pomyślał, że jeszcze może być z tego chryja. Upił trochę „coli", mocnej i cuchnącej wódką, potem szybko włożył świeżą gumę do ust.

– To druga. Pierwszą do Radomia zrobiliśmy.

– Zarąbiście – powiedział, żeby powiedzieć cokolwiek.

Walter pociągnął z butelki gestem rasowego alkoholika, tak że tylko niewidomy by nie spostrzegł, czym smaruje swój piętnastoletni organizm. Marcin poczuł się zażenowany jego ostentacją i tym, że bierze udział w tandetnym przedstawieniu, szybko przesunął się bliżej środka grupy, która już schodziła do sandomierskich podziemi. Części kolegów mimo najlepszych starań nie udało się ukrywać ekscytacji przygodą, tylko panny pozostawały niewzruszone wobec takich atrakcji, Mary jedną ręką trzymała się Stefy, żeby się nie przewrócić, drugą pisała coś w komórce. Nie wiedzieć do kogo, wszyscy byli tutaj.

– ...Sandomierz był wtedy bogatym miastem, jednym z najbogatszych w Polsce, obowiązywało w nim prawo składu, co oznaczało, że każdy z podróżujących kupców musiał wystawić tu swoje towary na sprzedaż, przez co był Sandomierz gigantycznym, non stop otwartym centrum handlowym, gdzie można było dostać wszystko. – Mary oderwała od komórki znudzony wzrok na dźwięk słów „centrum handlowe", ale szybko dała spokój. – Mieszczanie sandomierscy bogacili się i w trosce o swój dobytek, towary, a także bezpieczeństwo przez wieki drążyli pod miastem piwnice, które z biegiem lat zamieniły się w monstrualny labirynt. Połączone pomieszczenia sięgały ośmiu pięter w głąb lessowej skały, korytarze biegły pod Wisłą aż do zamku w Baranowie, do innych sąsiednich wsi. Do dziś nikt nie wie, ile tak naprawdę ich jest.

Przewodniczka miała przyjemny, zadziorny głos, który nie zmieniał faktu, że przynudzała, zwłaszcza jeśli się musiało wysłuchać tej samej historii drugi raz w przeciągu kilku miesięcy. Ale nawet gdyby nie przynudzała, nie zmieniłoby to faktu, który już poprzednio tak zadziwił Marcina – że słynne sandomierskie lochy wyglądały jak piwnica w bloku z wielkiej płyty. Ceglane ściany, betonowe stropy, podłoga z lastryko, jarzeniowe światło. Zero magii, zero tajemnicy, zero czegokolwiek. Niezwykłe, jak im się udało spieprzyć taką atrakcję.

– I nagle Mongołowie otoczyli miasto – powiedziała niskim głosem przewodniczka, co ją ośmieszyło, zamiast dodać dramatyzmu opowieści. – Halina Krępianka, nieutulona w żalu po stracie całej rodziny, poszła do obozu wroga. Tam opowiedziała wodzowi Tatarów, że wprowadzi ich tajnymi korytarzami do miasta, ponieważ chce się zemścić na mieszkańcach za to, że ją pohańbili... – Przewodniczka zawstydziła się nagle, pewnie nie była pewna, czy dzieci rozumieją, co dokładnie ma na myśli.

– Pohańbili? To czemu uciekała, głupia jakaś – mruknęła Mary.

– Lol – zawtórowała jej najlepsza przyjaciółka.

– Kiedy Tatarzy zaufali dziewczynie, długo prowadziła ich labiryntem korytarzy, a przez ten czas mieszkańcy zamurowali wejście do podziemi. Zginęli wszyscy najeźdźcy, zginęła też bohaterska dziewczyna...

– Jak się kapnęli, to ją dopiero pohańbili. – Mary była niezastąpiona.

– He, duże lol.

– ...a na dowód tego, że w każdej legendzie jest ziarenko prawdy, mogę wam powiedzieć, że wąwóz Piszczele od tego ma swoją nazwę, że do dziś można tam wykopać ludzkie kości, być może właśnie szczątki żywcem pogrzebanych Tatarów.

Przeszli noga za nogą do następnej sali, o tyle ciekawej, że przypominała górniczy chodnik, Marcin słuchał wykładu o tym, jak już po wojnie ratowano miasto przed zawaleniem. To było ciekawe, ciekawsze niż legendy o bohaterskich dupach. Jak górnicy wiercili szyby na rynku, jak domy na starówce musiano rozebrać i zbudować na nowo, jak puste tunele i piwnice wypełniano specjalną masą, żeby wzmocnić podziurawioną jak sito skałę. Oparł się plecami o ścianę, słuchanie nie przeszkadzało mu gapić się na wystającą z biodrówek Mary tasiemkę liliowych stringów. Może on był niedzisiejszy, ale drażniło go trochę, że one prawie wszystkie usiłowały wyglądać jak przechodzone dziwki. Dobrze, że Ola taka nie była.

Przewodniczka zawiesiła na moment głos, zapanowała cisza.

W ciszy usłyszał delikatne, odległe, dobiegające jakby z głębi ziemi wycie.

– Słyszycie?

Mary odwróciła się do niego i podciągnęła spodnie.

– Czy co słyszymy, zboku?

– No wycie takie z głębi ziemi. O, cicho, cicho, teraz... Dziewczyny wymieniły spojrzenia.

– Oł-em-dżi. Oszalałeś?

– Ale posłuchajcie, naprawdę słychać wycie.

– Takie wycie, jakby ktoś kogoś hańbił, czy raczej szatańskie? Bo chyba tylko to pierwsze mnie interesuje.

– Lol.

– Jezu, ale z ciebie głupi lachon. Ty weź się zamknij na chwilę i posłuchaj.

– A ty weź się idź leczyć, psycho freak normalnie, Oli muszę powiedzieć.

Dziewczyny zachichotały wspólnie i dołączyły do grupy, która przechodziła do następnej sali. Marcin został, przykładał ucho do ściany w różnych miejscach, w końcu znalazł takie, gdzie wycie słychać było najlepiej. Przedziwny był to dźwięk, ciarki przechodziły od niego po plecach. Długie, modulowane, prawie nieprzerwane wycie torturowanego człowieka albo zwierzęcia. Cokolwiek wydawało ten dźwięk, musiało być w opłakanym stanie. Chociaż może mu się wydaje, może to wiatr, wentylacja jakaś.

Zgasło światło, delikatna, połączona z szeptami łuna dobiegała jedynie z kierunku, gdzie zniknęła jego klasa. Położył się z uchem przy podłodze, coś nie dawało mu spokoju w tym dźwięku, czegoś nie słyszał do końca. Szukając najlepszej jakości, szurał uchem po zimnym lastryku, coraz lepiej słyszał wycie, był już pewien, że dobywało się z więcej niż jednego gardła. I oprócz wycia było coś jeszcze, inny rodzaj dźwięku, znajomy, zwierzęcy...

Już miał go nazwać, kiedy poczuł bolesne uderzenie w bok.

– Co jest, kurwa... – Ciemność rozjaśniło trupie światło komórkowego wyświetlacza. – Mario? Ocipiałeś?

Marcin wstał, otrzepał ubranie.

– Bo takie wycie...

– Ta, jasne, na skrzypcach wycie. Ty weź się lepiej napij, Vivaldo.

3

Doktor nadkomisarz Jarosław Klejnocki siedział z nogą założoną na nogę, pykał fajkę i patrzył na nich spokojnym spojrzeniem, ukrytym za grubymi okularami. Okulary były naprawdę grube, nie było w tym żadnej przenośni, na tyle grube, że można było dostrzec wybrzuszony kształt soczewek i żeby widoczny za nimi fragment twarzy naukowca wydawał się znacznie węższy od reszty. Do tego krótkie siwe włosy, broda równie krótka, niżej golf, tweedowa marynarka, spodnie od garnituru i czerwone sportowe buty w stylu House'a.

Ubranie delikatnie na nim wisiało, Szacki pomyślał, że jeszcze niedawno musiał być gruby, pewne zmizernienie, odrobina nadmiarowej skóry na policzkach, sposób ubierania się i powolne ruchy świadczyły o tym, że przez lata przyzwyczajał się do swojej tuszy. Którą mu pewnie zabrała choroba albo litościwa żona, uznawszy, że nie chce, aby przedwcześnie owdowił ją cholesterol.

Oprócz Klejnockiego i Szackiego w sali konferencyjnej prokuratury byli Basia Sobieraj i Leon Wilczur, który wcześniej oprowadzał naukowca po miejscach zbrodni. Okna były zasłonięte żaluzjami, na dużym rozkładanym ekranie wyświetlano zdjęcia zwłok. Sobieraj siedziała tyłem do ekranu, nie chciała na to patrzeć.

Klejnocki pyknął jeszcze raz fajeczkę i odłożył ją na specjalny stojaczek, który wcześniej wyjął z kieszeni. Gdyby ktoś zorganizował konkurs na typowego krakowskiego wykształciucha, nadkomisarz miałby prosty wybór – albo grand prix, albo przewodniczący jury. Szacki nagle poczuł irytację. Pozostawała tylko nadzieja, że za tym przerostem formy kryje się inna treść niż jasnowidztwo w naukowym przebraniu.

– Wziąłem ostatnio, wyobraźcie sobie państwo, udział w konkursie na najbardziej polski wyraz. Wiecie, co zaproponowałem?

Chuj-kurwa-złamany, pomyślał Szacki, uśmiechając się uprzejmie.

– Żółć – powiedział z emfazą Klejnocki. – Z dwóch powodów. Po pierwsze, składa się ono z samych znaków diakrytycznych charakterystycznych ekskluzywnie dla języka polskiego i w ten sposób zyskuje rangę tyleż oryginalności, co niepowtarzalności.

Kurwa mać, to nie może być prawda. To nie jest tak, że on tutaj siedzi i słucha tego wykładu, niepodobna.

– Po drugie, mimo że wyraz ten językowo jest tak dystynktywny, zawiera pewne treści uogólniające, w symboliczny sposób stanowi o naturze wspólnoty, która się nim, przyznajmy, że niezbyt często, posługuje. Oddaje pewien charakterystyczny nad Wisłą stan mentalno-psychiczny. Zgorzknienie, frustrację, drwinę podszytą złą energią i poczuciem własnego niespełnienia, bycie na „nie" i ciągłe nieusatysfakcjonowanie.

Klejnocki przerwał, wytrząsnął popiół z fajki i w zamyśleniu zaczął ją ponownie nabijać, czerpiąc tytoń z aksamitnego woreczka w kolorze sukna na stole bilardowym. W pomieszczeniu rozszedł się zapach wanilii.

– Dlaczego o tym mówię?

– Też zadajemy sobie to pytanie – nie wytrzymała Sobieraj.

Klejnocki skłonił jej się uprzejmie.

– Zapewne, droga pani prokurator. Mówię o tym, bo zauważyłem, że oprócz zbrodni w afekcie istnieje coś takiego jak zbrodnia, nazwijmy to, w żółci. Dość charakterystyczna dla tego miejsca na Ziemi, które chcąc nie chcąc, nazywamy ojczyzną. Afekt to nagły wybuch emocji, chwila podniecenia i zaślepienia, która znosi wszystkie narzucone przez kulturę hamulce. Na oczy spada czerwona kotara i ważna jest tylko jedna myśl: zabić. Żółć to co innego. Żółć zbiera się powoli, małymi kropelkami. Najpierw tylko czasami się odbija, potem zamienia się w nieprzyjemną zgagę, przeszkadza żyć, jest irytującym coraz bardziej szumem tła, niczym ćmienie zęba, z tą różnicą, że przyczyny żółci nie usuniemy w czasie jednego zabiegu. Mało kto wie, jak sobie z nią poradzić, a tymczasem każda chwila to kolejna kropelka drażniącej emocji. Kap, kap, kap. – Każdemu „kap" towarzyszyło pyknięcie fajki. – W końcu czujemy już tylko żółć, nic innego w nas nie ma, zrobilibyśmy wszystko, żeby z tym skończyć, żeby nie czuć więcej tej goryczy, tego upokorzenia. To moment, kiedy ludzie rzucają wszystko w diabły, na przykład jeśli żółć zbierała się w pracy. Niektórzy rzucają siebie. Z mostu lub z dachu wieżowca. Niektórzy rzucają się na kogoś. Na żonę, na ojca, na brata. I myślę, że z tym przypadkiem mamy do czynienia tutaj. – Wskazał fajką na bladego trupa Eli Budnik.

– Czyli przechodzimy do konkretów – wtrącił Szacki.

– Jak najbardziej, chyba nie przypuszczali państwo, że będę tak pierdolił cały dzień.

Sobieraj podniosła brew, ale nic nie powiedziała. Wilczurowi nawet nie drgnęła powieka. Do tej pory absolutnie nieruchomy i milczący, uznał chyba, że skończyła się gra wstępna i pora wkroczyć do akcji. Oznaczało to, że pochylił się na krześle – Szacki dałby głowę, że usłyszał skrzypienie i nie było to skrzypienie krzesła – oderwał filtr od papierosa i zapalił.

– Przyznaję, dziwna jest to sprawa – zaczął Klejnocki, a Szacki pomyślał, że się zaczyna. Zawsze miał profilerów za rodzaj jasnowidzów, którzy dają tyle informacji i tak mnożą wątpliwości, że coś musi pasować. O nietrafionych fragmentach nikt potem nie pamięta. – Gdyby nie to, że raczej oczywisty i nie budzący wątpliwości jest fakt, że sprawcą jest ta sama osoba, sugerowałbym, że w wypadku drugiego zabójstwa macie do czynienia z naśladowcą. Zbyt wiele jest tu różnic.

– Na przykład? – spytał Szacki.

– Obie ofiary wykrwawiły się na śmierć. Niby podobieństwo. Ale spójrzmy na szczegóły. Denat ma precyzyjnie podcięte tętnice udowe. Rozwiązanie w pewien sposób eleganckie, krew wypływa szybko, spływa po nogach, koniec. Denatka z kolei ma rozpłatane gardło tak, że przypomina ono skrzela, co oznacza wiele wściekłych cięć. Chciał ją ukarać, upokorzyć, oszpecić, nie przeszkadzało mu, że krew zalewa ofierze twarz i tułów, że ochlapuje sprawcę. Przy takim sposobie poderżnięcia gardła tam musiało być wszystko we krwi.

Szacki przypomniał sobie karmazynową rozległą kałużę na piętrze opuszczonego dworku.

– Czyli że pierwsza zbrodnia została dokonana „w żółci" i teoretycznie powinna zamknąć sprawę. Mord dokonany, żółć wypłynęła razem z krwią ofiary, pojawia się spokój, potem poczucie winy, wyrzuty sumienia. Taka jest dynamika. Dlaczego zabił jeszcze raz? – Klejnocki wstał, zaczął się przechadzać wzdłuż pomieszczenia. – Poza tym obie ofiary były rozebrane. Niby podobieństwo. Ale spójrzmy na szczegóły. Denatka jest porzucona goła w publicznym miejscu, upokorzona po raz kolejny, wszystko to wyraźnie pokazuje, jak silna była potrzeba zabójstwa. Dlatego możemy wykluczyć, że sprawca jest osobą obcą lub przypadkową. Denat wisi w ustronnym miejscu, mało tego, beczkę można potraktować nawet jako rodzaj okrycia, w końcu nie zrobiła ona wielkiej krzywdy, to raczej gadżet. Wygląda, jakby sprawca tym razem podświadomie wstydził się swojego czynu, podczas gdy wcześniej chciał, żeby usłyszał o nim cały świat. Dlaczego? Na razie nie wiemy, ale radzę przyjąć, że kluczem do zagadki jest pierwsze zabójstwo i stojące za nim motywy. Drugie jest, jak by to powiedzieć, uzupełniające, nie kluczowe. Przepraszam za cyniczny ton, ale rozumiem, że na tym etapie przede wszystkim zależy państwu na ujęciu sprawcy.

– Mówi pan cały czas „on" – wtrąciła Sobieraj. – Czy profil pasuje do mężczyzny?

– Bardzo dobre pytanie, właśnie chciałem o tym powiedzieć. Niestety, nie możecie państwo wykluczyć kobiety z kilku względów. Przede wszystkim ofiara nie została zgwałcona. Bardzo rzadko zdarza się, żeby opętany żądzą mordu mężczyzna nie wykorzystał nieprzytomnej kobiety, bo oznacza to dla niej dodatkowe upokorzenie. Poza tym twarz ofiary jest nietknięta. Mimo że sprawca pociął ostrym narzędziem gardło ofiary na strzępy. To może wskazywać na kobietę. Dla kobiet twarz jest bowiem wizytówką, manifestacją piękna, które świadczy o wysokiej wartości, o płodności, o lepszej pozycji. Zniszczenie tej wizytówki jest dla kobiety silniejszym tabu niż dla mężczyzny. I w końcu to, o czym mówiłem wcześniej. Pierwsze zabójstwo to typowy mord o silnym podłożu emocjonalnym, drugie jest popełnione jakby ze wstydem, z obowiązku, bo zakładał to plan na przykład zemsty. A kobiety są znacznie bardziej systematyczne. Facet zarżnąłby, napięcie by go opuściło, dałby spokój. A kobieta odfajkowałaby punkt pierwszy i zaczęła realizować punkt drugi. Oczywiście nie twierdzę, że sprawcą jest kobieta. Twierdzę, że niestety nie można tego wykluczyć.

– Bardzo nam pan pomaga – skomentował zgryźliwie Szacki. – Niczego nie może pan potwierdzić, niczemu zaprzeczyć, wszystko jest możliwe. Nie posuwa nas to do przodu.

– Ofiary nie zginęły w tym samym miejscu. Co pan powie na taki konkret, panie prokuratorze?

– Myli się pan – zaskrzypiał z tyłu Wilczur.

– Stopień nie gwarantuje nieomylności, inspektorze – żachnął się Klejnocki, pokazując tym samym, że nie jest przyzwyczajony do tego, aby małomiasteczkowe gliny legitymowały się wyższą szarżą.

– Badania wykazały, że pod denatem była też krew pierwszej ofiary.

– Być może wykazały, być może była. Radzę sprawdzić jeszcze raz, wziąć próbki z kilku miejsc. Nie jest psychologicznie prawdopodobne, żeby mord pod wpływem emocji został z takim trudem zrealizowany. Drugi jest na chłodno zainscenizowany, ale pierwszy nie, absolutnie wykluczone. Jeśli jednak sprawca zadał sobie trud, żeby podrzucić tam krew pierwszej ofiary, oznacza to, że bardzo mu zależy, abyście nie znaleźli miejsca, gdzie została zamordowana.

Szacki spojrzał na Wilczura, ten tylko skinął potakująco głową. Trzeba będzie sprawdzić.

– Dziękujemy – powiedział do Klejnockiego. – Potwierdzenie będzie dla nas bardzo ważne.

– Czy zaatakuje jeszcze raz? Czy może być seryjnym zabójcą?

– Nie, nie pasuje do profilu seryjnego mordercy. Jak mówiłem wcześniej, bardziej to wygląda na realizowanie jakiegoś planu, zemsta to oczywiście narzucający się motyw. Jeśli więc plan zakłada dalsze ofiary, to tak, zabije.

– Co na to wskazuje?

– Napis pozostawiony na miejscu zbrodni. Gdyby sprawa była skończona, nie chciałoby mu się bawić w żadne gierki.

– Czyli to gierka?

– Albo sposób zakomunikowania, czego dotyczy zemsta. Często mścicielom nie wystarcza śmierć osoby, którą obwiniają o swoją krzywdę. Ważna jest też infamia, świat musi się dowiedzieć, za co ofiary poniosły karę. Oczywiście jest

210

też trzecia możliwość, w końcu zabójcy tak samo jak i my egzystują w pewnej przestrzeni metakryminalnej.

– Wiem, dokąd pan zmierza – westchnął Szacki. – Że oglądają te same filmy i że morderca po prostu nabazgrał parę przypadkowych cyferek, żeby nam namieszać w głowach.

– Dokładnie.

Klejnocki sięgnął ręką i wyłączył projektor.

– Przepraszam, ale nie mogę już patrzeć na tego trupa.

W pomieszczeniu zapanowała cisza. Szacki myślał, że spotkanie mimo wszystko było owocne i musiał oddać Klejnockiemu sprawiedliwość: rozumował bardzo logicznie, nie pozwalał, aby nadmiar teorii przysłonił mu rzeczywistość.

– Zakładając, że jest jeszcze ktoś na liście do odfajkowania. Kto to może być?

– Ktoś powiązany – odparł zgodnie z przeczuciem Szackiego krakowski naukowiec. – Najpierw żona, potem mąż, nie sądzę, żeby teraz przyszła kolej na ekspedientkę z Białegostoku. Ktoś z rodziny, może wieloletni przyjaciel, ktoś z tego samego układu. Jeśli uda wam się dowiedzieć, czego dotyczy sprawa, jeśli znajdziecie kolejną osobę, zanim zaatakuje...

Klejnocki nie musiał kończyć, Szacki bez przerwy słyszał w głowie tykanie zegara, odkąd ta sprawa w ogóle się zaczęła, teraz zegar po prostu zaczął tykać głośniej i szybciej. Jeśli znajdą potencjalną ofiarę, znajdą też mordercę. Może mężczyznę, może kobietę, pewnie kogoś powiązanego z Budnikami, kogoś znanego. Może kogoś, kogo minął na ulicy, a może nawet kogoś, kogo już zna. Spojrzał na rozpytującą jeszcze o jakieś drobiazgi Sobieraj, spojrzał na Wilczura, który rozmawiał przez komórkę w kącie pomieszczenia. Pomyślał o innych, o Szyllerze, o Miszczyk, o mężu Sobieraj, o dziwacznym anatomopatologu Rzeźnickim, o sędzi Tatarskiej, o facecie, który go rano zaczepił przed sklepem. Wszyscy oni byli w jakiś sposób powiązani, znali się od dziecka, razem chodzili na imprezy, rozpuszczali plotki, wyjawiali sekrety, poznawali tajemnice. Nie był paranoikiem, nie dopuszczał do siebie myśli o ogólnomiejskiej zmowie milczenia, ale zauważył, że coraz częściej się cenzuruje w kontaktach z nowymi ziomkami.

Do tej pory tylko przeczuwał, że rozwiązanie zagadki kryje się w murach starego, istniejącego od zarania polskiej historii miasta. Teraz był tego pewien.

4

Z przyczyn oczywistych ominęła go konferencja prasowa, każde pytanie o Teodora „szeryfa żydożercę" Szackiego było zbywane przez Miszczyk w ten sam sposób. Chłodnym stwierdzeniem, że prokurator nadzorujący śledztwo zajmuje się czynnościami służbowymi. Nie rozmawiali wcześniej zbyt długo o pierwszej stronie „Faktu", szefowa lakonicznie poinformowała go, że odbyła długą rozmowę z prokuratorem generalnym i nie była to rozmowa przyjemna. O tym, że śledztwo nie zostało im odebrane i przeniesione do okręgowej w Kielcach, zadecydował – nomen omen – fakt, że prokurator generalny nienawidził tabloidów po tym, jak zobaczył tam swoje zdjęcia w kąpielówkach (*Sauna Temidy*), a jakiś tajemniczy, wysoko postawiony w strukturach władzy obywatel potwierdził, że jeśli ktoś w ogóle potrafi posprzątać ten małomiasteczkowy bajzel, to właśnie białowłosy prokurator. Szacki był realistą, wiedział, co to oznacza – ktoś bardzo nie chciał, żeby wrócił do Warszawy. Spokojnie, nie miał takiego zamiaru.

Obejrzał konferencję w telewizji. Koszmar, połowa pytań kręciła się wokół żydowskich mordów rytualnych, połowa wokół seryjnego zabójcy. Czwarta władza z trudem ukrywała podniecenie tym, że w końcu nad Wisłę zawitał być może prawdziwy seryjny morderca. Poprawka: nie ukrywała. Większość wygłaszających komentarze teflonowych prezenterów sprawiała wrażenie, jakby cały czas trzymała rękę w spodniach i przy słowie „seryjny" mocniej obciągała skórkę. Żenujący spektakl. Zauważył też, że coraz wyżej podnosili głowy narodowi prawicowcy, objęci ostracyzmem za swoje poglądy politycy wrócili do łask, żeby dodać salonowi kolorytu. Różne typy upeerowsko-elpeerowskie siedziały w telewizji i starały się ubrać antysemicką agitkę w szatki intelektualnej publicystyki spod znaku „ja tylko pytam", a czwarta władza udawała, że bierze to za dobrą monetę.

„Należałoby sobie zadać pytanie, czy lud Izraela zawsze był jedynie ofiarą? Oczywiście jest koszmar Holokaustu, ale jest też krwawy Stary Testament, jest zbombardowanie Libanu i mur rozdzielający palestyńskie rodziny. Nie twierdzę, że Żydzi stoją za wydarzeniami w Sandomierzu – choć akurat w tym mieście, gdzie zdarzały się w przeszłości różne incydenty, byłaby to straszna symbolika. Twierdzę, że nieroztropnością byłoby udawać, że jest na świecie naród absolutnie niezdolny do agresji. Bo akurat w tym wypadku takie założenie może prowadzić do eskalacji tragedii".

Cóż, na głupotę nie ma rady, postanowił odciąć się od tego szumu, skupić na dowodach, przejrzał jeszcze raz wszystkie protokoły, stare i nowe. Nie wyglądało to najlepiej. Opuszczony dwór na Zamkowej stał w takim miejscu, że nikt nie mógł nic widzieć i oczywiście nikt nic nie widział. Miejsca nie obejmowała też żadna z kamer. Sześciocyfrowe numery nie były numerami starych legitymacji milicyjnych, również sprawdzanie numerów obozowych i identyfikatorów gadu-gadu było ślepą uliczką. Małym krokiem naprzód było potwierdzenie hipotezy Klejnockiego, że faktycznie Budnikowa nie została zamordowana w tym samym miejscu, co jej mąż. Jej krew znaleziono w kilku miejscach, podejrzanie równo rozmieszczoną, na pewno wyglądałoby to inaczej, gdyby tam została zaszlachtowana. Szacki wiedział, że to istotna informacja. Skoro sprawcy tak bardzo zależało, żeby przestali szukać miejsca popełnienia pierwszej zbrodni, musi ono wskazywać na jego tożsamość. Co by potwierdzało, że na pewno nie jest to osoba przypadkowa. Dlatego polecił pod kątem obecności krwi przeszukać dokładnie całą posesję. Może zabójca popełnił błąd, wylał gdzieś trochę, wskazując kierunek, z którego przyszedł, może nieświadomie zostawił im szlak z okruszków chleba. Chleb i krew, znowu jakaś pokręcona symbolika.

Po konferencji spotkał się jeszcze raz z Miszczyk i Sobieraj, podsumowali wszystko dokładnie. Prawie wszystko, ponieważ Szacki zataił efekt całonocnej kwerendy, dotyczącej Konspiracyjnego Wojska Polskiego. Wspomniał o tym, a jakże, ale ani nie wpiął tego do akt jako dodatkowej wersji śledczej, ani nie przedstawił jako ważnego wątku. Dlaczego? Ponieważ czuł, że to rzuca zbyt duży cień na to cukierkowe miasto, żeby mógł zaufać wychowanym tutaj i zakochanym w Sandomierzu obywatelom. Poza tym wkręcał się coraz bardziej w myślenie, że nie są z nim do końca szczerzy. Że jest tym obcym, któremu się mówi tylko tyle, ile trzeba, i ani słowa więcej. Może było to nie w porządku w stosunku do Sobieraj, łącząca ich sympatia krzepła z rozmowy na rozmowę, a obecność rudej piczki-zasadniczki sprawiała Szackiemu autentyczną przyjemność. Ale ona była stąd, co znaczyło, że nie mógł jej zaufać do końca.

Po spotkaniu wrócił do akt. Musiał być pewien, że nie przeoczył żadnego zdania, żadnego słowa, żadnego fragmentu zdjęcia. Musiał być pewien, że w aktach na pewno nie kryje się rozwiązanie zagadki.

Gruba wskazówka wiszącego nad drzwiami zegara zbliżała się do dziesiątej, a on ciągle ślęczał nad papierami, obracał w wyobraźni każdy element układanki, różne wersje wyświetlały mu się w głowie na podobieństwo filmów. Skupiony, pogrążony w innym świecie – gwałtownie wciągnął powietrze ze strachu, kiedy tuż pod jego nosem rozdzwoniła się komórka. Komenda Powiatowa Policji. Czy prokurator Szacki? Zdecydowanie. Na śmierć zapomniał, że ma dziś dyżur, łatwo było zapomnieć w Sandomierzu o dyżurach, zazwyczaj nie działo się nic, co by wymagało obecności prokuratora na miejscu zdarzenia, czasami wypadek na obwodnicy. Słuchał oficera dyżurnego i znowu poczuł się jak rano w sklepie. To nie mogła być prawda, ktoś sobie z niego robił jaja.

– Będę za dziesięć minut – rzucił.

W samochodzie zerknął jeszcze do planu miasta, wydawało mu się, że wie, gdzie to jest, ale nie chciał ryzykować. Blisko, jakżeby inaczej, tutaj wszędzie było blisko. Jadąc, słuchał Trójki, rozdawali właśnie Fryderyki, Nosowska została wokalistką roku. Zaklął głośno. Niewiarygodne, no po prostu, kurwa, niewiarygodne. Uwielbiał Osiecką, cenił Nosowską, kupił płytę zaraz po premierze, żeby sprawdzić, co rockowa diwa zrobiła z tekstami poetki, jak zaaranżowała słynne songi, czy będzie w stanie zmierzyć się z kompozycjami Komedy, Satanowskiego, Krajewskiego. Po pierwszym przesłuchaniu był wstrząśnięty. Ponieważ Nosowska nic nie zrobiła. Było to po prostu kilkanaście coverów legendarnych kawałków Osieckiej. Ani jednej nowej nutki, po prostu covery. Tyle tylko, że zamiast zróżnicowanych głosów Fettinga, Jędrusik czy Rodowicz cały czas to zachrypnięte wycie, przejęte, egzaltowane i pretensjonalne. Szacki był autentycznie zażenowany sposobem, w jaki artystka ekshumowała poetkę. Aż bał się, co będzie dalej. Która tam jeszcze zapomniana szansonistka wybierze się na cmentarz? Wyobraził sobie Kasię Kowalską wyjącą piosenki Republiki i parsknął śmiechem. No nie, bez przesady.

Minął dworzec autobusowy, skręcił w lewo i zaparkował za radiowozem. Ciemność na tyłach akademika zespołu szkół spożywczych rozświetlona była blaskiem pochodni. Jak tylko wyłączył radio, do samochodu zaczął się wdzierać śpiew.

– ...a łez, krwi naszej popłynęły rzeki. Jakże okropnie to musi być z temi, którym ty wolność odbierzesz na wieki. Przed Twe ołtarze zanosim błaganie...

Szacki położył głowę na kierownicy w geście rezygnacji. Błagam, tylko nie to. Tylko nie kolejna patriotyczna jatka. Jeszcze na dodatek podkład z tej katolickiej, ksenofobicznej grafomanii. My lepsi, wy gorsi, nas nagrodzić, was ukarać, naprawdę nie widział różnicy między *Boże_coś Polskę* a *Horst Wessel Lied*. To drugie przynajmniej mniej jęcząco-zawodzące. Zapiął marynarkę, założył na twarz stalową maskę prokuratora i wyszedł w zimny wieczór, pachnący mgłą i wilgocią. Nie uszedł dziesięciu kroków, kiedy z mroku wyłonił się Marszałek i zaniepokojony zastąpił mu drogę.

– A pan prokurator co tutaj robi?

– Spaceruję – żachnął się Szacki. – Dyżurny dzwonił, że jest zdarzenie.

– A... – machnął ręką Marszałek. – Nocul jest trochę nadgorliwy, tak naprawdę nic się nie dzieje. Młodzież popiła, pohałasowała, sąsiedzi się przestraszyli, że rozruchy.

– Tak sobie popiła, że zapaliła pochodnie? – Szacki nie potrafił zrozumieć, jakie jest źródło niepokoju w oczach Marszałka. O co tutaj chodzi? Wyminął go zdecydowanym krokiem, idąc w stronę zgromadzenia, które grzmiało teraz *Marsz, marsz, Polonia*. No tak, oczywiście, jęknął w myślach, jakżeby mogło w tej sprawie zabraknąć szalonych narodowców, niepodobna.

Na ulicy stała grupka kilkunastu chłopaków, w wieku od siedemnastu do może dwudziestu pięciu lat, część chyba wstawiona, część z pochodniami. Na początku Szacki zastanawiał się, co tutaj robią, słyszał plotki o sandomierskich narodowcach i o tym, że ich tradycyjnym miejscem spotkań jest z jakichś powodów stary cmentarz żołnierzy radzieckich na obrzeżach miasta. Zespół szkół spożywczych jakoś mu nie pasował do patriotycznych misteriów, chyba że chodzi o chleb, cholera wie. Zagadka szybko się wyjaśniła, zaraz za kompleksem szkolnym znajdował się mały cmentarz żydowski, w świetle latarni i pochodni widać było lapidarium, kilkumetrową piramidę zbudowaną z fragmentów macew.

– Polak pada dla narodu, dla matki ojczyzny – zawodzili chłopcy w czarnych koszulkach. – Chętnie znosi głód i trudy, a najczęściej blizny. Marsz, marsz, Polonia...

Ciekawe, czy wiedzieli, że to ukraińska melodia, pomyślał Szacki.

Jego pierwszym odruchem było rozgonić towarzystwo, zanim zlecą się media i napiszą, że szeryf Sandomierza razem ze swoimi wiernymi pretorianami ściga sprawców żydowskiego mordu rytualnego. Brawo, panie prokuratorze! Tak trzymać! *Sieg Heil*! Swoją drogą, to interesujące, że tabloidy na całym świecie są identycznie ksenofobiczne. Wiedzą, że ich zapijaczony i tłukący żonę czytelnik niczego tak nie potrzebuje, jak wskazania wroga, którego może obarczyć winą za swoje niepowodzenia. Po krótkiej chwili wahania Szacki zwalczył pierwszy odruch, kiwnął na Marszałka i kazał mu sprowadzić jak najszybciej Szyllera i trzy suki z Tarnobrzega.

– Ale po co, panie prokuratorze? – Marszałek miał prawie łzy w oczach.

– Natychmiast – warknął Szacki i musiał mieć w głosie coś takiego, co sprawiło, że policjant w dwóch susach doskoczył do radiowozu. Ale za chwilę wrócił.

– Młodym, wiadomo, nudzi się, gówno mają w głowie – zaczął znowu swoje. – Kółko patriotyczne zrobili sobie takie, lepsze to przecież niż narkotyki.

– Kółko patriotyczne, jasne, faszystowskie pedały i tyle. – Szacki z chwili na chwilę robił się coraz bardziej wściekły.

– No ale mój chłopak tam jest, panie prokuratorze. Po co robić aferę, rozgońmy ich i już.

Szacki spojrzał lodowato i już miał ostro skomentować, ale pomyślał o Helci, która nie chciała się z nim widywać, która stawała się coraz bardziej odległa, blakła nawet we wspomnieniach. Kim on jest, żeby dawać dobre rodzicielskie rady? Żal mu się zrobiło policjanta, w każdej innej sytuacji powiedziałby, żeby mu nie zawracali głowy i rozpędzili towarzystwo. Ale teraz, po pierwsze, potrzebował przykładnego ukarania, po drugie, zaczął już swój, nazwijmy to, eksperyment procesowy. Poza tym nie cierpiał narodowców, hobbyści z pochodniami, psia ich mać.

– Jest wolność zgromadzeń! – wrzasnął w ich stronę śniady brunet o bardzo niearyjskiej urodzie. – Do ciszy nocnej możemy tu stać! Gówno nam zrobicie!

Szacki uśmiechnął się do niego. Jakiś tam paragraf by się znalazł, ale na razie chciał z jednej strony uśpić ich czujność, a z drugiej prowokować obecnością swoją i policji.

– I wolność słowa! – dorzucił inny, ten już bardziej w typie lebensbornskim. – Możemy mówić, co chcemy, nie zamkniecie ust Polakom!

Znowu nie była to do końca prawda, ale Szacki uśmiechnął się po raz kolejny.

– To co, walczyka? – krzyknął do kompanów niearyjski i wszyscy zaczęli śpiewać na melodię megaprzeboju Jerzego Połomskiego.

– Był raz goj, sprytny goj, co z Żydami bez przerwy zadzierał... Żydzi wnet rzekli „oj", trzeba jakoś uciszyć frajera...

Szacki zdławił w sobie wybuch śmiechu. Cała ta sytuacja była surrealistyczna, bez dwóch zdań, a weselny hicior przerobiony na antysemicką przyśpiewkę nadawał wszystkiemu kabaretowego sznytu. Weseli chłopcy doszli do refrenu.

– ...caaaaa...ła sala strzela z nami, a jewreje padają setkami! Rozprawimy się z parchami, Arafata oddziały są z nami...

Z jednej strony czuł satysfakcję, bo właśnie weszli pod paragraf, z drugiej czuł się ubrudzony. Wierzył, że na początku każdego działania jest słowo, że słowa o nienawiści prowadzą do nienawiści, o przemocy – do przemocy, a o śmierci – do śmierci. Każda znana ludzkości masakra zaczynała się od gadania.

– ...a Murzynów z pedałami ogrodzimy w obozie drutami. Lewactwo, parchactwo, wpuścimy im gaz, endecki walczyk w szabas!

Dokładnie z ostatnim wykrzyknikiem zatrzymał się radiowóz, ze środka wyszedł Szyller. W dżinsach i czarnym golfie wyglądał jak wilk morski. Na chór patriotycznej młodzieży nawet nie spojrzał, od razu podszedł do Szackiego.

– Co to za szopka? – warknął.

– Przepraszam za kłopot, ale potrzebowałem pańskiej pomocy. Pomyślałem, że lepiej, żeby pan uciszył swoich przydupasów, zanim do tego miasta będą waliły pielgrzymki jako do światowego skansenu antysemityzmu. Wystarczająco dużo mamy problemów.

– Co to za bzdura?! To, że jestem patriotą, nie oznacza, że znam każdego świra w glanach.

Szacki podszedł bliżej, stara sztuczka naruszenia przestrzeni intymnej.

– Niech pan, za przeproszeniem, przestanie pieprzyć – wyszeptał. – Myśli pan, że śledztwo polega na uprzejmym gadaniu? Prześwietliliśmy dokładnie pana finanse, pańską działalność filantropijną, doskonale wiem, jakie organizacje dostają od pana pieniądze. Oczywiście do protokołu pan wszystkiemu zaprzeczy, okaże się, że jakiś księgowy robił to za pana plecami, a z organizacji patriotycznych to zna pan tylko kółka różańcowe. To potem. Ale teraz niech pan pójdzie do swoich chłopców i każe im iść do domu, zanim ci pijani faszyści wpakują nas wszystkich w kłopoty.

Mężczyźni mierzyli się wzrokiem. Szacki nie miał pojęcia, o czym myśli Szyller, ważne dla niego było tylko jedno: nie dać po sobie poznać, że cała historyjka z finansami to blef. Po dłuższej chwili biznesmen odwrócił się i podszedł do „niearyjskiego". Rozmawiali cicho.

I to by było na tyle, jeśli chodzi o eksperyment procesowy.

– Boże, dziękuję panu, panie prokuratorze – powiedział z ulgą Marszałek. – Już się bałem, że pan prokurator... a to przecież dzieciaki. Pan musi zrozumieć, że u nas inaczej jest, ludzie się znają, przyjaźnią, tutaj chodzi o całą społeczność, musimy być razem, prawda? Nawet jak im głupoty takie w głowie, żeby świętować urodziny tego wariata. Na szczęście z tego się wyrasta.

Szacki nie miał pojęcia, o czyich urodzinach policjant mówi, ale zrobiło mu się smutno, że musi sprawić mu przykrość. Od strony miasta zajechały tarnobrzeskie suki, na bombach, ale bez sygnału. Zatrzymały się w tej samej chwili, kiedy Szyller wrócił ze swojej misji.

– Załatwione – zakomunikował chłodno.

– Powiem, żeby wracali – rzucił Marszałek, ale Szacki powstrzymał go gestem.

– Zgarnąć ich wszystkich – powiedział spokojnie.

– Co? – wrzasnęli jednocześnie Marszałek i Szyller.

– Zgarnąć ich wszystkich i wsadzić na cztery osiem. Widzę tu czternaście osób, rano chcę mieć na biurku czternaście protokołów zatrzymań, ani jednego mniej. Zarzuty będą postawione do wieczora.

– Ale panie prokuratorze...

– Ty skurwysynu...

– Nie przechodziliśmy na ty, Szyller – wycedził zimno Szacki. – A po tym, jak właśnie powiązał się pan z ultraprawicowymi organizacjami narodowymi, zalecałbym grzeczność wobec wymiaru sprawiedliwości. Proszę zawieźć pana

Szyllera z powrotem do domu, środek zapobiegawczy pozostaje w mocy.

– Ale panie prokuratorze...

– Jebać policję! Jebać policję! – zaczęło skandować kółko pieśni patriotycznej.

– Dawaj świnię! – ktoś wrzasnął. – Dawaj, kurwa, świnię! Szacki odwrócił się. Jeden z chłopaków, „lebensbornski", wyciągnął z czarnego worka na śmieci świńską głowę i rzucił nią w stronę lapidarium. Głowa groteskowo utknęła pomiędzy połamanymi macewami, różowe ucho kołysało się miarowo. Zaraz za świnią nad murem cmentarza przefrunął słoik i rozbił się z hukiem o kamień, czerwona ciecz spłynęła na tablice, wypełniając wolno żłobienia hebrajskich liter.

– Krew za krew! Krew za krew! Krew za krew!

– Panie prokuratorze, błagam! – jęczał Marszałek.

– Zaczynam pracę o ósmej, panie kapitanie. Lepiej, żeby te protokoły na mnie czekały.

Funkcjonariusze tarnobrzeskiej prewencji bez emocji skuwali wierzgających demonstrantów i ładowali do suk. Szyller odjechał, Marszałek płakał, mieszkańcy patrzyli bez emocji na całe zajście.

Prokurator Teodor Szacki obojętnie odwrócił się i poszedł do samochodu. Najwyższy czas odgwizdać fajrant i zastanowić się, kto z zewnątrz może mu pomóc w rozsupłaniu tego wiejskiego węzła zbrodni. Miał już nawet pewien pomysł.

Z tyłu zatrzymani, zgodnie z najlepszymi tradycjami patriotycznych chórów, bisowali jakimś hymnem na melodię *Międzynarodówki*.

– Polsce niesiem odrodzenie, depcząc podłość, fałsz i brud. W nas mocarne wiosny tchnienie, w nas jest przyszłość, z nami lud...

Co za kraj, pomyślał Szacki. Nic tylko covery i przeróbki. Jak tu ma być normalnie?

6

W życiu nie można mieć starych rzeczy, w życiu można mieć tylko rzeczy nowe. Pragnienie jakiegokolwiek powrotu jest niemożliwe i gdybyśmy ten powrót wymyślili i zapisali na papierze – to także musimy się zawieść, bo powrót na papierze jest tylko wyborem fragmentów, poszczególnych słów, poszczególnych barw i poszczególnych kawałków uczucia. Cały prąd tamtego czasu minął bezpowrotnie. Dlatego, czekając na swoją kolejną ofiarę, czuje spokój. Nie tęskni, nie rozpamiętuje, nie żałuje. Trzeba się zająć sprawami praktycznymi, zastanowić się co dalej. W końcu w życiu można mieć tylko rzeczy nowe.

7

Zegar na ratuszowej wieży obwieścił czterokrotnym uderzeniem pełną godzinę, potem wybił jedenastą, nie rezygnując z żadnego dźwięku – o tej porze taka dokładność wydawała się zbędnym okrucieństwem. Inna rzecz, że w Sandomierzu poza dziećmi i policjantami przed domem Jerzego Szyllera mało kto spał. Wszyscy gadali. Zazwyczaj w kuchniach, tam gada się najlepiej, ale też w sypialniach, na kanapach, przed ściszonymi telewizorami. Gadali tylko o jednym. O znajomych zwłokach, o znajomych podejrzanych, o znajomych-którzy-na-pewno-to-zrobili, o znajomych-którzy-na-pewno-tego-nie-zrobili, o motywach i brakach motywów, o tajemnicach, plotkach, nieprawdopodobnych wytłumaczeniach, spiskach, mafiach, policjantach, prokuratorach i jeszcze raz o zwłokach. Ale też o starych zabobonach, o wiecznie żywych legendach, mitach przekazywanych z pokolenia na pokolenie, dawnych sąsiadach i w końcu – o ziarnie prawdy.

Ariadna i Mariusz gadali przed głoszącym wiecznie złą nowinę kanałem informacyjnym, to znaczy bardziej gadał on, ona słuchała, sprzeciwiając się dość oszczędnie. Nie chciała awanturą obudzić śpiącego w pokoju obok synka, poza tym z mężem nie chciało jej się nawet kłócić, odkąd oficjalnie uznała go za swoją największą życiową pomyłkę.

– Nie rozumiem. Wisi obraz od trzystu lat w kościele, katedrze nawet. Były procesy, byli skazani, jeszcze przed wojną proceder był powszechnie znany. A teraz udają wielkie zdziwienie, że prawda wyszła na jaw.

– Jaka prawda, oszalałeś? Nikt tego nigdy nie udowodnił.

– Nikt nie może udowodnić, że to jest nieprawda.

– Mariusz, zmiłuj się, to tak nie działa. Nie musisz udowadniać niewinności, tylko winę. Nie trzeba prawa studiować, żeby to wiedzieć, to jest... sama nie wiem, elementarz człowieczeństwa to jest.

– To był normalny zwyczaj u Żydów. Proste? Zresztą nie tylko u nas, podobno też we Francji, w innych krajach. A poza tym myślisz, że kto czarną wołgą jeździł?

– Niech zgadnę: Żydzi?

– A skąd legendy, że dzieci do wołgi były na krew porywane? Hmm? Może jednak coś tutaj pasuje?

– Tak, jedno kłamstwo do drugiego, takie same bzdury. Zawsze jak dziecko zginęło, bo rodzice popili albo nie mieli głowy do pilnowania, to się pojawiały strzygi, Żydzi, Cyganie, czarne wołgi, co tam akurat było modne. Nie rozumiesz, że to bajki?

– Na pewno w każdej bajce jest coś z prawdy, jakieś ziarno, choćby malutkie.

– Nie dobijaj mnie, przecież krew nie jest koszerna, żaden Żyd by nie tknął macy z krwią, kurna, przecież jesteś wykształcony człowiek, powinieneś wiedzieć takie rzeczy.

– Dlatego że jestem wykształcony, to wiem, że nie ma w historii rzeczy czarnych i białych. I że można opowiadać wszystkim o koszerności i szabasie, a robić co innego. Myślisz, że jak Izrael prowadził wojnę z Libanem, to w soboty przestawali? No właśnie.

– Ale nie nauczyli cię, że w historii to Polacy mordowali Żydów, a nie odwrotnie? Że to Polacy organizowali pogromy i przypadkowe podpalenia, a w czasie okupacji lubili donieść na jakieś dziecko, co się w lesie ukrywało, albo wziąć na widły kogoś, komu się cudem udało uciec?

– To tylko jedna wersja historii.

– A w drugiej chodzą nocami zakutani w chałaty i polują na dzieci? Boże, niewiarygodne.

– Umówmy się, że teraz inaczej polują. Pieniądze teraz rządzą bardziej niż te beczki z gwoździami. Zobacz, które banki są dziś w nieżydowskich rękach? Który jest w Polsce polski? To lepsze utaczanie krwi niż jakieś gwoździe.

– Jasne. Ty weź lepiej załóż drugi zamek w drzwiach, żeby ci syna nie uprowadzili. Taki gruby katolicki bobasek, byłoby na macę dla całego miasta.

– Uważaj, kobieto. Dobrze ci radzę: uważaj. Uważaj, co mówisz o moim synu.

– Albo nie, gorzej, bo mogą mu konto w banku założyć, to by dopiero była tragedia, z każdym przelewem parchy by się kosztem Kubusia bogaciły. Na Chrystusa Pana, Króla Polski i Wszechświata, nie dopuścimy do tego! Zawsze będzie nasz Kubuś pieniądze w skarpecie trzymał!

Ksiądz Marek i jego parafianka Aniela gadali przy stole w jej kuchni. Oddajmy im sprawiedliwość: ponieważ dobry Bóg obdarzył Anielę łaską wielkiej wiary i jeszcze większym talentem kulinarnym, częściej było słychać z kuchni energiczne mlaskania niż antropologiczne w gruncie rzeczy dyskusje.

– Grzeszę, wiem, że grzeszę, poza tym już późno i iść trzeba. Ale jak pani nalega, to może malutki kawałeczek, ten taki

z boku, ze skórką przypieczoną, no, najbardziej taki lubię. /
Święty Tomasz by zjadł kawałek tego sernika, od razu by
musiał jeden dowód na istnienie Pana Boga dopisać.

– Co też ksiądz, takie żarty!

– Przez takie żarty będę musiał znowu sutannę oddać
do krawca. A tu raczej zeszczupleć by trzeba było, turyści
przyjeżdżają, chcą ojca Mateusza oglądać, a nie jakiegoś
grubasa.

– Ksiądz nie opowiada, dobrze ksiądz wygląda.

– Za dobrze.

– A co ksiądz myśli, znowu się szum o tych bohomazach
z katedry robi?

– A robi, robi. Nawet myślałem o tym ostatnio, pani Anie-
lo, myślałem, że powinniśmy się uczyć od tych obrazów
de Prevota, że każde morderstwo, każda nienawiść, każde
posądzenie fałszywe, że to zawsze jest złe i powinniśmy się
tego wystrzegać. Żaden fanatyzm nie jest dobry, żadna przesada, nawet jeśli w dobrej wierze ktoś przesadza.

– Ładnie to ksiądz mówi.

– Ale oczywiście jest wiele interpretacji, akurat jeśli chodzi o ten obraz. Myślałem też, że on mówi o ważnym dziś
problemie aborcji, przecież kiedyś też ten problem istniał,
a mówiono, że oni akurat umieli dokonywać aborcji.

– Żydzi?

– Nic wiadomo, czy Żydzi, czy ktoś, i tylko im podrzucano
niemowlęta po aborcji.

Pan Stanisław, zwany przez przyjaciół Stefanem, od dwudziestu trzech lat dyplomowany przewodnik, oprowadzają-
cy wycieczki po Sandomierzu, kończył kolację w restaura-
cji hotelu Basztowy. Zaprosili go księgowi z pewnej firmy
budowlanej, którym wcześniej przez cały dzień pokazywał
ukochane miasto.

– Proszę państwa, ja może i jestem stary, ale przed wojną
nie żyłem, jak to mogło być naprawdę, nie mam pojęcia. Ale

tak na logikę się zastanówmy. Są różne sekty religijne w Polsce i na świecie, prawda?

– Są.

– I w tych sektach, widzimy to przecież, niestety, w telewizji, zdarzają się samobójstwa, zdarzają się też morderstwa. Prawda?

– Prawda.

– Sataniści na przykład i inni. Czyli tak na logikę, mogły być też w historii różne sekty żydowskie?

– No, mogły.

– I takie sekty mogły robić rzeczy straszne?

– Oczywiście.

– I być może tutaj leży prawda. Że tak się, niestety, zdarzało i pamięć o strasznych wydarzeniach na tym obrazie przetrwała.

Pani Hela, jak wszyscy dawni mieszkańcy miasta, którzy znali innych Żydów niż tylko drewniane figurki ze sklepu z pamiątkami, przestała być na jeden dzień ciężarem i stała się autorytetem, który wie, jak to kiedyś było. A ona, jak większość z tych, którzy żyli w przedwojennym polsko-żydowskim mieście, nie pamiętała beczek, tylko wspólne wylegiwanie się na błoniach w ciepłe dni. Myślała o tych ciepłych dniach, kiedy na dole wnuczka dyskutowała z mężem.

– Sylwia mówi, że nie posyła, że po co ryzykować. Niech dzieciak w domu posiedzi, krzywda mu się nie stanie. Wiesz przecież, jaka legenda tu jest.

– Legenda, srenda. Może babci się zapytamy, ona pamięta, jak to przed wojną z Żydkami było.

– To chodźmy na górę do niej, faktycznie. Ale nie mów „Żydkami", Rafał, to obrzydliwe jakieś.

– To jak mam mówić? Hebrajczycy?

– Bez tego zdrobnienia mów, no... Uważaj na ten schodek ostatni... Śpi babcia?

– Ja już się wyspałam swoje.

– Babcia, widzę, kwitnie.

– Przekwita raczej, daj, Rafałku, całusa, wnukozięciu mój ulubiony.

– Już tak go babcia nie rozpieszcza. Babcia pamięta, jak to przed wojną było, prawda?

– Lepiej. Kawalerowie się za mną oglądali.

– A Żydzi?

– Ba, najlepsi Żydzi, Mojsiek Epsztajn, ach, ten to był gładki.

– A tam, co opowiadali, wie babcia, bo teraz też gadają, jak to z tą krwią, co niby dzieci porywali?

– A to gadanie takie, ale wtedy też głupoty opowiadali. Pamiętam miałam taką koleżankę, niezbyt ona była rozgarnięta, poszła raz w niedzielę do sklepu, co to go miała Żydówka przy ulicy, matka ją pewnie po coś wysłała. Bo to tak wtedy działało, że Polacy mieli otwarte w sobotę, Żydzi w niedzielę, wszyscy byli zadowoleni.

– I ta koleżanka...

– I ta koleżanka poszła w niedzielę do sklepu, a że procesja kościelna szła, to Żydówka przymknęła drzwi, coby nie drażnić, rozumiecie. Jak ta koleżanka, nawet nie pamiętam, jak ona na imię miała, Krysia chyba, to zobaczyła, zaczęła się drzeć, że ją na macę chcą wziąć. Rwetes się zrobił, akurat moja matka była w tym sklepie, to uratowała sytuację, dała Krysi w tyłek i do domu odprowadziła. Ale wrzask był taki straszny, że faktycznie, pół miasta musiało uwierzyć. Taka to była maca i takie żydowskie łapanie, wszystko bzdura i nieprawda, aż mówić żal.

– Ale w kościele wisi. Jakby była nieprawda, toby zdjęli chyba.

– Bo w kościele sama prawda musi być, wiadomo. Ty, Rafałku, pomyśl trochę.

– No tak, ale chyba przed wojną nie układało się Polakom z Żydami, no nie?

– A bo to Polakom z Polakami się układało? Co wy się żeście tutaj, młodzi, wczoraj ze Szwajcarii sprowadzili? Czy to się Polacy z kim układają? Ale powiem wam, że ja mieszkałam po jednej stronie rynku, a po drugiej rodzina żydowska, oni mieli córkę w moim wieku, Mala miała na imię. A ja często zapadałam na anginy i tak siedziałam w domu sama, koleżanki nie chciały tak dnia marnować i ze mną siedzieć. A Mala przyszła zawsze. I zawsze mówiłam: „Tatusiu, przyprowadź mi Malę, będę się z nią bawić". Mala siedziała cały dzień i bawiła się ze mną. I tak ją bardzo miło wspominam.

– A co się z nią stało?

– A nie wiem, wyjechała gdzieś. Idźcie już. I pomyślcie trochę, mówię, bo aż żal, że to takie głupie. Krew na macę...

– Już babcia nie przesadza...

– Idźcie, mówię. Zmęczona jestem, późno.

Jak tylko młodzi wyszli, babcia Helena Kołyszko od lat wyćwiczonym gestem wyciągnęła złożony kawałek gazety, służący za zamek do szafki w kredensie, wyjęła „Nalewkę Babuni", napełniła do połowy szklankę włożoną w plastikowy koszyczek i zdrowo golnęła, z wprawą osoby, która pierwszy kieliszek wychyliła na weselu kuzynki Jagódki w 1936 roku, miała wtedy szesnaście lat. To dopiero było wesele, po raz pierwszy wtedy całowała się z chłopakiem, maj był taki piękny i ciepły. Mama Jagódki miała sklep i dobrze żyła z Żydami, śmiała się na weselu, że w katedrze „mało Polaków było, tylko cały kościół Żydów przyszedł". A jak orszak przechodził przez miasto, cała grupa weselników, to wszystkie Żydóweczki wyszły: „Jagódka! Żeby ci się życie jasno świeciło!". Szły sobie z Malą, trzymały się za ręce i się śmiały głośno, i kwiatów było tyle, każde drzewko w Sandomierzu wtedy chyba kwitło.

No ale Mala wyjechała, pomyślała babcia Kołyszko i wychyliła do końca nalewkę. Pamiętała, jak wyjeżdżała. Doktor Weiss też wtedy wyjechał, ten co jej anginę od maleńkości leczył. Bardzo był zachwycony Niemcami, że to kulturalny naród, że on nigdy czegoś podobnego... nie zrobi krzywdy

228

Żydom. Ojciec babci Kołyszko go namawiał: „Panie dokto-
rze, niech pan nie podpisuje, nie przyznaje się". A on swoje:
„Ależ skąd, Niemcy są kulturalni". W Dwikozach podobno
się otruł na rampie. Nie wszedł do tego wagonu, tylko wolał umrzeć tak. Widziała z okna, jak go prowadzą, strasznie
płakała, bo była z doktorem zżyta, doktór tak się w ich okna
patrzył, jakby chciał się pożegnać, ale matka nie pozwoliła.
Potem szła pani Kielman z bliźniaczkami, dwie dziewczynki
czteroletnie, prześliczne. Niemiec strzelił do jednej małej,
pod ich domem ta dziewczynka została. Co to za ludzie, co
to za naród, co strzelał, jak dziecko płacze, małe dziecko
trzyma matka, a ten przychodzi i strzela. Ojciec wieczorem
wrócił, opowiadał, że tylu znajomych było, że chcieli kogoś
uratować, chcieli komuś rękę podać i nie dało się w ogóle,
byli tak obstawieni.

A Mala wyjechała. Mówili, co byli w Dwikozach, że się
potknęła i przez taki rów nie przeskoczyła, co go Niemcy
wykopali naprzeciw stacji, żeby sprawdzić, kto silny i kto
się nadaje. Ale gdzie by tam Mala nie przeskoczyła, bardziej
była zwinna niż one wszystkie razem wzięte.

Już potem nigdy takiej przyjaciółki nie miała.

8

Kiedy wysadzili go przed furtką, życząc miłego wieczoru,
mało nie rzucił im się do gardła. Bydło, cholerne bydło
z awansu społecznego; szmondaki, którym słoma z butów
wystaje, wysypuje się z cholewek całymi snopkami. Pan
prokurator nie lepszy. Mylą mu się socrealistyczne pedały,
nie dziwne, w chałupie pewnie tylko trylogia stała.

Wszedł do domu, rzucił kurtkę na wieszak i nie zapalając światła, nalał sobie pół szklanki metaxy. Miał słabość do

tej przesłodzonej greckiej brandy. Usiadł w fotelu, zamknął oczy. Nie minęło pięć minut, a ryczał jak bóbr. Znał teorię, wiedział, że ciągle jest w fazie niewiary i ta faza mu odpowiadała, ale czasami przez niewiarę, przez przeświadczenie, że to tylko gra, ściema, że jak skończy się spektakl, to wszystko będzie jak dawniej – przebijał się doprowadzający go do granicy utraty przytomności ból. Wtedy przepływały przez niego falą wszystkie obrazy ostatnich miesięcy, ich najszczęśliwsze chwile i na pewno najszczęśliwsze chwile jego życia. Eli pije kawę, rękaw swetra naciągnięty na dłoń, żeby nie parzyła jej szklanka. Eli czyta książkę, nogi zarzucone na oparcie kanapy, włosy zebrane na jednym ramieniu, żeby nie przeszkadzały. Eli nawija włosy na palec. Eli się kąpie, włosy w kok, głowa oparta na poduszce z piany. Eli żartuje. Eli paple. Eli na niego krzyczy. Eli, Eli, Eli.

Nagle poczuł, że nie jest sam. Oczy przyzwyczaiły się do ciemności na tyle, że dostrzegł ducha. Ciemną postać wbitą w fotel w rogu salonu. Postać drgnęła i wstała, wolnym krokiem ruszyła w jego stronę. Z tej strony było jaśniej, mimo zgaszonych lamp, z ulicy wpadało wystarczająco dużo żółtego, rozproszonego przez mgłę światła latarni, aby coraz wyraźniej widział rysy postaci, w końcu ją rozpoznał.

– Czekałem na ciebie – powiedział.

Rozdział siódmy

Punktualnie o godzinie 10.00 Izrael zamiera na dwie minuty, uroczyście obchodzony jest Jom Ha-Szoah, Dzień Holokaustu. W Oświęcimiu odbywa się Marsz Żywych, uczestniczący w nim wicepremier Izraela porównuje politykę Iranu do nazistowskich Niemiec. Irańska prokuratura zapowiada, że zażąda kary śmierci dla schwytanych autorów internetowych stron pornograficznych. Na Białorusi posadę traci trener klubu hokejowego, który śmiał wygrać z drużyną Aleksandra Łukaszenki – do tej pory niepokonaną w krajowych rozgrywkach, dostawali łupnia tylko od Rosjan. Posłowie przyjmują rządowy raport o przygotowaniach do Euro 2012 (jest nieźle), fiskus nie zgadza się, aby rodzice żyjący w konkubinacie rozliczali się wspólnie z dzieckiem, a wrocławskie strażaczki skarżą się, że nie wolno im jeździć na akcje, bo nie ma damskich szatni. Okazuje się, że wspólne szatnie nie przeszkadzają ani im, ani tym bardziej ich kolegom. Pogoda taka sama jak wczoraj. Słonecznie, zimno.

Zresztą zacytuję panu, to akurat ukazało się w „Twoim Week-endzie": „Bezpruderyjna trzydziestka poszukuje pana lub panów w wieku 55–65, gotowych do erotycznych eksperymentów bez zobowiązań, za to ze związaniami". I taka buźka ze średnika, że śmieszne. „Francuski bez, kakaowe oko, bilard na dwie dziury, wiązanie i odrobinka przemocy na niby". I znowu taka buźka z przymrużonym oczkiem. I mój numer telefonu. Pan sobie wyobraża, co się dzieje, jak się napisze w takiej gazecie, że kobieta szuka podstarzałego faceta do erotycznych zabaw, prawda? Pół Polski dzwoni. A drugie pół esemesuje, proszę, to jest ogłoszenie z internetu sprzed dwóch tygodni: „Chętnie poświntuszę esami, nudzi mi się na wsi, a chciałabym trochę pomarzyć i zwilżyć swoją kłoptuszkę...".

– Kłoptuszkę?

– Tak się na Podlasiu mówi na, no wie pan na co. Ale to jeszcze nie koniec. „Pisz, na pewno odpiszę, a może nawet wyślę ememes, chętnie panowie ZK". Pan wie oczywiście, co to znaczy ZK?

– Jestem prokuratorem.

– No właśnie. Ja potem przez dwa dni dostaję co kwadrans wiadomość, która jest wulgarnym streszczeniem pornola, na dodatek nudne to wszystko, nie rozumiem, czemu co drugi zek musi pisać o wkładaniu przez kraty. Mają jakieś szablony? Moda jest taka? I niech mi pan nie mówi, żebym zmieniła numer, ja ciągle zmieniam numery, wydałam majątek, a nie mija tydzień i znowu to samo. A przecież w handlu robię, nie mogę nie mieć telefonu, mam kontrahentów, hurtownie. I tak jest coraz gorzej, ludzie narzekają, że kontaktu nie ma, a jak ma być, jak co tydzień nowy numer. Myślałam, że to minie, ale nie mija. Dlatego chciałabym złożyć oficjalne zawiadomienie o popełnieniu, to znaczy, zawiadomienie o podejrzeniu popełnienia przestępstwa i niech ta ujeżdżająca cudzych mężów dziwka idzie siedzieć w końcu.

Prokurator Teodor Szacki żywił naturalną sympatię do zbyt szybko mówiących i zbyt ekspresyjnych pań w typie peerelowskich królowych bazaru, być może dlatego, że przypominały mu matkę i wiedział, że za tymi wszystkimi słowami, lokami, pierścionkami i mechatymi garsonkami – zawsze ozdobionymi broszką z bursztynem – kryje się zazwyczaj złote serce i organiczna niezdolność do robienia ludziom krzywdy. Tym bardziej było mu przykro, że nie ma dobrych wiadomości dla siedzącej po drugiej stronie biurka pani Zgorzelskiej.

– Po pierwsze, musi pani z tym iść na policję, sprawa podchodzi pod kodeks wykroczeń i nawet jeśli przyjmę zawiadomienie, to i tak zajmie się tym policja, nie ma co wydłużać papierkowej roboty.

– Wykroczenie! Dobre sobie. A to, że koledzy moich synów w szkole zawsze się dziwnym trafem o tym dowiedzą? A to, że kontrahenci też się dziwnie uśmiechają? Przecież ja już bym wolała, żeby mnie pobiła, napadła czy coś i żeby było z głowy. A tak to się nie da żyć. Ile ona za to może dostać maksymalnie?

– Jeśli da się jej to udowodnić, półtora.

– Roku?

– Tysiąca złotych grzywny.

– Co?!

– Przykro mi. Chodzą słuchy, że mają zmienić przepisy i wpisać stalking do kodeksu karnego, wprowadzić jakieś rozsądne zagrożenie jako straszak, pewnie dwa albo trzy lata. Na razie jest tylko paragraf sto siedem kodeksu wykroczeń, który mówi o złośliwym nękaniu.

Zgorzelska była zdruzgotana.

– Ale ona śpi na forsie. Półtora tysiąca? Zapłaci i jeszcze mi faksem potwierdzenie przelewu przyśle. A co, jeśli nie przestanie? Drugie półtora tysiąca?

Szacki potwierdził skinieniem głowy. Nie pierwszy raz, rozmawiając z poszkodowanymi, musiał się wstydzić za polskie rozwiązania prawne. Przestarzałe, zawiłe, nie potrafiące nadążyć za czasami przepisy, które albo były kuriozalnie łagodne, de facto zdejmowały odpowiedzialność karną ze sprawcy, albo – efekt dwóch dekad populistycznych rządów – absurdalnie penalizujące, sprawiające, że więzienia w Polsce były pełne osób, których nie powinno tam być, uczestników pijackich bójek, gdzie nic się nikomu nie stało, ale scyzoryk z otwieraczem do piwa został zakwalifikowany jako niebezpieczne narzędzie.

– Ale jeśli będzie karana za to samo powtórnie, sędzia może jej wlepić areszt. Od pięciu do trzydziestu dni. Wydaje się niewiele, ale nie sądzę, aby pani... – ugryzł się w język, o mało nie powiedział „konkurentka" – prześladowczyni była aż tak zdesperowana. Poza tym po pierwszym wyroku może ją pani skarżyć o straty, ale to już do adwokata.

– Skarżyć w Polsce – parsknęła Zgorzelska. – Ja mam prawie pięćdziesiątkę, mogłabym pierwszej rozprawy nie dożyć.

Co miał powiedzieć? Że najrozsądniej wynająć kogoś, żeby postraszył babę? Uśmiechnął się przepraszająco i spojrzał wymownie. Tak naprawdę w ogóle nie powinno być tej rozmowy. Przypadek sprawił, że kiedy wchodził przed siódmą do prokuratury, chcąc dzięki wczesnej porze uniknąć dziennikarzy i wykorzystać czas na kolejne przejrzenie papierów, Zofia Zgorzelska czekała na schodach. Była tak zmarnowana i zziębnięta, że nie miał litości jej odprawić, widać robi się miękki na stare lata.

Wstał, chcąc się pożegnać, i w tej samej chwili, bez pukania, gwałtownie otworzyły się drzwi, stanęła w nich zadyszana Basia Sobieraj, jeszcze w czapce i szaliku, cała zarumieniona. Wyglądała uroczo. Szacki pomyślał, że przy jej problemach z sercem nie powinna biegać. I że bardzo nie chce usłyszeć tego, co ma mu do zakomunikowania. To nie mogła być dobra wiadomość.

2

Najgorsze były rogi. W czasie poprzedniej wizyty wydały mu się po prostu tandetne, ot, małomiasteczkowa ozdoba, chyba wszędzie je tutaj widział. Teraz każda głowa dzika i każda jelenia czaszka wydawały się z niego nabijać. Betonowo spokojny na zewnątrz, w środku dyszał żądzą zniszczenia, złapania pogrzebacza i rozpierdolenia tego wszystkiego w drobny mak. Aż mrowiło go w palcach.

– Ona ma siedemdziesiąt lat, skąd mieliśmy przypuszczać, panie prokuratorze, to nie Warszawa, tutaj ludzie życzliwi, pomagają sobie – powtórzył policjant.

Niski, drobny, z dużym nosem, przypominał komiksowego Kajka. Szacki przymknął oczy, żeby go nie widzieć. Bał się, że jeśli jeszcze raz zerknie na ten czerwony kinol i przepraszające oczy, to nie wytrzyma i rzuci się na niego. To wszystko było jak zły sen. Dwójka mundurowych odwiozła wczoraj Jerzego Szyllera do domu, zaparkowała przed furtką i szykowała się do całonocnej warty. Zaraz potem, było około dwudziestej trzeciej, sąsiadka Szyllera, pani o dziwacznym greckim nazwisku Potelos, przyniosła policjantom termos z kawą. Robiła tak codziennie, bo miała dobre serce i wiedziała, że to niewdzięczna praca, jej syn był policjantem w Rzeszowie. Dała kawę, pogadała chwilkę, poprzynudzała o chorobach i poszła, życząc dobrej nocy. Słowa te były prorocze, wystarczył jeden kubek kawy i policjanci zapadli w bardzo głęboki sen, z którego obudzili się dopiero po siódmej, tak przemarznięci, że lekarz stwierdził odmrożenia uszu, nosa i palców. Co, swoją drogą, wiele mówiło o jakości wiosny Roku Pańskiego 2009.

– Czy to możliwe, żeby Szyller się z nią spotkał? Żeby poszedł do niej, dodał narkotyk do kawy?

– Nie ma mowy. Mieliśmy go cały czas pod obserwacją, na zmianę chodziliśmy wokół posesji. Wyciągnęliśmy go tylko, żeby pojechać tam na Suchą, co się widzieliśmy z panem prokuratorem. A potem ona przyszła chwilę po tym, jak drzwi się za nim zamknęły.

Za Szackim coś zaskrzypiało. Wilczur.

– Nic nie widziała, nic nie wie, jest spanikowana. Śladów włamania nie ma, ale też nie jest pewna, czy wszystkie drzwi i okna były pozamykane. Termos i puszkę z kawą wysłaliśmy do analizy. Stawiam na termos, kobieta twierdzi, że była zdziwiona, że stoi na blacie, a nie na ociekaczu. Ale w tym wieku, wiadomo, człowiek się tylko przez chwilę dziwi.

Szacki skinął głową, że przyjął to do wiadomości. Najbardziej doskwierało mu, że nawet nie było kogo opieprzyć. Nigdy nie mieli na Szyllera tyle, żeby postawić mu zarzuty i go zamknąć, tak naprawdę było uprzejmością z jego strony, że zgodził się zostać w chałupie – każdy sąd w pięć minut obaliłby decyzję o areszcie domowym. Że gliniarze wzięli kawę od starej, dobrze im znanej sąsiadki? No wzięli, on też by wziął. Najgorsze, że nie wiadomo, co dalej. Uciekł? Ktoś go porwał? Zrozumiał, że tak naprawdę jest wściekły na siebie. Może gdyby myślał szybciej, lepiej kojarzył fakty, gdyby potrafił dostrzec coś, co na pewno już widział, tylko nie zrozumiał znaczenia – może, może, może.

– Nie ma śladów walki – powiedział.

– Nie ma – mruknął Wilczur. – Albo wyszedł, albo został wyniesiony.

– Myślałem o tym. Wyślijcie do sprawdzenia butelki z barku i szklankę, która stoi na pianinie. Może jemu też coś dosypali. I zostawili odciski na dodatek. To by była miła odmiana.

– List gończy?

– Nie ma mowy, dość mam upokorzeń jak na jedną sprawę. Nie chcę dowiedzieć się za chwilę, że kolejny główny podejrzany wisi gdzieś na haku. Wyślijcie do mediów ogłoszenie, że poszukujemy ważnego świadka w sprawie, i tej wersji będziemy się trzymali. Świadek, ważny świadek.

Z kuchni Szyllera wyszła Basia, stanęła przy nich.

– I co? – spytała. – Myślisz, że to kolejny z serii? Teoretycznie ten sam styl. Ofiary znikają bez śladu z domu, po paru dniach pojawiają się ze spuszczoną krwią.

– Odszczekaj, ta się jeszcze nie pojawiła. Trzymaj kciuki, żeby Szyller się znalazł żywy, przyznał do wszystkiego i żebyśmy mieli to z głowy.

Klik. Znowu coś zaskoczyło w mózgu. To on coś powiedział czy Sobieraj coś powiedziała?

– Ale masz rację, myślałem o tym. Tylko jak to możliwe, że w mieście Budnik wyparował pod nosem policjantów, a tutaj ktoś musiał sobie zadać trud ogłuszenia ich. Mimo że teoretycznie łatwiej stąd prysnąć przez podwórko i dalej przez park.

– Ktoś nie chciał ryzykować.

– A wcześniej chciał? Dlaczego wyprowadzenie Budnika miałoby być mniejszym ryzykiem niż wyprowadzenie Szyllera? Coś mi tutaj nie gra.

Sobieraj wzruszyła ramionami i usiadła na kanapie. Wydawała się blada.

– Słabo mi trochę, a powinnam odwiedzić ojca w szpitalu – powiedziała cicho.

– Tutaj w Sandomierzu? – zdziwił się.

– Tak, podle się czuję, ostatnio częściej tam jeżdżę na trupy niż do niego. A to przecież przez niego tutaj wylądowałam – westchnęła i sięgnęła do stojącej na stole miski z chrupkami. Szacki bezwiednie podążył wzrokiem za jej ręką, miała śmieszny kolor lakieru do paznokci, bardzo ciemnoróżowy.

– Stój! – wrzasnął.

Sobieraj cofnęła rękę i spojrzała na niego przestraszona. Szacki bez słowa wskazał jej miskę z chrupkami, którymi o mało co się przed chwilą nie poczęstowała. Nie było w niej ani chipsów, ani słonych paluszków, ani rybek z makiem, ani krakersów czy chrupek kukurydzianych. Były – jakżeby inaczej – pokruszone kawałki macy, charakterystycznie perforowane i poprzypalane na wybrzuszeniach.

– Pieprzony żartowniś – mruknął. – Aż dziwne, że nie polał tego keczupem, widać mu się spieszyło.

Wszyscy pochylili się nad drewnianą miseczką do przekąsek, jakby to było jakieś rytualne naczynie.

– Skąd w ogóle ta maca? – spytał jeden z policjantów.

– Jak uciekali z Egiptu, nie mieli czasu czekać, aż ciasto na chleb wyrośnie – wyjaśnił swoim grobowym głosem Wilczur – musieli szybko upiec jakiś prowiant i wyszła im maca.

Szackiemu kliknęło w głowie i tym razem na tyle głośno, że zrozumiał, co powinien zrobić.

– Przełóż wizytę z ojcem – powiedział szybko do Sobieraj – i ogarnij tutaj wszystko, tym razem to nie spleśniała ruina, niech zbiorą mikroślady, maca oczywiście jak najszybciej do labo. Ja muszę lecieć.

– Co? Gdzie? Dokąd? – Sobieraj wstała, zaniepokojona jego pośpiechem.

– Do kościoła! – krzyknął Szacki i wybiegł.

Basia Sobieraj i inspektor Leon Wilczur wymienili zdziwione spojrzenia. Ona po chwili usiadła, on wzruszył ramionami i oderwał filtr od papierosa. Rozglądał się chwilę, szukając śmietnika albo popielniczki, w końcu schował filtr do kieszeni.

3

Katedra Narodzenia Najświętszej Maryi Panny w Sandomierzu przypominała w tych dniach oblężoną twierdzę. Wokół ogrodzenia kręcili się dziennikarze, dostępu do budynku bronili duchowni, zaufani świeccy i naprędce sporządzone znaki o „zakazie fotografowania", „zakazie nagrywania", „zakazie zakłócania spokoju w Domu Bożym", „zakazie wstępu poza godzinami sprawowania Liturgii". Szacki wszedł do środka, korzystając z tego, że akurat wychodziła wycieczka seniorów. Był przygotowany na tłumaczenia i nawet wyciągnął legitymację z kieszeni marynarki, ale nie był przez nikogo niepokojony. Może rozpoznali we mnie swojaka, nieustraszonego szeryfa, co się Żydom nie kłania, pomyślał gderliwie, przechodząc przez portal. Stanął w bocznej nawie, czekając, aż oczy przyzwyczają się do półmroku.

Był sam. No, prawie sam. Jednostajny, szurający dźwięk powiedział mu, że starzy znajomi z poprzedniej wizyty nigdzie się stąd nie ruszyli. Faktycznie, zza kolumny oddzielającej go od nawy głównej wyszedł smutny mężczyzna i zaczął myć podłogę, po chwili mokry ślad oddzielił go od zachodniej ściany kościoła, gdzie była kruchta, chór, przepiękne organy, a pod nimi nieprzepiękne obrazy osiemnastowiecznego pacykarza i miłośnika horroru, Karola de Prevot. W tym jeden wstydliwie zasłonięty bordową kotarą. Szacki ruszył w tamtą stronę zdecydowanym krokiem. Smutny mężczyzna przestał szurać, spojrzał na niego pustym wzrokiem.

– Nie po mokrym – ostrzegł, zyskując tylko tyle, że Szacki machnął ręką i wszedł na mokrą posadzkę, nawet nie zwalniając. Bardzo to było westernowe, tyle tylko, że poślizgnął się, zachwiał i z trudem utrzymał równowagę, machając rozpaczliwie rękami. Uratowało go tylko to, że złapał się nogi putta z kolumny.

– Mówiłem, nie po mokrym – powtórzył z rezygnacją mężczyzna, jakby widział taką scenę setki razy.

Szacki nie odpowiedział, podszedł do kotary, odpiął portret Jana Pawła II i postawił pod ścianą.

– Halo, co pan robi, nie wolno! – wydarł się mężczyzna. – Leć po księdza kanonika, Żasmina, znowu jacyś chuligani przyszli.

– Teodor Szacki, prokuratura rejonowa w Sandomierzu, przeprowadzam czynności procesowe! – krzyknął Szacki, pokazując bumagę biegnącemu w jego stronę mężczyźnie. I myśląc jednocześnie, że gdyby dostał tysiąc szans na to, aby zgadnąć, jak ma na imię smętna kobieta myjąca podłogę sandomierskiej katedry, i tak by nie zgadł.

Mężczyzna zatrzymał się, niepewny, jak potraktować intruza. Ale też wyraźnie ciekawy, co się wydarzy. Szacki tymczasem zebrał w dłoniach pluszową storę i z całej siły szarpnął. Puściła większość żabek, zasłona wydała z siebie ostatnie tchnienie w formie chmury kurzu i opadła. Przebijające się przez wysokie okno słońce trafiło w burzową chmurę i zamieniło ją w oślepiający obłok świetlistych drobinek, przez który niczego nie można było dojrzeć. Szacki zamrugał oczami, cofnął się o dwa kroki, żeby lepiej zobaczyć ogromny obraz.

Po wszystkich opowieściach spodziewał się uderzenia, naturalistycznej rzezi, silnych barw i zdecydowanych kształtów, podświadomie oczekiwał, że przed jego oczami ożyje stary zabobon, że zamiast starego płótna zobaczy kinowy ekran, a na ekranie film nie tyle o mordzie rytualnym, co o współczesnych wydarzeniach. Że coś zadrga, coś się stanie, pojawi się rozwiązanie zagadki. Tymczasem stare płótno, cóż, wyglądało po prostu jak stare płótno. Poczerniałe, z popękanym werniksem, na którym blikowało słoneczne światło, z trudem można było rozróżnić poszczególne kształty.

Smętny czyściciel posadzek musiał stać pod lepszym kątem.

– Boże wszechmogący – wyszeptał i przeżegnał się energicznie.

Prokurator Teodor Szacki przesunął się w jego stronę i zamiast się przeżegnać, sięgnął po telefon i zadzwonił do Sobieraj.

– Jestem w katedrze. Powiedz Wilczurowi, że potrzebuję tu na już dwóch mundurowych do zabezpieczenia, techników, jak tylko skończą u Szyllera, a ciebie i tego pomarszczonego psa najszybciej jak się da... Nieważne, szkoda czasu na gadanie, przyjeżdżajcie.

Rozłączył się i komórką obfotografował obraz. Teraz, kiedy jego oczy nauczyły się już wyławiać z powodzi czerni te mniej czarne kształty, mógł porównać oryginał z reprodukcjami. Akurat w tym wypadku rozmiar miał znaczenie. Reprodukcje oglądał w książkach lub na ekranie małego laptopa, tutaj przedstawienie mordu rytualnego miało jakieś dziesięć metrów kwadratowych, tyle co mały pokój w mieszkaniu. Na pierwszy rzut oka wydawało się, że jak na ironię ten obraz najlepiej wyszedł de Prevotowi pod względem artystycznym i kompozycyjnym, choć narracyjnie pozostawał wierny komiksowemu stylowi opowieści o męczeństwie. Szacki rozpoznawał poszczególne etapy legendy o misterium krwi. Po prawej dwóch Żydów zajmowało się zaopatrzeniem. Jeden, wyraźnie bogatszy, w kapeluszu i płaszczu, proponował matce kupno od niej niemowlęcia. Drugi nęcił małego chłopca czymś, co może było cukierkiem, a może zabawką, jednocześnie łapiąc go za szczękę gestem nabywcy na targu niewolników. Po przeciwnej stronie Żydzi zajmowali się uśmiercaniem lub torturowaniem (albo jednym i drugim) ułożonego na prześcieradle dziecka. A centralne miejsce kompozycji zajmowała oczywiście beczka, dwóch Żydów trzymało beczkę najeżoną gwoździami niczym zębami, przypominającą fantastycznego morskiego stwora, z którego otworu gębowego wystawały pulchne niemowlęce nogi. Skapującą krew zbierał do miseczki rozanielony właściciel ogromnego nochala. De Prevot nie byłby sobą, gdyby w prezentowaniu makabry nie poszedł o krok za daleko. Na ziemi walało się trochę dziecięcych zwłok, upiorne wrażenie robiło rozszarpane przez psa małe ciało. Z pyska zwierzęcia wystawała oderwana noga, na deser czekała druga noga, ręce i głowa – wszystko oddzielnie.

Ale Szacki nie dlatego robił zdjęcia, żeby zawsze mieć przy sobie to poruszające dzieło sztuki. Robił zdjęcia, ponieważ w poprzek obrazu nabazgrany był czerwoną farbą hebrajski napis:

עין תחת עין

Rdzawe litery świeciły w słońcu niczym karmazynowy neon, sprawiając upiorne wrażenie, i Szackiego nie zdziwiła reakcja smętnego pomywacza, ale pomyślał też, że był to typowy odruch katolika na widok hebrajskich liter – traktowanie ich tak, jakby miały zejść z obrazu, przemaszerować przez nawę i jeszcze raz uśmiercić Pana Naszego Jezusa Chrystusa, amen.

Sobieraj i Wilczur pojawili się chwilę później, równocześnie z księdzem kanonikiem i wikarym, których przyprowadziła Żasmina. Stanowili zaskakującą parę. Szacki, słysząc o kanoniku i wikarym, spodziewał się komediowych postaci, zażywnego grubaska i młodzika o odstających czerwonych uszach. Tymczasem stał przed nim wypisz, wymaluj Sean Connery i Christopher Lambert, jakby dopiero co zeszli z planu *Nieśmiertelnego*. Obaj diablo przystojni.

Po krótkiej awanturze obecni wyjaśnili sobie, że w interesie wszystkich jest trzymać gębę na kłódkę, i dopiero to uspokoiło sytuację. Śledczy zajęli się śledztwem, a kapłani powołali się na obowiązek ochrony domu Bożego, żeby móc bezkarnie przyjąć rolę gapiów. Nie byli do końca udobruchani, ale wyraźnie bardziej od obecności policji i prokuratury martwiła ich perspektywa wizyty biskupa, który na złamanie karku pędził do swojej katedry z Kielc i podobno był bardzo, ale to bardzo niezadowolony. A że cieszył się zasłużoną opinią choleryka, to mogło się jeszcze okazać, że przykrości dnia dzisiejszego dopiero przed nimi.

– Jeśli to nie farba, tylko krew, to trzeba sprawdzić, czy ludzka, zrobić badania DNA, porównać z krwią denatów i Szyllera. Poza tym każdy centymetr przestrzeni wokół obrazu ma być prześwietlony. Napis jest wysoko, ktokolwiek go zrobił, musiał przystawić drabinę, wleźć pod kotarę, oprzeć się, powiesić kubełek. To dawało dziesiątki okazji, żeby pozostawić ślad, i ten ślad muszę mieć. Nawet jeśli teraz wydaje nam się gówno wart, potem w sądzie może być na wagę złota jako małe ogniwo w łańcuchu poszlak. Dlatego jeśli jakikolwiek technik piśnie, że nie ma sensu, to pogonić.

Sobieraj spojrzała na niego kwaśno.

– A ty mnie, przepraszam, przyjmujesz teraz na asesurę?

– Ja cię uprzedzam, że jeśli tu przyjdzie jakaś Kasia, z którą chodziłaś do przedszkola, i zacznie błagać, że musi z dzieckiem do lekarza i że już nie ma potrzeby, bo to takie szczegóły, to wtedy mówisz jej, że ma tu siedzieć do wieczora i wszystko fotografować, nawet gdyby się do ciebie miała nigdy więcej nie odezwać. Jasne?

– Nie ucz mnie...

– Trzydzieści dziewięć.

– Mój wiek nie ma nic do...

– Prowadziłem trzydzieści dziewięć spraw o zabójstwo, dwadzieścia pięć skończyło się skazaniem. I ja cię teraz nie proszę, Basiu. Ja wydaję polecenia. Prokuratura to instytucja hierarchiczna, a nie lekcja demokracji.

Jej oczy ściemniały, ale nic nie powiedziała, skinęła tylko głową. Za nią stał nieruchomo Wilczur, oparty o konfesjonał. Wikary przyglądał się scenie z zachwytem, widać było, że Dana Browna zna nie tylko z teorii jako szatana w pisarskiej skórze, ale też poświęcił kilka wieczorów na dogłębne poznanie swojego wroga. Odchrząknął.

– Pierwsze i trzecie słowa są takie same. To musi być jakiś szyfr – powiedział cicho.

– Nawet wiem jaki – warknął Szacki. – Nazywa się alfabet. Ksiądz zna hebrajski? – zapytał bez większych nadziei kanonika, przekonany, że w odpowiedzi ksiądz proboszcz się przeżegna i zacznie odprawiać egzorcyzmy.

– Potrafię przeczytać. Pierwsze i trzecie słowo to „ein", środkowe „techet" albo „tachat". Niestety nie wiem, co oznaczają. „Ein" to może jeden, tak z niemiecka, tylko wtedy to byłby jidysz, nie hebrajski. – Musiał zauważyć zdziwiony wzrok Szackiego, bo dodał zgryźliwie: – Tak, mieliśmy biblistykę z elementami hebrajskiego w seminarium. Tylko nie zawsze uważałem, pierwsze zajęcia, rano byliśmy zmęczeni po pogromach.

– Przepraszam – powiedział Szacki po chwili. Było mu autentycznie przykro, zrozumiał, że odpowiadając stereotypem na stereotyp, nie różni się niczym od pijanych neofaszystów, których kazał wczoraj zgarnąć. – Bardzo przepraszam. I dziękuję za pomoc.

Ksiądz skinął głową, a Szackiemu kliknęło. To się zaczynało robić nieznośne, jeśli te puste kliknięcia się nie skończą, będzie musiał poszukać pomocy neurologa. O co mogło chodzić tym razem? Pogromy? Seminarium? Biblistyka? A może coś zobaczył kątem oka? Może jego mózg odnotował coś ważnego, co umknęło jego świadomości? Rozejrzał się uważnie po wnętrzu kościoła.

– Teo... – zaczęła Sobieraj, ale uciszył ją gestem.

Dostrzegł w jednej z bocznych kaplic coś, co przyciągnęło jego wzrok. Obraz Chrystusa Miłosiernego, taki sam jak wszędzie, kopia tego namalowanego na podstawie wizji siostry Faustyny. Dookoła wota, pod obrazem cytat z Ewangelii: „To jest moje przykazanie, abyście się wzajemnie miłowali, tak jak Ja was umiłowałem – J 15,12".

Klik.

O co chodzi? O Chrystusa? O Faustynę? O cytat? O miłosierdzie? Akurat tego w tej sprawie brakuje. Może o świętego Jana Ewangelistę? Babki w sklepie rozmawiały o jakimś konkursie biblijnym, też mu wtedy kliknęło. Tyle tylko, że głowę miał zajętą Hitlerem i George'em Michaelem. Boże, jak to brzmi, wstydził się własnych myśli czasami. Skup się! Konkurs biblijny – klik. Jan Ewangelista – klik. Seminarium – klik.

Próbował połączyć ze sobą te fakty, gapiąc się cały czas na obraz.

Klik.

Mało brakowało, a zakląłby, ile sił w płucach. Jak mógł być taki głupi, no jak?!

– Potrzebuję Pisma Świętego. Natychmiast! – rzucił w stronę wikarego, który nie czekając na przyzwolenie proboszcza, rzucił się biegiem w stronę zakrystii; sutanna filmowo zafurkotała.

– Jakie ksiądz zna księgi zaczynające się na literę K? – zapytał.

– Cóż, nie ma dokładnie takiego siglum w Biblii Tysiąclecia – odpowiedział kanonik po chwili zastanowienia.

– A na literę K zaczyna się Księga Kapłańska, dwie Królewskie, dwie Kronik i Koheleta. W Nowym Testamencie mamy dwa listy do Koryntian i jeden do Kolosan. Tak myślę, ale po łacinie nic się nie zaczyna na K, na C mamy Canticum Canticorum, czyli Pieśń nad Pieśniami w Starym, i oczywiście te same listy do Koryntian i Kolosan.

Wikary pokonał drogę do zakrystii i z powrotem niczym wytrawny sprinter, z trudem wyhamował przed zgromadzoną pod przedstawieniem mordu rytualnego grupką, dzierżąc olbrzymią księgę formatu A3, oprawioną w skórę, zdobioną okuciami i złoceniami.

– Czyś ty zwariował? – zapytał kanonik. – Nie mogłeś normalnie wziąć z półki?

– Chciałem, żeby każdy widział dokładnie – wydyszał wikary, choć jasne było dla wszystkich, że zwyczajna niebieska Biblia Tysiąclecia nie pasowała mu do podniosłej, godnej Dana Browna chwili.

– Zacznijmy od Kapłańskiej – powiedział Szacki. – To część Pięcioksięgu, Tory, prawda?

– Prawda – potwierdził kanonik.

– Rozdział dwudziesty czwarty, wersety od dziewiętnastego do dwudziestego pierwszego.

– No jasne... – jęknęła z tyłu Sobieraj.

Wikary odnalazł odpowiednie miejsce, pomagając sobie kolanem, z szacunkiem podsunął do przeczytania proboszczowi.

– Ktokolwiek skaleczy bliźniego, będzie ukarany w taki sposób, w jaki zawinił. Złamanie za złamanie, oko za oko, ząb za ząb. W jaki sposób ktoś okaleczył bliźniego, w taki będzie okaleczony. Kto zabije zwierzę, będzie obowiązany do zwrotu. Kto zabije człowieka, będzie ukarany śmiercią.

Ksiądz kanonik miał donośny, niski głos, słowa wypowiedział powoli, z szacunkiem należnym Pismu. Groźnie zabrzmiały w ciszy świątyni, rezonowały od prastarych kamieni, odbijały się od ścian i sklepienia, wypełniając dźwiękiem i znaczeniem sandomierską katedrę. Nikt nie drgnął, dopóki dalekie echa nie umilkły całkowicie.

– Księga Wyjścia, rozdział dwudziesty pierwszy, wersety od dwudziestego drugiego do dwudziestego piątego – powiedział Szacki, nie pytając już o literki.

Wikary zaszeleścił kartkami.

– Gdyby mężczyźni, bijąc się, uderzyli kobietę brzemienną, powodując poronienie, ale bez jakiejkolwiek szkody, to winny zostanie ukarany grzywną, jaką nałoży mąż tej kobiety, i wypłaci ją za pośrednictwem sędziów polubownych. Jeżeli zaś ona poniesie jakąś szkodę, wówczas on odda życie za życie, oko za oko, ząb za ząb, rękę za rękę, nogę za nogę, oparzenie za oparzenie, ranę za ranę, siniec za siniec.

– I na „P", to chyba będzie Księga Prawa, tak?

– Powtórzonego Prawa – poprawił z tyłu Wilczur. Szacki drgnął, zaskoczył go głos tuż za plecami. I zdziwił się, ale tylko trochę.

– Tak, oczywiście. Rozdział dziewiętnasty, wersety od szesnastego do dwudziestego pierwszego.

Szelest. I wypieki na twarzy wikarego – wyglądał, jakby płonął, cały był postanowieniem zrzucenia sutanny i zamienienia jej na kurtkę i kapelusz Indiany Jonesa.

– Jeśli powstanie świadek złośliwy przeciwko komuś, oskarżając go o przekroczenie Prawa, dwu ludzi wiodących między sobą spór stanie wobec Pana przed kapłanami i przed sędziami urzędującymi w tym czasie. Jeśli ci sędziowie, zbadawszy sprawę dokładnie, dowiodą fałszu świadkowi, jeżeli świadek taki fałszywie oskarżył brata swego, uczyńcie mu, jak on zamierzał uczynić swemu bratu. Usuniesz zło spośród siebie, a reszta, słysząc to, ulęknie się i nie uczyni więcej nic takiego pośród siebie. Twe oko nie będzie miało litości. Życie za życie, oko za oko, ząb za ząb, ręka za rękę, noga za nogę.

Ostatnie zdanie proboszcz przeczytał, nie patrząc na stronice Biblii, zamiast tego wodził wzrokiem po twarzach słuchaczy. Na koniec zawiesił pytające spojrzenie na Szackim.

– To wszystko. Wygląda na to, że wyjaśniło się znaczenie hebrajskiego napisu.

– Oko za oko – zaskrzypiał złowrogo Wilczur. Szacki drgnął ponownie.

– Zapewne – skomentowała Sobieraj. – Wyjaśnił się też nasz tajemniczy szyfr. Okazuje się, że nie chodziło o Komendę Wojewódzką Policji. Zawsze coś.

I znowu klik. Nieznośny, upierdliwy klik.

– Taaak – przeciągnął Szacki. – Tylko dlaczego nie w kolejności? Dziwne.

– Ale co dziwne?

– Cytaty nie są po kolei – odpowiedział jej wikary szybko, aby nikt go nie ubiegł. – W Pięcioksięgu najpierw jest Księga Rodzaju, potem Wyjścia, Kapłańska, Liczb i Powtórzonego Prawa.

– Czyli powinno być WKP? Dlaczego litery są zamienione?

– Nie mam pojęcia – odparł Szacki. – Ale się dowiem. Muszę znaleźć jakiegoś rabina.

Basia Sobieraj spojrzała na zegarek.

– Musisz być za pięć minut na Koseły. Masz przesłuchanie Magiery, specjalnie go z Kielc dowieźli.

Prokurator Teodor Szacki zaklął szpetnie. Wilczur parsknął śmiechem, kanonik spojrzał na niego z pełną wyrozumiałości naganą, wikary był zachwycony.

4

PROTOKÓŁ PRZESŁUCHANIA PODEJRZANEGO. Sebastian Magiera, urodzony 20 kwietnia 1987 roku, zamieszkały w Zawichoście przy ulicy Topolowej 15a, obecnie przebywa w AŚ Kielce. Wykształcenie średnie techniczne, przed zatrzymaniem bezrobotny, pracujący dorywczo jako ogrodnik. Stosunek do stron: syn ofiary. Niekarany, pouczony o obowiązkach i prawach podejrzanego, wyjaśnia, co następuje:

Chciałbym zmienić swoje wyjaśnienia składane poprzednio kilkakrotnie w toku postępowania i przyznać się do tego, że 1 listopada 2008 roku nieumyślnie zabiłem swojego ojca Stefana Magierę w jego domu przy ul. Topolowej 15a w Zawichoście. Zrobiłem to w emocjach i pod wpływem kłótni, nie miałem intencji pozbawienia życia swojego ojca. Powodem kłótni był fakt, że mimo wielokrotnie składanych obietnic ojciec mój nie chciał udostępnić mi, mojej żonie Annie i trzyletniemu synowi Tadeuszkowi pomieszczeń do mieszkania w swoim domu, który zamieszkiwał samotnie, oraz oddać w użytkowanie rodzinnej ziemi, która leżała odłogiem. Fakt ten bardzo negatywnie odbijał się na naszych warunkach bytowych.

Żonę swoją poznałem w technikum ogrodniczym w Sandomierzu przed pięcioma laty, mieszkałem wtedy samotnie z ojcem w Zawichoście, nadmieniam tutaj, że ojciec, były sportowiec, zawsze nadużywał alkoholu i był agresywny. Zakochaliśmy się w sobie i kiedy Anna zaszła w ciążę, a było to jeszcze przed naszym ślubem, poprosiłem ojca, żeby mogła zamieszkać z nami, w mieszkaniu bowiem u jej rodziców w Klimontowie nie było ku temu warunków. Pijany ojciec ubliżał mi i Annie, nie pozwolił zamieszkać nam u niego oraz wyrzucił mnie z domu. Na początku mieszkaliśmy mimo wszystko u rodziców Ani, ale jak Tadzio się urodził, wynajęliśmy pokój w Klimontowie. Warunki były bardzo złe, nie mieliśmy pieniędzy. Dorywczo pracowałem jako ogrodnik, ale moje dochody nie były duże. Kiedy Tadzio trochę podrósł, pracy szukała też Ania, ale bez powodzenia. Przez cały ten czas próbowałem rozmawiać z ojcem, żeby nam udostępnił chociaż jeden pokój, ale ojciec był nieugięty, nawet po tym, jak wzięliśmy ślub w 2007 roku, ciągle lżył mnie i moją żonę. Mieliśmy problemy, zasiłek nie wystarczał na życie, szczególnie gdy okazało się, że Tadzio jest chory na astmę i potrzebuje drogich leków. Dlatego z pokoju w Klimontowie przenieśliśmy się do baraków socjalnych na Krukowie w Sandomierzu. Warunki nie były tam dobre. Moja żona Anna jest bardzo ładna i w 2007 roku znalazła pracę jako modelka. Zaczęła jeździć po Polsce z pokazami, a ja opiekowałem się dzieckiem. I rozmawiałem z ojcem, cały czas bezskutecznie. Ojciec powtarzał, że jemu udało się zdobyć brązowy medal na olimpiadzie w Monachium swoją ciężką i długą pracą i że powinienem brać z niego przykład.

Okazało się, że praca nie satysfakcjonuje Ani, że zajęcie modelki polega trochę na striptizie. Najpierw prezentowała bieliznę na dyskotekach, potem doszły do tego występy takie jak walki w kisielu i walki bokserskie z innymi dziewczynami. Było to dla niej i dla mnie bardzo upokarzające. Najpierw opowiadała o innych dziewczynach, o swojej szefowej, która była nieprzyjemna i agresywna, i o jej mężu, który odnosił się do pracownic bez szacunku i próbował je wykorzystywać. Potem przestała opowiadać, a ja nie pytałem, bo myślałem, że to jest dla niej przykre i nie chce o tym mówić. Poza tym było mi wstyd, bo to ja powinienem utrzymywać rodzinę. To był straszny czas, poszedłem do ojca z dzieckiem i zacząłem go błagać i zaklinać, że to nasza ostatnia nadzieja, że przecież ta ziemia tylko odłogiem leży i ojciec nawet na nią żadnych dotacji nie bierze, nic. A to nie tylko dotacje, uprawiać można, hodować różne rzeczy, ja zawsze do tego taką smykałkę miałem. I zlitował się ojciec i powiedział, że dobrze, że będziemy mogli mieszkać razem z nim i że ziemię mi przepisze, on jej nie potrzebuje, bo mu renty starcza. I że do końca roku załatwimy wszystkie formalności i od 1 stycznia możemy się wprowadzić. To było wtedy lato 2008 roku, jak mieliśmy tą rozmowę. Przyznaję, że poza dniem ślubu i narodzin Tadeuszka był to wtedy najszczęśliwszy dzień mojego życia.

Głównie ja się zajmowałem przygotowaniami, bo Ania jeździła na pokazy, przyznaję, że coraz gorzej układało się wtedy między nami. Nie dlatego, że się kłóciliśmy, tylko mało rozmawialiśmy, myślę dziś, że miała mi za złe, że musi się tym zajmować, ale nie mieliśmy wyjścia, na leki wydawaliśmy nawet po trzysta złotych miesięcznie. Mimo to udało mi się jeszcze trochę pożyczyć po ludziach, żeby kupić narzędzia ogrodnicze do tej ziemi. Z ojcem nawet wtedy było dobrze, planowaliśmy razem, co będę robił, bywałem u niego, pokazywał Tadeuszkowi swój dysk, ale on był jeszcze za ciężki, nawet go dzieciak utrzymać nie mógł. Bałem się, że ojciec się zdenerwuje, ale on się śmiał tylko, że nic, nic, jeszcze do tego podrośnie.

We Wszystkich Świętych 2008 roku pojechaliśmy we trójkę do Zawichostu na groby i oczywiście odwiedzić ojca, trochę się tego spotkania bałem, bo po kłótniach z przeszłości Ania prawie wcale go nie widywała. Było nawet miło, jedliśmy, rozmawialiśmy i piliśmy trochę, ale niewiele. Ja głównie opowiadałem, jak to z tą ziemią będzie, ale ojciec w ogóle tematu nie podchwytywał. Tylko włączył muzykę z radia i powiedział, że teraz Ania pokaże, jak tam jako modelka tańczy i różne popisy robi. Ania nie chciała, a ja się zdenerwowałem i powiedziałem, że nie ma mowy. Na co on, cytuję, że „skoro ta kurwa przed wszystkimi się rozbiera, to przed nim też może". I że jeśli ona przed nim nie zatańczy, to ani domu nie będzie, ani ziemi, a swoimi grabkami to się będę mógł z Tadzikiem w piaskownicy bawić. I zaczął się śmiać, i ja zrozumiałem, że to wszystko były kłamstwa. Że on nigdy nie chciał ani mieszkania dać, ani ziemi, ani mi pomóc, ani w ogóle nic. Że się gdzieś o Ani dowiedział i tylko to wszystko wymyślił, żeby nas upokorzyć i upodlić, nic w tym prawdy nie było.

I wtedy zobaczyłem, że Ania zaczyna się rozbierać, takimi obojętnymi, mechanicznymi ruchami to robiła. A ojciec jeszcze głośniej w śmiech, że on się na niej poznał jeszcze jak w szkole byliśmy, a ja mu nie chciałem wierzyć, to niech teraz patrzę, że taka lekcja to zupełnie za darmo, a przecież więcej warta niż dom i ziemia, bo może zmądrzeję w końcu. I ja wtedy poczułem, że teraz to już nic – ani przyszłości, ani żony, ani leków dla Tadzika – i taka czerwona mgła mi na oczy zaszła, i wziąłem z półki ten dysk z Monachium i ojca uderzyłem w głowę, a potem, jak leżał, jeszcze kilka razy.

Na swoją obronę chciałbym dodać, że działałem pod wpływem szoku, bólu psychicznego i silnych emocji.

Prokurator Teodor Szacki spojrzał na siedzącą przed nim kupkę nieszczęścia. Chłopak był drobnym blondynkiem o wielkich oczach i długich czarnych rzęsach, wyglądał jak ministrant marzenie. Spojrzał na monitor z tekstem protokołu. Nie dawał po sobie tego poznać, ale ciążyła mu odpowiedzialność, los chłopaka i jego rodziny zależał od niego. I nie chodziło tu o klasyfikację czynu. Zabójstwo było ewidentne, nawet jak się biegły zlituje i uzna wyjątkowe wzburzenie, to i tak z paragrafu czwartego dostanie z górnej półki, pewnie z osiem lat. Chodziło o to, czy Szacki uwierzy w jego kłamstwa, czy nie.

– Gdzie teraz mieszka pańska żona? – spytał.

– No, po sprawie spadkowej odziedziczyłem dom i ziemię, ona tam mieszka z dzieckiem. Podobno nawet ładnie zrobiła, pisała kuzynka.

– Za co?

– Do Unii w końcu ten wniosek złożyła, w gminie są ludzie, co wypełniają papiery. Plus zasiłek. Ja, gdybym już był w więzieniu, a nie w areszcie, to też bym coś dorobił, wysłał.

Magiera patrzył na niego błagalnie. Wiercił się na krześle, nie wiedział, co oznacza milczenie prokuratora. Milczenie prokuratora tymczasem oznaczało, że próbuje przypomnieć sobie wszystkie podobne sprawy z przeszłości. Nie pamiętał dokładnie chwili, kiedy po raz pierwszy dla jakiegoś wyższego dobra postawił się nad kodeksem, bardziej ufając swojemu osądowi niż bezlitosnej ustawie. Może i były w niej błędy, może była niesprawiedliwa, ale stanowiła podstawę porządku w Rzeczpospolitej. Moment, w którym uznał, że prześlizgnie się między jej paragrafami, powinien być tym, w którym przestał być prokuratorem.

Miał wybór między dwiema opcjami. Opcja pierwsza to kupić wersję Magiery. Co oznaczało oskarżenie go o zabójstwo i łatwe obronienie tez z aktu na sali. Oskarżony się przyznaje, żona potwierdza jego wersję, świadków nie ma, rodziny ojca i oskarżyciela posiłkowego nie ma, apelacji oczywiście nie ma. Odsiedzi kilka lat i wróci do Zawichostu, żona na niego będzie czekała. Co do tego Szacki nie miał wątpliwości.

Opcja druga oznaczała, jak to się mówi, „ustalenie prawdy materialnej". Co w tym wypadku oznaczało oskarżenie zarówno Magiery, jak i jego żony o zabójstwo z paragrafu pierwszego i wyroki od piętnastu lat w górę dla każdego, Tadeuszek do domu dziecka. Na dysku były odciski obydwojga. Żadne z nich nie miało alkoholu we krwi. Dziecko dziwnym trafem wylądowało przed zabójstwem u sąsiadki dwie ulice dalej. Z oględzin zwłok wynikało, że stary Magiera umarł półtorej godziny przed wezwaniem karetki – chcieli mieć pewność, że go nie odratują.

Ale też wszystko, co mówił cherubinek-ogrodnik o swoim życiu z Anną i o stosunkach z ojcem, było prawdą, potwierdzili to świadkowie. Nawet notariusz zeznał, że to było wyjątkowo obrzydliwe, jak stary przyszedł do niego niby obgadywać sprawy ziemi, a tak naprawdę wyśmiewać się z syna i jego żony dziwki. A zbrzydzić notariusza – to jest naprawdę wielka sztuka.

Magiera wiercił się, pocił i błagał wzrokiem coraz bardziej. Szacki obracał w dłoni monetę, a w głowie jedną myśl: prawda czy pół prawdy?

5

Jest takie żydowskie przysłowie: pół prawdy to całe kłamstwo – powiedział rabin Zygmunt Maciejewski, wznosząc toast koszernym winem. Było pyszne, niestety Szacki nie mógł wypić już ani kropli, jeśli nie chciał zostawać w Lublinie na noc.

Kiedy kilka godzin wcześniej przemierzał dziurawą i wąską drogę z Sandomierza do Lublina, nie pokładał wielkich nadziei w czekającym go spotkaniu. Chciał pogadać z kimś, kto zna kulturę żydowską, dowiedzieć się czegoś, co nawet jeśli nie będzie przełomowe, to pozwoli mu w krytycznej chwili nie przegapić pozostawionej przez ich wariata poszlaki. I zrozumieć, czy ta dziwaczna gra ma jakieś drugie dno, ukryte znaczenie, którego nie potrafi dostrzec, ponieważ brakuje mu wiedzy.

Nie rozmyślał nad tym zbyt wiele, ale pukając do drzwi mieszkania w centrum Lublina, spodziewał się zobaczyć sympatycznego staruszka z ostrym nosem i siwą brodą, spoglądającego z mądrą dobrocią zza okularów połówek. Takie połączenie Albusa Dumbledora z Benem Kingsleyem. Tymczasem drzwi otworzył mu krępy mężczyzna w koszulce polo, o wyglądzie tyleż inteligentnego, co niebezpiecznego żula z Grochowa. Rabin Zygmunt Maciejewski miał około trzydziestu pięciu lat i przypominał Jerzego Kuleja. Ale nie starego posła Kuleja, tylko Kuleja z czarno-białych zdjęć, z czasów, kiedy zdobywał złote medale na igrzyskach. Trójkątna twarz z ostro zarysowanym podbródkiem, zadziorny uśmiech zabijaki, płaski nos boksera, nad nim głęboko osadzone, czujne jasne oczy. I zakola wrzynające się w krótko obcięte czarne kędziory.

Prokurator Teodor Szacki starannie ukrył swoje zaskoczenie wyglądem żydowskiego nauczyciela, ale w głębi mieszkania nie wytrzymał i musiał zrobić zdziwioną minę na widok jego wystroju, ponieważ młody rabin parsknął śmiechem. Że salon zastawiony był regałami pełnymi książek w kilku językach – tego można było się spodziewać. Ale że pomiędzy symetrycznie rozstawionymi półkami ściany zajmowały fototapety naturalnych rozmiarów piękności w kostiumach kąpielowych – to już wydawało mu się dziwne. Szackiego ciekawił klucz doboru, nie były to chyba Żydówki, bo tylko jedna, z burzą obsydianowych loków związanych w koński ogon, wyglądała jak oficer izraelskiej armii. Spojrzał pytająco na Maciejewskiego.

– Miss Israel z ostatnich dziesięciu lat – wyjaśnił rabin. – Powiesiłem je, bo uznałem, że trzeba dawać inne świadectwo niż szmoncesy, szabasowe świece, targowanie się w chałatach i skrzypcowe recitale na dachu.

– Te ukraińskie modelki też? – spytał Szacki, wskazując na wyginające się na kilku plakatach smukłe blondynki.

– Myślał pan, że wszystkie wyglądają jak Gołda Tencer? W takim razie zapraszam do Izraela. Tylko proszę wcześniej czule pożegnać żonę. Pewnie jestem nieobiektywny, ale nie znam bardziej seksownych kobiet. A to sporo znaczy w ustach kogoś, kto mieszka w akademickim polskim mieście.

Rabin miał naturalną skłonność do skracania dystansu i choć w wypadku Szackiego nie było to normą, obaj mężczyźni dość szybko przeszli na „ty". Przy okazji wyjaśnił, że żydowskie pochodzenie odziedziczył po matce z Izraela, imię po wielkim Żydzie Zygmuncie Freudzie, a nazwisko po polskim inżynierze, który czterdzieści lat temu wyjechał na kilkudniową delegację do Hajfy i już nie wrócił stamtąd do pozostawionej w Poznaniu żony i dwójki dzieci.

– Proszę sobie wyobrazić, że teraz przyjaźnię się ze swoim przyrodnim rodzeństwem. – Szacki nie wyobrażał sobie, żeby ktokolwiek mógł się nie zaprzyjaźnić z będącym samą serdecznością rabinem Maciejewskim. – Mimo iż przez całe swoje dzieciństwo słuchali, że Żydówa im ojca ukradła. Zawsze to podaję jako optymistyczny przykład, kiedy ktoś mnie pyta o stosunki polsko-żydowskie. A rozumiem, że o tym będziemy rozmawiali?

Zaczęli jednak od Sandomierza. Od popełnianych w mieście zabójstw, które prokurator opisał ze szczegółami. Od katedry, starego obrazu i legendy o mordzie rytualnym, która mogła w jakiś sposób być kluczem do sprawy. Choć tę akurat hipotezę Szacki chciał zgodnie z intuicją raczej wykluczyć niż potwierdzić. Od napisu na obrazie. Rabin dokładnie obejrzał fotografię i najpierw zmarszczył brwi, mamrocząc, że to dziwne i że musi jedną rzecz przemyśleć, a nagabywany przez prokuratora wytłumaczył, że słowa należy czytać „ajin tachat ajin", że dosłownie oznaczają one „oko pod okiem" i faktycznie pochodzą z Pięcioksięgu.

– Chrześcijanie i muzułmanie często przytaczają te fragmenty jako dowód na agresję i brutalność judaizmu – tłumaczył Maciejewski, rozlewając wino, które wcześniej zareklamował jako koszerne. Nazywało się l'chaim i było przyzwoitym stołowym cabernet. – Tymczasem zapis ten nigdy nie był traktowany przez Żydów dosłownie. Nie wiem, czy zdaje pan sobie sprawę, że wedle tradycji Mojżesz otrzymał od Boga oprócz spisanej Tory, także tradycję ustną, czyli Talmud?

– Coś w rodzaju żydowskiego katechizmu?

– Dokładnie. Talmud stanowi oficjalną interpretację zapisów Tory, które cóż, bywają dyskusyjne. Gdybym był, Boże uchowaj, sceptyczny wobec wiary, to powiedziałbym, że to było bardzo mądre posunięcie ludu Izraela: szybko napisać życiowe interpretacje nieżyciowych zapisów i uznać je za głos Boga, tyle tylko, że przekazany podczas pogawędki. Ale ponieważ jestem bardzo bogobojny, to będziemy trzymać się wersji, że mądry Bóg wiedział, co kazać Mojżeszowi zapisać, a co tylko mu powiedzieć ku pamięci.

– I co miał do powiedzenia w kwestii wydłubywania oczu?

– Wytłumaczył Mojżeszowi, że tylko kretyn mógłby to traktować dosłownie. Słynny jest następujący przykład: osoba, która oślepiła kogoś na jedno oko, sama jest jednooka. Gdyby zastosować dosłownie zapis z Tory, za karę trzeba byłoby wykłuć pozostałe oko sprawcy, co uczyniłoby go zupełnie niewidomym. Czy to byłaby sprawiedliwa kara? Oczywiście nie. Dlatego Tradycja bardzo szybko wytłumaczyła, że w zapisie „ajin tachat ajin" chodzi o sprawiedliwe, monetarne zadośćuczynienie, proporcjonalne do szkody. Inna jest bowiem w przypadku utraty nogi szkoda pisarza, a inna zawodowego piłkarza. Innymi słowy, w prawie żydowskim nigdy nie było zasady, że karą za oślepienie powinno być oślepienie. Czy to jasne?

– W takim razie skąd to przekonanie? – zapytał Szacki.

Rabin dolał sobie wina, kieliszek prokuratora był pełny.

– Spora w tym zasługa Mateusza Ewangelisty, który zacytował, jak Jezus wykłada, że kiedyś nauczano „oko za oko, ząb za ząb", a on teraz mówi, żeby nie stawać przeciwko złu, tylko nadstawić drugi policzek. Urodził się z tego zabobon, który przeciwstawia miłosiernych chrześcijan krwawym Żydom. Co jest nawet dość zabawne.

– Czyli że Żydzi nie nadstawiają drugiego policzka? – zapytał Szacki, zastanawiając się, na ile rabin jest otwarty, a na ile poprawny politycznie, i czy nie wypieprzy go za drzwi, jak się dowie, że tak naprawdę sprawdza teorię o żydowskim szaleńcu, który postanowił zabawić się w mordy rytualne.

– Nie – odpowiedział krótko Maciejewski. – Rebe Schneerson, ostatni lubawicki rabin, lubił powtarzać, że najlepszym sposobem walki ze złem jest czynienie dobra. Ale są sytuacje, kiedy ta strategia słabo się sprawdza. Były momenty w historii, kiedy byliśmy ofiarami, ale nasza mitologia nie jest mitologią ofiar. Proszę spojrzeć na żydowskie święta. Pascha to wspomnienie utopienia egipskiej armii w Morzu Czerwonym. Chanuka to udane powstanie Machabeuszy i pokonanie okupanta. Purim to wspomnienie tego, jak szykowana Żydom rzeź zamieniła się w wycięcie w pień agresora.

– A zemsta?

– Tora i Talmud są w tym temacie jednogłośne: zemsta jest wbrew Prawu. Nie wolno szerzyć nienawiści, nie wolno szukać pomsty, nie wolno żywić urazy, należy miłować bliźniego jak samego siebie. Ta sama Księga Kapłańska, z której pochodzi twój cytat. Tylko kilka rozdziałów wcześniej.

Szacki zamyślił się.

– A po wojnie? Wydawałoby mi się to naturalne.

Rabin Zygmunt Maciejewski wstał i zapalił stojącą na stole lampę – zaczynało zmierzchać. W półmroku roznegliżowane piękności wydawały się bardziej żywe niż przedtem, bardziej przypominały czające się po kątach prawdziwe osoby niż zdjęcia na ścianie. A między nimi stał młody Jerzy Kulej w roli lubelskiego rabina.

– Nie lubię rozmawiać o Zagładzie – powiedział. – Nie lubię tego, że koniec końców każda rozmowa między Żydami i Polakami wraca do wydarzeń sprzed siedemdziesięciu prawie lat. Tak jakby nie było siedmiuset lat wspólnej historii wcześniej i wszystkiego później. Tylko morze trupów i nic więcej. Dlatego wieszam te modelki, których obecność wydaje mi się teraz surrealistyczna, a tobie pewnie jeszcze bardziej.

Maciejewski gapił się w okno i nic nie wskazywało na to, aby miał kontynuować rozmowę. Szacki wstał, żeby rozprostować kości, podszedł do niego. Dziwna panowała atmosfera w mieszkaniu rabina. Poczuł, jak opada jego zawodowa garda, jak odpływa cynizm i ironia, chce tak po prostu porozmawiać. Być może wynikało to z faktu, że od dawna musiał pilnować każdego słowa – w Sandomierzu wszyscy byli podejrzani i żadna rozmowa nie była tam po prostu rozmową. Stanął obok rabina i nabrał ochoty, żeby opowiedzieć o swoim wielkim marzeniu: zawsze chciał się przejść po dawnej Warszawie, poczuć i posmakować jej różnorodność, chodzić ulicami, na których polski mieszał się z rosyjskim i jidysz. Czuł potrzebę wyrażenia nostalgii za innością, ale zamknął otwarte już usta, bojąc się, że po prostu wyjdzie na to, że ględzi coś bez sensu, bo jak każdy wykształcony Polak śmiertelnie boi się wyjść na antysemitę. Nagle poczuł irracjonalną złość na siebie i szybko wrócił na fotel. Upił trochę wina, resztę rozcieńczył wodą gazowaną. Zamyślony rabin dalej stał przy oknie, z profilu wyglądał jak bokser rozpamiętujący przegraną walkę.

– Rozumiem, że masz jakiś powód, dla którego pytasz o żydowską zemstę – powiedział w końcu, wracając do stolika. – Mówiąc krótko, nie za bardzo tutaj było komu i na kim się mścić. Żydów niewiele, Niemców po przejściu Armii Czerwonej tak samo. Część Żydów, nikogo nie osądzam, stwierdzam fakt, polscy chłopi wzięli na widły, przestraszeni, że się upomną o swój majątek. Część nie miała najmniejszej ochoty na zemstę, zemsta oznaczała ryzyko, a cudem ocalone życie było zbyt kruche, żeby ryzykować nim w jakikolwiek sposób. Były wyjątki. Coś ci mówią nazwiska Wiesenthal i Morel?

– Pierwsze tak, drugie nie.

– Szymon Wiesenthal, nasz łowca nazistów numer jeden, podobno jeszcze w czasie wojny, tutaj, w sowieckim już Lublinie, założył razem z towarzyszami tajną organizację o nazwie Nekama, czyli Zemsta. Brzydzę się rewanżyzmem, ale jestem w stanie wyobrazić sobie taką sytuację, kiedy paru ocalonych z Zagłady do tego stopnia pała żądzą zemsty, aby powołać specjalną organizację. Może szybko okazało się, że mogą działać jawnie i coś, co powstawało w Polsce jako Nekama, stało się potem ośrodkiem dokumentacji historycznej, które Wiesenthal założył w Austrii. Jasne?

– Jasne – odparł lakonicznie Szacki.

– Czyli na jednym ręku mamy Wiesenthala – Maciejewski wykonał odpowiedni gest – i jego zemstę, polegającą na tropieniu nazistów. Czyste rozwiązanie. Na drugiej dłoni z kolei ciąży nam Salomon Morel. Szlomo miał to szczęście, że jakiś dobry Polak ocalił go od Zagłady, dzięki czemu mógł przystać do Gwardii Ludowej i kiedy Wiesenthal zakładał Nekamę, Morel organizował czerwonym milicję w tymże Lublinie. Potem został komendantem obozu Zgoda na Górnym Śląsku, w którym komuniści przetrzymywali głównie Niemców i Ślązaków, ale też niewygodnych dla władzy Polaków. W obozie, urządzonym zresztą w byłym obozie koncentracyjnym, umarło prawie dwa tysiące osób, podobno wskutek celowych zaniedbań Morela.

– I? – Szacki pomyślał, że wszystko to bardzo interesujące, ale w żaden sposób mu nie pomaga.

– I masz dwa oblicza żydowskiej zemsty z tamtych czasów. Z jednej strony izraelscy urzędnicy tropiący esesmanów po argentyńskich willach, z drugiej kompulsywne zaspokajanie niskiego instynktu zemsty. Niskiego, ale jakoś tam zrozumiałego. Wyobraź sobie, że wracasz do swojej wioski, a w twoim domu mieszka szmalcownik, przez którego donos cała twoja rodzina zginęła w obozie. Żona, dzieci. Powstrzymałbyś się? Przebaczył? Umiłował jak siebie samego?

Szacki milczał. Nie potrafił odpowiedzieć na to pytanie, nikt, kto nie stanął przed takim wyborem, nie potrafił.

– Masz rodzinę? – zapytał rabin.

– Mam. Miałem. Do niedawna.

Maciejewski spojrzał uważnie, ale nie skomentował.

– W takim razie pewnie i tak możesz sobie lepiej wyobrazić takie emocje niż ja. Dla mnie to abstrakcja, akademickie rozważanie. Tyle wiemy o sobie, ile nas sprawdzono.

– Talmud?

– Nie, Szymborska. Mądrość dobrze jest czerpać z różnych źródeł. Akurat to cytat z wiersza o kobiecie, zwykłej nauczycielce, która zginęła, ratując czwórkę dzieci z pożaru. Lubię ten wiersz i ten cytat i lubię przeświadczenie, które stoi za tymi słowami: że nigdy nie wiemy, ile w nas dobra. Oglądałem dokument o amerykańskim Żydzie, który jedzie do Polski szukać korzeni i pomiędzy tymi potłuczonymi macewami i zamienionymi w warsztaty synagogami znajduje chłopską rodzinę, która ocaliła jego ojca. Potem w Izraelu pyta tegoż ojca, dlaczego tym Polakom nigdy nie przysłali chociaż kartki. I dostaje odpowiedź: bo jak? Jak za coś takiego podziękować? I ostatnie pytanie: czy w odwrotnej sytuacji zrobiłby to samo? I staruszek odpowiada cicho: nie, nigdy.

– Mówisz jak antysemita.

– Nie, mówię jak ktoś, kto wie, że wielka historia to zbiór małych historii, z których każda jest inna. Bo ten stary Żyd w odwrotnej sytuacji może, jak mówi, nie zrobiłby nic, a może tak samo nosiłby kaszę do stodoły, wiedząc, że w każdej chwili mogą rozstrzelać całą jego rodzinę. Tyle wiemy o sobie, ile nas sprawdzono.

Maciejewski dolał sobie wina.

– Znam setki takich historyjek – powiedział, siadając na powrót w fotelu naprzeciwko Szackiego. – Wiesz, jak to wygląda z polskiej strony, te wszystkie łyse gnojki. A wiesz, jak wygląda z naszej?

Szacki zaprzeczył ruchem głowy, trochę ciekaw dalszego ciągu, ale tylko trochę. Czuł, że czas ucieka. Że powinien się czegoś dowiedzieć i wracać do pracy jak najszybciej.

– Tak, że jak przyjeżdża wycieczka z Izraela do obozu w Majdanku, do dyskoteki zabierają własną ochronę. A zanim wsiądą do autokaru na Okęciu, muszą wysłuchać pogadanki o tym, jak się zachowywać na wypadek antysemickich zamachów. Wychowywałem się w Izraelu, byłem na takiej wycieczce, która składa się głównie z epatowania Szoah. – Maciejewski wypowiedział to słowo z chrapliwym zaśpiewem, Szacki zrozumiał teraz, że dziwna, szarpana melodia, jaką od początku słyszał w jego płynnej polszczyźnie, to musiały być ślady hebrajskiego. – Ale nie tylko. W tej samej mierze składała się z pieprzenia o wszechobecnym antysemityzmie, ze wzbudzania podejrzliwości, ksenofobii i żądzy odwetu. Doprawdy, w budowaniu tożsamości na trupach zrobiliśmy się lepsi niż Polacy.

Szacki mimo powagi tematu wybuchnął śmiechem i wzniósł kieliszek.

– Za to wypiję, bo jeśli to prawda – zawiesił głos – dokonaliście niemożliwego.

Stuknęli się.

– Mówi ci coś skrót KWP? – spytał prokurator, wekslując rozmowę na interesujące go tematy. Chciał ją doprowadzić do końca.

– Komenda Wojewódzka Policji?

– A Konspiracyjne Wojsko Polskie?

– Nie wiem, coś dzwoni, ale daleko, to jakiś rodzaj WiN-u albo NSZ?

– Tak, należeli do żołnierzy wyklętych.

Rabin westchnął i spojrzał w ciemne okno, jakby pozował do sesji, w której sportowcy udają myślicieli.

– Dlaczego pytasz?

– Różne poszlaki wskazują, że obecne wydarzenia mogą być z tym związane. Coś ci to mówi?

– Kolejny drażliwy temat. Wyklęci walczyli z komunistyczną władzą, niektórzy aż do lat pięćdziesiątych. Czytałem o nich, sprawa ma mnóstwo odcieni, przez wieki narosło wokół niej sporo legend i jak to zwykle w Polsce bywa, nie ma żadnej prawdy pośrodku. – Rabin uśmiechnął się niespodziewanie. – Na marginesie: uwielbiam tę waszą cechę, to poruszanie się po skrajnościach, euforia albo czarna depresja, wielka miłość albo ślepa wściekłość. U Polaków nigdy normalnie. Szlag mnie czasami od tego trafia, ale i tak to lubię, nauczyłem się traktować uzależnienie od polskiego charakteru jako nieszkodliwy nałóg. Nieważne zresztą, ważne, że o waszej partyzantce antykomunistycznej też się mówi skrajnie. Dla jednych to bohaterowie bez skazy, dla drugich szkodliwi pieniacze, którzy szukali pretekstu do awantury i rozróby, jeszcze dla innych krwawi żydożercy od urządzania pogromów.

– Były takie przypadki?

– Szczerze: nie mam aż takiej wiedzy. Pamiętaj, że to były oddziały raczej prawicowe, lewica jakoś tam, mniej lub bardziej, wierzyła nowej władzy. A to była przedwojenna, endecka prawicowość, podszyta antysemityzmem, dotyczy to zwłaszcza Narodowych Sił Zbrojnych. Ale też pamiętajmy, że od Zagłady każdy czyn wymierzony w Żyda przedstawiany jest jako przejaw antysemityzmu, a to nie musi być prawda. Wyklęci walczyli z aparatem państwa, z jego funkcjonariuszami, ofiarą walki padali Żydzi, ponieważ było ich sporo w bezpiece.

– Myślałem, że to antysemickie kłamstwo.

– Antysemickie mogą być interpretacje faktów, ale nie fakty jako takie. Z przykrością, bo nie jest to zbyt jasna karta w historii mojego narodu, przyznaję, że do połowy lat pięćdziesiątych ponad jedna trzecia funkcyjnych w Ministerstwie Bezpieczeństwa Publicznego to byli Żydzi. Taki jest fakt, nic w nim antysemickiego nie ma. Oczywiście przedstawianie tego jako wymierzonego w Polskę żydowskiego spisku to już inna historia. Zwłaszcza że większość to byli zwyczajni komuniści, żydowskie mieli jedynie pochodzenie.

Szacki porządkował w głowie zdobyte informacje. Był zadowolony, teza, z którą tutaj przyjechał, zaczynała nabierać ciała.

– Dlaczego aż tylu?

Maciejewski powtórzył gest bezradności.

– Bo każda władza inna niż niemiecka wydawała im się dobra? Bo już przed wojną dla żydowskiej biedoty komunistyczna ideologia była atrakcyjna? Bo władza wolała z natury kosmopolitycznych Żydów niż niechętnych Rosjanom patriotycznych Polaków? Bo tyle samo prawdy jest w plotkach o antysemityzmie Polaków, co w tych o antypolonizmie Żydów? – Rabin nagle zawiesił głos i smutno zanucił: – Bo ja chciałem być kimś, bo ja byłem Żyd, a jak Żyd nie był kimś, to ten Żyd był nikt.

– Bo dla niektórych był to sposób na odwet na sąsiadach? – dopowiedział Szacki.

– Jasne. Szukanie winnych jest najprostszym sposobem radzenia sobie z traumą. Jeśli wskażesz kogoś, kto jest sprawcą twoich krzywd, od razu jest prościej. Niemców nie było, pod ręką byli Polacy. I czerwoni, szepczący do ucha, jak to endeckie bandy urządzają sobie pogromy. Nie przez przypadek departamentem do walki z „bandytyzmem" kierowali komuniści żydowskiego pochodzenia, technika jątrzenia i szczucia zawsze się sprawdza.

Szacki słuchał ze zdumieniem.

– Nie spodziewałem się usłyszeć czegoś takiego.

– Jasne, że nie, jesteś przewrażliwiony jak każdy wykształcony Polak. Boisz się, że miaukniesz i zaraz ci wyciągną Kielce i Jedwabne. Dlatego, niestety jak reszta świata, nie jesteś zdolny do rzetelnej oceny. Ja sam jestem wierzącym Żydem i patriotą, ale uważam politykę Izraela za szkodliwą. Zamiast być liderem regionu, jesteśmy warowną twierdzą, zamieszkaną przez paranoików z syndromem oblężenia, antagonizujących i tak już nienawidzące nas narody. Przedstawiane oczywiście jako terroryści i poplecznicy Hitlera. Zresztą nie wiem, czy słuchałeś dziś radia, jest Dzień Pamięci o Szoah, a nasz wicepremier w Auschwitz wykorzystuje to, żeby porównać Iran do nazistowskich Niemiec. Normalnie ręce opadają, niektórzy nasi politycy, jakby nie wyciągali Hitlera przy każdej okazji, straciliby rację istnienia.

Szacki uśmiechnął się w duchu, bo w publicystycznym zapale Maciejewskiego, w rytualnym psioczeniu na władzę było coś bardzo polskiego. Zapachniało wódką, sałatką jarzynową i wędlinami ułożonymi na srebrnym półmisku. Czas kończyć.

– Wiesz oczywiście, dlaczego pytam o to wszystko?

– Bo rozważasz opcję, że to może być sprawka jakiegoś Żyda, i chcesz wiedzieć, czy to możliwe. Gdyby chodziło o normalną osobę, powiedziałbym, że nie, ale osoba, która ma na rękach krew dwóch osób, to szaleniec. A u szaleńców wszystko jest możliwe. I jest jeszcze coś...

– Tak? – Szacki pochylił się w fotelu.

– Wszystko to, o czym opowiadałeś: Sandomierz, obraz, cytaty, nóż do szechity, zwłoki w beczce... – Maciejewski zrobił swój gest zamyślonego boksera. – Takiej wiedzy nie da się zdobyć w weekend. Teoretycznie musisz po prostu być Żydem, i to Żydem doskonale obeznanym ze swoją kulturą. Albo badaczem tejże.

– Dlaczego teoretycznie? – Szacki włączył wszystkie radary, w tonie rabina było coś, co kazało mu zwiększyć czujność.

Maciejewski obrócił w jego stronę fotografię hebrajskiego napisu na obrazie w katedrze i wskazał środkową literę w środkowym słowie.

– To chet, ósma litera hebrajskiego alfabetu. Jest źle napisana, ale nie tak źle, żeby można to wytłumaczyć dysleksją na przykład. Jest lustrzanym odbiciem poprawnie napisanej litery, łuk powinien być z prawej, nie z lewej strony. Żaden

Żyd nie napisze tego w ten sposób, tak samo jak ty, choćbyś nie wiem jak się upił czy naćpał, nie napiszesz B z brzuszkami z lewej strony. Myślę, że ktoś jest po prostu cwany i chce wskrzesić tyle demonów, aby móc się między nimi schować. Pytanie, mój drogi prokuratorze, czy potrafisz w tłumie zjaw i upiorów dostrzec twarz zabójcy?

6

Słowa o upiorach rezonowały w głowie Szackiego, kiedy wracał nocą do Sandomierza. Mijając wsie i miasteczka Lubelszczyzny, zastanawiał się, ile z nich było przed wojną żydowskimi sztetlami. Ilu było Żydów w Kraśniku? W Annopolu? W Olbięcinie, Wilkołazach, Gościeradowie? I gdzie skończyli? Na Majdanku, w Bełżcu, niektórzy może dożyli marszów śmierci? Upokarzający koniec, bez pochówków, bez rytuałów pogrzebowych, bez przeprowadzenia duszy na drugą stronę. Jeśli wierzyć ludowym wierzeniom, wszystkie te dusze powinny tułać się po świecie, uwięzione od siedemdziesięciu lat między wymiarami. Czy w takie dni jak ten, Jom Ha-Szoah, czują, że są wspominani? Czy wracają wtedy do Kraśnika albo Annopola, szukając znajomych kątów, a polscy mieszkańcy oglądają się przez ramię, częściej niż zwykle czują chłód i wcześniej zamykają okna?

Prokurator Teodor Szacki poczuł niepokój. Droga była dziwnie pusta, ciemne lubelskie wioski wyglądały na opuszczone, od Kraśnika po szosie snuły się mgły, czasami ledwo widoczne, niczym brud na szybie, czasami gęste jak wata, w widoczny sposób rozstępujące się przed maską citroena. Prokurator poznawał swój lęk po tym, że bardziej niż zwykle wsłuchiwał się w pojękiwania starego samochodu. Lekkie stukanie z lewej strony zawieszenia, posykiwania pompy płynu hydraulicznego, burczenie sprężarki od klimatyzacji. Było to zupełnie irracjonalne, ale bardzo nie chciał stanąć teraz we mgle i ciemności.

Zaklął i gwałtownie skręcił kierownicą, kiedy z mgły wyłoniła się czarna postać, w ostatniej chwili ominął stojącego prawie na środku jezdni autostopowicza. Zerknął w tylne lusterko, ale zobaczył tylko krwawą ciemność, mgłę rozżarzoną czerwonymi światłami. Przypomniało mu się nagranie Wilczura, przypomniał mu się Żyd rozpływający się w gęstej, nadwiślańskiej mgle.

Żeby zająć czymś myśli, zaczął przewijać w głowie rozmowę z Maciejewskim, przypominać sobie momenty, kiedy czuł znajome łaskotanie neuronów. Raz przy okazji zemsty za śmierć rodziny, na pewno. A drugi raz pod koniec, kiedy rabin mówił, że takiej wiedzy nie da się zdobyć w weekend. Jakaś myśl przemknęła mu wtedy przez głowę, nieoczywista i cenna. Nie, nie chodziło o to, żeby szukać wśród znawców kultury żydowskiej, nie. Maciejewski w opowieści Szackiego dostrzegł dużo szczegółów, detali składających się na obraz.

– A ja? – powiedział głośno Szacki, zachrypnięty głos zabrzmiał obco wewnątrz samochodu.

Czy ja dostrzegłem wszystkie szczegóły? Czy w tym koszmarze nie skupiłem się na tym, co najbardziej widoczne? Kiedy pod powałą wiszą zamknięte w beczce zwłoki, nikt się nie zastanawia, dlaczego mają dziwne, zdeformowane stopy – a teraz mu się to przypomniało. Kiedy w krzakach leży goła kobieta, a kawałek dalej rzeźnicka brzytwa, nikt nie myśli, skąd piasek pod paznokciami. A teraz mu się to przypomniało – zwłoki miały pod paznokciami nie ziemię, nie brud, ale właśnie żółty, nadmorski piasek. Ile takich detali przegapił, ile uznał za nieistotne? Całe zajście w katedrze, cytat na obrazie, „oko za oko, ząb za ząb". Poszedł oczywistym, narzucającym się tropem żydowskiej zemsty. Dokładnie tak, jak chciał tego morderca. Zamiast, wbrew jego oczekiwaniom, szukać błędów w tym spektaklu, daje się prowadzić na smyczy. Jak idealny widz pokazu iluzjonisty, który na wszelki wypadek nie patrzy, co robi druga ręka, żeby nie popsuć sobie wieczoru.

Mijał właśnie Annopol, wystarczyło przejechać przez Wisłę, skierować się na południe – za pół godziny powinien być na miejscu. Miasteczko było puste i zasnute mgłą, mimo to poczuł się bezpieczniej w obecności latarni. Na tyle, że zjechał na bok i sięgnął po komórkę, żeby połączyć się z internetem. Znalazł serwis biblijny, czekając na połączenie, uchylił okno, żeby zwalczyć pojawiającą się senność. Do środka wlały się chłód i wilgoć, samochód wypełnił intensywny ziemny zapach roztopów, zapowiedź wiosny, która miała za chwilę wybuchnąć gwałtownie, chcąc nadrobić stracone tygodnie.

Pamiętając notację, znalazł biblijne cytaty. Czemu były takie długie? Wystarczyłoby podać ten jeden wers, zawierający zwrot „oko za oko", i wszystko byłoby jasne. Przepisał wszystkie do notesu. Ten z Księgi Kapłańskiej był najkrótszy i najprostszy, mówił o karze za okaleczenie i za śmierć. „Kto zabije człowieka, będzie ukarany śmiercią". Szackiego uderzył kodeksowy charakter zwrotu, tak samo zaczynał się paragraf 148 kodeksu karnego Rzeczpospolitej: „Kto zabija człowieka, podlega karze pozbawienia wolności...".

Drugi cytat mówił o karze nakładanej za skrzywdzenie brzemiennej kobiety w czasie walki między mężczyznami, co było zapewne sposobem określenia wojny lub konfliktu. Za spowodowanie poronienia groziła tylko grzywna, jednak jeśli kobieta umarła – śmierć.

W końcu trzeci, z Księgi Powtórzonego Prawa, był najbardziej pokręcony – nieomalże tak jak współczesne kodyfikacje karne. I jednocześnie był to zapis najbardziej surowy, wymierzony przeciwko krzywoprzysięstwu czy – ujmując rzecz współcześnie – przeciwko składaniu fałszywych zeznań. Żydowski ustawodawca – co jest doprawdy dziwnym określeniem Boga, pomyślał Szacki – kazał karać procesowego kłamcę tą samą karą, jaka zostałaby wymierzona, gdyby jego kłamstwa wzięto za prawdę. Innymi słowy, jeśli wskutek czyichś niesłusznych oskarżeń ktoś mógł zostać skazany na śmierć, a sprawa się wydała – to krzywoprzysięzcę czekał stryczek czy co tam wtedy stosowano. Ciekawy był też fakt, że surowość przepisu podyktowały zasady prewencji ogólnej. Zapisane było wprost, że „reszta, słysząc to, ulęknie się i nie uczyni więcej nic takiego pośród siebie". W pewien sposób kłamstwo traktowano jako najgorszą ze zbrodni.

Być może słusznie, pomyślał Szacki i zamknął notes, zamknął też okno i zapiął marynarkę, noc była pierońsko zimna. O czym mówiły cytaty? O zabójstwie, skrzywdzeniu ciężarnej i krzywoprzysięstwie. Przypadek czy istotny szczegół?

Zgasił lampkę zamontowaną nad lusterkiem wstecznym, zamrugał kilka razy, żeby przyzwyczaić zmęczone oczy do zamglonego mroku za oknem i zamarł, widząc tłoczące się przy samochodzie ciemne postacie. Cienie krążyły niepewnie wokół auta. Czując rosnącą w gardle panikę, uruchomił silnik, reflektory wypełniły mleczną mgłę światłem. Nie było żadnych cieni. Tylko wyludnione nadwiślańskie miasteczko, chodnik z kostki bauma i reklama piwa Perła nad sklepem spożywczym.

Ruszył gwałtownie, odjeżdżając w stronę rzeki. Mgła zawirowała za szerokim zadem citroena.

Prokurator Teodor Szacki nie wiedział, bo nie mógł wiedzieć, że opuszcza właśnie jeden z typowych przedwojennych sztetli, miasteczek zamieszkanych w większości przez ubogą ludność żydowską, która w Annopolu stanowiła tuż przed wojną ponad siedemdziesiąt procent mieszkańców. Była tu szkoła hebrajska stowarzyszenia Tarbut, chedery, Towarzystwo Talmud Tora i świeckie szkoły dla dziewcząt i chłopców, była nawet skromna jesziwa, po której chłopcy kontynuowali rabinackie nauki w Lublinie. Został mały i brzydki pamiątkowy kamień w miejscu starego kirkutu na obrzeżach miasteczka, otoczony dla ozdoby chodniczkiem z różowej kostki bauma.

7

Na twarzy dziewczyny pojawiło się niedowierzanie, ale ciągle pozwalała mu trzymać rękę na udzie, dobry znak. Roman Myszyński pozwolił sobie przesunąć ją wobec tego trochę wyżej, na kawałek skóry ponad koronką pończoch, tyle tylko, że nie było tam ani koronki, ani skóry. No nie, nie mówcie, że ktoś dziś chodzi do klubu w rajstopach. Co to jest, jakieś vintage party czy jak, zaraz się okaże, że ma stanik z elastanu i nieogolone pachy. Czy on raz w życiu nie mógłby trafić normalnie? Nie że raz na miesiąc, nawet nie raz na pół roku i nie raz na rok. Raz, raz w ogóle.

– Czyli że jesteś kimś w rodzaju detektywa? – zapytała, nachylając się w jego stronę.

– Nie tyle w rodzaju, co po prostu detektywem – odkrzyknął, notując w pamięci, żeby nigdy, przenigdy nie zapraszać już nikogo przed randką na kalmary w sosie czosnkowym. – Wiem, jak to brzmi, ale tak jest. Siedzę w biurze, przychodzi ktoś, najpierw coś kręci, sprawdza, czy można mieć do mnie zaufanie. A potem – zawiesił głos – a potem wyjawia mi swoje najskrytsze tajemnice i dostaję od niego zlecenie. Nawet nie masz pojęcia, jak pokrętnie układają się ludzkie losy.

– Chciałabym zobaczyć twoje biuro. Wyjawić ci swoje tajemnice.

– Te najskrytsze? – zapytał, czując, jak tandeta tej odzywki sprawia, że odchodzi mu ochota na wieczór pełen wrażeń.

– Nie masz pojęcia! – odkrzyknęła przez muzykę.

Chwilę potem siedzieli już w taksówce, która wiozła ich z centrum do jego „biura", czyli małej kawalerki na Grochowie. Miejsce nie było może luksusowe, ale klimatyczne, w porośniętej winem przedwojennej willi z ogrodem, przycupniętej pod blokami osiedla Ostrobramska, zwanego w okolicy Mordorem. Całowali się namiętnie, kiedy zadzwonił telefon. Numer prywatny. Odebrał, zaklinając w duchu bogów wszystkich religii, żeby to nie była matka.

Słuchał przez chwilę.

– Oczywiście, że kojarzę, panie prokuratorze – powiedział rzeczowym, niższym niż zazwyczaj głosem, rzucając dziewczynie wymowne spojrzenie. – Takich spraw się nie zapomina... Tak, teraz akurat w Warszawie... Jasne... Aha, aha... Rozumiem... Oczywiście... Muszę się przespać kilka godzin, trzy godziny na dojazd, mogę być u pana o ósmej... Tak, jasne, do zobaczenia.

Ruchem rewolwerowca zamknął futerał telefonu i schował go do kieszeni marynarki. Dziewczyna patrzyła na niego z podziwem.

– Wie pan co, żeby prokurator do ludzi o północy wydzwaniał – rzucił taksówkarz, patrząc na niego w lusterku. – Normalnie, kurwa, Związek Radziecki nam tutaj zrobią, platfusy, kondominium, panie.

Rozdział ósmy

Ziemia świętuje swój dzień, Jack Nicholson 72. urodziny, Donald Tusk – 52., a znawcy motoryzacji fetują 7. rocznicę śmierci poloneza. W Polsce prawie pół miliona gimnazjalistów pisze kończący szkołę egzamin, poza tym rząd zapowiada całkowity zakaz palenia, 25-letni alpinista wspina się bez zabezpieczeń po ścianie na szczyt hotelu Marriott w Warszawie, a konkurs na kabareciarza roku wygrywa minister infrastruktury, zapowiadając, że autostrady A1, A2 i A4 będą skończone przed Euro 2012. U zachodnich sąsiadów rozpoczyna się wielki proces islamskich terrorystów, u wschodnich zostaje przywrócony trener hokejowy, zwolniony wcześniej za to, że jego drużyna śmiała wygrać z drużyną prezydenta Łukaszenki. W Sandomierzu policjanci zatrzymują mężczyznę, który oskarżył kilku czternastolatków o kradzież na bazarze 74 butelek piwa oraz butelki wódki i w ramach odszkodowania wymusił od nich pieniądze. Tymczasem prawdziwi złodzieje wynoszą z otwartego mieszkania torebkę, a w niej 180 złotych. Właściciele siedzieli na balkonie. I nie dziwne, bo choć temperatura nie przekracza 18 stopni, a w nocy potrafi spaść do dwóch, to dzień słoneczny i piękny.

1

Odkąd w autobusie na pierwszym gimnazjalnym wyjeździe Marcin wylądował obok Saszy – tylko obok tego przerośniętego dryblasa o wyglądzie mordercy było wolne miejsce – obu chłopców połączyła może nie tyle przyjaźń, co specyficzna znajomość. Nie wiedzieli o sobie zbyt wiele, nie odwiedzali się w domach, nie zapraszali na imprezy, nie chodzili nawet do tej samej klasy. Obaj byli dość osobni i obaj swoją osobność szanowali. Marcin był raczej chuchrem, niskim słomianym blondynkiem w okularach, tyleż znanym, co wyśmiewanym skrzypkiem, grającym czasami, ku swojej rozpaczy, na szkolnych imprezach. Trochę komponował, kręciła go myśl, że mógłby kiedyś pisać muzykę do filmów, ale jego kompozycje znała tylko Ola i właśnie Sasza.

O Saszy chodziły słuchy, że handlował narkotykami i był związany z ruską mafią, plotki na tyle rozpowszechnione, że nawet nauczyciele traktowali go z zaskakującą pobłażliwością, bojąc się zapewne, że przez zbyt niską ocenę semestralną jakiś mafioso w szeleszczącym dresie przewierci im kolano w szkolnej szatni. Z natury milczący Sasza milczał w tej sprawie szczególnie, co oczywiście tylko potęgowało plotki, a kiedy ktoś odważył się podejść do niego i zapytać o towar, Sasza najpierw długo milczał, gapiąc się na klienta bez mrugnięcia powieką, a w końcu nachylał się i mówił z celowym zaśpiewem: „Nie dla ciebie".

W rzeczywistości Sasza nie handlował niczym, jego największą, nieznaną nikomu pasją było kino dokumentalne, którego miał w swoim komputerze terabajty. Podrzucał co jakiś czas Marcinowi co lepsze i co bardziej kontrowersyjne kawałki ze swoich zbiorów. Ostatnio dzięki Saszy Marcin obejrzał niezwykły film o amerykańskim Żydzie, który jedzie z dzieciakami szukać w Polsce ludzi, którzy uratowali jego ojca. Najbardziej uderzył go stary, chory, podpięty do różnych rurek Żyd, który od sześćdziesięciu lat mieszka w Izraelu, już nie kontaktuje i tylko powtarza, że chciałby do domu. Tłumaczą mu, że przecież jest w domu, a on swoje – że do domu. „Tato, a gdzie jest ten twój dom?" – ktoś w końcu pyta. „Jak to gdzie? Zawichojska siedem" – odpowiada. Marcin nie potrafił wytłumaczyć dlaczego, ale bardzo go ta scena wzruszyła.

Sasza stał oparty o parapet, z założonymi na piersi rękami, i gapił się w przestrzeń, w luźnych ciuchach i jasnej bluzie wydawał się jeszcze potężniejszy niż zwykle. Marcin podszedł, skinął głową na powitanie i oparł się o parapet obok niego.

– Pion na e4 – powiedział.

Sasza zmarszczył brwi, pokiwał z uznaniem głową.

– Skoczek na c4 – mruknął.

Rozgrywali partie szachowe właściwie bez przerwy, od momentu poznania się w autobusie, kiedy Sasza na komórce grał w szachy właśnie. Teraz wyglądało to tak, że każdy miał w domu swoją szachownicę, a w szkole codziennie wymieniali się jednym ruchem. Tyle tylko, że Marcin miał na obmyślenie i przygotowanie swojego ruchu cały dzień, Saszy odpowiedź na jego często godzinami opracowywane posunięcia nie zajmowała więcej niż kwadrans. Raz poprosił o czas do namysłu do następnej przerwy, Marcin wtedy chodził dumny przez tydzień. Ale nie wygrał nigdy, jakiś ruski gen sprawiał, że Sasza był niepokonany.

– Słuchaj, czy ja dobrze pamiętam, że twój stary jest przestępcą, łapówkarzem, oprawcą i gnidą?

– Zgadza się, faktycznie jest oficerem policji – odparł Sasza.

– Byłem w poniedziałek na wycieczce w Sandomierzu.

– Przykro mi.

– Zwiedzaliśmy takie lochy pod starówką, kiedyś podobno były tego całe piętra, teraz został taki korytarz beznadziejny, a może pokazują tylko tyle.

– No.

– No i słyszałem wycie.

– Czyli Mary w końcu znalazła łechtaczkę. To koniec, teraz nikt nie jest bezpieczny.

– Takie... takie piekielne wycie, z głębi ziemi. Jakby tam kogoś męczyli albo torturowali.

Sasza spojrzał z góry na przyjaciela. Podniósł jedną brew.

– Tak, wiem, jak to brzmi. Doskonale wiem. Ale to mi nie daje spokoju. Wiesz, co tam się teraz dzieje, grasuje seryjny morderca, były już dwa trupy, dziś przeczytałem, że podobno ludzie przestali posyłać dzieci do szkoły, histeria. No i rozumiesz, to pewnie nic, raczej na pewno nic, ale jeśli coś? Głupio by było, nie?

– Wycie, mówisz? No dobra, powiem staremu, niech tam nada psiarni, może im się przyda. Coś jeszcze?

– Wycie, głównie wycie, takie trochę jak wiatr, trochę jęk, trochę krzyk. I jeszcze jeden dźwięk, wtedy nie mogłem go rozpoznać, za słaby był, ale dziś rano usłyszałem podobny i mi się skojarzyło.

– No?

– Ujadanie. Takie psie, wściekłe ujadanie, jakby gdzieś w tych lochach hodowali psy piekielne albo, ja wiem, wilkołaki mieszkały. Tak, wiem jak to brzmi.

2

Rozmowa była krótka, owocna i Szacki cieszył się, że udało mu się ściągnąć Myszyńskiego z Warszawy. Inteligentny, szybko myślący gość, odrobinę niepasujący do formy, którą sobie stworzył. Był fajnym, dobrym człowiekiem, takim, co to nikomu krzywdy nie zrobi i zawsze będzie się tak samo dziwił, jeśli jego to spotka. A próbował grać starego wyjadacza, zimnego i wyrachowanego cynika, którego interesuje jedynie profesjonalizm w jego robocie – i więcej nic. Rola sama w sobie przyzwoita, zwłaszcza w tym fachu, ale sens ma tylko wtedy, jeśli potrafi się ją zagrać bez fałszu. Szacki potrafił, a gość – prawie wcale. Na szczęście jego zdolności aktorskie były tutaj najmniej istotne.

Wyszedł z gabinetu, żeby umyć kubek po kawie, i zrobił to na tyle gwałtownie, że zderzył się w korytarzu z Basią Sobieraj. Wypadła jej z rąk mała paczuszka. Szybko schylił się, żeby ją podnieść – kartonowe pudełko z pocztową naklejką miało wielkość grubej książki, ale było bardzo lekkie, jakby pozbawione zawartości. Dworskim gestem zwrócił paczkę.

– Proszę, oto pani zguba.

Ze zdumieniem zauważył, że Sobieraj zaczerwieniła się jak dorastająca dziewczynka przyłapana na wstydliwej i intymnej czynności. Gwałtownym gestem wyrwała mu paczkę z rąk.

– Proszę patrzeć, jak pan chodzi, szanowny panie.

Miał ochotę się odgryźć, ale otworzyły się drzwi gabinetu Miszczyk, szefowa wyjrzała i wezwała go zdecydowanym gestem: uczeń proszony do dyrektora. Poszedł, ciągle trzymając w dłoni pusty kubek po kawie, zdobny w logo Legii Warszawa. U Miszczyk siedział mężczyzna o spuchniętej gębie alkoholika i wyglądzie kloszarda, wierzący zapewne, że jego zaniedbanie to sportowa elegancja. Budził niechęć. Wstał na widok Szackiego i przywitał się wylewnie.

– Ja kibicuję Polonii – powiedział, wskazując na kubek.

– Przepraszam, komu?

– No... drugiej warszawskiej drużynie...

– Ale jak to? Przecież w Warszawie jest tylko jedna drużyna – zażartował Szacki, czego tamten nie zrozumiał.

– Pan redaktor przyjechał z Warszawy, pisze duży reportaż o naszej sprawie – Miszczyk wybawiła idiotę z opresji. – Obiecałam, że będzie mógł zabrać panu kwadrans, panie prokuratorze, nie dłużej.

W Szackim zabulgotało, ale uśmiechnął się zdawkowo i zaproponował, żeby załatwili sprawę od razu, co pozwoli mu jak najszybciej wrócić do pracy.

Rozmowa na początku toczyła się wokół śledztwa, mechanizmów postępowania w wypadku podejrzenia działania seryjnego zabójcy i różnych niuansów prawa karnego. Szacki odpowiadał na pytania szybko i precyzyjnie, mimo starań dziennikarza nie pozwalał, aby wywiad zamienił się w miłą, niezobowiązującą pogawędkę, brutalnie ucinał też wszelkie próby skracania dystansu. Czekał na nieuniknione, czyli podróż w stronę żydowskich motywów i polskiego antysemityzmu. Nieuniknione zachowało się zgodnie ze swoim zakresem semantycznym – nadeszło.

– Zastanawia mnie ponura symbolika tego wszystkiego, coś wyjątkowo brudnego jest w tej krwawej zabawie motywami. Tutaj, w mieście słynącym z obrazu, który jest w jakiś sposób credo antysemityzmu. W województwie świętokrzyskim, w którego stolicy wydarzył się największy pogrom od czasu Zagłady. Wydawało się, że to wszystko stare blizny, a tymczasem wystarczy podrapać i co się okazuje? Że to niepogojone, ropiejące rany.

– Symbolika mnie nie interesuje – skwitował chłodno Szacki.

Dziennikarz uśmiechnął się.

– To takie bardzo polskie, nie uważa pan? Mnie nie interesuje. Jak się pojawia drażliwy temat, to zaraz ktoś powie „a po co to wyciągać", „a dajcie sobie spokój", „a po co to jątrzyć niepotrzebnie".

– Przykro mi, ale nie wiem, co jest typowo polskie, mam dyplom z prawa, nie z antropologii. Poza tym pan mnie nie słucha. Może pan wyciągać i jątrzyć, ile dusza zapragnie, nie namawiam pana, żeby pan cokolwiek odpuszczał. Informuję pana tylko, że jako urzędnika w służbie Rzeczpospolitej Polskiej nie interesuje mnie symbolika, nawet brudna i krwawa.

– To czemu kazał pan zatrzymać pijanych gówniarzy, którzy urządzili sobie antysemicką demonstrację?

– Sto dziewięćdziesiąt sześć, dwieście pięćdziesiąt sześć, dwieście pięćdziesiąt siedem, dwieście sześćdziesiąt jeden, dwieście sześćdziesiąt dwa.

– Słucham?

– To przepisy kodeksu karnego, które w tym wypadku mają zastosowanie. Przede wszystkim znieważenie miejsca pamięci, znieważenie miejsca spoczynku zmarłego i nawoływanie do nienawiści na tle różnic narodowościowych. Moja praca polega na stawianiu przed sądem osób, które naruszyły przepisy prawa. Nie kieruję się w tym ideologią, nie kieruję się symboliką.

– Rozumiem, to oficjalne stanowisko. A nieoficjalnie co pan o tym sądzi?

– Nieoficjalnie nic nie sądzę.

– Czy spotyka się pan z przejawami antysemityzmu?

– Nie.

– Czy stereotypy przeszkadzają w prowadzeniu śledztwa?

– Nie.

– Czy wie pan, że w Sandomierzu ludzie nie posyłają dzieci do szkoły?

– Tak.

– Czy sądzi pan, że spowodowane jest to powrotem wiary w legendę o krwi?

– Nie.

– Czy wie pan, co mówi sandomierska ulica?

– Nie.

– A co piszą prawicowe media?

– Nie.

– Nie rozumiem, skąd u pana totalne odrzucenie takiej rozmowy, skąd ta panika. Musi pan się przecież zastanawiać, jakie jest źródło tych wydarzeń, ich geneza. Nie wiem, czy czytał pan książki Grossa?

– Nie – skłamał Szacki.

– Szkoda. On opisuje falę powojennego antysemityzmu, gniew sąsiadów na widok ocalałych z Zagłady, nienawiść. Ja tak myślę, że to pokolenie powojennych antysemitów wychowało następne pokolenie, a ono wychowało następne. Wierzące w żydokomunę, w światowy spisek, w międzynarodową finansjerę. A jednocześnie pozbawione przeciwwagi. Przeciwwagi w formie zwykłego żydowskiego sąsiada, z którym wspólnie chodziliby na ryby, znaliby go i dzięki temu mogliby, słysząc te straszne stereotypy, wzruszyć ramionami i powiedzieć: „E, pieprzenie, Szewek taki nie jest". I gdzieś z tego pokolenia wyrósł pana sprawca, nosiciel najstraszniejszych polskich stereotypów, pozbawiony wiedzy, nierozliczony, pałający nienawiścią do wszystkiego, co obce. I ta jego nienawiść znalazła tutaj, na antysemickiej ziemi, swoją straszną realizację.

Zegar koło godła wskazywał, że Szackiego czekały jeszcze dwie minuty tych męczarni. Zamierzał wstać dokładnie w tej sekundzie, kiedy minie kwadrans rozmowy, która go męczyła, nużyła i wkurwiała. Martwił się, że tak dużo potrzebnej mu dziś energii marnuje teraz na to, aby nie wybuchnąć, nie pokłócić się z debilem, któremu zależało tylko na jednym: udowodnić tezę o żydożerczych Polakach. Był zaskoczony, że jak na razie najwięcej empatii, woli zrozumienia i zdrowego rozsądku w tej sprawie zobaczył u młodego, urodzonego w Izraelu rabina. Maciejewski miał rację: same skrajności, tutaj nigdy nic normalnie.

– A co, jeśli jest odwrotnie? – zapytał dziennikarza.

– Czyli?

– Jeśli się okaże, że sprawca to szalony ortodoksyjny Żyd, który razem ze swoją wychowaną w duchu antypolonizmu szajką przyjechał z Jerozolimy, aby mordować katolików? Co, jeśli w piwnicy jego domu znajdziemy martwe dzieci, beczki wypełnione krwią i wytwórnię macy?

– To... to niemożliwe... To byłoby straszne. Tutaj, w tym kraju, który powinien zmierzyć się z czarnymi kartami historii. Któremu trzeba przypominać bez przerwy o jego winach. Pan nie może rozważać takiego scenariusza poważnie.

– Moja praca polega na tym, żeby każdy scenariusz rozważać poważnie. Powiem więcej: nie wzbudza to we mnie większych emocji, czy sprawcą okaże się polski biskup, czy przewodniczący sanktuarium Yad Vashem. Bylebyśmy go znaleźli.

– Naprawdę jest to panu obojętne?

Na szczęście czas dobiegał końca.

– Tak.

– Pan nie rozumie chyba swoich obowiązków wykształconego, myślącego człowieka. Musi się pan opowiedzieć po jednej ze stron. Nasza strona musi dawać świadectwo, nauczać, wyjaśniać. Inaczej ta druga, ciemna, zdobędzie rząd dusz.

– Jaka znowu ciemna strona? – żachnął się Szacki. – Czy wy po prostu nie możecie informować o tym, co się dzieje? Czy tutaj każdy musi uprawiać jakąś pokręconą propagandę?

– Nam nie jest wszystko jedno.

– Ale mnie jest. Kwadrans minął.

3

Lubił kobiety, lubił ten stan, kiedy spotykał nową i czuł przebiegający po kręgosłupie dreszcz, zachwyt spowodowany czasami urodą, czasami seksapilem, gestem lub brzmieniem głosu, uśmiechem lub błyskotliwą odzywką. Czasami, bardzo rzadko, podobne uczucie, narastające ni to w kręgosłupie, ni to w dole brzucha, towarzyszyło mu w czasie kontaktu z mężczyznami. Kiedyś się go bał, potem zrozumiał, że to podziw. Mieszanka podziwu, lekkiej zazdrości, trochę ekscytacji. Takie chłopięce „kurczę, chciałbym być kiedyś taki jak ten facet".

Roman Myszyński w takim właśnie stanie opuścił gabinet prokuratora Teodora Szackiego. Kiedy w swojej karierze archiwisty do wynajęcia, tropiciela ukrytych na pożółkłych kartach rodzinnych tajemnic, przyjmował nowego klienta i starał się na nim wywrzeć wrażenie, starał się być kimś takim. Rzeczowy, ale nie małomówny. Profesjonalny, ale nie zimny. Zdystansowany, ale nie chamski. Spokojny, ale czujny. Obcy, ale budzący zaufanie. Teodor Szacki dokładnie taki był. Dumny szeryf, który wiele widział i wiele wie, ale nie ma potrzeby, żeby o tym opowiadać. Jasne, rozwodnione jakby, niepokojące spojrzenie, wąskie usta, klasyczne rysy twarzy. I te mlecznobiałe gęste włosy, które nadawały mu wyjątkowy, trochę demoniczny wygląd. Było w prokuratorze coś z szeryfa, z Gary'ego Coopera i Clinta Eastwooda, ale też coś z archetypu polskiego oficera, zadziorna niezłomność i granitowe przekonanie, że jest właściwym człowiekiem na właściwym miejscu.

Zazdrościł też Szackiemu misji. Widocznego przeświadczenia, że jest po właściwej stronie, że wszystkie jego działania służą dobru i sprawiedliwości. A kim był on? Historykiem gryzipiórkiem, który dla paru złotych ukrywał żydowskich przodków przed wąsatymi Polakami i znajdował im szlacheckie korzenie, żeby mogli sobie powiesić herb nad telewizorem. Tak naprawdę to teraz po raz pierwszy w życiu robił coś, co ma znaczenie.

Dlatego nie czuł żadnego dyskomfortu związanego z tym, że tak szybko wrócił do miejsca swojej największej życiowej traumy – Archiwum Państwowego w Sandomierzu. Może przez chwilę, krótkie ukłucie niepokoju, kiedy w sali modlitewnej starej synagogi wyszukiwał odpowiednie akta. Znowu musiał przejść obok miejsca, z którego zwodzony mostek prowadził do okna wychodzącego na krzaki pod synagogą. Minął je ostrożnie, miał wrażenie, że namalowane przez żydowskiego artystę zodiakalne symbole śledzą jego ruchy. Szybko jednak otrząsnął się z tego wrażenia i zaniósł księgi hipoteczne do czytelni. Położył obok nich materiały, które dostał od Szackiego. Krótką listę osób, które miał sprawdzić, i dotyczące ich wydruki z bazy danych PESEL na dobry początek. Pokryte pieczątkami upoważnienia, które gwarantowały mu dostęp do wszystkich danych, jakie jeszcze nie wylądowały w archiwach państwowych. I jedną kartkę, na której napisane było, czego miał szukać: zabójstwo, śmierć ciężarnej, krzywoprzysięstwo.

Wyjął swój amerykański notes, gruby notatnik z żółtymi kartkami, i zaczął zapisywać listę instytucji do odwiedzenia. Zacznie od Urzędu Stanu Cywilnego i akt wyznaniowych, od naszkicowania krótkiego drzewa genealogicznego każdej z osób. Nie trzeba sięgać dalej jak dwa pokolenia wstecz, to nie powinno być trudne. Potem akta sądowe i powojenne gazety, też łatwizna. Gorzej może być z dokumentami bezpieki – ipeenowcy cierpieli na zaawansowaną manię prześladowczą i paranoję. Ale może nie będzie w ogóle takiej potrzeby.

Na razie jednak na pierwszy ogień pójdą akta własnościowe. Jeśli prokurator ma rację, to kluczem do całej sprawy jest opuszczony dworek przy Zamkowej, jego obecni i poprzedni właściciele.

4

Telefon od Olega Kuzniecowa był niczym głos z zaświatów, uświadomił Szackiemu, jak delikatna i łatwa do naruszenia jest jego równowaga emocjonalna.

Gdy tylko usłyszał lekko śpiewną wymowę warszawskiego policjanta, swojego wieloletniego przyjaciela i towarzysza, momentalnie się rozkleił. Wpadł w tęsknotę za poprzednim życiem. Kuzniecow oznaczał wizytę na miejscu zbrodni w chłodny poranek, późniejszą kawę na placu Trzech Krzyży, spotkania na czynnościach, w czasie których policjant udawał, że ma go za upierdliwego dupka, a on – że uważa podkomisarza za patentowanego lenia. Wspólne sukcesy i wspólne klęski, wspólna walka na salach sądowych, w czasie których Oleg bywał często najważniejszym świadkiem. Wspólne imprezy w jego mieszkaniu na Pradze. Helcia spała w swoim pokoju, oni pili we czwórkę. Kuzniecow opowiadał dowcipy albo śpiewał Wysockiego, Natalia opieprzała męża za przynudzanie, Szacki z ciepłą złośliwością pointował rozmowę. Weronika wtulała się w niego, alkohol zawsze tak na nią działał, że chciało jej się spać, ale i tak po wygonieniu gości znajdowali czas na przyjacielski, łagodny, satysfakcjonujący seks. Zasypiała zawsze wcześniej, odwrócona do niego plecami. Gest, którym obejmował ją pod piersiami, tak żeby czuć ich obecność, przylegał brzuchem do pleców i wtulał twarz we włosy na karku, był ostatnim jego świadomym gestem przed zaśnięciem prawie codziennie, przez prawie piętnaście lat.

– Ale w ogóle chcesz, żebym ci o tym opowiadał? – w głosie Kuzniecowa usłyszał wahanie. To było przykre, dawniej Oleg nie wpadłby na pomysł, żeby się cenzurować w czasie rozmowy z przyjacielem.

– Nie, no co ty. Przecież chcę, żeby jej było jak najlepiej, jak jej jest dobrze, to Helci też jest dobrze. Poza tym, wiesz, ciekaw jestem.

– Okej – powiedział Kuzniecow po pauzie na tyle długiej, że była zauważalna. – Wpadliśmy do nich, nawet nie musiałem się wpraszać, Wiera sama zadzwoniła, że nowe śmiecie, że Helcia chce nas zobaczyć, no i musimy poznać Tomka.

– No.

– No i nie wiem, jak u ciebie, czy już mieszkasz w świętokrzyskim pałacu z ogrodem i widokiem na Wisłę, ale twoją byłą spotkał pewien awans cywilizacyjny. Nie jest to może willa w Konstancinie, ale całkiem przyjemne pół bliźniaka w Wawrze, trochę w głąb od Patriotów. Kawałek ogródka z hamakiem dla Helci, w środku przyjemnie, tak wiesz, nie-ikeowsko, raczej skórzany wypoczynek i kredens, znać, że gość nie z awansu, tylko ze starej rodziny.

– A jak on w ogóle?

– W porządku raczej. Starszy od ciebie, gabarytowo więk-szy, mniej siwy. Chyba przystojny, Natalia twierdzi, że po-dobny do tego gościa z *Gladiatora*, tylko z późniejszych fil-mów. Trochę nudzikoń, jeśli mam być szczery, męczą mnie te radcowskie opowieści, ale może po prostu musimy się jeszcze dograć.

Musimy się dograć. Szkoda, że nie znalazłeś czasu przez pół roku, żeby mnie odwiedzić, przyjacielu.

– Ale Wiera wydaje się, no, zadowolona.

Ocenzurowano. Chciał powiedzieć: szczęśliwa.

– Hela tak samo, więc chyba w sumie dobrze się stało, co nie? Byłem na was wkurzony wcześniej, bo tak szczerze, to nie znałem lepszej pary, ale coś musiało być nie tak, skoro teraz tak fajnie układacie sobie życie. He, Natalii to chyba dało do myślenia, bo zaczęła nosić koronki i piec ciasta. Taa, to jednak stara prawda, krótko trzeba trzymać babę. À pro-pos baby, to jak tam?

– Kawalerskie życie, nie ma nudy, ostatnio mnie tutejsza sędzia zaskoczyła.

– Sędzia? Czekaj, moment. Pięć lat studiów, dwa lata apli-kacji, trzy lata asesury... Chcesz powiedzieć, że zmieniłeś życie, żeby dymać laski po trzydziestce? Czy to jakiś żart? Ale rozumiem, że masz tam pewną różnorodność?

– Raczej. – Szacki poczuł, że męczy go ta rozmowa.

– Boże, najwspanialsze uczucie świata, zdjąć bluzkę z no-wego ciała. Ale ci zazdroszczę.

Nie ma czego, pomyślał Szacki, który poznał już, co ozna-cza fizjologiczny seks, i – jak każdy mężczyzna – zachował prawdę o nim dla siebie. Prawdę o tym, że ciało sprowadzone do ciała składa się z samych irytujących niedoskonałości. Kwaśnego zapachu, nieforemnych piersi w brzydkim staniku, pryszczy na dekolcie, rozstępów wokół pępka, spoconej krawędzi majtek, włażących między zęby włosów łonowych, odcisku z boku małego palca u nogi i krzywego paznokcia.

– Ba! – powiedział, żeby powiedzieć cokolwiek.

– Taaa – rozmarzył się Kuzniecow. – Ale ja z czymś innym dzwoniłem, czekaj. Tylko jeszcze powiedz, jak z Helcią, Wiera mówiła, że tam różnie jest.

– No różnie. Przyjeżdża do mnie w ten weekend, ale faktycznie, jakoś tak, rozumiem, że jest na mnie wkurwiona za to wszystko, nie wiem, chyba zacznę częściej jeździć do Warszawy – Szacki nie mógł słuchać sam siebie. Gubił się, tracił wątek, pieprzył jakieś farmazony bez sensu.

– O, o, właśnie, częściej do stolicy to świetny pomysł. Trzeba będzie się napić, jak za starych czasów. Albo może ja do ciebie wpadnę, co ty na to? Tylko to nieprędko, wiesz, jak jest.

– Jasne, wiem. Słuchaj, jeśli...

– To ty słuchaj, to pewnie bzdura, ale może ci się przyda.

– No.

– Powiedział mi Sasza, syn mój umiłowany, że gadał ze swoim jednym kumplem. Kumpel był w poniedziałek na wycieczce szkolnej w Sandomierzu, i aha, kumpel jest podobno bardzo uzdolniony muzycznie, ma świetny słuch, komponuje, gra na instrumentach itede. To ważne. Niczego nie nadużywa, to też ważne.

Szacki słuchał, poczuł lekkie napięcie w mięśniach. Czy Bóg naprawdę ma takie poczucie humoru, żeby przełom przyszedł od starego towarzysza śledczych przygód?

– Kumpel zwiedzał podobno jakieś lochy pod starówką, macie tam coś takiego?

– Tak, wielka atrakcja.

– I twierdzi, że w tych lochach, w komnacie z archeologicznymi skorupami słyszał dziwne dźwięki, dobiegające zza ściany. Ledwo słyszalne, dalekie, ale wyraźne.

– Jakie dźwięki?

– Wycie. Wycie i ujadanie.

5

Wycie i ujadanie jest naprawdę nieznośne. Mimo zatyczek w uszach powietrze wibruje od nieprzyjemnych dźwięków, czuje je przez skórę, czuje je, obserwując wirujące w świetle reflektora kropelki śliny, czuje je w gorzkim, zwierzęcym zapachu. To jeden z tych momentów, kiedy ma już wszystkiego dość, chce to skończyć i mieć z głowy, móc zacząć wszystko od nowa. Czuje irytację, czuje też strach i wie, że każde z tych uczuć to bardzo zły doradca. Musi zadzwonić. Sięga bez sensu po komórkę i bezgłośnie klnie, przecież nie ma mowy, żeby w tym miejscu był zasięg. Wie, że musi wyjść, wie też, że bardzo nie chce tutaj wracać. Może nie musi? Zna drogę, wystarczy uruchomić mechanizm i wyjść. Jeśli wszystko zadziała tak, jak powinno, nie zostanie żaden ślad. Później ich tutaj skieruje, żeby znaleźli wszystko, kiedy będzie już w bezpiecznym miejscu.

6

Szacki biegał po korytarzu prowincjonalnej prokuratury półżywy z wściekłości. Normalnie w tej cholernej dziurze wszyscy się o siebie obijali na trzech ulicach na krzyż, a kiedy ktoś był potrzebny, to znikali, jakby to był Nowy Jork, kurwa jego mać. Wilczur miał bez przerwy zajęty numer, komórka najbardziej mu potrzebnej Sobieraj była wyłączona, Miszczyk gdzieś zniknęła, udało mu się zdobyć numer do męża Sobieraj, ale i u niego zgłaszała się sekretarka. Pieprzona prowincja, odrobina technologii i się gubią, nie wyszli jeszcze z etapu sygnałów dymnych.

Zauważył, że cały czas biega z tym idiotycznym piłkarskim kubkiem w dłoni, wszedł do kuchni, umył go tylko po to, żeby zająć czymś ręce, odstawił na ociekacz tak gwałtownie, że stłukł archaiczną biurową szklankę. Zakląć głośno. I zaraz znowu, kiedy skaleczył się, zbierając odłamki szkła. Skaleczenie było dość paskudne, krew ściekała mu po kciuku do wnętrza dłoni. Cholera, gdzie on widział apteczkę? W sekretariacie chyba.

Prokurator Teodor Szacki nie dotarł jednak do sekretariatu, ponieważ po drodze zaiskrzyło mu w neuronach. Myśl z apteczki przeskoczyła na opatrunek, z opatrunku na pierwszą pomoc, z pierwszej pomocy na pogotowie, z pogotowia na szpital i już wiedział, gdzie znajdzie Basię Sobieraj – w szpitalu u chorego ojca.

Wybiegł z budynku prokuratury ze skaleczoną dłonią w ustach, ale zamiast wsiąść do samochodu, zawrócił na górę. Nie dlatego, że skaleczenie wydało mu się poważne i że uznał, że jednak lepiej poświęcić dwie minuty na jego opatrzenie. Wrócił, kierowany irracjonalnym i gwałtownym przeczuciem niebezpieczeństwa. Wrócił, żeby zrobić coś, co w jego wieloletniej karierze prokuratora zdarzyło się do tej pory tylko raz.

Wrócił po broń.

Nie miał czasu na zakładanie kabury, wyjął z szafy pancernej małego glocka, sprawdził bezpiecznik i wrzucił do kieszeni marynarki.

W szpitalu szybko zlokalizował odpowiednią salę, oczywiście wystarczyło powiedzieć, że szuka ojca Basi Sobieraj, żeby pielęgniarka skierowała go w odpowiednią stronę. Stanął w drzwiach i zawahał się, intymność zastanej sceny była dla niego krępująca.

W czteroosobowej sali tylko jedno łóżko było zajęte, leżał na nim staruszek. Z jednej strony łóżka miał monitor z latającymi kolorowymi kreskami i stojak z dwiema kroplówkami, z drugiej, lekko oddalony, wieszak na ubrania. Wisiała na nim toga. Prokuratorska toga, pięknie wyprasowana, ze starannie ułożonym kołnierzem. Musiała mieć swoje lata, może nawet kilkadziesiąt lat. Czerwona lamówka była już nieco wyblakła, czerń gabardyny straciła głębię.

Basia Sobieraj i jej ojciec odwróceni byli do niego plecami. On leżał na boku, pokazując światu plecy, pośladki i uda z widocznymi sinoróżowymi plamami odleżyn. Ona przecierała mu skórę gąbką moczoną w misce z jakimś roztworem, stojącej na szpitalnym taborecie.

– Nie płacz, tato, to tylko ciało – szeptała, jej szept był zmęczony i zrezygnowany.

Ojciec mruknął w odpowiedzi coś, czego Szacki nie dosłyszał.

Zakasłał cicho. Basia Sobieraj odwróciła się i po raz kolejny tego dnia lekko zarumieniła. Spodziewał się, że zostanie ofuknięty, ale uśmiechnęła się ciepło. Zaprosiła go gestem do środka, szybko odwróciła ojca i nakryła dokładnie pościelą. Przeprosiła za wyłączoną komórkę, ale po prostu musiała być przez chwilę sama z ojcem, nie chciała, żeby ktoś jej przeszkadzał. Szacki opowiedział o wyciu i ujadaniu, na szczęście nie musiał tłumaczyć, jakie to ma znaczenie i czego potrzebują. Wyjęła telefon z wiszącej na oparciu krzesła torebki i wybiegła, zostawiając Szackiego ze swoim ojcem.

Staruszek gasł. Nie trzeba było kończyć medycyny, żeby to stwierdzić. Żółtawa skóra nieprzyjemnie opinała czaszkę, zwisała na szyi i na ramionach chorego, wyblakłymi, jakby pokrytymi galaretką oczami, z wysiłkiem wodził za Szackim. Jedynie bujne siwe wąsy kpiły z praw natury, zdrowo błyszcząc i przyozdabiając twarz chorego. Szacki pomyślał, że Sobieraj musiała być późnym dzieckiem, sama była pod czterdziestkę, staruszek na pewno miał koło osiemdziesiątki.

– Pan Teodor – nie tyle zapytał, co stwierdził staruszek.

Szacki drgnął zdziwiony, ale podszedł do łóżka i delikatnie uścisnął dłoń chorego.

– Teodor Szacki, miło mi – powiedział zbyt głośno, wstydząc się, że jego głos brzmi tak mocno i dźwięcznie. Wydało mu się to nie na miejscu.

– O, w końcu ktoś, kto nie szepcze jak w kostnicy – uśmiechnął się staruszek. – Andrzej Szott. Basia dużo o panu opowiadała.

– Mam nadzieję, że same dobre rzeczy – odparł Szacki najbardziej wyświechtanym tekstem świata. Jednocześnie poczuł swędzenie w głowie. Andrzej Szott. To nazwisko powinno mu coś mówić. Tylko nie pamiętał co.

– Wręcz przeciwnie. Chociaż ostatnio mniej na pana klnie.

Prokurator uśmiechnął się i wskazał na togę.

– Pańska?

– Tak, moja. Trzymam ją tutaj, bo bywa, że mózg mi się buntuje i, jak by to powiedzieć, odpływa. Toga pomaga przypomnieć sobie różne rzeczy. Na przykład, kim jestem. Przyzna pan, że taka wiedza się przydaje czasami.

Potwierdził uprzejmym skinieniem głowy, dziwiąc się jednocześnie, że stary prokurator wybrał togę zamiast zdjęcia żony albo córki. Dziwiąc się tylko przez chwilę. Gdyby on mógł wybrać tę jedną rzecz, która określa go najlepiej, to czy nie byłaby to właśnie toga z czerwoną lamówką?

– Zastanawia się pan, czy też by powiesił togę. – Szott czytał w jego myślach.

– Tak.

– I?

– Nie wiem. Być może. – Podszedł do togi, przejechał palcem po prążkowanej wełnianej tkaninie.

– Ta – Szott wskazał delikatnym ruchem palca – jest wyjątkowa. Widziała ostatni wykonany w Polsce podwójny kaes.

– Kraków, rok osiemdziesiąty drugi.

– Zgadza się. Wie pan, kogo powiesili?

Klik. I już wiedział, co powinno mu mówić nazwisko staruszka. Odwrócił się i podszedł do łóżka.

– Mój Boże, prokurator Andrzej Szott. To zaszczyt, wielki zaszczyt, proszę wybaczyć, że nie skojarzyłem od razu, naprawdę, bardzo przepraszam.

Staruszek uśmiechnął się łagodnie.

– Cieszę się, że ktoś pamięta.

Swoją drogą, Sobieraj naprawdę jest niezła, pomyślał Szacki, żeby się nie wysypać, że jej staruszek wsadził Sojdę i Adasia. Albo nie jest przyzwyczajona, że ktoś tutaj tego nie wie, albo – też możliwe – pan Szott był doskonałym prokuratorem, a niedoskonałym ojcem, niechętnie wspominanym przez własne dzieci.

Inaczej spojrzał na małą, spreparowaną jakby, pomarszczoną twarz, na słaby uśmiech pod wąsami, na blade oczy pod ciemnymi brwiami. A więc tak wygląda prokurator Andrzej Szott, oskarżyciel w jednej z najsłynniejszych i najbardziej bulwersujących spraw kryminalnych w historii Polski.

– Który to był rok? – zapytał.

– Siedemdziesiąty szósty. Sroga zima.

– Połaniec to powiat sandomierski?

– Staszowski, tuż obok. Ale wtedy to było jedno wojewódz-
two tarnobrzeskie. Ja pracowałem tutaj, proces też był tutaj.
Sąd wojewódzki w Tarnobrzegu z siedzibą w Sandomierzu,
tak to się wtedy nazywało. W Tarnobrzegu mieli wojewódz-
two i siarkę, ale poza tym nic, wszystko było tutaj. Pamiętam,
na Bramie Opatowskiej ktoś nabazgrał: „Brama Opatowska
w Tarnobrzegu z siedzibą w Sandomierzu".

Tak, Połaniec, a ta wieś pod Połańcem to chyba Zrębin,
z każdą kolejną nazwą Szackiemu przypominały się książki, jakie czytał o tej sprawie. Krall, Bratny i ten dziennikarz,
Łuka chyba. Przypominały się fakty, pojawiały obrazy. Była
wigilijna noc, Sojda...

– Jak Sojda miał na imię?

– Jan.

...Jan Sojda, nazywany „królem Zrębina", w każdej wsi
jest taki, zwiózł całą wieś autosanem na pasterkę do kościoła w Połańcu, ale zamiast pójść do kościoła, pili razem
w autobusie, była to swego rodzaju wigilijna zrębińska tradycja. Trzydzieści osób w wozie, nikt wtedy nie wiedział,
że są częścią większego planu. Zgodnie z tym planem pod
pretekstem rodzinnej awantury znajoma wywabiła z kościoła małżeństwo Krystyny i Stanisława Łukaszków. Młodzi byli
krótko po ślubie, ona miała osiemnaście lat, była w ciąży.
Razem z nimi był brat Krystyny, dwunastoletni chłopak.
Cała trójka miała nadzieję zabrać się autobusem ze wszystkimi, ale Sojda ich pogonił, „król" od dawna miał na pieńku
z rodziną Kalitów, z której wywodziła się młoda i jej brat.
Tym bardziej na pieńku, że w czasie jej wesela padło oskarżenie, że siostra Sojdy kradnie kiełbasę. Nie będzie nikogo
podwoził, niech hołota maszeruje w śniegu pięć kilometrów
do Zrębina.

No to hołota pomaszerowała. Autobus pełen biesiadników
ruszył za nimi niedługo potem, dogonili młodych w połowie drogi. Najpierw potrącili dzieciaka, wtedy jeszcze mogło
to wyglądać na wypadek. Ale kiedy Sojda i jego zięć Adaś

wypadli z autobusu i zakatowali kluczem do kół Stanisława Łukaszka – już nie. Ciężarna dziewczyna uciekła w pole, błagała wujka – Sojdowie i Kalitowie byli spokrewnieni – żeby jej darował, że już jej męża zabili. Nie darowali, tym samym kluczem zatłukli. Został jeszcze dwunastolatek, Miecio, połamany, ale żywy. Położyli go na drodze i kilka razy przejechali samochodem, żeby upozorować wypadek. Tak samo postąpili z małżeńskimi zwłokami. Ułożyli wszystkich w rowie i wrócili do kościoła, żeby zapewnić sobie alibi. Wcześniej biesiadnicy zdążyli jeszcze w czasie dziwacznego rytuału złożyć Sojdzie przysięgę, że będą milczeć. Całowali krzyż, przysięgali, upuszczali kroplę krwi na kartkę papieru.

Śledztwo prowadzono pod kątem wypadku drogowego długie miesiące, coś śmierdziało w tej sprawie, ale mało kto myślał, że smród dotyczy zaplanowanej z premedytacją zbrodni. Raczej tego, że nikt się nie chce przyznać do prowadzenia po pijaku. Noc, ślisko, nieszczęśliwy wypadek. Pod takim zarzutem zatrzymano Adasia – spowodowanie wypadku ze skutkiem śmiertelnym. W śledztwie pojawiały się nowe fakty, ale też fakty znikały – zniknął na przykład świadek, który jako jedyny twierdził, że w wigilijną noc dopuszczono się morderstwa z zimną krwią. Utopił się w przepływającej przez Połaniec rzeczce kilkunastocentymetrowej głębokości. Nikt nie podejrzewał jednego – że trzydzieści normalnych osób, będących świadkami potwornej zbrodni na trzech osobach, w tym na ciężarnej kobiecie i dwunastoletnim chłopcu, nie puści pary z gęby w imię wiejskiej solidarności.

Nikt poza prokuratorem Andrzejem Szottem.

– To była w pewien sposób sprawa podobna do pańskiej – skomentował Szott myśl Szackiego. – Z tego, co mi Basia opowiadała.

– W jaki?

– Stara nienawiść. Trzeba mieszkać na prowincji, żeby znać taką nienawiść, w dużym mieście tego nie ma. Ludzie raz się widzą, raz nie, muszą się umówić, żeby się w ogóle zobaczyć. A we wsi na co dzień każdy każdemu w okno zagląda. Czyli jeśli żona się panu puści, to nawet jak się między wami ułoży, codziennie na ulicy i co tydzień w kościele będzie pan widział faceta, któremu obciągała. Żółć wzbiera, nienawiść rośnie, nawet jak pan nic nie zrobi, to pan gada, jakie ci Iksińscy szmondaki. Syn słucha. I jak się w szkole z synem Iksińskiego pobije, to nie tylko za siebie, ale i za pana. Czyli mocniej. I tak cegiełka do cegiełki, aż w końcu ktoś ginie, znika, topi się. Myśli pan, że taki Zrębin to jeden na świecie? Nie sądzę.

– Tak, ale nie wiem, czy to można porównywać. Tam to była pijacka rzeź, tutaj koronkowa robota.

– Pijacka rzeź? Niech mnie pan nie rozśmiesza. Przygotowane dwa autobusy, w tym jeden dla niepoznaki. Przygotowana kuzynka do wyciągnięcia ich z kościoła. Przygotowany krucyfiks, agrafka do upuszczania krwi, przygotowana kiełbasa i pieniądze na łapówki za milczenie. Wymyślone alibi. Sojda to przygotowywał tygodniami, może nawet miesiącami, odkąd to oskarżenie o kradzież kiełbasy na weselu przepełniło czarę. A myślę, że są wsie, gdzie takie wendety przygotowuje się latami, gdzie przechodzą z pokolenia na pokolenie.

Poczuł niepokój. Dlaczego? Dlatego że Szott wspomniał o nienawiści przechodzącej z pokolenia na pokolenie? To była też jego teoria, dlatego kazał Myszyńskiemu grzebać w archiwach. Tak, to chyba to. Ale poczuł niepokój, swędzenie pojawiało się zwykle wtedy, kiedy coś przegapił, nie wtedy, kiedy potwierdzały się jego teorie. Czy sprawa ze Zrębina miała faktycznie coś wspólnego z wystylizowanym zabójstwem Budników? W tamtej bardziej szokująca od samego mordu była zmowa milczenia. Straszna, niezrozumiała zmowa milczenia. Zmowa rozmontowana przez Szotta.

– Skąd pomysł, żeby dopaść ich na sali sądowej? – zapytał starego prokuratora. – Dlaczego zwlekano?

– Ci ludzie byli już przyzwyczajeni do ciągłych przesłuchań przez milicję i prokuraturę, powtarzali swoje wersje jak katarynki, żadne prośby i groźby nie przynosiły rezultatu. Mogliśmy to robić do sądnego dnia, śledztwo i tak się dłużyło, trzeba było napisać akt oskarżenia, wszystkie terminy były przewalone. To było ryzykowne zagranie, iść do sądu z poszlakowym procesem, licząc, że na sali pojawią się twarde dowody. Długo się zastanawialiśmy z kapitanem, czy ma sens postawienie wszystkiego na jedną kartę.

– Ale się udało?

– Tak, sąd był dla nich nowym doświadczeniem, zaczęliśmy razem z sędzią przyciskać ich na sali, rozprawy zostały utajnione, żeby rodziny nie mogły słuchać i żeby nie mogli dogrywać wersji. Zaczęło się źle. Oskarżeni szli w zaparte, świadkowie też, niektórzy zaczęli odwoływać zeznania złożone w trakcie śledztwa.

– I?

– Co działa najlepiej na prosty lud? Obrazek. Wiedzieliśmy, który ze świadków był najgłupszy, najbardziej się gubił, mylił. A przy tym robił potwornie złe wrażenie, budził naturalną niechęć. Przycisnęliśmy go na sali, tak gubił się w zeznaniach, że sędziego trafił szlag i ukarał go aresztem. Jak ludzie zobaczyli, że ziomka wyprowadzają z sali w kajdankach, zmiękli. Bali się Sojdy, ale siedzieć nikt iść za niego nie chciał. Potem następny w kajdankach. I następny. A potem jeden zaczął mówić, drugi.

– Dostali chyba wysokie wyroki, z tego co pamiętam?

– Osiemnaście osób odsiedziało po kilka lat za składanie fałszywych zeznań.

Zabójstwo. Śmierć ciężarnej. Krzywoprzysięstwo.

Szacki poczuł suchość w ustach. Nieprzypadkowo to wracało jak refren – zabójstwo, śmierć ciężarnej, krzywoprzysięstwo. Ale na Boga, jaki związek mogła mieć z obecnymi mordami sprawa sprzed trzydziestu lat? Co je łączy? Ta sama okolica. Ta sama premedytacja. Ta sama rodzina śledczych.

Kościelne motywy – tam pasterka, tu obraz w katedrze. Być może ten sam motyw narastającej przez lata nienawiści. Być może zmowa milczenia? Nie wiedział tego, nie miał na to cienia dowodu, ale intuicja kazała mu ściągnąć Myszyńskiego w tajemnicy przed wszystkimi, prosić go o tropienie osób, które teoretycznie były po jego stronie, z którymi razem pracował.

A może to przypadek, może te zbrodnie są tylko do siebie podobne? Może to znak, że musi pójść śladami Szotta w swoim rozumowaniu? Co miał Szott, czego on nie ma? Co pozwoliło mu odkryć prawdę o połanieckiej zbrodni? Wiedział to, gdzieś tam to wiedział, miał na końcu języka, odpowiedź chowała się przed nim w gąszczu neuronów, bawiła w chowanego – ale była tam.

– Jezu, tato, a ty znowu o tych Sojdach, no ile można. – Sobieraj zmaterializowała się w pomieszczeniu, machinalnie poprawiła ojcu poduszkę, podciągnęła go do góry. – Jakbyś rozumiał, co oznaczają te cyferki – wskazała na monitor – tobyś nie gadał tyle.

Spojrzała na Szackiego.

– Idziemy. Znalazłam chłopaka, który wie wszystko o naszych lochach. Doktoryzował się z tego na AGH, szczęśliwie akurat jest u rodziny w Sandomierzu, mamy się z nim spotkać koło seminarium, tam podobno jest jakieś wejście. No, już, już – zaczęła go wyganiać gestem z sali, jak niesfornego dzieciaka, Szacki jednak ominął ją i podszedł do starego Szotta.

– Dziękuję – powiedział i uścisnął rękę prokuratora. Ręka nawet nie drgnęła, wzrok stał się bardziej zamglony i nieobecny, bystry uśmiech zniknął z jego twarzy. Szacki pogłaskał dłoń człowieka, który jako jeden z nielicznych w Polsce widział wykonanie kaesu. Musi tu przyjść jeszcze kiedyś, spytać, jak to jest. Czy on sam wierzy w taką karę? Czy wierzy w zbrodnie niewybaczalne?

Wychodząc, musnął dłonią stary prokuratorski mundur.

– Piękną togę odziedziczysz – powiedział do Sobieraj.

– Ona jej nie dostanie – wyszeptał staruszek tak cicho, że Szacki bardziej się domyślił słów, niż je usłyszał.

– Dlaczego? – zapytał, wracając do łóżka.

Zniecierpliwiona Sobieraj stała w drzwiach i wymownie przewracała oczami.

– Bo ona nie rozumie.

– Czego nie rozumie?

Stary prokurator dał znak ręką, młody nachylił się nad nim nisko, prawie przytknął ucho do warg umierającego.

– Za dobra jest. Nie rozumie, że wszyscy kłamią.

7

Zaparkowali pod Bramą Opatowską, sandomierskie Wyższe Seminarium Duchowne znajdowało się dokładnie naprzeciwko, w pięknym barokowym zespole klasztornym, zajmowanym kiedyś przez benedyktynki. To niestety była cała wiedza Szackiego dotycząca tego miejsca, którego nigdy nie odwiedził, choć kościół Świętego Michała wielokrotnie polecano mu jako turystyczny musik. Może dlatego, że nie lubił baroku, a może dlatego, że położony poza starymi murami i przy ruchliwej ulicy kościół wydawał się mniej zapraszający od innych.

Pod bramą klasztoru zobaczył Wilczura, obok stał przystojny blondyn w typie młodego Paula Newmana, przez ramię miał przerzucony plecak. Szacki drgnął, blondyn kogoś mu przypominał. Nie tylko aktora, było jeszcze w jego twarzy coś znajomego, cień bliskiej osoby.

– Prokurator Teodor Szacki – przedstawił go Wilczur, jak tylko przebiegli przez jezdnię.

Blondyn uśmiechnął się szeroko i wyrżnął Szackiego pięścią prosto w przeponę. Uderzenie było jak taran, prokurator skulił się i padł na ziemię niczym worek kartofli. Klęcząc, z nosem przy trotuarze, gwałtownie próbował złapać oddech, ale powietrze zatrzymywało się na zębach i nie chciało się przecisnąć ani milimetr dalej. Przed oczami zaczęły mu latać czarne i czerwone plamki, bał się, że straci przytomność, i jednocześnie marzył o tym, przestałby wtedy czuć rozlewający się po całym ciele mdlący ból.

Blondyn ukucnął obok niego.

– Pamiętaj, koleś – powiedział ledwie słyszalnym szeptem prosto do ucha prokuratora – że mam jeszcze drugą rękę, i mój starszy i większy brat ma jeszcze dwie ręce, i że zwyczajnie bardzo nie lubimy, jak nasza siostrzyczka płacze. Rozumiesz?

Szacki zdołał wciągnąć minimalną ilość powietrza, tyle, żeby nie stracić przytomności. Spojrzał na blondyna, oderwał jedną rękę od chodnika i tuż przed jego nosem wyprostował środkowy palec. Blondyn zaśmiał się, chwycił go za dłoń i postawił na nogi.

– Marek Dybus, bardzo przyjemnie poznać pana – powiedział z wylewną serdecznością. – Przepraszam za ten wypadek, potknąłem się nieszczęśliwie.

Prokurator skinął głową. Wilczur i Sobieraj stali obok siebie z kamiennymi minami, co zapewne oznaczało, że z trudem hamują śmiech. Bez słowa poszli za Dybusem, prowadzącym ich do stojącego nieco na uboczu budynku, tuż obok muru, oddzielającego teren seminarium od spadającej w dół, do targowiska i Wisły, ulicy Zawichojskiej. Trzykondygnacyjna kamienica była ozdobiona szczytami stylizowanymi na barokowe, ale poza tym wyglądała na współczesną konstrukcję. Spytał o to Dybusa.

– Tak, postawili to w międzywojniu na Niższe Seminarium Duchowne, pod koniec lat dwudziestych chyba, nazywa się Nazaret. Jak na razie jednak dłużej tu rządzili świeccy niż duchowni. W czasie wojny była to gestapowska katownia, po wojnie ubecja, potem milicja i prokuratura. Sojdę tutaj przesłuchiwali, kojarzy pan sprawę?

– Tak.

– Dopiero w latach dziewięćdziesiątych oddali budynek diecezji, teraz jest tutaj akademik, czy jak to się u nich nazywa, dla kleryków i mieszkania dla wykładowców.

– Dlaczego tam idziemy? – spytał Szacki, wchodząc za przewodnikiem do wnętrza budynku i potem schodami na dół do wąskiej piwnicy.

– Bo w tym pełnym kleryków świętym budynku znajdują się wrota do piekieł. Jak go budowali, to przez przypadek natknęli się na średniowieczne tunele, na szczęście, zamiast po prostu zabetonować, mądry międzywojenny Polak zamontował drzwi. Proszę. – Wyjął z plecaka i dał każdemu z nich po czołówce.

Latarki były małe, ale dawały zaskakująco jasne, białe światło. Dybus wyglądał w niej jak wytrawny grotołaz, Wilczur jak upiór, a Sobieraj jak przedszkolna dekoracja świąteczna. Po minach, z jakimi na niego patrzyli, mógł przypuszczać, że on także, niestety, jak wytrawny grotołaz nie wyglądał.

– Zapnijcie się – powiedział chłopak, otwierając jednocześnie zamek w drzwiach, które wyglądem niczym nie różniły się od pozostałych. – Na dole jest dość chłodno, nigdy więcej niż kilkanaście stopni.

Gęsiego weszli do środka, podziemny korytarz zbudowany był z czerwonych cegieł i nie wyglądał na stary, na ziemi stały jakieś zakurzone słoiki. Przeszli kilka metrów, skręcili raz, potem drugi, potem zeszli kawałek po drewnianych schodkach, też niewyglądających na takie, co to pamiętają tatarskie czasy, tam Dybus otworzył kolejne drzwi i weszli z nich do małej sklepionej sali o wysokości mieszkania w bloku i powierzchni dziesięciu, może dwunastu metrów.

– Dobra, teraz dwa słowa wyjaśnienia – zagaił przewodnik, przekręcając pasek z czołówką na bok, żeby nie razić ich w oczy. – Jesteśmy siedem metrów pod ziemią, prawie dokładnie pod Żeromskiego, w tę stronę jest Brama Opatowska i Stare Miasto, w tamtą Wisła. Ciocia Basia mówiła, że ktoś słyszał dziwne dźwięki z trasy turystycznej, tyle tylko, że trasa jest absolutnie odcięta od pozostałych podziemi. To znaczy, że można tam coś usłyszeć, ale bez kilofa nie da się stamtąd nigdzie dalej wejść, wszystko jest albo zasypane, albo zamurowane, albo zalane.

– Zalane?

– Nie wodą. Nie będę się wdawał w szczegóły, opowiem w skrócie, żeby pan wiedział, o co chodzi. Sandomierz jest na lessie, less jest fajny, bo zarazem twardy i plastyczny, z jednej strony można na nim budować praktycznie bez fundamentów, z drugiej da się w nim kopać tunele paznokciami, nie martwiąc się o stemple i podpory. Dlatego przodkowie, odkąd tutaj ta wiocha stoi, kopali pod nią piwnice. Płyciej na ziemniaki, głębiej na kosztowności, najgłębiej na schrony. Zryli całe wzgórze jak krety, korytarzy było kilkanaście poziomów, dziesiątki kilometrów. I tak sobie to stało. Czasami coś się zapadło, ale jak na miasto wybudowane na serze szwajcarskim – i tak nieźle. Ale jest też less niefajny. Niefajny, bo pod wpływem wilgoci zachowuje się jak bryła piasku wrzucona do miski, rozpada się momentalnie, pstryk, ni ma. I w latach sześćdziesiątych nagle zaczął się Sando zwyczajnie walić, jak zbudowany na ruchomych piaskach. Dlaczego? Przez cywilizację. Miastu założono kanalizację, z kanalizacji ciekło, cieknięcie rozpuszczało wzgórze staromiejskie. Katastrofa. Jasne?

– Jasne. Bardzo też ciekawe, ale czas...

– Moment. Sprowadzili speców z AGH, sprowadzili górników z Bytomia. Górnicy rozebrali Stare Miasto, podrążyli szyby, zrobili plan lochów i te pod budynkami i jezdniami zalali mieszaniną lessu i szkła wodnego, która po zastygnięciu tworzy coś w rodzaju pumeksu, taką lekką, sztywną konstrukcję. A potem odbudowali starówkę.

– Tyle że wysiedloną inteligencję zostawili w blokach, a sprowadzili czerwonych – zaskrzypiał Wilczur. – Dlatego to teraz jak jakiś slums wygląda, menele i brudne okna.

– Co niespecjalnie należy do naszych rozważań, ale oczywiście dziękujemy za tę uwagę – skomentował Dybus z wdziękiem. Szackiemu podobał się ten chłopak, miał fajną, żywą inteligencję. I pomyśleć, że on mógł się wżenić w taką sympatyczną rodzinę. Przypomniało mu się miodowe ciało Klary i poczuł ukłucie żalu. Może jeszcze to jest jakoś do odbudowania?

– Część pozostałych piwnic zamienili na trasę turystyczną, resztę odcięto od miasta, ale ostała się i tak naprawdę nikt się nią nie zajmował, wszyscy byli przekonani, że to parę wilgotnych lochów. Dopiero my – zabrzmiało w tym trochę dumy – zaczęliśmy badać dokładniej. I okazało się, że nawet po zalaniu części tuneli pod Starym Miastem został tutaj labirynt. Bez żadnej przesady labirynt, rok siedzieliśmy w tych lochach prawie codziennie i zewidencjonowaliśmy nie więcej jak dwadzieścia procent korytarzy. Idziemy, za mną gęsiego.

Ruszyli, przeszli jeszcze kawałek sklepionym korytarzem, za nim był już nieprzyjemny, niski chodnik, jakby wydrążony w wysuszonym brązowawym błocie. Szacki dotknął ściany, w dotyku przypominała piaskowiec. Wystarczyło poskrobać paznokciem, żeby posypały się drobinki żółtego piasku.

Doszli do rozwidlenia.

– I teraz uwaga, muszę podać kilka zasad porządkowych. Po pierwsze, rządzę ja, nie obchodzą mnie zwyczajnie wasze tytuły i wasze szarże. – Rzut okiem na Wilczura, który wydawał się dziwnie spięty, być może cierpiał na klaustrofobię. – Po drugie, gdybyśmy się jakimś cudem rozdzielili, to na każdym skrzyżowaniu lub rostaju jest na poziomie metra wyryta strzałka wskazująca drogę do wyjścia przy seminarium. Ale ponieważ strzałki są tylko na zbadanym przez nas terytorium, nie będziemy się rozdzielać. Po trzecie, uciekajcie z miejsc wilgotnych z widoczną cieknącą lub kapiącą wodą. To oznacza, że less jest tam niestabilny i może was pogrzebać. Jasne? Jasne, to idziemy.

Prokurator Teodor Szacki nie miał klaustrofobii, ale czuł się nieswojo. Korytarz był niski i wąski, jego piaskowa konstrukcja nie dawała poczucia bezpieczeństwa, miał wrażenie, że w zimnym, lekko zatęchłym powietrzu nie ma dość tlenu, żeby zaspokoić jego płuca. Oddychał głęboko, a ledwo nabierał powietrza. Choć możliwe, że to zdefasonowana przez Dybusa przepona miała problemy ze znalezieniem swojego miejsca. Wciąż kłuło go pod żebrami przy każdym kroku.

Szli w milczeniu przez kilka minut. Parę razy skręcili, wszystkie korytarze były do siebie bliźniaczo podobne. Niepokojąco podobne, skóra cierpła na samą myśl o możliwości zostania tutaj samemu i zgubienia drogi.

– Okej, jesteśmy – młody przewodnik zatrzymał się gwałtownie przy ścianie z desek. Jednej brakowało, widać było za nią szary beton. – Za tym murem jest trasa turystyczna, właśnie sala z różnymi skorupami. Jeśli faktycznie coś się tutaj dzieje i jeśli ktoś w środku słyszał hałasy, my powinniśmy usłyszeć je tym bardziej.

Umilkli. Trasą turystyczną musiała przechodzić wycieczka, słyszeli kroki, stłumione słowa, śmiech. Wysoki głos przewodniczki, która opowiadała o czyimś niespotykanym bohaterstwie. Wszystkie dźwięki oddaliły się po chwili i zostali w nieprzyjemnej, gęstej ciszy. Szacki wzdrygnął się, czując, że coś chodzi mu po ręce – była to dłoń Sobieraj. Spojrzał na nią zdziwiony, ale Basia uśmiechnęła się tylko przepraszająco. Ręki nie puściła, było to nawet przyjemne. Ale tylko przez krótką chwilę, potem wszystkie inne uczucia wyparło gwałtowne uderzenie lęku. Z plątaniny czarnych korytarzy doleciało ich dalekie, ale wyraźne zwierzęce wycie.

– O kurwa – powiedział Dybus.

Sobieraj głośno westchnęła, kurczowo zacisnęła dłoń.

– Potrafisz powiedzieć, gdzie to? – spytał Szacki, zadowolony, że w jego głosie nie słychać drżenia.

– Echo oszukuje, ale stawiałbym na zachód, w stronę synagogi i kościoła Świętego Józefa. Do Podwala mam wszystko opisane, potem zobaczymy.

Szli teraz znacznie wolniej i ostrożniej. Najpierw Dybus, potem Szacki i ciągle uczepiona jego ręki Sobieraj. Milczący Wilczur zamykał stawkę. Szackiemu przeszło przez głowę, żeby wyprowadzić stąd starego policjanta. Jeśli faktycznie ma klaustrofobię i dostanie w tych lochach ataku serca, to trochę skomplikuje ich wycieczkę.

– Gdzie teraz jesteśmy? – zapytał. Przeszli około stu metrów, chodnik schodził łagodnym łukiem w dół, minęli do tej pory jedno skrzyżowanie i jedno boczne odgałęzienie, zasypane lessowym gruzem.

– Pod murami, z lewej strony mamy Stare Miasto, z prawej Podwale. Słyszycie?

Wycie powtórzyło się, nawet jeśli było głośniejsze, to tylko trochę. Sobieraj spojrzała na zegarek.

– Która?

– Za chwilę trzecia.

Szli pomału dalej, słabe potępieńcze wycie było słyszalne za każdym razem, kiedy się zatrzymali. W pewnej chwili dobiegł ich wyraźny, metaliczny dźwięk, jakby ktoś upuścił klucz francuski na betonową podłogę warsztatu. Dybus zatrzymał się.

– Słyszeliście?

– Idziemy – ponaglił Szacki i pociągnął Sobieraj, jej ręka wyślizgnęła się z jego spoconej dłoni.

– O mój Boże – wycedziła głucho, takim tonem, że wszyscy na nią spojrzeli. Basia Sobieraj podniosła pomału do góry dłoń, w białym świetle latarek było widać, że jest cała czerwona od krwi. Kobieta zgięła się wpół, wyraźnie miała zamiar zwymiotować.

301

– Basiu, hej, spokojnie – Szacki delikatnym ruchem wyprostował koleżankę. – Nic się nie stało, skaleczyłem się w prokuraturze, przepraszam, nie zdążyłem tego opatrzyć. Nie czułem, że krwawię, przepraszam.

Spojrzała na niego wrogo, ale z ulgą. Bez słowa wyjęła z kieszeni cienki jedwabny szalik i prowizorycznie opatrzyła jego dłoń.

– Nie wiem, czy nie powinniśmy wysłać tutaj kogoś lepiej wykwalifikowanego – mruknęła. – Dziwne lochy, dziwne wycie, nie wiemy, czego szukamy, jeszcze ta krew, zły znak.

– Szukamy Szyllera – powiedział Szacki. – Do tej pory jak ktoś w tej sprawie ginął, to potem znajdował się sprawiony jak wieprzek.

– Jagnię raczej – poprawił Wilczur. – Wieprzek trefny.

– Trefny?

– Niekoszerny.

– W każdym razie jest szansa, że tym razem znajdziemy kogoś szybciej.

– Skąd w ogóle wiesz, że to ma związek?

– Wycie, ujadanie, wszystko pasuje.

– Zwariowałeś? – Sobieraj wykonała swój gest zdziwienio-oburzenia, z którym było jej bardzo do twarzy. – Gdzie ci ujadanie pasuje?

– A co masz na obrazie w katedrze? Porwanie dziecka, jego zamordowanie, wytaczanie w beczce krwi i rzucanie resztek psom na pożarcie. Czego jeszcze nie widzieliśmy?

– O Boże – jęknęła Sobieraj, ale nie dlatego, że ta informacja ją przeraziła. Tym razem wycie było wyraźniejsze, słychać też było wściekłe, szczekliwe ujadania. Zniekształcony przez pokręcone korytarze dźwięk wydawał się piekielny, cierpła od niego skóra, sztywniały włosy, mięśnie napinały się, czekając na sygnał do ucieczki.

– Nie przeszliśmy tak daleko – jęknął Dybus. – Może lepiej spieprzajmy.

– Spokój – zakomenderował chłodno Szacki. – Czego się spodziewacie? Psa Baskerville'ów? Piekielnej bestii, ziejącej płomieniami? Pies to pies. Ma pan broń, inspektorze?

Wilczur odchylił połę marynarki, koło jego zapadniętej klatki piersiowej kołysało się w kaburze coś, co wyglądało na klasycznego policyjnego walthera.

– Idziemy. Szybko.

Ruszyli, potępieńcze zwierzęce dźwięki zbliżały się do nich błyskawicznie, Szacki nie mógł pozbyć się wrażenia, że stoi pośrodku drogi złapany w reflektory pędzącego samochodu i zamiast uskoczyć, zaczyna szarżować w jego stronę. To pies, to tylko przestraszony pies i akustyka małego pomieszczenia, nic więcej, tylko pies, powtarzał sobie w myślach. Idący przed nim Dybus zatrzymał się gwałtownie, prokurator siłą rozpędu wpadł na niego i dalej wszystko potoczyło się szybko, niestety zbyt szybko i zbyt chaotycznie.

Brat Klary zatrzymał się, ponieważ za zakrętem korytarza zaczynały się wykute w lessie schody, schodzące ostrą spiralą w dół, gdzie czekała granatowa ciemność i skąd dochodziło wściekłe ujadanie, już nawet nie tyle głośne, co ogłuszające. Być może chciał ostrzec pozostałych, być może chciał ustalić, co dalej, jego intencje stały się nieistotne w momencie, kiedy pchnięty przez Szackiego runął z krótkim okrzykiem w dół. Prokurator zachwiał się i upadł na kolana, jakimś cudem udało mu się utrzymać równowagę i zastygł w przedziwnej pozycji: stopy i kolana zostały mu na poziomie korytarza, dłońmi natomiast zaparł się o ściany – z braku lepszego słowa – klatki schodowej. Ktoś z tyłu, może Sobieraj, a może Wilczur, chwycił go za połę marynarki i już miał odetchnąć z ulgą, kiedy tuż przed jego twarzą pojawiła się morda wściekłego psa o szalonych ślepiach, czarna, kudłata, pokryta kurzem, śliną i zaschniętą krwią. Chciałem psa Baskerville'ów? No to mam, pomyślał Szacki.

Pies, kundel wielkości owczarka, nie rzucił mu się do gardła, zastygł kilka centymetrów od jego twarzy i ogłuszająco ujadał, nie potrafił złapać równowagi na wąskich stopniach, drapał je tylko pazurami, wzbudzając duszącą chmurę lessu. Przestraszony i oszołomiony Szacki oderwał jedną rękę od ściany, żeby zasłonić się przed zębami spłoszonego zwierzęcia, i to był jego drugi największy błąd tego dnia – pierwszy miał jeszcze przed sobą. W momencie kiedy machnął psu przed pyskiem zakrwawioną ręką z przesiąkniętym krwią szalikiem, zwierzę oszalało. I tak jak jeszcze ułamek sekundy wcześniej przytrzymywany Szacki miał szansę na zachowanie równowagi, to gwałtownie ugryziony stracił ją całkowicie i wyjąc z bólu, stoczył się razem z psem na dół schodów, uderzając na koniec w coś miękkiego, co musiało być Markiem Dybusem. Czołówka oczywiście spadła mu z głowy i teraz pod jakimś dziwnym kątem oświetlała jego walkę z potwornym, wściekłym kundlem. Jedną dłoń miał cały czas uwięzioną między jego szczękami, drugą bezskutecznie próbował odciągnąć głowę zwierzęcia. Szarpał za mokre kudły, drąc się i wrzeszcząc, ale pies nie zamierzał odpuścić, wgryzał się tylko coraz mocniej, czuł wyraźnie, jak kolejne tkanki pękają pod naporem szczęk. Działając bardziej instynktem niż rozumem, puścił łeb i sięgnął do kieszeni marynarki po glocka. Wijąc się gwałtownie, próbując wyszarpać ciało spod łap psa, które teraz ryły pazurami po jego brzuchu, zamiast po lessie, jakimś cudem odbezpieczył pistolet, wsadził go w pysk zwierzęcia tuż koło swojej dłoni i strzelił.

Jego ryk bólu zlał się w jedno z ogłuszającym, rozrywającym bębenki hukiem wystrzału; chmura tkanki, którą strzał wyrzucił z czaszki psa, spadła Szackiemu na twarz mokrymi, lepkimi kropelkami. W tej samej chwili u wylotu schodów pojawiło się białe światło czołówki, oświetlając coś, czego Szacki nie widział, ale co ciągle ujadało jak szalone. Pod czołówką pojawił się błysk ognia. Jeden, drugi, trzeci.

Ujadanie zamieniło się w ciche skomlenie umierającego zwierzęcia.

Inspektor Leon Wilczur podszedł do prokuratora i pomógł mu wstać, kawałek dalej z ziemi gramolił się Dybus, na szczycie schodów widać było światło czołówki Sobieraj. Wyglądało na to, że nic się nikomu nie stało. No, prawie.

– Kurwa mać, chyba odstrzeliłem sobie kawałek palca.

– Pokaż – powiedział rzeczowo Wilczur, po raz pierwszy zwracając się do niego per „ty", i brutalnie pociągnął rękę Szackiego, który syknął z bólu. – Masz wodę? – spytał Dybusa. Dybus miał, wyciągnął butelkę z plecaka. Wilczur przemył dłoń prokuratora, wyglądało to paskudnie. Szklankowe skaleczenie na kciuku ciągle krwawiło, na grzbiecie dłoni widać było głębokie ślady po kłach pieprzonego kundla (Szacki nigdy nie lubił psów), a rozerwana tkanka między kciukiem a palcem wskazującym bezbłędnie wskazywała, którędy przeszła kula, zanim spenetrowała mózg zwierzęcia. Stary policjant obejrzał rany ze znawstwem, po czym kazał zszokowanemu jeszcze ciągle Dybusowi zdjąć koszulę, porwał ją na pasy i starannie opatrzył dłoń Szackiego. Prokurator był pod wrażeniem zimnej krwi policjanta.

– Okej, to możemy już wracać? – zapytał ich przewodnik i znawca podziemi, rozbiegane oczy wskazywały, że był na granicy paniki. – Ja w każdym razie nie zapuszczam się dalej w ten mordor nawet na centymetr.

– Nie ma mowy – Szackiemu co prawda chciało się wymiotować, żółć zbierała mu się w ustach kwaśną falą, ale przez lata wypracowywana forma po raz kolejny zwyciężyła. – Muszę zobaczyć miejsce, z którego przybiegły.

– Ale jak – głos Dybusa był histerycznie płaczliwy. – Przecież nie ma już wycia.

– Ale jest ślad z okruszków – powiedział prokurator i wskazał na podłogę, gdzie pazury pędzących psów wyryły symetryczne żłobienia.

Zostawili za sobą dwa truchła i ruszyli dalej, tym razem Szacki na przodzie wycieczki. Był zdesperowany, za wszelką cenę musiał się dowiedzieć, co czekało na końcu korytarza.

8

Muszę?

Weronika wiedziała, że w tym obrażonym, naburmuszonym pytaniu nie kryje się brak tęsknoty za ojcem, ponieważ ta tęsknota była niewyobrażalna, nie do ogarnięcia, przepalająca duszę małej dziewczynki na wylot w każdej sekundzie na nowo. Wiedziała, bo sama była z rozbitej rodziny. Jej rodzice rozstali się, kiedy już była na studiach, a i tak było to najgorsze wspomnienie jej życia. Rozwód z Teodorem był przykry, co chwilę zalewały ją fale wściekłości, miała ochotę dorwać go i wydrapać mu oczy za to, że ją zdradził i oszukał. Ale nic nie mogło się równać z tym, kiedy ojciec zabrał ją do pijalni czekolady na Szpitalnej i poinformował, że on i mama nie będą już razem. Nigdy więcej u Wedla nie była.

To nie był brak tęsknoty, Helcia, gdyby mogła w mgnieniu oka teleportować się na kolana swojego taty, na pewno by to zrobiła. To był bunt, wyparcie, testowanie tego, na ile może sobie pozwolić. Naciąganie łączących ją z rodzicami emocji do granic wytrzymałości i sprawdzanie, czy pękną. I też manifestacja lojalności wobec niej, sposób na powiedzenie: spójrz, akceptuję twoje życie, lubię Tomka, to tata jest zły, tata nas zostawił, ukarzmy go.

I oczywiście miała ochotę wejść w te wygodne buty, przygarnąć córkę, żeby stanęła po jej stronie, żeby razem się odegrały na złym chuju, ramię w ramię. Ale to była szkodliwa łatwizna. Helcia nie ma z tym nic wspólnego, nie powinna mieć, niech buduje swoje życie z mamą i tatą za plecami, nawet jeśli mama i tata nie stoją już obok siebie przytuleni.

– Owszem, musisz. Ale poza tym chcesz i nie rozumiem, czemu się nakręcasz.

– No bo jechać tym autobusem tyle godzin. Tak to mogłabym z Tomkiem iść na kajaki. Już jest ciepło. Obiecał, że pójdziemy, jak będzie ciepło.

Uśmiechnęła się, ale szlag ją trafiał. Atencja córki wobec jej nowego partnera irytowała ją niemożebnie, mimo że powinna się z tego cieszyć. Opowieści znajomych, którzy wprowadzali dzieci w nowy związek, mroziły krew w żyłach, a u niej wyglądało to jak jakaś idylla. A mimo to czuła irytację, kiedy słuchała takich odzywek swojej córki. Nie miała pojęcia dlaczego, musi o tym porozmawiać z terapeutą. A może nie musi, może wie, że tak naprawdę ciągle go kocha, ciągle jest z nim związana, a Tomka ma w dupie i wie, że cały ten związek jest na pokaz, obliczony na to, żeby utrzeć nosa siwemu skurwielowi. I tutaj nagle jej córka w tym pokazowym związku, w którym jej matka jeszcze ani razu nie doświadczyła porządnego orgazmu, rozpływa się z zachwytu nad jakimś obojętnym jej facetem. Szlag by to trafił.

– Powiem tak, córeczko. Pojedziesz i będziesz się dobrze bawiła, i zwiedzisz nowe miejsca, i zaprezentujesz tatusiowi swojego najlepszego focha, takiego jak mnie w poniedziałek, żeby on też wiedział, że jego córeczka dorasta. Rozerwiesz go trochę, biedaczyna siedzi cały czas w biurze i się nudzi, przyda mu się trochę emocji. Hmm?

9

Ból poranionej dłoni był nieznośny, wędrował w górę ramienia falami, jakby głupie psisko cały czas tam wisiało i prokurator Teodor Szacki miał szczerą nadzieję, że to koniec emocji na dziś.

Ślady psich pazurów doprowadziły ich do niewielkiej sali, podobnej do tej koło seminarium, w której zaczęli swoją wyprawę. Znaleźli tam trzy amatorsko zespawane klatki, trochę psiego gówna, mnóstwo krwi i trupa Jerzego Szyllera. Znalezisko zostało skomentowane w różny sposób. Dybus puścił monstrualnego pawia, musiał chyba sięgnąć do głębin układu trawiennego. Ciocia wyłączyła czołówkę, żeby wyłączyć ten widok. Wilczur zapalił papierosa. Szacki, czując wszechogarniające zmęczenie, wywołane odpływającą z krwi adrenaliną, usiadł na jednej z klatek i wyciągnął rękę po papierosa. Wilczur usłużnie oderwał filtr i podał prokuratorowi zapalniczkę. W pierwszej chwili Szacki chciał zaprotestować i poprosić o egzemplarz z filtrem, ale dał spokój i przypalił. Dym uspokoił zbierające się w gardle wymioty, wydmuchany nosem zatkał na chwilę receptory węchowe, dając wytchnienie od prosektoryjnego smrodu. Ze zdumieniem skonstatował, że camel bez filtra smakuje lepiej niż zwykły. Ba, w ogóle smakuje.

– Gdzie jesteśmy? – zapytał, także dlatego, że chciał czymś zająć myśli Dybusa, nie miał ochoty na uspokajanie napadu paniki, którego cień widział w rozbieganych oczach.

Dybus wyjął mapkę pełną niezrozumiałych kolorowych kresek i rozłożył ją obok prokuratora.

– Akurat w tym miejscu nigdy nie byłem, ale jakoś tutaj – pokazał punkt na mapie miasta już poza murami miejskimi, niedaleko zbiegu Zamkowej i Staromiejskiej. Niedaleko opuszczonego dworku. Wedle wiedzy Szackiego w miejscu tym była łąka.

– Nic tam nie ma – powiedział.

– Teraz nie – zgodził się Dybus. – Ale kiedyś była cała dzielnica. Tyle tylko, że domy w większości drewniane, dlatego nic nie zostało. Ta sala to pewnie pozostałość po jakimś cwanym kupcu, który uznał, że rabusie prędzej będą szukać pod kamienicami niż pod domami biedoty na Podwalu.

– Trzeba sprawdzić, czy można w jakiś sposób dojść stąd w kierunku dworku na Zamkowej, katedry i domu Budnika na Katedralnej. Mam wrażenie, że właśnie odkryliśmy sposób, dzięki któremu zwłoki teleportowały się z jednego miejsca na drugie.

– Jesteś pewien? – Sobieraj doszła trochę do siebie, ale ciągle była sinoblada.

– Raczej tak. Od wczoraj nie daje mi spokoju jedna rzecz, mianowicie zwłoki Budnikowej. Miała za paznokciami piasek, taki żółty nadmorski piasek. W czasie sekcji nie zwróciłem na to uwagi, wytłumaczyłem sobie, że może lubiła grzebać się w ziemi albo że to piasek z miejsca zbrodni. Ale dziś rano sprawdziłem i krzaki pod synagogą, i jej ogródek, w obu miejscach jest zwykła czarna ziemia.

– Co innego tutaj – mruknął Wilczur i skrobnął po ścianie, pod długim paznokciem zostało trochę żółtawego lessu.

– Dokładnie. – Szacki poszedł w kąt pomieszczenia, jak najdalej od trupa, żeby skiepować papierosa.

Dopiero wtedy zrobił to, na co do tej chwili nie mógł się zdobyć, czyli spojrzał wprost na zwłoki Szyllera, jednocześnie oświetlając go swoją latarką. Biznesmen-patriota był rozpoznawalny tylko dlatego, że przykuto go do ściany na tyle wysoko, że psy nie mogły pożreć jego twarzy. Cała reszta, od mniej więcej linii klatki piersiowej w dół, była krwawym strzępem, Szacki nawet nie chciał zgadywać, w które miejsca pasują porozrzucane po całym pomieszczeniu kawałki. Biegli, biegli się tym zajmą.

– Możemy już iść? – spytała cicho Sobieraj.

– I tak nic tutaj nie zdziałamy. – Wilczur wstał, skrzypiąc, zerknął na zegarek, ciągle było w nim jakieś podenerwowanie i zniecierpliwienie, zupełnie niepasujące do flegmatycznego zwykle policjanta. – Trzeba przysłać biegłych, reflektory, torebki na dowody. Muszą zbadać to pomieszczenie i całą okolicę, myślę, że jest też tutaj miejsce, gdzie trafili Budnik i Budnikowa, muszą tam być jakieś ślady.

– Może nawet więcej, niż nam się wydaje. – Szacki wolno obrócił głowę, oświetlając pomieszczenie. – Do tej pory działaliśmy na warunkach zabójcy, znajdowaliśmy wszystko wysprzątane i przygotowane dla nas, a to miejsce odkryliśmy zbyt wcześnie.

– Jak to?

– Ten szczęk, który słyszeliśmy, zanim dopadły nas psy, spójrzcie, na klatkach jest jakiś mechanizm czasowy, który je otworzył przed naszym przyjściem. Tyle tylko, że gdyby nie jeden dzieciak obdarzony absolutnym muzycznym słuchem, nie byłoby nas tutaj. Psy by się rozbiegły po podziemiach, może jeszcze trochę by pożyły, może zjadły resztki Szyllera, może jakoś wydostały się z labiryntu, a my byśmy je znaleźli nad Wisłą i mieli kolejną zagadkę. A gdybyśmy nie znaleźli, pewnie podsunięto by nam wskazówkę. W każdym razie na pewno jesteśmy tu za wcześnie i na pewno niezgodnie z planem zabójcy. Musimy to wykorzystać, jak najszybciej ściągnąć techników.

– I powiedzieć im, żeby byli ostrożni – dodała Sobieraj.

– Ha, wiedziałem, że ten zboczeniec nie siedział tutaj o świeczce! – doleciało ich z bocznego korytarza, w którym niepostrzeżenie zniknął Dybus. – Chodźcie, znalazłem akumulator!

Szackiemu neurony rozżarzyły się do czerwoności w tej tysięcznej sekundy, jaka była potrzebna, aby skojarzyć fakty, ale Wilczur i tak był szybszy od niego.

– Zostaw! – wydarł się potwornie policjant, Szacki nigdy nie słyszał takiego krzyku. Wydarł się za późno.

Prokurator Teodor Szacki najpierw zobaczył biały błysk, potem usłyszał grzmot, a potem fala uderzeniowa miotnęła nim o ścianę jak szmacianą lalką. Ostatkiem świadomości odnotował zaskakujące uczucie ulgi, odpływanie w ciemność oznaczało, że przestanie go boleć. Może na chwilę, może na zawsze – ale przestanie.

10

Wyglądało na to, że dowiedział się wszystkiego, czego mógł się dowiedzieć w sandomierskim archiwum. Czas wyruszyć dalej, na szczęście zapowiadało się, że nie będzie musiał opuszczać województwa, żeby zdobyć wszystkie potrzebne prokuratorowi informacje. Kto wie, przy odrobinie szczęścia jutro robota może być skończona. Śmieszne, praca dla wymiaru sprawiedliwości przy trudnej sprawie okazała się prostsza niż tradycyjne tropienie herbowej szlachty.

Mógł zostawić wszystkie akta w czytelni i wyjść, tak to zawsze wyglądało, ale tym razem wziął je pod pachę i wrócił do sali modlitewnej. Dlaczego? Na pewno udzielił mu się nastrój kryminalnego śledztwa, co u laików zawsze powoduje wzrost podejrzliwości, ostrożności i paranoi. Nie chciał zostawiać akt istotnych dla prokuratora tak po prostu na wierzchu, żeby każdy mógł do nich zajrzeć. Każdy – czyli w domyśle sam zabójca, jego wspólnik albo bliska im osoba. Poza tym drażniło go, że główna sala archiwum ciągle budziła w nim pewien lęk, przez co nie potrafił myśleć o niej spokojnie. Czy naprawdę jest aż tak miękki? Jedno dziwne wydarzenie, jeden trup zobaczony przez mgłę, z daleka, i teraz jojczy jak stara baba.

Dlatego Roman Myszyński dziarskim krokiem przeszedł przez próg ciężkich, stalowych drzwi i wszedł do głównego pomieszczenia synagogi. W świetle wpadającego przez okna popołudniowego słońca nie wyglądała na straszną, wyglądała przede wszystkim na zakurzoną. Wymalowane na sklepieniu znaki zodiaku nie sprawiały wrażenia ponurych i groźnych, tylko nieporadnych, zdradzały niewprawną rękę osiemnastowiecznego artysty. Mimo to nie czuł się do końca pewnie, wchodząc na górę rusztu po trzęsących się schodach – bo księgi hipoteczne były oczywiście na samej górze, koło pieprzonych mostków i pieprzonych okien, z których widać trupy.

Odłożył archiwalia w odpowiednie miejsce i stanął obok „swojego" okna, myśląc o tym jak o terapii. O, proszę, stoję i nic mi nie jest. Miejsce jak miejsce, luz.

I dokładnie w tej samej chwili przez ruszt przebiegła dziwna wibracja, cała konstrukcja zatrzeszczała na nitach, spawach i spojeniach, a mostek urwał się z zaczepu, spadł i huknął metalicznie o parapet okna, jakby zapraszając do znalezienia nowego trupa.

Roman Myszyński podskoczył i wrzasnął z przerażenia.

– Panie, co pan zwariował, czy jak? – na dole stał dyrektor archiwum i patrzył na niego z dezaprobatą.

– Co ja? Co ja? Nie moja wina, że macie tutaj jakieś ruchy tektoniczne.

Dezaprobata zniknęła z oczu dyrektora, pojawiła się łagodna pobłażliwość dla wariata.

– Oczywiście, ruchy tektoniczne. Mogę panu jeszcze w czymś pomóc? Bo jak nie, to chciałbym zamknąć – uśmiechnął się złośliwie – nasz lokalny ośrodek badań sejsmicznych.

11

Wiedział, że jest źle. Obejrzał w swoim życiu wystarczająco wiele dokumentów o wojnie, żeby wiedzieć, że jest bardzo źle. Teraz jego organizm pracuje w innym trybie, w żyłach ma więcej hormonów niż krwi, biologia chce mu dać maksymalną szansę na przetrwanie. Ale tak naprawdę ma poodrywane kończyny, bebechy zbierają się w kałuży, nie może otworzyć oczu, jak to zobaczy, na pewno dostanie jakiejś frontowej histerii, będzie się czołgał z oderwaną nogą w ręku albo próbował włożyć jelita na powrót do środka. Trochę szkoda, że tak się to wszystko kończy, ale z drugiej strony – może jednak jest jakieś potem albo jakieś od nowa, kto wie.

– Wstawaj, Teo! Nie możemy tutaj zostać! – Białe światło oślepiło go nawet przez powieki, zasłonił twarz ręką, myśląc, że to oznacza, że ma rękę, dobry znak.

– A moje nogi? – spytał bez sensu.

– Co twoje nogi? Wstawaj na swoje nogi, musimy stąd wynieść Marka, może jeszcze jest szansa, żeby go uratować. Szybko, Teo, błagam! – w głosie Sobieraj pojawiły się płaczliwe, histeryczne tony.

Prokurator Teodor Szacki zakasłał i zdecydował się otworzyć oczy. W powietrzu było tyle lessowego pyłu, że światła czołówek ryły w nim kreskówkowe, wręcz białe tunele. Twarz Basi Sobieraj pokryta była grubą warstwą lessu, w kurzu świeciły przestraszone oczy, wilgotne, oblizywane nerwowo usta i miejsce, gdzie znajdował swoją drogę cieknący z nosa gruby gil. On sam był zakurzony i pokiereszowany, ale cały, mógł ruszać wszystkimi członkami, potwornie tylko bolała go głowa i plecy w miejscu, gdzie wyrżnął o ścianę. Nie bez trudu wstał, zakręciło mu się w głowie.

– Wilczur?

– Opatruje Marka.

– Leć jak najszybciej na zewnątrz, wezwij karetkę. Do psów masz prostą drogę, potem pamiętaj o strzałkach. Trzymaj. – Wcisnął jej w rękę swojego glocka.

– Oszalałeś?

– Po pierwsze, inne psy, po drugie, sprawca. Nie dyskutuj, biegnij! – Popchnął ją w stronę wyjścia i zataczając się, poszedł w stronę tunelu, w którym zniknął Dybus, skąd dobiegała poświata latarek i niepokojące, pełne bólu jęki.

Wilczur nachylał się nad ciałem chłopaka, jedną latarkę miał na czole, drugą zamocował na rumowisku, które powstało po wybuchu, blokując przejście do dalszej części jaskiń.

Słysząc kroki, odwrócił się do Szackiego, był tak samo zakurzony i zapylony jak wszyscy, ale na jego długiej, pobrużdżonej starej twarzy wyglądało to wyjątkowo upiornie; ozdobiona wąsami i bladymi oczami przypominała rytualną maskę. Szackiego uderzyło, że oczy policjanta były pełne autentycznego bólu. Jakby żałował, że w feralny korytarz nie wszedł on, tylko młody chłopak, mający całe życie przed sobą.

– Jeszcze jest w szoku, ale jeśli ma mieć jakiekolwiek szanse, musi być w ciągu kwadransa na stole – powiedział policjant.

Jego szacunki wydawały się optymistyczne. Dybus miał otwarte złamania jednej ręki, polar w widoczny sposób nasiąkł mu krwią, a z dziury w twarzy wyzierała odsłonięta szczęka. Najgorsza jednak była oderwana pod kolanem noga. Wzrok Szackiego przyciągała wystająca z kikuta biała, brzydko poszarpana kość.

– Zrobiłem opaskę uciskową na udzie, opatrzyłem ranę na brzuchu, kręgosłup chyba jest cały, bo reaguje na bodźce, wydaje mi się, że nie ma też żadnej przerwanej tętnicy, to dobrze. A długo to nie potrwa.

Szacki wrócił i rozejrzał się po „komnacie Szyllera", nawet nie zwracając uwagi na zwłoki. Szukał czegoś, z czego można by zaimprowizować nosze, jego wzrok padł na drzwiczki od psich klatek. Wyjął je z zawiasów, ułożył obok siebie na ziemi i tak zakleszczył, że razem stworzyły konstrukcję wielkości mniej więcej ogrodowej furtki. Niewielkiej furtki. Wilczur obserwował jego poczynania.

– Dobrze, że jest krótszy – zachichotał upiornie, na co Szacki zareagował wbrew sobie tym samym chichotem, który nie miał nic wspólnego z czarnym humorem, był objawem przerażenia i narastającej histerii.

Musieli się spieszyć.

Przenieśli jęczącego Dybusa ostrożnie na nosze i podnieśli je z obu stron; ciężar był nieznośny. Chłopak należał do mocnych i postawnych, a klatki zostały pospawane z prętów zbrojeniowych. Mimo to ruszyli w głąb korytarza, Szacki lekko kuśtykając. Po paru krokach zauważył, że ból uda nie jest bezzasadny, ponieważ nogawka spodni od garnituru pomału przesiąkała krwią.

Klnąc, jęcząc i stękając, dotarli do schodów i psich zwłok. To była mniej więcej połowa drogi, a Szacki nie był w stanie zrobić ani kroku więcej. Mięśnie ramion wyły z bólu, dłonie poobcierał sobie o pręty do żywego mięsa. Nawet nie chciał wyobrażać sobie, co czuje starszy o trzydzieści lat Wilczur. A sam Wilczur nie chciał nikogo informować, jak się czuje, oparł się tylko o ścianę i dyszał chrapliwie. Szacki odnalazł w sobie rezerwę woli, najpierw zaciągnął po schodach na górę jęczącego coraz ciszej Dybusa, potem nosze, a na koniec pomógł wejść Wilczurowi.

– Nie dam rady – powiedział cicho stary policjant, kiedy po niego wrócił.

– Dasz, dasz, to jeszcze kawałek.

– Jakbym nie dał, musisz coś wiedzieć...

– Och, pierdol się, człowieku. Po prostu wyjdźmy stąd.

Złapał za nosze z cięższej strony, tam gdzie była głowa znów położonego na nich Dybusa, zaczekał, aż Wilczur podniesie swój koniec. Zataczając się, walcząc z bólem, zawrotami głowy, mdłościami i latającymi przed oczami plamami, zmuszając każdą komórkę do krańcowego naprężenia, chrapliwie łapiąc powietrze, szedł do przodu i ciągnął za sobą nosze, rannego i Wilczura. Skupiał się wyłącznie na myśli o zrobieniu następnego kroku.

– W lewo – jęknął z tyłu Wilczur. – W lewo.

Rzeczywiście, poszedł automatycznie, nie poszukał strzałki. Konieczność cofnięcia się o dwa kroki przygnębiła go, przestraszył się, że teraz to już na pewno nie starczy mu sił, i rozpłakał się. Chlipiąc i pociągając nosem, zmusił się jednak do skręcenia w inną odnogę i znowu mógł się skupić tylko na krokach. Jeden, drugi, trzeci. Był na granicy utraty przytomności, cudem jakimś po tej stronie trzymało go poczucie obowiązku, odpowiedzialność za Dybusa. Kiedy zobaczył światła skaczące po ścianach tunelu, zbliżające się z kierunku, w którym szli, nawet nie pomyślał, co to oznacza, po prostu postawił kolejny krok. Nie mógł zaufać światłom, mógł zaufać tylko nogom. Raz, dwa, trzy.

Dopiero kiedy sanitariusz wywlókł go na trawę przed Nazaretem, dopiero kiedy ułożono go na noszach i zobaczył nad sobą nieskażone żadną chmurką błękitne niebo nad Sandomierzem – prokurator Teodor Szacki stracił przytomność.

Rozdział dziewiąty

czwartek, 23 kwietnia 2009

W Turcji Dzień Dziecka, Święto Orderu Podwiązki w Wielkiej Brytanii, wszędzie – Światowy Dzień Książki. W dwóch samobójczych zamachach w Iraku ginie 76 osób, w Meksyku epidemia grypy zabiera dwudziestą ofiarę. Nepal montuje nadajniki GSM pod Everestem, a szkoccy naukowcy poszukują 40 ochotników do jedzenia czekolady. Lublin: funkcjonariusze, chcąc zapobiec publicznej defekacji, zatrzymują mężczyznę i znajdują przy nim pistolet sygnałowy, a w mieszkaniu – arsenał broni z okresu drugiej wojny światowej. Gliwice: przy stoisku mięsnym w Biedronce umiera klient, kupujący musieli omijać ciało w plastikowym worku. Poznań: Rossmann żąda okazania dowodu osobistego od nastolatka, który chce kupić prezerwatywy. Łódź: LPR donosi do prokuratury, że na basenie organizowane są noce naturystów. I znowu Łódź: okazuje się, że policjanci z jednostki antyterrorystycznej masowo dorabiali u gangsterów. Tylko w Sandomierzu nuda, nawet pogoda się nie zmienia: słonecznie, chłodno. Ciśnienie spada, wszystkim spać się chce.

1

Nawet jeśli ojczyzną moreli są Chiny, to warto wiedzieć, że w Polsce jest to owoc typowo sandomierski, którego sprowadzenie do Polski zawdzięczamy cystersom. To właśnie mnisi w białych habitach, po tym jak zbudowali w XII wieku swoje opactwo w Jędrzejowie i zaczęli krzewić cywilizację na okolicznych ziemiach, założyli pierwszy sad morelowy pod Sandomierzem.

Prokurator Teodor Szacki z nudów przeczytał cały reportaż o morelach i ich patriotycznej lokalnej historii, uznał, że go nic lepszego ze strony „Tygodnika Nadwiślańskiego" już nie spotka, i odłożył gazetę na taboret stojący obok łóżka. Rano jeszcze bawiły go szpitalne procedury, badania, leki, rozmowy z lekarzami, ale teraz nudził się śmiertelnie i miał wrażenie, że marnuje bezcenny czas. Przyjął leki przeciwtężcowe i szczepionkę przeciw wściekliźnie, pozwolił się wysmarować i zabandażować, ale leku przeciwbólowego odmówił. Wczoraj nie miał takich obiekcji, dał się czymś nafaszerować i odpłynął w dziesięciogodzinny sen, dziś bał się jakiegokolwiek otumanienia, musiał myśleć szybko i sprawnie, musiał przeanalizować dotychczas zebrane fakty i wszystkie nowe, jakie będą wynikiem badania podziemi. Wyrzeczenie miało swoją cenę – wracał ból mięśni, przykre szczypanie otartych dłoni, a przede wszystkim rwący, miarowy, powodujący od czasu do czasu jęk i zaciskanie warg ból pogryzionej ręki.

Zadzwonił telefon.

– Przepraszam, ale dlaczego ja się muszę dowiadywać z paska w Polsacie, że jesteś w szpitalu?

Weronika.

– Przepraszam, ale prokuratura jeszcze nie kontroluje mediów. Może niedługo, jak PiS wygra następne wybory.

– Bardzo śmieszne.

– Nic mi nie jest.

– Nie pytam się, czy coś ci jest, bo gówno mnie to interesuje. Pytam się, dlaczego moja córka dzwoni ze szkoły cała rozhisteryzowana, że tata jest w szpitalu, a ja jedyne, co mam jej do powiedzenia, to chwileczkę, zaczekaj, zaraz włączę telewizję, może się czegoś dowiem. Naprawdę nic ci nie jest?

– Siniaki. Ale nafaszerowali mnie czymś wczoraj, spałem. Nie miałem pojęcia, że jest coś w mediach.

Do sali weszła Basia Sobieraj. Zatrzymała się w progu, widząc, że rozmawia, ale skinął ręką, żeby podeszła bliżej.

– Wyobraź sobie, że jest. O tobie, o jakichś podziemnych wybuchach, o strzelaninie.

Zaklął w myślach. Kto, do jasnej cholery, im o tym wszystkim donosił. Tymczasem Weronika rozkręcała się w znajomy, jakże znajomy sposób.

– Podziemne wybuchy? Strzelanina? Czyś ty kompletnie oszalał? Zapomniałeś, że masz dziecko? Rozumiem, kryzys wieku średniego, kup sobie, kurwa, motor, człowieku, czy coś, ale nie zamieniaj biurka na podziemne strzelaniny. Wystarczy mi, że jestem rozwódką, nie mam ochoty na bycie wdową. Jak to brzmi? Jakbym miała sześćdziesiątkę.

– Nie możesz być chyba wdową, skoro jesteś rozwódką.

– Nie będziesz mi mówił, kim mogę być, a kim nie, te mroczne czasy na szczęście się skończyły. Wystarczy, żebyś mnie nie straszył i nie denerwował. Dziecko masz, tak? Pamiętasz? Codrugoweekendowy tatusiu?

– Poniżej pasa.

– Może. Zabroń mi. I co teraz? Czy Helcia ma do ciebie w ogóle przyjeżdżać jutro? Czy jedyne, co masz chwilowo do zaoferowania, to wymiana kaczki i pielęgnacja odleżyn? – głos jej się załamał.

Chciał powiedzieć coś miłego, przytulić przez telefon, wyznać, że też tęskni i mu żal, i przykro jak cholera. Ale nie chciał tego robić przy siedzącej obok Sobieraj.

– Oczywiście, niech przyjeżdża, wychodzę stąd za chwilę, jutro będę na chodzie – wyrzucił z siebie urzędowym tonem, którego chłód zaskoczył nawet jego. Tym bardziej Weronikę po drugiej stronie. Poczuł wyraźnie, że sprawił jej przykrość.

– Tak, oczywiście. To wyślę ci jutro esemesa, jak ją wsadzę do autobusu. Trzymaj się.

I odłożyła słuchawkę. Sobieraj spojrzała pytająco.

– Matka mojej córki – wyjaśnił, przyoblekając twarz w dziwny grymas, przepraszający za to, że Sobieraj musiała być świadkiem, jak jakaś dawno zapomniana baba mu dupę zawraca, no ale wiadomo, dziecko.

– Ślicznie wyglądasz – powiedział, żeby wzmocnić fałszywe wrażenie, jakoby przeszłość od dawna należała do przeszłości. – A oni?

– Staremu nic nie jest, wszystkich nas przeżyje. Zrobili badania i wygonili z przykazaniem, żeby wypił pół litra i się wyspał. Gorzej z Markiem, sam widziałeś.

– Gorzej... czyli? – zapytał ostrożnie, bojąc się najgorszego.

– Żyje, jeśli o to pytasz. Gdyby trafił na stół kilka minut później, pewnie by go nie odratowali. – Sobieraj patrzyła na niego jak na bohatera, usiadła obok na łóżku i zaczęła go delikatnie głaskać po obandażowanej dłoni. – Byłam u niego, ale cały czas trzymają go na oiomie, w śpiączce farmakologicznej. Noga amputowana, niestety, powyżej kolana, choć podobno najgorsze były obrażenia wewnętrzne, jakiś problem z łożyskiem naczyniowym, nie zrozumiałam do końca, o co chodzi. Ale poradzili sobie, poskładali. Młody, silny organizm, będzie dobrze, tak mówią.

Nagle zaczęła płakać.

– To moja wina, ja go tam ściągnęłam. N-n-nie n-n-nie... – jąkała się – nie powinniśmy schodzić w ogóle, trzeba było wysłać techników, biegłych z reflektorami, przyrządami. Teo, my jesteśmy urzędnikami, a nie jakimiś agentami, co to w ogóle była za chora akcja.

– Myśleliśmy, że jest szansa na uratowanie Szyllera.

– To źle myśleliśmy!

– Przykro mi.

Dokładnie w chwili, kiedy to mówił, korytarzem przeszła Klara w objęciach starszego mężczyzny, pewnie ojca. Spojrzała na niego, ale nawet nie zwolniła kroku. Mimo to Szacki przez ten krótki moment skleił się z nią spojrzeniem, szukając w ciemnych oczach wybaczenia za to, co stało się z jej bratem. I nadziei na kolejną szansę? Nie, chyba już nie. Ciekawe, czy w końcu jest w tej ciąży, czy nie, pomyślał, kiedy ich spojrzenia się rozkleiły. Byłoby to raczej niefortunne w obecnej sytuacji.

– Tak, przykro – wyszeptała Sobieraj, bardziej chyba do siebie. – Łatwo powiedzieć. Trudniej pomyśleć zawczasu.

– Zwłaszcza że akurat nie on miał zginąć, prawda?

Prokurator Barbara Sobieraj w milczeniu pokiwała głową, pogrążona we własnych myślach. Chwilę to trwało, Szacki jej nie przeszkadzał, też musiał sobie parę rzeczy poukładać.

– Mówią, że potrzymają cię do poniedziałku. Na wszelki wypadek.

– Wychodzę po wieczornym obchodzie.

– Oszalałeś?

– Potrzebuję swojego gabinetu, akt i dzbanka mocnej kawy. Nie możemy sobie pozwolić teraz na wczasy. Poza tym nic mi nie jest. Ale mam do ciebie prośbę, potrzebuję trzech rzeczy.

– Tak?

– Chcę na bieżąco wiedzieć o wszystkich nowych informacjach, to raz. Mój komputer z internetem, to dwa. Telewizor ze wszystkimi kanałami informacyjnymi, to trzy.

– Nie wiem, czy da się tutaj podłączyć...

– To niech mnie przeniosą do innej sali.

Wstała, dopiero teraz puściła jego rękę. Może była to kwestia przeżytych wspólnie emocji, może doceniał ten świat bardziej teraz, kiedy cudem na nim został, ale wydała mu się bardzo ładna. Jej pomarańczowy golf w połączeniu z marchewkowymi włosami stanowił miły, pełen życia kontrapunkt dla zielono-białej sali, a odsłonięte przez podwiniętą dżinsową spódnicę nogi biły wszystko, czego można oczekiwać od kobiety w jej wieku.

Wiosna przyszła. Basia Sobieraj poprawiła spódnicę i wyszła, nie oglądając się za siebie.

2

Mało brakowało, a granica pomiędzy precyzyjnie obmyślaną wendetą a morderczym wariactwem zostałaby przekroczona. Kto wie, może jeszcze zostanie, jeśli chłopak umrze. Patrzy w okno i bezsilnie zaciska dłonie na parapecie. Jak to się mogło stać? Jak? Teraz trzeba pomyśleć na chłodno, czy to coś zmienia. Chyba nie, wręcz przeciwnie, paradoksalnie może się teraz czuć bezpieczniej.

3

Prokurator Teodor Szacki czuł się fatalnie. Nie dlatego, że bolało go całe ciało. I nawet nie dlatego, że każdy z członków szpitalnego personelu, którzy pomagali mu się przenosić do sali z telewizorem, musiał zażartować, że pewnie prokurator chce się obejrzeć w telewizji. Czuł się fatalnie, ponieważ po raz pierwszy od początku tej sprawy – nie licząc słynnej pierwszej strony „Faktu" – zadał sobie trud sprawdzenia, jak wydarzenia sandomierskie są relacjonowane w mediach, i dowiedział się, że pojawia się tam w nazbyt wielu odsłonach. Na konferencjach prasowych, jasne, ale było też mnóstwo przebitek z jego wchodzenia lub wychodzenia z urzędu, raz go przyłapano, jak szybkim krokiem przemierza rynek koło ratusza, raz, jak wychodzi z Trzydziestki. Utrata, zapewne tylko chwilowa, anonimowości była przykra, ale fatalne samopoczucie Szackiego wiązało się przede wszystkim z utratą dobrego wyobrażenia o sobie samym.

Nie miał się za jakiegoś wielkiego twardziela, ale lubił o sobie myśleć jak o szeryfie, który zamiast sumienia ma kodeks karny, jest jego ucieleśnieniem, strażnikiem i egzekutorem. Wierzył w to i na tej wierze zbudował całą swoją społeczną rolę, która po latach stała się jego uniformem, służbowym mundurem, obejmującym ubiór, mimikę, sposób myślenia, mówienia i kontaktowania się z ludźmi. Kiedy Weronika mówiła „powieś prokuratora w szafie i siadaj do stołu", to nie żartowała.

Cóż, kamera widziała to ciut inaczej. Na konferencjach wyglądał jak prokurator – sztywny, konkretny, nadmiernie poważny, niekokietujący publiczności i niewchodzący w niepotrzebne interakcje. Miszczyk i Sobieraj wyglądały przy nim na asystentki. Tyle tylko, że miał dość nieprzyjemny, wysoki głos, może nie piskliwy, ale nie był to głos Clinta Eastwooda.

Im mniej oficjalna sytuacja, tym było gorzej. W scenie na schodach przed prokuraturą, kiedy wypowiedział niefortunne słowa, odebrane przez niektórych jako deklaracja antysemityzmu, widać było, że puszczają mu nerwy, a razem z nerwami – kontrola roli. Na twarzy pojawił się brzydki grymas agresji, jedno oko mrugało, szybko wypowiadane słowa zlewały się ze sobą i chwilami bełkotał niewyraźnie. Wyglądał jak ci, z których zawsze się wyśmiewał – urzędniczyna w szarym garniturku, agresywny, sfrustrowany, sepleniący, nie potrafiący skonstruować składnej wypowiedzi.

Najbardziej przygnębiło go jednak nagranie z rynku. Nie pojawiał się na nim szlachetnie siwy orzeł Temidy, posuwistym krokiem kawalerzysty przemierzający centrum prastarego grodu. Tylko chudy, blady, przedwcześnie podstarzały facecik, kurczowo przyciskający do zapadłej klatki piersiowej poły marynarki, żeby zatrzymać trochę cennego ciepła. Skrzywiony, z zaciśniętymi ustami, poruszający się drobnym, szybkim krokiem człowieka, który wypił za mocną kawę i teraz biegnie do toalety.

Koszmar.

Przebrnięcie przez informacje na stronach telewizji, w archiwach gazet i na portalach informacyjnych było robotą upiorną, doniesienia były bowiem niekompetentne, chaotyczne, podane w histerycznym tonie i sprowadzone do najtańszej, najpodlejszej sensacji. Gdyby Szacki nie znał sprawy, to tylko na podstawie tekstów prasowych podjąłby decyzję o jak najszybszym opuszczeniu powiatu, albo jeszcze lepiej, województwa, w którym krwiożerczy szaleniec poluje na swoje ofiary, czyniąc z morderstw krwawe misteria, i w którym nikt – nikt, na Boga! – nie jest bezpieczny.

Na szczęście nie musiał się zagłębiać w to morze egzaltowanego gówna, ponieważ interesowała go tylko jedna rzecz, roboczo nazwana informacją alfa. O co chodziło? Otóż znał funkcjonowanie mediów na tyle, żeby wiedzieć, że z grubsza polega ono na zjadaniu swoich własnych rzygowin. Obieg informacji był tak błyskawiczny, że nie było czasu na szukanie źródła ani na weryfikację, sama informacja stawała się źródłem, a fakt, że ktoś ją podał – wystarczającym uzasadnieniem jej powtórzenia, potem trzeba ją tylko było powtarzać w kółko, dodając słowo komentarza własnego lub zaproszonego gościa. Trzymając się wymiotnego porównania, wyglądało to tak, że ktoś dostawał do jedzenia jajecznicę, po czym ją zwracał. Ktoś inny dosmażał kawałek boczku, zjadał, zwracał. Następny ktoś wymiociny solił, pieprzył, zjadał, zwracał. I tak dalej, i tak dalej. Im mniej było na początku jajecznicy, tym więcej potem musiano dodawać garnirunku. Co nie zmienia faktu, że gdzieś tam na początku ktoś musiał rozbić jajka – i właśnie ich Szacki w pocie czoła szukał.

Szukał, ponieważ w tej sprawie od początku chodziło o szum medialny. Pamiętał zdziwienie, kiedy pod budynek prokuratury zajechał pierwszy wóz transmisyjny, zdarzyło się to szybko, zbyt szybko, zwłaszcza biorąc pod uwagę odległość Sandomierza od Warszawy i Krakowa. Zdziwił się, ale nie zwrócił na ten szczegół uwagi, bo w ogóle największym problemem tej sprawy, nadmiernie obfitującej w szokujące, wyreżyserowane wydarzenia, był fakt, że prokurator Teodor Szacki nie zwracał uwagi na szczegóły.

Teraz naprawiał ten błąd. Podzielił sprawę na kilka istotnych etapów. Przede wszystkim znalezienie ciała Budnikowej, identyfikacja brzytwy jako noża do uboju rytualnego, znalezienie Budnika. I starał się odnaleźć miejsce, w którym suche informacje pojawiły się najszybciej, stając się pożywką dla pozostałych mediów. Przez chwilę myślał, że to Polsat News, tam na przykład o Budnikowej powiedzieli już przed ósmą. Ale w pozostałych przypadkach Polsat był mocno spóźniony. Zetka była szybka, ale nie aż tak szybka, żeby wyprzedzić Polsat w przypadku Budnikowej czy TOK FM w przypadku Budnika. TVN24 trzymało dość równy poziom, nigdy się znacząco nie spóźniło, ale nie było pierwsze w żadnym przypadku. Może to jednak ślepa uliczka? Może informacje nie pochodziły z jednego źródła?

Nie wierzył w to, cholera, no nie wierzył. Zbyt dużą rolę w zaciemnianiu sprawy odgrywała medialna histeria, żeby nikt tym nie sterował.

Nagle rozdzwonił się monitor nad jego głową. Szacki stężał, nie miał pojęcia, co to oznacza, na pewno nic dobrego. Nie minęło piętnaście sekund, jak do pokoju wbiegła pielęgniarka. Podbiegła do niego, ale szybko zwolniła, niepokój na jej twarzy zastąpił uspokajający uśmiech. Wsunęła mu rękę pod szpitalną koszulę.

- Pan się tak nie kręci, bo czujnik spada i alert się załącza – powiedziała bardzo niskim, prawie męskim głosem. – Po co to straszyć siebie i personel, hmm? Poprawiła, mrugnęła i wyszła. Szacki nie odmrugnął, bo zajął się ściganiem uciekającej po neuronach myśli. Alert. Dlaczego to ważne? No jasne, Alert. Tak się nazywał serwis portalu „Gazety", który służył do tego, aby czytelnicy przysyłali informacje razem ze zdjęciami i filmami. Genialne rozwiązanie w dobie dyktatu informacji z jednej i cięć budżetowych w redakcjach z drugiej strony.

Przejrzał szybko serwis i oczywiście nic nie znalazł. Zaklął głośno, stukanie w klawiaturę nie podobało się jego poranionej dłoni, ból promieniował teraz aż do barku, co miało swoje dobre strony, trzymało go na obrotach, nie pozwalało na odpłynięcie w drzemkę lub pogrążenie się w nieistotnych myślach.

Myśl, myśl, Teodorze, ponaglał się, Alert nie, ale muszą być inne takie miejsca. Szukał. W TVP nazywało się to Twoje Info, w Radiu Zet Infotelefon, jedno i drugie było gówno warte. Zaczął się zastanawiać, czy może są jakieś blogi informacyjne, zmartwiał na myśl o zanurzeniu się w otchłani twittera, blipa i facebooka. Zajrzał jeszcze raz na TVN24, które też miało swoją społeczność donosicieli (wyobraził sobie facebooka w latach osiemdziesiątych – ciekawe, ile osób lubiłoby SB, a ile by przyjęło do swoich przyjaciół), nazywała się ona Kontakt24. Była najlepiej zorganizowana ze wszystkich, każdy użytkownik mógł tam prowadzić swój miniserwis informacyjny na kształt bloga, redakcja przeglądała wpisy, najciekawsze trafiały na główną stronę serwisu, a nawet były wykorzystywane w telewizji, co zresztą oznaczano w specjalny sposób. Z kolei wiadomości serwisu były w odpowiedni sposób otagowywane, zaznaczano, informacje jakich użytkowników zostały wykorzystane.

Pod tym kątem zaczął czytać wszystkie newsy związane z jego sprawą, poczynając od najstarszego, od znalezienia ciała Budnikowej. W Sandomierzu, bladym świtem, bla, bla, bla, historyczne miasto, zwłoki pod starówką, zagadka godna ojca Mateusza, bla, bla, bla. Wiele osób przyłożyło się do powstania chaotycznego tekstu. Sando69, KasiaFch, OlaMil, CivitasRegni, Sandomiria...

Ożeż kurwa mać.

Jednym z wymienionych był użytkownik o nicku „Nekama". Szacki kliknął, aby wyświetlić jego stronę. Wpisów było tylko dziesięć, wszystkie dotyczyły sandomierskich morderstw. Przy każdym była adnotacja, że została wykorzystana zarówno w serwisie, jak i na antenie stacji. Krótkie, napisane suchym, prostym językiem, przekazywały najważniejsze informacje.

Pierwszy wpis z 15 kwietnia brzmiał: „Na Starym Mieście w Sandomierzu obok budynku starej synagogi znaleziono nagie zwłoki kobiety. Kobieta została bez wątpliwości brutalnie zamordowana, jej gardło było wielokrotnie poderżnięte".

Prokurator Teodor Szacki gapił się w ekran i czuł, jak serce łomocze mu się po klatce piersiowej, jeszcze chwila i alert przywoła pielęgniarkę, która pewnie bardzo się zdziwi, że czujnik pod koszulą jest na swoim miejscu. Jego stan nie był spowodowany jednak ani treścią informacji, ani nawet nickiem jej autora, tylko godziną publikacji.

Pamiętał chwilę, kiedy dostał telefon od Miszczyk, że ma się jak najszybciej pojawić na Żydowskiej. Klara ciągnęła go do wyra, moment wcześniej stał w oknie i obserwował, jak zbliżający się świt sprawia, że w ciemności zaczęły się pojawiać pierwsze cienie zamieszkujących ją bytów, zapowiedź nadchodzącego dnia. W podobnym tonie Myszyński opisywał chwilę dostrzeżenia zwłok. Nawet biorąc poprawkę na mgłę, wszystko działo się o świcie.

Sprawdził, 15 kwietnia 2009 roku słońce w Sandomierzu wynurzało się znad horyzontu o 4.39.

Wpis na Kontakcie pojawił się 15 kwietnia o 4.45. Co oznaczało, że jego autorem był albo morderca, albo któraś z osób od początku biorąca udział w śledztwie. Albo jedno i drugie, od wczoraj nabierał przekonania, że zna zabójcę, że to musi być jedna z osób, z którą na co dzień współpracuje, z którą pija kawę, przegląda akta i planuje, co zrobić następnego dnia. I mimo że rozważał taką opcję od rana, to właśnie potwierdzenie tej tezy sprawiło, że jego serce nie mogło się uspokoić.

Teraz potrzebował informacji od Myszyńskiego, musiał też zadzwonić do Kuzniecowa. Ale przede wszystkim potrzebował akt. Potrzebował akt jak jasna cholera.

4

Okej, potrzebował akt, ale to była pewna przesada. Śliczna asystentka kieleckiej delegatury IPN, taki typ mini-michelina, co to ma same okrągłości, ale żadnej zbędnej, podjechała do niego wózkiem pełnym akt, uśmiechnęła się przyjaźnie i zaczęła wypakowywać teczki na stół. Teczek było chyba ze sto.

– To na pewno wszystko dla mnie?

– Procesy żołnierzy wyklętych z powiatu sandomierskiego, lata 1944–1951, tak?

– Dokładnie tak.

– No to na pewno wszystko dla pana.

– Przepraszam, tak się tylko upewniam.

Spojrzała na niego lodowato.

– Proszę pana. Ja tutaj pracuję od siedmiu lat, robiłam z wyklętych magisterium, doktorat i habilitację, napisałam kilkanaście artykułów i dwie książki. Akurat te teczki mogę zdjąć z półki z zawiązanymi oczami.

Oczy mu się uśmiechnęły na wspomnienie zawiązanych oczu, przypomniał mu się jeden dowcip, dość sprośny, ale zabawny.

– I ostrzegam, że jak pan spróbuje wyciągnąć dowcip o zawiązanych oczach, myśliwych i saperce, to zabiorę akta, pana wyprowadzi ochrona, a następnym razem będzie pan musiał przysłać pełnomocnika. Na waszą szowinistyczną, seksistowską bandę żaden stopień naukowy nie działa, trzeba prać kijem po gębie i kopać po jajach, żeby nakopać trochę kultury do głupiego łba. Zresztą nieważne, w czymś jeszcze panu pomóc?

Pokręcił tylko przecząco głową, bojąc się zdradzić, jak na niego działa taki temperament, dałby teraz wszystko za jej numer telefonu. Asystentka spojrzała na niego groźnie, odwróciła się i odeszła, ostentacyjnie kołysząc biodrami.

– Moment! Jest jedna rzecz...

– Bóg mi świadkiem, że jeśli chodzi o numer telefonu albo podobną zagrywkę...

– Przeciwnie. Chodzi o wiedzę.

Wyciągnął z notesu kartkę z wypisanymi nazwiskami, które go interesowały, podał je młodej kobiecie.

– Budnik, Budnik z domu Szuszkiewicz, Szyller – czytała na głos, przerwała na chwilę i spojrzała na niego podejrzliwie. – Wilczur, Miszczyk, Sobieraj, Sobieraj z domu Szott.

– Mówią coś pani te nazwiska?

– Nie wszystkie.

– Ale niektóre?

– Oczywiście. Czy ja sobie naprawdę muszę stopnie naukowe wytatuować na czole albo obciąć cycki, żeby mnie któryś z was, wielkich męskich badaczy historii, potraktował poważnie?

– Byłaby to niepowetowana strata...

Spojrzała na niego jak rzeźnik na półtuszę.

– ...oszpecić czoło, za którym kryje się tak przenikliwy, analityczny umysł.

5

Jest pan tam, panie komisarzu?

– Oczywiście.

– Przepraszam, że tak długo to trwało, ale musiałam sprawdzić wszystko dokładnie z działem informatycznym.

– Jasne.

– Otóż każdy z wpisów użytkownika „Nekama" został przysłany z numeru IP, który jest bramką sieci Orange.

– Czyli ktoś korzystał z internetu w gwizdku?

– Nie sądzę, ponieważ wpisy zostały wysłane z przeglądarki Skyfire uruchomionej na systemie Symbian.

– Co oznacza...

– Co oznacza, że ktoś swoim telefonem, nokią, zrobił zdjęcia, na telefonie odpalił Kontakt, na telefonie napisał tekst i z telefonu przysłał.

– Okej, rozumiem, może mi pani podać te numery, żebym mógł je sprawdzić w Orange?

– Oczywiście.

Oleg, proszę cię, wiesz, że to tak nie działa.

– Ostatni raz, obiecuję.

– Oleg, u ciebie dwa razy w tygodniu jest ostatni raz! Nie możesz raz, tylko raz, jeden jedyny raz załatwić tego po bożemu? Przysłać pismo z pieczątką, zaczekać na odpowiedź? Żebym miała podkładkę, jakąkolwiek podkładkę, żebym mogła powiedzieć: tak, komisarz Oleg Kuzniecow z Wilczej też nam przysyła oficjalne pisma.

– No wiesz co, krewnemu takie słowa.

– Nie jesteśmy spokrewnieni.

– Jak to? Przecież jesteś szwagierką ciotecznej siostry mojej żony.

– Nazywasz to więzami krwi?

– I co, pojawiło ci się już na monitorku?

– Nie wierzę, że to robię, ale słuchaj... wszystko zostało wysłane z numeru 798 689 459, to prepaid kupiony 24 marca gdzieś w Kielcach, nie w salonie, więc nie mam dokładnych danych. Numer rzadko logował się do sieci, zawsze do BTS-a o numerze 2328 w Sandomierzu, który się znajduje... moment... na wieży ciśnień przy ulicy Szkolnej. Właściciel korzysta z telefonu Nokia E51, popularny biznesowy model, do kupienia wszędzie.

6

Pozostał wierny postanowieniu o rezygnacji ze środków przeciwbólowych, ale kazał taksówkarzowi zatrzymać się po drodze ze szpitala do prokuratury przy delikatesach Kabanos i kupił sobie małą butelkę jacka danielsa. Trochę przeciwbólowe, trochę relaksacyjne i można dawkować precyzyjniej niż ketonal. Pierwszą rzeczą, jaką zrobił w gabinecie, było nalanie sobie odrobiny do kubka z Legią i wychylenie prawie duszkiem kilku łyków śmierdzącego spalenizną burbona. Och tak, potrzebował tego sto razy bardziej niż wczasów na koszt NFZ w sandomierskim szpitalu – wbrew przekonywaniom, namowom i groźbom doktora Sowy. Naprawdę tak się nazywał i Szacki powstrzymał się od pytania o doktora Sztrosmajera jedynie dlatego, że nie chciał drażnić lekarza, który w swojej karierze musiał słyszeć ten dowcip od każdego pacjenta.

Wyjął z szafy pancernej akta śledztwa (glock znajdował się chwilowo w policyjnym depozycie) i rozłożył je przed sobą na biurku. Gdzieś w nich, był tego pewien, kryje się odpowiedź na pytanie, kto zamordował trzy osoby, kto wodzi go za nos od dwóch tygodni i kto o mało co nie wykończył go w tych pieprzonych lochach. Tak, trudno mu było pozbyć się z głowy wczorajszych obrazów, ale to dobrze, to bardzo dobrze – myślał. Dobrze, ponieważ tak naprawdę była to jedyna sytuacja, która nie została wyreżyserowana, jedyna, która nie została ładnie przygotowana dla prokuratora Teodora Szackiego.

Dlatego wyjął ze świeżutkiej teczki odbitki zdjęć zrobionych dziś przez techników i ułożył pod lampą. Wejście koło seminarium, leżące na podłodze lessowego korytarza zakrwawione nosze, wąskie schody, truchła kundli, pokryty kurzem trup Szyllera i pozbawione drzwiczek klatki dla psów, wystająca z rumowiska w bocznym korytarzu noga Dybusa. Każde spojrzenie na fotografię powodowało, że ręka bolała go bardziej. Ale to dobrze, bardzo dobrze. Musi przyjrzeć się wczorajszej wycieczce minuta po minucie, przeanalizować każdy gest i każde zdanie jego towarzyszy.

Usiadł i zaczął zapisywać wszystko, co się wczoraj wydarzyło.

Po dwóch godzinach pracy miał zapisanych kilka kartek, ale tylko parę elementów zakreślonych na czerwono. Przepisał je na osobny arkusz:

• LW od początku przestraszony i spięty. Pierwszy raz taki.

• BS patrzy na zegarek i niepokoi się, która godzina, tuż przedtem, zanim słychać dźwięk otwieranych klatek. Potem nalega, żeby zawrócić.

• LW wspomina o tym, że Szyller powinien być sprawiony jak jagnię, a nie świnia, bo świnia nie jest koszerna. Używa też słowa „trefny". Znajomość obyczajów żydowskich. Tak jak wcześniej w domu Szyllera i w katedrze.

• Ani LW, ani BS nie chcą badać lochów, biernie idą.

• LW i BS puszczają wszystkich przodem tuż przed spotkaniem z psami.

• BS nalega, żeby jak najszybciej wyjść z „komnaty Szyllera".

• LW tak samo, cały czas gapi się na zegarek.

- LW nie zauważył momentu wychodzenia Dybusa, kiedy się spostrzegł, zareagował bardzo gwałtownie, histerycznie.
- BS bez problemu znalazła w labiryncie drogę do wyjścia.
- LW chciał coś powiedzieć w czasie ewakuacji. Wyznać coś ważnego. Zauważył też od razu, że skręciliśmy w złą stronę.
- BS w szpitalu przyznała, że Dybus nie miał być ofiarą, zachowywała się dziwnie.

Stukał czerwonym flamastrem w kartkę i myślał. Wszystko to były poszlaki, bardzo słabe poszlaki, może nawet nie tyle poszlaki, co ukłucia intuicji. Ale intuicja rzadko go zawodziła. Przypomniał mu się lodowaty ranek sprzed dwóch tygodni, ślizganie się na kocich łbach rynku, przedzieranie się przez krzaki do trupa Budnikowej. Kto tam czekał? Prokurator Barbara Sobieraj i inspektor Leon Wilczur. Przypadek? Może.

Stary policjant już dawno mógł przejść na emeryturę albo przenieść się do innej komendy, awansować. Ale postanowił zostać w tej dziurze. Pięknej, bo pięknej, ale dziurze. Zwłaszcza dla policjanta. Szacki czytał codziennie w „Echu" kronikę kryminalną – kradzież komórki w szkole to było tutaj wydarzenie. Mimo to Wilczur został. Przypadek? Może.

Każde z nich na wyprzódki dzieliło się z nim swoją wiedzą o mieszkańcach, o mieście, o relacjach. Tak naprawdę wszystko, co wiedział, wiedział od nich. Przypadek? Może.

Każde z nich kręciło się po miejscach wszystkich tych zbrodni, pozostawiając tam swoje ślady, zdobywając wytłumaczenie dla obecności włosa lub odcisku palca. Przypadek? Może.

Oboje byli sandomierzanami, znali miasto od podszewki, jego małe i duże tajemnice. Przypadek? Może.

A może w ogóle nie powinien rozpatrywać ich osobno? Może poza tym śledztwem jest jeszcze coś, co ich łączy?

O czym mogli mu nie powiedzieć? Co zataić? W końcu – jak powiedział ojciec Sobieraj, stary małomiasteczkowy prokurator – wszyscy kłamią.

Przysypiający raz po raz Szacki ocknął się gwałtownie. Ojciec Sobieraj powiedział coś jeszcze. Opowiadając o śledztwie zrębińskim, wspomniał, jak to wahali się, czy z kapitanem postawić wszystko na jedną kartę. Czyżby? Wiek się zgadzał, stary Szott i Wilczur mogli być kolegami przed trzydziestu laty. A jeśli Wilczur brał udział w rozwikłaniu jednej z najgłośniejszych zbrodni PRL? To by też tłumaczyło jego niespotykanie wysoką szarżę, kto to widział inspektora w powiatowej dochodzeniówce.

Szacki wstał, uchylił okno gabinetu i zadrżał, wpuszczając chmurę powietrza, która chyba w lutym zabłądziła w tej okolicy i do tej pory nie znalazła drogi powrotnej.

Nawet jeśli... Nawet jeśli założymy, że Wilczur i ojciec Sobieraj razem pracowali przy sprawie połanieckiej. Nawet jeśli założymy, że w związku z tym jeden i drugi mają jakąś zaszłość. Że łączy ich zabójstwo, śmierć ciężarnej i krzywoprzysięstwo. Że to jest odprysk tamtej sprawy. Że Sobieraj wyręcza ojca w jakimś pokręconym zbrodniczym planie, zemście czy cholera wie czym, to...

To co?

Nic.

Jaki jest sens mordowania ludzi, którzy z tamtymi wydarzeniami nie mogą mieć nic wspólnego, bo są zwyczajnie za młodzi?

Jaki jest sens mordowania z powodu emocjonalnego trójkąta? Mąż, żona i ten trzeci. Czy był jakiś czwarty albo czwarta? Czy to nie przesada, nawet jak na tę rozerotyzowaną prowincję?

I przede wszystkim: jaki jest sens stylizowania tego na antysemicką legendę? Jasne, wzbudzenie medialnej histerii zawsze pomaga, ale żeby zadać sobie aż tyle trudu? Te beczki, te lochy, te psy, totalny bezsens.

Klejnocki tłumaczył, że to nie musi być zasłona dymna ani dzieło szaleńca, to może być celowe działanie, które w jakiś pokrętny sposób usprawiedliwia zabójstwa, wyjaśnia, daje motywację. Motywację. Motyw. Nie miał nawet cienia motywu, żadnego podejrzenia, żadnej nitki, której mógłby się uczepić, aby dojść po niej do odpowiedzi na pytanie: dlaczego? Jeśli zrobi jakikolwiek krok w tę stronę, odpowiedź na pytanie „kto?" będzie już tylko formalnością.

Westchnął, otworzył szerzej okno, wylał do doniczki resztkę burbona z kubka i poszedł zaparzyć sobie mocnej kawy. Dochodziła północ, organizm dopominał się o spłatę zadłużenia, a on zamierzał dotąd czytać akta, aż znajdzie motyw.

7

Motyw ten znał już bardzo dokładnie Roman Myszyński, tyle tylko, że kontakt z prokuratorem był chwilowo daleko na liście jego priorytetów. Starsza inspektor delegatury IPN w Kielcach wbrew buńczucznym zapowiedziom nie była aż tak niedostępna i Myszyński zamiast zapoznawać się z jej krągłym pismem, zapoznawał się w kieleckim mieszkaniu ze zgoła innymi krągłościami, zgrabnie opakowanymi w obłędny czerwony stanik chantelle.

Szkoda, ponieważ gdyby poświęcił kilka minut na telefon do Teodora Szackiego i zreferowanie mu, jak trochę nienawiści, trochę kłamstw i trochę zbiegów okoliczności doprowadziło do zagłady żydowskiej rodziny w Sandomierzu w 1947 roku, oszczędziłby nieprzespanej nocy i tak nadmiernie sponiewieranemu przez życie prokuratorowi.

Ale z drugiej strony odebrałby spokojną noc komu innemu, więc może trochę sprawiedliwości w tym było.

Rozdział dziesiąty

piątek, 24 kwietnia 2009

Izrael świętuje niepodległość i rozpędza palestyńską demonstrację przeciwko „murowi bezpieczeństwa", Armenia wspomina ludobójstwo Ormian w Turcji, Kościół katolicki wspomina świętą Dodę. Z badań wynika, że 53 procent Polaków nie ufa premierowi, a 67 procent prezydentowi. Janusz Palikot porównuje prezesa PiS do Hitlera i Stalina. IPN przyznaje się do błędu i wycofuje z żądania zmiany nazwy ulicy Brunona Jasieńskiego w Klimontowie. Wcześniej nazwał poetę propagatorem stalinizmu, a jego śmierć i tortury – wewnętrznymi rozgrywkami w partii komunistycznej. Wisła rozbija Górnika 3:1 w meczu rozpoczynającym 25. kolejkę, Robert Kubica nieźle wypada na treningach przed GP Bahrajnu, a Stadion Śląski prezentuje maskotkę jeża, ciągle mając nadzieję, że jednak ktoś na nim zagra w czasie Euro 2012. W Sandomierzu odnotowano przestępstwo kryminalne w postaci kradzieży telefonu komórkowego ze spodni 16-latka pozostawionych pod salą gimnastyczną. Pogoda bez zmian, może troszkę chłodniej.

Trzymali go na smyczy jak psa, traktowali też jak psa. Kopali, ciągnęli, wyzywali od najgorszych, w końcu wepchnęli do klatki. Pospawana z prętów zbrojeniowych klatka była dla niego za ciasna, musiał wygiąć głowę boleśnie pod jakimś nieprawdopodobnym kątem, żeby się do niej zmieścić, a i tak się nie zamykała, ktoś zaczął walić drzwiczkami, żeby dopchnąć je na siłę, drzwiczki uderzały w wysuniętą dłoń, powodując okropny ból, udało mu się ją schować, ale drzwiczki waliły cały czas, jednostajny dźwięk wypełniał mu czaszkę. Nie wiedział, co się dzieje, kim są i czego od niego chcą. Dopiero kiedy ktoś otworzył puszkę pedigree i on zobaczył w środku twarz Szyllera, zrozumiał, że to sen, i ocknął się gwałtownie.

Ból dłoni niestety nie zniknął, nie zniknął też ból szyi, spowodowany tym, że usnął z głową złożoną na aktach i tak spędził noc. Nie zniknęło też walenie, tyle tylko, że ucichło i zamieniło się w natarczywe pukanie do drzwi. Pojękując i postękując, zwlókł się z obrotowego krzesła, za drzwiami stał blady i niewyspany, ale wyraźnie szczęśliwy Roman Myszyński.

– Całą noc siedziałem w archiwum – powiedział z dziwnym uśmiechem, machając plikiem skserowanych kartek.

– To pewnie napije się pan kawy – wybełkotał w odpowiedzi Szacki, jak już udało mu się odkleić jedną wargę od drugiej, i uciekł do kuchni, żeby doprowadzić się do porządku.

Kwadrans później słuchał niezwykłej historii, którą nie bez swady opowiadał jego archiwista do specjalnych poruczeń.

– Zima roku czterdziestego szóstego nadeszła wcześnie, bo już pod koniec listopada, skuła lodem i przykryła śniegiem ziemię, nad którą jeszcze niedawno unosiły się dymy pogorzelisk. Ludzie z trwogą patrzyli w przerażone oczy sąsiadów, puste spiżarnie i przyszłość, gdzie czekał jedynie ból, głód, choroba i upokorzenie.

– Panie Romanie, litości.

– Chciałem tylko jakoś wprowadzić w nastrój.

– Udało się. Mniej barokowo, proszę.

– Okej, w każdym razie zima przyszła ostra, kraj był wyniszczony po wojnie, nie było leków, jedzenia i mężczyzn, byli za to komuniści, nowy porządek i nędza. Nawet w Sandomierzu, który jakimś cudem nie został zamieniony przez żadną ze stron w kupę cegieł. Zresztą jest taka opowieść o podpułkowniku Skopence, który razem z Armią Czerwoną zatrzymał się na drugim brzegu Wisły...

– ...i tak mu się spodobało miasto, że je oszczędził dzięki swojej strategicznej mądrości i umiłowaniu piękna architektury – wpadł mu w słowo Szacki, myśląc, że jeśli Myszyńskiego nie uda się wyrwać z grzęznącej w dygresjach narracji, to będzie to najdłuższy piątek jego życia. – Znam, każdy ją tutaj opowiada. Słyszałem też kontropowieść, jak to podpułkownik miał takiego kaca, że nie pozwolił używać artylerii. Panie Romanie, błagam.

Archiwista obdarzył go smutnym spojrzeniem, malujący się w jego oczach wyrzut zranionego miłośnika dobrej anegdoty poruszyłby najtwardsze serca. Prokurator tylko wskazał wymownie błyskającą czerwono diodę na dyktafonie.

– Sroga zima, zdziesiątkowani ludzie, głód, bieda. Oczywiście puste miejsce tam, gdzie kiedyś była dzielnica żydowska, oczywiście najlepsze mieszkania i kamienice zajęte przez Polaków. Ale nie wszystkie, z tego, co udało mi się ustalić, trochę starozakonnych po wojnie wróciło, niestety, nie byli witani kwiatami, nikt tu na nich nie czekał. Nieruchomości zagospodarowano, pozostawione na przechowanie majątki tak samo, każdy Żyd był wyrzutem sumienia, że być może nie wszyscy w czasie wojny zachowali się tak, jak powinni. Nie wiem, czy pan czytał opowiadania Kornela Filipowicza, on wspaniale opisuje ten dylemat, że nawet jak się robiło dużo, to i tak zawsze było za mało, zawsze wyrzut sumienia. A jak się w ogóle nic nie robiło, biernie obserwowało Zagładę albo jeszcze gorzej, oczywiście dziś trudno sobie wyobrazić...

– Panie Romanie!

– Tak, oczywiście. No więc nieliczni Żydzi wracali na zgliszcza i musieli wysłuchiwać opowieści o zwojach Tory wykorzystywanych jako podszewka do cholewek, o wykopywaniu zwłok swoich bliskich, zastrzelonych przez Niemców, w poszukiwaniu dolarów i złotych zębów. Krążyły opowieści o żołnierzach wyklętych, zwłaszcza tych z NSZ, którzy polowali na ocalałych Żydów. Niektóre prawdziwe, widziałem dokumenty z procesów. Dziwny, ciemny czas... – Myszyński na chwilę zawiesił głos. – Jedni Polacy potrafili wymordować całe żydowskie rodziny, a inni, oba przypadki z Klimontowa, byli gotowi ryzykować życiem, żeby dalej ukrywać Żydów, tym razem przed antykomunistyczną partyzantką. Tak, wiem, nie za szeroko. W każdym razie Żydzi nie mieli czego szukać w takim Klimontowie czy Połańcu. Sandomierz to było jednak miasto, ci, którzy nie mieli ochoty na emigrację do Łodzi, przyjeżdżali tutaj, starali się za wszelką cenę ułożyć sobie życie.

– Ale to zaraz po wojnie. A miała być zima z czterdziestego szóstego na czterdziesty siódmy.

– Zgadza się. Jesienią przyjechała żydowska rodzina. Obca, nikt ich wcześniej w Sandomierzu nie widział. On był lekarzem, nazywał się Wajsbrot, Chaim Wajsbrot. Razem z nim kobieta w ciąży i dzieciak dwu-, może trzyletni. Z tego, co zrozumiałem, pomogło im to, że byli obcy. Nie wracali na stare śmiecie, nie trzeba było im patrzeć w oczy jak sąsiadom, tłumaczyć się z nowego kredensu w kuchni, ot, ofiary wojny. Spokojni, nie wadzili, nie upominali się, na dodatek on potrafił pomóc. Przed wojną też był w Sandomierzu żydowski lekarz, Weiss, bardzo szanowany, to i tego ludzie jakoś tak naturalnie poszanowali.

– Niech zgadnę, jego jest domek przy Zamkowej?

– Domek przy Zamkowej jest niczyj, należy do gminy, ale kiedyś należał właśnie do doktora Weissa i podobno właśnie tutaj siłą rzeczy zamieszkał Wajsbrot z rodziną. Ale to już więść gminna, kwitów na to nie mam.

– A czemu to stoi puste?

– Oficjalnie sprawy własnościowe, nieoficjalnie miejsce jest nawiedzone.

– Nawiedzone?

– Że straszy.

– Dlaczego?

– Zaraz do tego dojdziemy.

Szacki pokiwał głową. Wiedział niestety, że to kolejna historia bez happy endu, wysłuchiwał jej niechętnie, ale nie tracił nadziei, że czegoś się dzięki niej dowie.

– Zima trwała, ludzie usiłowali przetrwać, Wajsbrot leczył, kobiecie rósł brzuch. Doktor zwłaszcza dzieciakom chętnie pomagał, ludzie mówili o dobrym podejściu, woleli prowadzać do niego niż do polskiego doktora. Tym bardziej że jak się okazało, żydowski doktor miał coś, czego nie mieli inni.

– Co?

– Penicylinę.

– Skąd miał żydowski doktor mieć penicylinę?

– Nie mam pojęcia i wtedy chyba też nikt nie wiedział, bo penicylina była amerykańska. Czy ją już ze sobą przywiózł, czy mu ją ktoś przemycał, czy miał jakieś kontakty dziwne na czarnym rynku? Nie wiem, wszystko tak samo prawdopodobne. Ale jak jednego i drugiego dzieciaka podniósł z suchot, gruchnęła wieść po okolicy. Mogę po colę?

– Słucham?

– Pójdę sobie po colę. Do kiosku. Zaraz wrócę.

– A tak, oczywiście.

Myszyński wybiegł, a prokurator wstał, żeby zrobić kilka ćwiczeń rozciągających, bolał go każdy – bez przesady każdy – mięsień. Było zimno, zaczął energicznie machać rękami, żeby się rozgrzać. Trudno powiedzieć, czy to ta wiosna trefna, czy udzielił mu się klimat opowieści. Sroga zima, zaspy pomiędzy szczątkami domów żydowskiej dzielnicy, powojenna martwota i opustoszenie. Słabe światło świecy albo naftowej lampy bije z okna murowanego dworku na Zamkowej. Tak zwanego na wyrost dworku, musiał już wtedy być w ruinie tak samo jak teraz, skoro pozwolili się osiedlić przybyszom. Pewnie doktorostwo przysposobili do mieszkania jakiś pokój na parterze, może dwa, o luksusach nie mogło być mowy. I stoi ta ruina z żółtym światłem w jednym oknie, matka z dzieckiem na ręku puka do drzwi, księżyc jest w pełni, kobieta rzuca długi cień na srebrnym śniegu, z tyłu ciemne bryły zamku i katedry zasłaniają gwiazdy. Mija długa chwila, zanim ciężarna kobieta z czarnymi lokami otwiera i wpuszcza niespokojną matkę do środka. Proszę, proszę, mąż już czeka. Czy tak to wyglądało? Czy może ponosi go wyobraźnia?

Wrócił zdyszany i zarumieniony archiwista z pięcioma puszkami coli. Szacki nie skomentował.

– No więc po okolicy gruchnęła wieść o penicylinie – powiedział, włączając dyktafon. – I rozumiem, że dotarła nie tylko do uszu zatroskanych matek.

– Nie tylko. Do Wajsbrota zgłosili się wyklęci...

– Niech zgadnę: KWP?

– Dokładnie. Zgłosili się i zażądali kontrybucji na walkę z czerwonym okupantem, kontrybucji w postaci antybiotyku. Wajsbrot ich pogonił, obili go strasznie, podobno ludzie cudem uratowali swojego doktora. Tamci zagrozili, że wrócą, że zabiją.

– Skąd to wiemy?

– Z wyjaśnień Wajsbrota, jakie złożył w swoim procesie o szpiegostwo.

Szacki zrobił zdziwioną minę, ale nic nie powiedział.

– Któremu to zresztą procesowi zawdzięczamy większość naszej wiedzy. I który wziął się stąd, że dowódca partyzantki nie przełknął obrazy, jaką była odmowa.

– Czyli wrócił i zabił?

– Złożył donos. Co z kolei wiemy z procesu jego towarzyszy. Uwierzyłbyś? Majorowi tak się rzuciła na mózg żydowska odmowa, że wydał go znienawidzonym czerwonym, co
z kolei wiele mówi o skali nienawiści w Polsce, ciekawe,
gdzie by się tutaj uplasowały pedały.

– Panie Romanie...

– Okej, okej. Nie trzeba było wiele, wystarczyło wspo-
mnieć o amerykańskiej penicylinie i bezpieka zamknęła
Wajsbrota w try miga, tym razem sandomierska ulica mogła
się tylko przyglądać. A było to już przedwiośnie, zbliżała się
Wielkanoc, zbliżało się święto Pesach, zbliżał się termin rozwiązania pani Wajsbrotowej.

Szacki zamknął oczy. Błagam, tylko nie to, pomyślał.

– Doktor siedział w więzieniu, podobno gdzieś na terenie
dzisiejszego seminarium, nie wiem, czy to prawda. A żona
nie była lekarką, nie miała penicyliny, na dodatek zwykle
raczej stała za jego plecami, więc z nikim się w miasteczku
nie zaprzyjaźniła. Ale mimo to ludzie jej pomagali, nie po-
zwalali, żeby z głodu umarła.

– I co się stało?

– Jak mówiłem, zbliżał się termin porodu. Żona Wajsbrota
była, jak to się mówiło, słabej konstytucji. Doktor szalał, wiedział, że go nie puszczą, ale błagał, żeby pozwolili jej na kilka
dni przyjść do aresztu, żeby mógł odebrać poród. Czytałem
protokoły, są wstrząsające, na zmianę przyznawał się do
wszystkiego i wszystkiemu zaprzeczał, byleby się podlizać
przesłuchującemu. Sypał jakimiś zmyślonymi nazwiskami,
obiecywał, że wyda międzynarodową szajkę imperialistycz-
nych kontaktów, jeśli tylko na to pozwolą. No cóż, nie pozwolili. Zresztą tak po brzmieniu nazwisk przesłuchujących
sądząc, to chyba bracia w wierze mu nie pozwolili.

– A Wajsbrotowa umarła?

Myszyński otworzył puszkę coli i wypił duszkiem, zaraz
potem następną. Szacki miał ochotę zapytać, czemu po

prostu nie kupił dwulitrowej butelki, ale odpuścił. Czekał spokojnie, aż archiwista zbierze myśli.

– Tak, chociaż nie musiała. Mieszkańcy lubili dobrego doktora, ściągnęli najlepszą położną, żeby odebrała poród. Pech chciał, że położna przyszła z córką i była przesądna. I ona, i córka. Cóż, resztę łatwo sobie dopowiedzieć. Weszła do domu i pierwsze, co zobaczyła, to stojącą w drzwiach do piwnicy beczkę z ogórkami, i oczywiście zrozumiała, że to nie żaden poród, tylko podstęp, że Żydzi się czają, żeby porwać jej śliczną córeczkę, utoczyć krwi na macę i noworodkowi oczy przemyć, coby nie było ślepe. To wzięła i wyszła.

– Przecież tam nikogo nie było.

– Duchów też nie ma, a ludzie się boją. Uciekła. Przyszła inna akuszerka, ale nie tak zdolna, a poród był ciężki. Wajsbrotowa całą noc krzyczała, nad ranem umarła razem z noworodkiem. Podobno do dziś można na Zamkowej usłyszeć jej krzyk i płacz niemowlaka. Wajsbrot powiesił się w celi następnego dnia.

Roman Myszyński zamilkł i poprawił leżące przed nim papiery, ułożył je w zgrabną kupkę. I otworzył kolejną puszkę. Szacki wstał i oparł się o parapet okna, patrząc na sandomierskie domy, na majaczące w oddali dachy Starego Miasta. Był w domu na Zamkowej, był w Nazarecie, starej ubeckiej katowni. Wszędzie trupy, wszędzie jakieś duchy, ile takich miejsc w życiu odwiedził, ile miejsc naznaczonych przez śmierć?

Myszyński odkaszlnął. Teoretycznie Szacki powinien bardzo chcieć słuchać, przecież to było dopiero tło, teraz archiwista dopasuje bohaterów dzisiejszego dramatu do bohaterów dramatu powojennego i wszystko stanie się jasne. Czemu zwleka, żeby się tego dowiedzieć? Przecież ta informacja oznacza aresztowanie, koniec sprawy, sukces. Zwleka, bo trawi go wewnętrzny niepokój, jakiś opór. Nie potrafi go zdefiniować, nie potrafi nazwać. Zaraz wszystko wskoczy na swoje miejsce, rozsypane puzzle zostaną w końcu do siebie dopasowane, wszystkie mniejsze i większe poszlaki zyskają wytłumaczenie. A mimo to, choć jeszcze nie zna szczegółów, trawi go dziwne uczucie fałszu, często towarzyszące widzom w kinie albo teatrze. Niby dobrze napisane, niby dobrze wyreżyserowane, zagrane też w porządku, a czuć, że to tylko teatr, zamiast postaci widać aktorów, widzów i żyrandol nad widownią.

– Jerzy Szyller? – zapytał w końcu.

– Jego ojciec był komendantem oddziału KWP, tego, który doniósł na Wajsbrota i oskarżył go o szpiegostwo. Ciekawa postać, przed wojną mieszkał w Niemczech i zakładał razem z innymi Związek Polaków. Kiedy wybuchła wojna, przyjechał tutaj walczyć i nawet zapisał się złotymi zgłoskami w historii podziemia, dużo dywersyjnych akcji na koncie, niektóre bardzo spektakularne. Potem jednak uznał, że bardziej od Niemców nienawidzi czerwonych, dlatego poszedł do lasu. Za czasów stalinowskich go nie złapali, a potem już nie był wrogiem publicznym, mimo to wyjechał do Niemiec, umarł w latach osiemdziesiątych. Syn Jerzy urodził się w Niemczech.

– Grzegorz Budnik?

– Syn naczelnika ubeckiego aresztu.

– Tego, który nie pozwolił doktorowi odebrać porodu żony?

– Miał więcej na sumieniu, ale tak, tego. Tata Budnik zresztą dożył późnego wieku, umarł spokojnie ze starości w latach dziewięćdziesiątych.

– A Budnikowa? W jaki sposób była powiązana z tymi wydarzeniami?

– Przyznaję, długo myślałem, że w ogóle nie była, założyłem, że była powiązana jedynie przez męża, dlatego zginęła. Uznałem, że jeśli ktoś jest na tyle szalony, aby tropić dzieci winowajców tragedii sprzed siedemdziesięciu lat, to może jest na tyle szalony, żeby polować też na ich rodziny.

Szacki skinął głową, rozumowanie było słuszne.

– Ale dla porządku chciałem sprawdzić wszystkie tropy, na szczęście poznałem jedną bardzo zdolną archiwistkę. Myszyński zarumienił się nieznacznie. – Zrobiła swoje czary--mary w różnych bazach danych i co się okazało? Pani Budnik przyjechała tutaj jeszcze jako panna Szuszkiewicz, z Krakowa, ale urodziła się w Sandomierzu w 1963 roku. Jej matka z kolei pochodzi z Zawichostu, urodzona w roku 1936.

– Czyli kiedy Wajsbrotowie umarli, miała jedenaście lat – powiedział Szacki i elementy układanki wskoczyły na swoje miejsce. – Taka mała dziewczynka wychowana w żydowskim sztetlu, gdzie należała do mniejszości i gdzie nasłuchała się różnych opowieści, taka mała dziewczynka mogła się bardzo przestraszyć, kiedy zobaczyła straszną beczkę w zrujnowanym żydowskim domu.

Myszyński nie skomentował, sprawa była oczywista. Szackiemu pozostało dowiedzieć się jednej rzeczy. Jednej jedynej. I znowu coś chwyciło go za gardło, jakby nie chciało pozwolić zadać tego ostatniego pytania. Bez sensu, po raz pierwszy doświadczał takiego uczucia. Zmęczenie? Nerwica? Wiek? Brak mu jakichś witamin? Przecież wszystko tak ładnie pasowało. Trzy ofiary przed laty, trzy trupy dzisiaj. Oko za oko, życie za życie. Syn partyzanta, który doniósł na doktora. Syn ubeka, który nie pozwolił mu odebrać porodu żony i pozwolił na samobójstwo. Córka dziewczynki, która swoją wiarą w legendę o krwi skazała na śmierć rodzącą doktorową. Tylko dlaczego teraz? Dlaczego tak późno? Przecież wcześniej można było dopaść osoby naprawdę odpowiedzialne, przecież nie wolno karać dzieci za grzechy rodziców. Czy to było celowe działanie? Czy może zabójca tak późno poznał prawdę? To była właściwie ostatnia rzecz, której należało się dowiedzieć. Pytanie ułożyło mu się na języku, jednak nie chciało się przepchnąć między zębami. Do kurwy nędzy, Teodorze, krzyknął na siebie w myślach. Musisz się dowiedzieć, kto to jest, nawet jeśli rozwiązanie bardzo ci się nie spodoba. Jesteś urzędnikiem w służbie

Rzeczpospolitej i za chwilę poznasz prawdę. Cała reszta jest nieważna.

– A jakie były losy drugiego dziecka Wajsbrotów? – zapytał chłodno.

– Oficjalnie nikt taki nie istnieje. Niemniej jest pewna osoba, której wiek by się zgadzał. Trafiłem na jej ślad trochę przez przypadek, ponieważ grzebała w archiwach Instytutu, zostało nazwisko w repertorium. Osoba ta została wychowana przez dom dziecka w Kielcach, wcześniej nie ma żadnego śladu w księgach ani po niej, ani po jej przodkach, szukałem dokładnie. Osoba ta ma jak najbardziej polskie nazwisko, rodzinę, córkę. Pracuje zresztą w pańskiej branży, czyli w wymiarze sprawiedliwości.

2

Wszystko się dokonało, nie ma już nic do zrobienia poza rozpoczęciem nowego życia. Jakie będzie to życie? Ile potrwa? Co przyniesie? Czy uda się zastąpić pustkę miłością i przyjaźnią? Gdzieś, kiedyś. Śmieje się. Miłością i przyjaźnią, dobre sobie. Nagle czuje ogromny żal za utraconą młodością i utraconą miłością. Chociaż myśli „na pociechę”, że nie ma prawdziwej młodości ani prawdziwej miłości... Po tych wszystkich czarnych czynach nie ma żadnej szansy na rozświetlenie swojej duszy. Ale nie szkodzi. Pustka i ciemność to niewygórowana cena za spokój, za to, że w końcu nie czuje tej dusznej nienawiści. Drga, kiedy rozlega się pukanie do drzwi. Dziwne, nie spodziewa się gości.

3

Myli się pan, panie prokuratorze.

Teodor Szacki milczał, akurat przy tej czynności nie miał za wiele do zrobienia, to była czysto policyjna robota. Marszałek co prawda jąkał się i patrzył przepraszająco, ale wypełnił wszystkie przewidziane prawem czynności. Przedstawił siebie, przedstawił podstawę prawną i sprawę, której dotyczyło zatrzymanie, wylegitymował zatrzymanego, przeszukał go, odebrał broń, skuł i poinformował o prawie do obecności adwokata oraz o prawie do odmowy składania wyjaśnień.

Inspektor Leon Wilczur poddał się procedurom spokojnie i bez słowa, w końcu znał je od drugiej strony. Nie wyglądał na zaskoczonego, nie szarpał się, nie kłócił, nie próbował uciekać.

– Myli się pan, panie prokuratorze – powtórzył z naciskiem.

Cóż miał powiedzieć? Bolały go wszystkie mięśnie, porozrywana ręka i jeszcze teraz szyja, był naprawdę kurewsko zmęczony. Spojrzał niechętnie na starego policjanta. Bez marynarki, tylko w rozchełstanej koszuli, spodniach i cienkich skarpetkach wyglądał jeszcze bardziej żałośnie niż zwykle. Stary dziadek, spędzający dzień zwolnienia lekarskiego przed telewizorem, w zaniedbanym mieszkaniu pełnym zakurzonych staroci. Zmusił się, żeby odwrócić wzrok i zderzyć się spojrzeniem z suchymi, lekko żółtawymi oczami Wilczura. Zawsze myślał, że kryje się za nimi niechęć do świata, zwykłe zgorzknicnie i typowa nadwiślańska frustracja. Ale nienawiść? Mój Boże, ileż serca trzeba włożyć przez lata w pielęgnowanie nienawiści, żeby dokonać trzech morderstw w imię wendety za wydarzenia sprzed siedemdziesięciu lat. Ile pracy, żeby nie pozwolić tej nienawiści zgasnąć, wyblaknąć, żeby nie stracić jej z oczu nawet na chwilę.

Biegli tego nie potwierdzą, i bardzo słusznie, ale dla niego Wilczur był szaleńcem. Widział różne zabójstwa i różnych zabójców. Płaczliwych, zadziornych, agresywnych, skruszonych. Ale to? To wymykało się jego skali. Jaki może być sens mordowania dzieci i wnuków sprawców sprzed lat, nawet jeśli tamta wina była okropna i bolesna? Żaden kodeks świata nie przewiduje odpowiedzialności dzieci za grzechy rodziców, to właściwie podstawa cywilizacji, granica pomiędzy myślącą rasą a napędzanym instynktami bydłem.

– Ojcowie nie poniosą śmierci za winy synów ani synowie za winy swych ojców. Każdy umrze za swój własny grzech – prokurator zacytował Księgę Powtórzonego Prawa.

Wilczur, nie odrywając ani na moment oczu od jego spojrzenia, zaświergotał niezrozumiałymi słowami o melodii raz śpiewnej, a raz chropowatej, przesiąkniętej bluesową tęsknotą, to musiał być jidysz albo hebrajski. Szacki pytająco podniósł brew.

– Bo Ja jestem Pan, Bóg twój, Bóg zazdrosny, karzący nieprawość ojców na synach w trzecim i czwartym pokoleniu. Ta sama Księga, kilka rozdziałów wcześniej. Jak pan doskonale wie, prokuratorze, na wszystko znajdzie się biblijny cytat. Ale to nieważne. Ważne, że pan się myli i że ta pomyłka może mieć straszne skutki.

– Mógłbym panu powiedzieć, inspektorze, ile razy słyszałem taki tekst od zatrzymywanych, ale po co? Przecież pan słyszał go częściej i wie pan lepiej ode mnie, ile w nim jest prawdy.

– Czasami trochę.

– W wypadku prawdy trochę to nic.

Ruchem głowy kazał Marszałkowi wyprowadzić Wilczura.

– Jutro spotkamy się na przesłuchaniu, niech się pan dobrze zastanowi do tego czasu, czy naprawdę chce pan utrudniać postępowanie. Te zabójstwa, ta stylizacja, ta chora inscenizacja, ta szalona zemsta. Niech pan przynajmniej odpowie za to z klasą.

Wilczur przechodził właśnie obok, jego twarz mijała się z twarzą Szackiego o centymetry, wyraźnie widział zgrubienia na białkach oczu, pory na skórze wyżłobionej grubymi zmarszczkami, żółty nalot papierosowego dymu na wąsach, ostre włoski w nozdrzach wydatnego nosa.

– Nigdy mnie pan nie lubił, prokuratorze, prawda? – zaskrzypiał z nieoczekiwanym żalem policjant, ziejąc w twarz Szackiego kwaśnym oddechem. – I ja wiem dlaczego.

Były to ostatnie słowa wypowiedziane przez Leona Wilczura w związku ze sprawą, w której został zatrzymany pod zarzutem potrójnego zabójstwa.

4

Nie wrócił do prokuratury. Odbył tylko dwie krótkie rozmowy telefoniczne z Miszczyk i Sobieraj, nie chciał się z nimi widzieć, nie chciał tłumaczyć i wyjaśniać, nie chciał reagować na egzaltowane „ochy", „achy" i „omójbożejaktomożliwe". Najważniejsze, czyli wynik kwerendy Romana Myszyńskiego, leżało na ich biurkach, a to wystarczyło, aby wystosować wniosek o areszt, czym zajmie się później Sobieraj. Do mediów miała też iść lakoniczna informacja, że zatrzymano podejrzanego. Reszta tak naprawdę zależała od Wilczura. Jeśli się przyzna, za trzy miesiące będzie gotowy akt oskarżenia, jeśli będzie szedł w zaparte – kogoś czeka długi i żmudny poszlakowy proces. Najprawdopodobniej nie jego, było zdrowym obyczajem, że sprawy dotyczące funkcjonariuszy i urzędników trafiały do innych prokuratur. Teodor Szacki miał nadzieję, że tym razem uda się jednak zatrzymać sprawę tutaj, ewentualnie skłonić ludzi w okręgowej, żeby dali mu to gdzie indziej. Bardzo chciał być tym, który napisze akt oskarżenia i obroni go przed sądem. Nie wyobrażał sobie, żeby miało być inaczej.

Tak czy owak nie musi się tym zajmować dzisiaj, dzisiaj może odpocząć, nie pamiętał, kiedy ostatnio był tak niewiarygodnie, potwornie zmęczony. Do tego stopnia, że zwykły chód sprawiał mu wysiłek, kiedy stanął pod Bramą Opatowską, vis-à-vis budynku seminarium, w którym wiele lat wcześniej powiesił się Chaim Wajsbrot i pod którym być może stał mały Leon Wilczur, wypatrując swojego taty – nie wytrzymał i usiadł koło jakiegoś menela na małej ławeczce. Tylko na chwilę. Menel wydał mu się znajomy, przez chwilę szukał w pamięci, tak, jasne, to on zaczepił Wilczura tego wieczoru, kiedy razem wychodzili z Ratuszowej, chciał szukać jakiegoś zaginionego kumpla. Pomyślał, czy nie zagaić, ale dał spokój. Zamknął oczy i wystawił twarz do słońca, nawet jeśli nie daje ciepła, to może opali trochę, nie dawało mu spokoju, że w telewizji był takim bladym, wychudzonym robakiem.

Czuł się dziwnie. Zawsze zakończeniu śledztwa i schwytaniu sprawcy towarzyszyła pewna pustka, depresja pośledcza, syndrom odstawienia. Ale tym razem to było coś innego, pustka w szybkim tempie wypełniała się niepokojem, znajomym niepokojem neuronów, sygnalizujących błąd, niedopatrzenie, przeoczenie.

Nie miał pojęcia, o co chodzi, i nie chciał się nad tym zastanawiać. Nie teraz. Teraz zwlókł się z ławki i poszedł Sokolnickiego w górę, do rynku. Minął bar z pierogami, minął Chińczyka, do którego nigdy nie odważył się zajrzeć, na chwilę zatrzymał się przy Małej, zastanawiając się, czy kawa z pianką i posypką z cukru pudru to nie jest to, czego potrzebuje. Ale nie, nie chciał kawy, nie chciał pobudzenia, chciał prysznica i łóżka.

Doszedł do rynku, kiedy zegar na wieży ratuszowej zaczął swoje harce, sygnalizujące godzinę drugą po południu. Zatrzymał się na moment, obserwując, jak miasto się zmienia, szykuje na sezon turystyczny, startujący jak wszędzie w długi weekend majowy. Nie widział jeszcze Sandomierza w tej odsłonie, zamieszkał tutaj pod koniec roku, kiedy wszystko było pozamykane, po złotej polskiej jesieni nie było śladu, a kocie łby na Starym Mieście były albo mokre, albo zaśnieżone, albo oblodzone. Teraz miasto wyglądało jak chory budzący się ze śpiączki, który nie wstanie od razu i nie pobiegnie, tylko delikatnie sprawdza, co mu wolno, a czego nie. Taras Kordegardy był już zagospodarowany, przed Małą właścicielka wystawiła na zewnątrz dwa stoliki, przed Kasztelanką dwóch kelnerów stawiało płotek ogródka. W głębi, chyba przed Cocktail Barem, ktoś czyścił wielki parasol z logo Żywca, przed Ciżemką zielona budka z lodami, do tej pory zabita na głucho, otwierała podwoje. Ciągle było zimno, ale stojące wysoko słońce wyraźnie nie zamierzało dać za wygraną i Szacki poczuł, że ten weekend będzie pierwszym weekendem prawdziwej wiosny.

Ale nie skusił się na żaden lokal, skręcił w stronę Wisły i po paru chwilach był już w swoim mieszkaniu, po raz pierwszy od środowego poranka. Nie przeszkadzały mu porozrzucane bety ani pusta lodówka, zdjął garnitur i zagrzebał się w pościeli, która ciągle pachniała słodkawymi, młodzieńczymi perfumami Klary.

Nie rozumiem, dlaczego nie czuję ulgi, do jasnej cholery, pomyślał.

I zasnął.

5

Kilka godzin później obudził go telefon od Basi Sobieraj. Musi się z nim zaraz zobaczyć. Okej, powiedział i poszedł wziąć prysznic, zapominając, że przy sandomierskich odległościach „zaraz" oznacza „natychmiast". Kiedy wyszedł z łazienki, z wodą kapiącą z włosów na kołnierz granatowego szlafroka, Basia stała pod drzwiami z nieforemnym pakunkiem w ręku i dziwnym wyrazem na twarzy.

Podała mu pakunek.

– To dla ciebie.

Otworzył brązowy, pakowy papier, w środku była prokuratorska toga, której czerń dawno przestała być czarna, a czerwień lamówki – czerwona.

– Ojciec prosił, żeby ci ją dać. Powiedział, że już nie chce na nią patrzeć, że chce umierać, widząc mnie, a nie ten kawał szmaty, który był jego przebraniem przez całe życie. I że mam dać ją tobie, bo tylko ty będziesz umiał zrobić z niej użytek. Bo podobno rozumiesz coś, czego ja nie rozumiem, nie wiem, o co chodzi.

Że wszyscy kłamią, pomyślał Szacki.

Nic nie powiedział, odłożył togę i kołnierzem szlafroka wytarł strużkę wody, która z białych włosów spłynęła na policzek. Gestem zaprosił Sobieraj do środka, zastanawiając się, dlaczego tak naprawdę przyszła do niego. Chciała rozmawiać o sprawie? O morderstwach? Trupach, winach i nienawiści? Gorzko pomyślał, że dobry z niego partner do takich rozmów, trudno o lepszego w Sandomierzu.

Nie chciało mu się odzywać. Usiadł na kanapie, nalał hojnie jacka do starych literatek z cieniutkiego szkła. Sobieraj usiadła obok, duszkiem wypiła. Spojrzał zdziwiony, nalał jeszcze raz. Ponownie wypiła duszkiem, zamrugała śmiesznie, zachowywała się jak dzieciak, który boi się powiedzieć, że stłukł wazon, choć i tak zaraz się wyda. Założyła za ucho kosmyk włosów i spojrzała na niego z nerwowym, przepraszającym trochę uśmiechem.

Błagam, nie dzisiaj, pomyślał. Był naprawdę kurewsko zmęczony.

Mimo to pochylił się i pocałował swoją koleżankę z pracy, zastanawiając się, czy ma na to ochotę, czy nie. Lubił ją, bardzo ją lubił, z dnia na dzień coraz bardziej, ale nie powiedziałby, że rodzi się między nimi romans albo namiętność, o miłości nie wspominając. Gdyby miał nazwać to uczucie, użyłby słowa „przyjaźń".

Postanowił jednak darować sobie na jakiś czas teoretyzowanie. Cały czas całując, zaciągnął ją do łóżka i zaczął delikatnie, ale systematycznie rozbierać.

– Bo jeśli nie, to wiesz, powiedz, inaczej będę się źle czuła. Nigdy nie byłam w takiej sytuacji – wyciągnęła ręce nad głowę, żeby mógł z niej ściągnąć cienki amarantowy golf – i za bardzo nie wiem, jak się zachować. Po prostu bardzo chciałam, ale jeśli ty nie chcesz...

– Trudno, jakoś się zmuszę – powiedział, wodząc palcem po jej obsypanym piegami dekolcie, który wyglądał jak obrazek typu „połącz kropki", przeskoczył nad fiszbinem przyciasnego stanika w kolorze swetra i dojechał do pępka.

– Warszawski dowcip. Słowo daję, nie wiem, czy dam radę. – Zaśmiała się jednak, kiedy z miną łobuza zajrzał jej do majtek. Które notabene też były ciut za małe, wrzynały się w brzuch, tworząc nad gumką sympatyczną fałdkę.

Klik.

– Hej, ta paczuszka, którą dostałaś w środę...

– Tak, jasne, wyśmiej mnie, bo chciałam mieć dla ciebie coś ładnego. Wyobraź sobie, że nie ma w Sandomierzu dziesięciu sklepów z markową bielizną. Tylko oczywiście nie pomyślałam, że przez zimę urosłam o rozmiar, i o, nie wygląda to superestetycznie, przepraszam...

Roześmiał się głośno.

– Zdejmijmy to jak najszybciej, zanim ci się porobią odciski.

– Uff, dzięki.

Wrócili do całowania, byli już oboje nago, kiedy Sobieraj nagle usiadła na łóżku i przykryła się wstydliwie kołdrą. Spojrzał pytająco.

– Boże, dziwnie się czuję, jakbym powinna poprosić go o pozwolenie. Tak żeby być w porządku.

– Okej – powiedział wolno, czekając na dalszy ciąg.

– Nigdy nie zdradziłam Andrzeja. Nie to że nie chcę, rozumiesz, bardzo chcę, tylko pomyślałam sobie, że powinieneś wiedzieć. Że nie jestem jakaś pierwsza puszczalska. No i strasznie się stresuję. O tobie chodzą opowieści, jest Klara, Tatarska też się zachwycała, a ona jest zwykle bardzo surowa...

Właśnie zrozumiał, dokładnie w tej chwili, co oznacza życie w małym miasteczku.

– ...a ja od piętnastu lat z jednym chłopem, i to nie za często, i po prostu boję się, że mój repertuar jest, rozumiesz, raczej na orkiestrę kameralną niż symfoniczną. I wiem, jak to brzmi, tylko nie chciałabym, żebyś mnie za szybko oceniał, rozumiesz?

– Woody Allen – powiedział, naciągając kołdrę na gołe ciało, zrobiło mu się zimno.

– Co Woody Allen?

– To scena jak z Woody'ego, zamiast się pieprzyć, rozmawiamy o pieprzeniu.

– No tak, wiem, wiem.

– To może tak pomalutku zacznijmy i zobaczymy, co dalej, hmm?

Zaczęli pomalutku i bardzo mu to odpowiadało po perwersyjnych akrobacjach, do jakich był zmuszany przez swoje kochanki ostatnimi czasy. Zamiast się spinać i starać, mógł powoli rozkoszować się bliskością, bawić w odnajdywanie przyjemności swojej i Basi, która w seksie okazała się zmysłowa i inteligentna, a przy tym dowcipna i rozkoszna w swoim skrępowaniu. Próbowała różnych rzeczy z ostrożnością zwierzątka, ale potem szybko nabierała tempa i nie minęło dużo czasu, kiedy z etapu ostrożnego pojękiwania doszli do tego, że chowała głowę w poduszkę, żeby nie zaalarmować Sandomierza swoimi krzykami. Przypomniał sobie o jej chorym sercu i przestraszył się.

– Wszystko w porządku?

– Zwariowałeś?

– Pomyślałem o twoim sercu.

– Spokojnie, wzięłam leki. Jeśli orgazm nie będzie zbyt intensywny, to może przeżyję.

– Bardzo śmieszne.

Orgazm był umiarkowanie intensywny i szczęśliwie obie strony go przeżyły. Szacki przytulał do siebie Basię i pomyślał, że jeśli zostaną kochankami, to będzie to dla niego zupełnie nowe doświadczenie, zwykle to on był tym zajętym.

– Ciągle jestem w szoku – wyszeptała – ciągle na etapie niewiary, naprawdę nie dociera do mnie, że to prawda.

– Daj mi się rozkręcić.

– Idiota, miałam na myśli Wilczura.

– Aha.

– Przeczytałam, co znalazł ten archiwista, wszystko do siebie pasuje, nie ma żadnych luk, jeśli chodzi o motywację. Potem przypomniałam sobie, że był pierwszy przy trupie Budnikowej, że asystował przy znalezieniu brzytwy, że on pokazywał nam nagrania z kamer i koordynował przesłuchania świadków, mógł sterować nami w dowolny sposób. Zwłaszcza tobą, nie znasz miasta, nie znasz ludzi, brałeś na wiarę rzeczy, których ja bym pewnie nie łyknęła.

– Jak jesteś taka bystra, to trzeba go było zamknąć wcześniej.

– Wiesz, że nie o to mi chodzi. Myślę, że nosił się z tym całym planem od dawna, ale możliwość pokazała się dopiero wtedy, kiedy ty pojawiłeś się w Sandomierzu. Mógł być pewny, że gwiazda z Warszawy dostanie sprawę. Gwiazda, ale obca.

– Pierwszego dnia powiedział, że mi pomoże, że będzie wyjaśniał, kto naprawdę jest kim.

– Nie wątpię.

Przez chwilę leżeli w milczeniu.

– To mnie przeraża, hodowanie nienawiści przez tyle lat. Ale kiedy czytałam akta sprawy Wajsbrota...

– Tak?

– To powojenne zezwierzęcenie, tutaj nigdy się o tym nie mówi, jak czasami to wyciągnie jakiś naukowiec albo publicysta „z Warszawy", to nawet nie staje się wrogiem publicznym numer jeden, po prostu się o tym nie mówi.

– Nie jesteście wyjątkiem. Tak jest w całej Polsce.

– Nie mogę przestać sobie tego wyobrażać. Jak ci ludzie po obozach wracają do domu, mając cały czas przed oczami to morze trupów, żyjąc nadzieją, że może cudem ocalała ich łazienka i kuchnia, że jak dotrą na miejsce, to zrobią sobie herbaty, popłaczą i jakoś się uda wrócić do życia. Tyle tylko, że w ich kuchni ktoś stoi, że ich życie nikomu nie jest na rękę, że kolega ze szkoły wrócił tydzień wcześniej i już go zakatowali, na witce brzozowej powiesili. To znaczy, wiedziałam, że takie rzeczy się działy, ale Wajsbrot daje twarz tym wydarzeniom, widzę go, jak wali pięściami w ścianę celi w Nazarecie i wyje, a jego żona umiera kilkaset metrów dalej, bo położna Żydówki się przestraszyła. Myślisz, że to możliwe, że umarła na rękach Wilczura? Musiał mieć wtedy cztery, pięć lat.

– To go nie usprawiedliwia.

– Nie. Ale pomaga zrozumieć.

Zadzwonił telefon. Odebrał i zerwał się na równe nogi.

– No jasne, już lecę, będę czekał na przystanku.

– Co się stało?

– Córka do mnie przyjechała na weekend.

– O, świetnie, to przyjdziesz jutro razem z nią?

– Ale jak to?

– Byliśmy umówieni na grilla. Nie pamietasz?

Od natłoku myśli i emocji czuje ból głowy. Chodzi z kąta w kąt, ale pomieszczenie jest małe i niewygodne, nie może się wychodzić, jak to ma w zwyczaju. Nie może się skupić, nie może się zdecydować, jak zwykle zresztą nie może się zdecydować. Wie, że najrozsądniej byłoby uznać, że to koniec, mieć wszystko z głowy. To tylko niepotrzebne ryzyko, które nie przyniesie żadnych korzyści, a może wszystko zniweczyć, wszystko! Wie to, ale nie potrafi odpuścić, nie tym razem. Poza tym – poza tym może ryzyko nie jest tak wielkie.

Rozdział jedenasty

sobota, 25 kwietnia 2009

Międzynarodowy Dzień Świadomości Zagrożenia Hałasem. Egipt świętuje 27. rocznicę wycofania się Izraela z półwyspu Synaj, irlandzcy socjaldemokraci i zieloni wygraną w przedterminowych wyborach parlamentarnych, a Al Pacino i Andrzej Seweryn – urodziny. Świat zaczyna żyć histerią na punkcie świńskiej grypy. W Niemczech anonimowy kolekcjoner płaci 32 tysiące euro za akwarele autorstwa Adolfa Hitlera. Przedstawiają rustykalne krajobrazy. Krystian Zimerman wywołuje skandal w USA, zapowiadając w czasie koncertu, że nie będzie więcej grał w kraju, którego armia chce kontrolować cały świat. W ojczyźnie pianisty PiS żąda od MON wyjaśnień, dlaczego żołnierze kompanii honorowej nie biorą udziału w uroczystych mszach; MON odpowiada: bo jeśli zemdleją od długiego stania na baczność, mogą komuś zrobić krzywdę bagnetem. W urzędach skarbowych całej Polski dzień otwarty, w przyszłym tygodniu mija termin rozliczeń z fiskusem. W Muzeum Okręgowym w Sandomierzu rusza wystawa tektografii i druków unikatowych Grzegorza Madeja. Sucho, słonecznie, odrobinę cieplej niż wczoraj, ale nie więcej niż 17 stopni.

1

Bał się spotkania z dzieckiem i choć nikomu by się do tego nie przyznał, z duszą na ramieniu jechał odebrać w piątkowy wieczór swoją córkę z dworca autobusowego w Sandomierzu, położonego nieopodal cmentarza żydowskiego, gdzie kilka dni temu kazał zgarnąć miłośników narodowego socjalizmu. Swoją drogą, dziwił się, że po wyjściu z dołka żaden się nie pofatygował, żeby mu namalować gwiazdę Dawida na drzwiach albo zwyczajnie obić ryj.

Helcia wyleciała z autobusu uchachana i uszczęśliwiona, pełna jedenastoletniego stęsknienia, podziwu i empatii. Empatii, ponieważ opatrunek na jego dłoni ciągle wyglądał odpowiednio poważnie, a podziwu, gdyż telewizyjne relacje w połączeniu z bujną wyobraźnią dziewczynki stworzyły obraz bohatera, który niepomny niebezpieczeństw walczy ze złem i występkiem.

Spędzili bardzo miły wieczór przy pizzy i cudne przedpołudnie, którego najważniejszymi elementami były spacer (połączony z gonitwami i grą w kometkę) nad Wisłą oraz śniadanie w Małej, z kawą, czekoladą i naleśnikami na słodko. Prokurator Teodor Szacki patrzył na pogrążoną w lekturze sfatygowanego egzemplarza jednego z *Tytusów* kasztanowowłosą iskrę, która zaczynała się właśnie przepoczwarzać z rozkosznego dziecka w nieforemną nastolatkę, i po raz pierwszy od bardzo dawna czuł spokój. Nie zmęczenie, tylko spokój. A Helcia, odbierając szóstym córczanym zmysłem, że jej rodzic ma za sobą kilka ciężkich dni, oszczędziła mu focha, histerii i rozdzierających płaczów, że ona chce, żeby było tak jak dawniej, albo że już nigdy nie będzie szczęśliwa.

A potem pojechali odwiedzić Basię i Andrzeja Sobierajów.

Sam plan odwiedzenia Basi i jej męża, nie dość, że z dzieckiem, to jeszcze po wczorajszym upojnym wieczorze, wydawał mu się tyleż kuriozalny, co atrakcyjny, i jedyne, co mu przeszkadzało w czerpaniu radości z tej perwersyjnej sytuacji, to fakt, że czeka go jeszcze rozmowa z Leonem Wilczurem. Najchętniej przełożyłby ją na poniedziałek, ale nie mógł. Gdyby bowiem Wilczur postanowił się przyznać – a Szacki przypuszczał, że stanie się to wcześniej czy później – dodatkowo wzmocniłoby to wniosek o tymczasowe aresztowanie. Na razie jednak zepchnął myśl o Wilczurze w kąt i radosnym gestem przerzucił piszczącą córkę nad niskim płotem ogródka Sobierajów, po czy sam go przeskoczył, co wydało mu się bardzo sportowe, a było możliwe jedynie dlatego, że ogrodzenie sięgało mu do kolan.

Helcia i Andrzej Sobieraj bardzo szybko znaleźli wspólny język, głównie dzięki pokazywanym przez niego gadżetom, których jego córka, wychowanka ramy H, nie znała. Bawiła się już sekatorem i kosiarką do trawy, teraz przyszła kolej na węża ogrodowego, który – sądząc po żywiołowej reakcji – był dla niej czymś w rodzaju świętego Graala doskonałej zabawy.

– W końcu nie wyglądasz jak Józef K.

Faktycznie, nie popełnił błędu sprzed tygodnia i przyszedł do ogródka Sobierajów w dżinsach i żeglarskim szarym golfie, garnitur, który miał włożyć na późniejsze przesłuchanie, został w pokrowcu w samochodzie.

– W końcu nie wyglądasz jak harcerka – odgryzł się.

Siedzieli razem przy stoliku na tarasie.

– Zbieraj kasę na dom z ogrodem! – krzyknął spod żywopłotu Sobieraj. – Ta mała ma zadatki na właścicielkę gospodarstwa ogrodniczego!

– Tak, tato, chcę mieć kosiarkę!

– Do włosów chyba!

Helcia podbiegła do stolika.

– Zapomniałeś, że ja chcę mieć długie włosy. O takie – machnęła ręką na wysokości nerek.

Za dzieckiem przyczłapał Sobieraj, wyraźnie zadyszany. Prokurator patrzył, jak bierze duży łyk z puszki piwa, i zastanowił się, czy Sobierajowie uprawiali wczoraj małżeński seks. Z jednej strony naprawdę by się zdziwił, z drugiej zdążył już się nauczyć, że wbrew obiegowej opinii to nie wielkie metropolie są siedliskiem wszelkiej rozpusty.

– Chodź, pomożesz mi zanieść ten szpej do kuchni – powiedziała Sobieraj do męża.

– Litości...

– A co z tym tańczącym kwiatkiem? – zapytała niewinnie Hela.

– Oczywiście, że ci pokażę tańczący kwiatek – ożywił się Sobieraj. – A z garami ci pomoże pan prokurator. Dziecko z miasta przyjechało, niech się nacieszy trochę.

Razem z Helą wrócili do ogrodu, żeby tam instalować tańczący kwiatek, czymkolwiek by on był, a Szacki z Basią Sobieraj zabrali talerze i poszli całować się w domu. Dopiero kiedy radosne okrzyki zakomunikowały sukces operacji „kwiatek", przestali i wrócili razem z blachą pełną ciasta na taras.

Tańczący kwiatek naprawdę tańczył, musiał być tak skonstruowany, że przepływająca przezeń woda miotała główką na wszystkie strony, co dawało radosny i komiczny efekt. Hela została przy kwiatku, żeby piszczeć, podskakiwać i bezskutecznie unikać pryskającej wody, a Sobieraj wrócił do stolika.

– Wspaniałą masz córkę – powiedział i wzniósł puszkę z piwem. – Za twoje geny.

Szacki w odpowiedzi podniósł swoją szklankę z colą. Jednocześnie przypomniał sobie, co Sobieraj opowiadała kiedyś o tym, że nie mogą mieć dzieci. Czy to oznacza, że nie używała żadnej antykoncepcji i że jest przyzwyczajona do tego, że seks nigdy nie oznacza prokreacji?

– Kiedy powiecie mediom o Wilczurze? – spytał szeptem zadyszany mistrz kwiatka. Wcześniej ustalili, że nie będą przy dziecku roztrząsać sprawy.

– O tym, że zatrzymany jest funkcjonariuszem policji, w poniedziałek. A resztę możliwie jak najpóźniej – wyjaśnił Szacki, nie spuszczając oczu z dziecka, stary ojcowski nawyk. – Ogólnikowo opowiemy o motywach osobistych, zdementujemy plotki o seryjnym mordercy, zasłonimy się tajemnicą śledztwa. Histeria ucichnie, a potem będzie jak zwykle. Śledztwo potrwa miesiącami, kiedy będzie można już zajrzeć do akt i poznać motywację Leona W., mało kogo to zainteresuje. Zrobi się szum przy procesie, ale to już pewnie nie nasz problem.

– Dlaczego?

– To nasze ostatnie dni z tą sprawą – w przeciwieństwie do białowłosego kolegi Sobieraj nie cierpiała z tego powodu, przeciwnie, wydawała się zachwycona. – Teo musi jeszcze przesłuchać Wilczura przed wystosowaniem wniosku o areszt, ale akta za chwilę powędrują do innej prokuratury, stawiam na okręgową w Rzeszowie.

– Szkoda. – Sobieraj zmiął puszkę i wrzucił ją do torebki ze śmieciami. – Chciałbym dowiedzieć się od was, jak to było naprawdę.

2

Przebranie się w garnitur trwało dłużej niż samo przesłuchanie. Leon Wilczur został doprowadzony, potwierdził swoje dane osobowe, po czym oznajmił, że odmawia składania wyjaśnień. Prokurator Teodor Szacki przez chwilę się namyślał, po czym podsunął protokół do podpisania. Wilczur był starym policyjnym wygą, który doskonale znał swoje opcje, nic by tu nie dały prośby, groźby i apele do sumienia. Strategia milczenia była idealna, gdyby Szacki był adwokatem policjanta – zaleciłby to samo nawet bez zaglądania do akt. Sprawa była zawiła, poszlakowa, historyczna motywacja wyjątkowo mętna, śledczych czekała ciężka praca szukania dowodów i świadków, na dobry początek trzeba było powtórzyć wszystkie czynności przeprowadzone przez policję, ponieważ obecność Wilczura je unieważniała.

Mimo to zatrzymał się w drzwiach, zanim przywołał mundurowego.

– A może jednak? – spytał. – Trzy zabójstwa. Trzy ofiary. Po tylu latach w policji, po tylu rozwikłanych sprawach, tylu złapanych przestępcach, nie uważa pan, że powinien się przyznać? Żeby sprawiedliwości mogło stać się zadość. Tak po prostu.

– Myli się pan, panie prokuratorze – zaskrzypiał Wilczur, nie odwracając nawet głowy w jego stronę.

Rozdział dwunasty

niedziela, 26 kwietnia 2009

Dla prawosławnych chrześcijan to Wielkanoc Umarłych, święto podobne do Dziadów lub Zaduszek, kiedy biesiadowanie na cmentarzach ma pomóc duszom zmarłych dostać się do nieba. Dla strażników więziennych w Polsce – Dzień Służby Więziennej. Urodziny obchodzą Jan Pietrzak i Anna Mucha. Świńska grypa szaleje. Media mówią w kółko o zarażonych w nowych krajach, polscy muzycy donoszą z Meksyku, że „ulice wyglądają jak oddziały OIOM", minister zdrowia zapewnia, że Polska jest gotowa. Do Rzymu przyjeżdża Aleksander Łukaszenka, to jego pierwsza zagraniczna wizyta od 1995 roku. Premier Tusk podpisuje oświadczenie, że zgadza się na przekazanie swoich organów do przeszczepu. Ku rozpaczy opozycji – dopiero po śmierci. Sandomierzanie reklamują swój gród na targach turystycznych w Warszawie, tymczasem w mieście koncertuje zespół etniczno-rockowy Jacyś Kolesie, na Wisłę wracają statki wycieczkowe, ale wiadomość dnia to wiosna, w końcu wiosna! Ciepło, słonecznie, temperatura przekracza magiczną barierę 20 stopni.

1

Pożegnanie z Heleną Ewą Szacką było rozdzierające. Im bliżej godziny odjazdu autobusu, tym bardziej psuła się atmosfera, mimo wysiłków Szackiego, żeby zabawa była przednia. W drodze na tak zwany na wyrost dworzec autobusowy, naprawdę budkę z dykty i blachy falistej, jedenastoletnia dziewczynka cicho płakała, a przed autobusem zaczęła szlochać i uczepiła się ojca tak histerycznie, że zaczął rozważać, czy nie odwieźć jej samochodem do Warszawy. Z odsieczą nadeszła zażywna pani, która podróżowała z wnuczką w zbliżonym wieku i widząc podbramkową sytuację, zaproponowała, że zaopiekuje się też drugą dziewczynką w czasie podróży. A „druga dziewczynka", jak tylko zwąchała imprezę, natychmiast pocałowała tatę radośnie w czoło i zniknęła we wnętrzu zaskakująco porządnie wyglądającego autokaru.

Mimo to prokurator Teodor Szacki smutny i zdołowany wracał do – no właśnie, gdzie? Do domu? To obce mieszkanie nie było jego domem. Do siebie? Już prędzej, u „siebie" to może być dom, ale też pokój hotelowy, łóżko w schronisku albo namiot na kempingu. O każdym tymczasowym lokum można tak było powiedzieć.

Toteż wrócił do siebie, ale wystarczyło mu spojrzeć w skrzynkowe okno kuchni, żeby odwrócić się na pięcie i ruszyć schodami prowadzącymi na dół, w stronę Wisły. Miał ochotę na naprawdę długi spacer, chciał się zmęczyć, zjeść obiad, wypić dwa piwa i usnąć snem bez snów.

Boże, jaki to był piękny dzień! Miała rację Sobieraj, kiedy mówiła tydzień wcześniej, że musi zobaczyć wiosnę w Sandomierzu. Wiosna postanowiła nadrobić wszystkie stracone dni, gołe do tej pory gałązki obrzuciła zieloną mgłą, na tych już zazielenionych pojawiły się białe kwiatki, w powietrzu słodkie zapachy kwitnienia mieszały się z wonią ziemi i zawiewającym znad Wisły błotnistym odorem podmokłych łąk. Szacki wciągał je w siebie jak narkoman, próbował doświadczyć wszystkich naraz i każdego z osobna, nigdy do tej pory w swoim życiu nie przeżył wiosny innej niż ta miejska, wyblakła, od samego początku jakaś taka zmęczona i przechodzona.

Zszedł na błonia i obok pomnika Jana Pawła II – przy którym kuriozalna tabliczka głosiła, że papież odprawił tu „mszę w obecności odradzającego się rycerstwa" – odbił w lewo i poszedł przez łąkę w stronę trasy na Kraków. Dopiero tam odwrócił się i spojrzał na Sandomierz. I pomyślał: okej, akurat w legendzie o pułkowniku Skopence musi być więcej niż marne ziarno prawdy. Nie wyobrażał sobie, żeby ktoś mógł z tej perspektywy ujrzeć miasto i wydać rozkaz artyleryjskiego ostrzału. Było piękne, było najpiękniejsze w Polsce, było włoskie, toskańskie, europejskie, niepolskie, było miastem, w którym chciało się zakochać od pierwszego wejrzenia, zamieszkać i nigdy nie wyjeżdżać. Było – ta myśl po raz pierwszy pojawiła się w głowie prokuratora – jego miastem.

Oderwał wzrok od spiętrzonych na wiślanej skarpie kamieniczek, od białej bryły Collegium Gostomianum, sąsiadującej z czerwonym ceglanym gotyckim Domem Długosza, od wieży ratusza i schowanej trochę z tej perspektywy sygnaturki katedry. I ruszył wzdłuż drogi, raz po raz zerkając na kojący oko architektoniczny przepych.

Pokręcił się trochę po bulwarze Piłsudskiego, przy którym pojawił się już statek białej floty, posiedział na ławce, obserwując wsiadających i wysiadających turystów. W zależności od osoby albo cieszył się, że nią nie jest, albo wręcz przeciwnie – zazdrościł jej życia. Mógł się tak bawić godzinami. Potem wspiął się tajemniczym i mrocznym wąwozem lessowym do kościoła Świętego Pawła i stamtąd wrócił pod zamek, po drodze wchodząc w tłum ludzi opuszczających po mszy kościół Świętego Jakuba.

Nie mógł niestety nie spojrzeć na rozciągającą się na dole łąkę, dokładnie to miejsce, pod którym kilka dni temu eksplozja rzuciła go na ścianę i uczyniła z Marka Dybusa kalekę na resztę życia. To nie było dobre wspomnienie.

Nie mógł też niestety udawać dłużej, że zajmuje go córka, widoki Sandomierza, spacery i poszukiwanie wiosny. Był niemiłosiernie, wyczerpująco niespokojny, rozedrgany, rozbity, pasowało do niego każde słowo w każdym języku, o ile tylko wyrażało niepokój. Który boleśnie odczuwał każdym fibrem swojej istoty. Niezależnie od tego, czy bawił się z córką, czy jadł, czy spał, czuł tylko jedną emocję. I widział tylko jedną rzecz: twarz Wilczura. I słyszał tylko jedną rzecz: pan się myli, panie prokuratorze.

Bzdura, pieprzona bzdura, nie może się mylić, bo wszystkie fakty – choć fantastyczne – idealnie do siebie pasują. Co z tego, że niecodzienne? Co z tego, że motyw wydumany? Z głupszych powodów ludzie mordowali, już Wilczur wie to lepiej od niego. Poza tym nikt mu nie zabrania mówić. Może wytłumaczyć, dlaczego się myli. Może udowodnić, gdzie był w czasie zabójstw. Może gadać bez końca, opowiadać dotąd, aż zabraknie papieru w prokuraturze. Ale tego nie zrobi, nie jest głupi, pieprzony stary dziad, szlag by to trafił.

Szacki już w czasie ostatniej bezsennej nocy nazwał to, co go trapi. Siedział w kuchni, słuchając, jak jego córka przewraca się z boku na bok, i kreślił możliwe wersje wydarzeń – teraz przynajmniej z podejrzanym za kratkami. Wersje różniły się niuansami, ale wszystkie odpowiadały na pytanie „dlaczego?" elegancko, na sposób właściwy powieściom kryminalnym. Wielka krzywda, przenoszona nienawiść, zemsta po latach. Zemsta zaplanowana w taki sposób, aby wszyscy usłyszeli o tym, co wydarzyło się mroźną zimą Roku Pańskiego 1947. Tak jak wyjaśniał Klejnocki: infamia to ważna część wendety, sam trup nie jest wystarczającym zadośćuczynieniem. No to Wilczur osiągnął swój cel, cała Polska będzie mówiła o nim i o jego krzywdzie.

Tak, w kwestii motywu wszystko się zgadzało. Gorzej było z odpowiedzią na pytanie „jak?". Jak ten stary, chudy, siedemdziesięcioletni dziad zamordował trzy osoby? Wiele znaków zapytania można było wytłumaczyć tym, że był doświadczonym sandomierskim gliną. Zawsze pierwszy na miejscu zbrodni, rozdawał karty, wydawał polecenia. Kontrolował przesłuchania i czynności, kontrolował całą śledczą machinę. On nadzorował odzyskiwanie nagrań z miejskiego monitoringu, jednocześnie udowadniając, że nie była mu obca współczesna technologia. Co tłumaczyło konto na serwisie informacyjnym i korzystanie z telefonu komórkowego do zawiadamiania mediów. Szkoda tylko, że telefonu nie znaleźli. Znał Sandomierz od podszewki, co może tłumaczyć jego znajomość sandomierskich lochów. Trzeba będzie przesłuchać Dybusa na tę okoliczność, jak dojdzie do siebie. Kto wiedział o ich badaniach, kto w nich uczestniczył, czy były w to zaangażowane służby miejskie, urzędnicy. Zakładając, że Wilczur znał podziemia, i zakładając fantastyczną tezę, że ukryte wejścia do nich są w różnych częściach miasta, mogło to wyjaśnić kwestię transportu zwłok. Postawienie policjanta w roli sprawcy wyjaśniało też niedającą wcześniej Szackiemu spokoju kwestię znaczka w dłoni Budnikowej. Wilczur wcisnął symbol rodła w dłoń trupa, aby skierować podejrzenia na Szyllera, aby od niego z kolei podejrzenie odbiło się w stronę Budnika i żeby na jaw wyszedł romans z sandomierskich wyższych sfer. Pasuje do teorii Klejnockiego o infamii.

Ale to mało, ciągle mało.

Szacki stał teraz na zamkowym dziedzińcu, lubił to miejsce i widok rozciągający się z tarasu na zakole niepokojąco szerokiej o tej porze roku Wisły. Lubił świadomość, że od kilkuset lat ludzie stawali tam i podziwiali ten sam pejzaż. No, może trochę piękniejszy, nieoszpecony złośliwie przez komin huty szkła. Wokół było pełno ludzi, którzy wysypali się z okolicznych kościołów po sumie. W charakterystyczny dla małego miasta sposób odświętnie ubrani: panowie w garniturach, panie w garsonkach o dziwacznych kolorach, chłopcy w błyszczących sportowych butach, dziewczyny w czarnych rajstopach i wieczorowym makijażu. Można było w każdym z nich osobno i we wszystkich razem znaleźć sto powodów do kpin, Szackiego jednak ten widok rozczulił. Przez lata mieszkania w Warszawie czuł, że coś jest nie tak, że ta najbrzydsza metropolia Europy nie jest miejscem przyjaznym, że jego przywiązanie do burych murów to tak naprawdę neurotyczne uzależnienie, urbanistyczny syndrom sztokholmski. Tak jak więźniowie uzależniają się od więzienia, a mężowie od złych żon, tak on uwierzył, że sam fakt życia w brudzie i chaosie wystarczy, aby tenże brud i chaos obdarzyć uczuciem. Prokurator Teodor Szacki, warszawiak. Warszawiak, czyli bezdomny. Teraz, na pełnym słońca i gwaru dziedzińcu zamku w Sandomierzu, widział to wyraźnie. Jako obywatel wielkiego miasta nie miał małej ojczyzny, nie miał krainy szczęśliwego dzieciństwa, swojego miejsca na ziemi. Miejsca, gdzie wracającego po latach witają uśmiechy, wyciągnięte dłonie i zmienione przez czas, ale te same twarze. Gdzie rysy sąsiadów i przyjaciół, którzy już odeszli, odnajduje się w ich dzieciach i wnukach, gdzie można poczuć się częścią większej całości, odnaleźć sens w byciu ogniwem mocnego i długiego łańcucha. Widział tutaj ten łańcuch, pod bazarowymi garniturami i garsonkami, i zazdrościł tym wszystkim ludziom. Zazdrościł tak bardzo, że aż bolało, ponieważ czuł, że jemu nigdy to nie będzie dane, nawet na najszczęśliwszej emigracji pozostanie zawsze i wszędzie bezdomnym bez ojczyzny.

– Panie prokuratorze? – Klara zmaterializowała się obok w beżowej, zwiewnej sukience. Otworzył usta, chciał przepraszać.

– Z Markiem już lepiej, odzyskał przytomność, udało mi się nawet z nim zamienić dwa słowa. Zobaczyłam cię i pomyślałam, że może chciałbyś wiedzieć.

– Dziękuję. To doskonała wiadomość. Chciałbym...

– Daj spokój, nie musisz przepraszać. Tam na dole, z Markiem, nie było w tym nic z twojej winy, mam tylko nadzieję, że ten dziad doczeka ostatniego oddechu za kratami. A jeśli chodzi o nas, cóż, jesteśmy dorośli. Spędziliśmy razem kilka chwil, które uważam za wyjątkowo miłe. Dziękuję.

Nie miał pojęcia, co powiedzieć.

– To ja dziękuję.

Skinęła głową, stali bez słowa, cisza była krępująca i w innych okolicznościach pewnie poszliby do łóżka, żeby jej nie słyszeć.

– Nie spytasz mnie, czy nasikałam na test?

– Nie spędza mi to snu z powiek. To byłby zaszczyt zostać ojcem twojego dziecka.

– No proszę, jednak potrafisz się zachować. Skoro tak, to... – stanęła na palcach i cmoknęła go w policzek – ...do zobaczenia. To małe miasto, na pewno będziemy na siebie wpadać co chwila.

Pomachała na pożegnanie i szybkim krokiem odeszła w stronę katedry. Szacki wrócił myślami do Dybusa, do podziemia, do Wilczura, do sprawy. I do męczącego jak zgaga pytania: jak? Jak, kurwa, jak? Nawet zakładając znajomość przez niego systemu tuneli, nawet zakładając, że w każdej bramie jest do nich wejście, to jak ten staruszek poradził sobie z trupami? Powiedzmy, że Budnikowa była lekka, jej mąż też chuderlawy, ale Szyller to już kawał przypakowanego byka. I co? Ma uwierzyć, że Wilczur go uśpił, a potem wrzucił na plecy i ukrzyżował w podziemiach? Że zadał sobie trud zatargania Budnika na piętro dworku przy Zamkowej? A Budnikowa? Przecież nie mógł wiedzieć, że akurat tego dnia o tej godzinie postanowi wyprowadzić się do kochanka. Obserwował posesję? Jak? Przez kamery?

No i napis na obrazie w katedrze. Wilczur był Żydem, kilka razy dał się poznać jako znawca kultury żydowskiej, potrafił cytować z pamięci Pismo po hebrajsku. Czy zrobiłby tak oczywisty błąd? Czy odwróciłby po dziecinnemu literkę w prostym słowie? Nie miałoby to przecież żadnego celu w jego planie. Czy to znaczy, że miał wspólnika? To by też tłumaczyło jego milczenie. To byłaby doskonała strategia, ale też gwarancja, że nikogo przez przypadek nie wyda.

Rozbolała go głowa, pomyślał, że to pewnie z głodu, zbliżała się pora obiadu, a on od rana nie miał niczego w ustach. Przedarł się przez zapach jabłoni kwitnących w ogrodzie przy katedrze i wspiął na poziom rynku, bez zastanowienia skierował swoje kroki prosto do Trzydziestki. Miejsca, gdzie szedł zawsze, kiedy nie miał ochoty na eksperymenty, gdzie pewnie żaden krytyk kulinarny nie dotrwałby do deseru i gdzie podawano najlepszą kaszę gryczaną na świecie. Nie chciał nawet myśleć, ile razy sympatyczna kelnerka stawiała przed nim kawał świeżutkiej karkówki z grilla w towarzystwie suszonych śliwek, góry kaszy i kufla zimnego piwa. Nie chciał, bo bał się, że jego wątroba podsłucha.

– Nasze stoliki są chyba w różnych wymiarach czasoprzestrzeni, panie prokuratorze – dobiegł go z tyłu zrzędliwy głos.

Odwrócił się i zdębiał. Przy stoliku obok siedziała jego była przełożona, szefowa prokuratury rejonowej Warszawa-Śródmieście, o której myślał zawsze jako o najmniej atrakcyjnej kobiecie świata. Cóż, jeden rzut oka po paru miesiącach rozłąki utwierdził go w przekonaniu, że zawsze miał rację. Szara twarz była tak samo szara, brunatne strąki lekko falujących włosów tak samo brunatne, zamiana urzędowego szarego żakietu na czerwony sweter zamiast złagodzić przygnębiające wrażenie, tylko je wzmacniała. Janina Chorko wyglądała jak kobieta, która wysłała prośbę do fundacji spełniającej życzenia śmiertelnie chorych, a fundacja przebrała ją w coś wesołego na ostatnie chwile. Upiorny efekt.

– Dobrze panią widzieć, pani prokurator. Doskonale pani wygląda.

Chorko nie była sama, razem z nią była Maria „Misia" Miszczyk ze swoim mężem, zaskakująco przystojnym, w typie

George'a Clooneya, dwójka ich dzieci miała około piętnastu–szesnastu lat, chłopak już teraz wyglądał jak kłopoty, dziewczynka w typie prymuski miała trochę zgaszoną urodę, ale jej oczy rzucały tak inteligentne błyski, że Szacki bałby się z nią zmierzyć na riposty.

Mimo skłonności mamy do nadmiaru cielesności i jej talentu do pieczenia ciast cała trójka była szczupła i wysportowana. Szackiemu zrobiło się nagle przykro, że Chorko z nimi siedzi, dla jej wymęczonej samotnej szarości bolesne musiało być obserwowanie tej szczęśliwej, pięknej rodziny.

– Nie wiedziałem, że panie się znają – powiedział cokolwiek, nie chcąc, żeby Chorko zauważyła emocje rysujące się na jego twarzy.

– Nie wiem, jak to o panu świadczy jako o śledczym, prokuratorze – zauważyła zgryźliwie. – Nie wyśledził pan, że dwie pana szefowe razem studiowały.

Miszczyk wybuchnęła śmiechem, Chorko do niej dołączyła. Nigdy nie słyszał śmiechu swojej byłej szefowej. A śmiała się ślicznie, radośnie, wygładzały jej się zmarszczki i rozżarzały oczy, nawet jeśli nie stawała się ładna, to przynajmniej przestawała przypominać pomoc naukową dla studentów medycyny.

– Ale, ale – powiedziała prokurator Janina Chorko. – Zwykle trzymam prywatne życie jak najdalej od świata zbrodni, lecz teraz... To jest prokurator Teodor Szacki, opowiadałam ci, Mariuszku, że jakbyś chciał mimo wszystko iść na prawo, to musisz pisać dyplom z jego spraw, niezwykłe historie w niezwykły sposób rozwikłane. A to mój mąż Jerzy, syn Mariusz i przysposobiona przez nas dziewczynka, Luiza.

– Jak to przysposobiona? – obruszyła się Luiza, ściągając na siebie uwagę.

– Bo to niemożliwe, żebym urodziła córkę, która w ten sposób trzyma łokcie na stole.

– Aha, więc to żart. Szkoda, już się ucieszyłam, że odnajdę swoją prawdziwą rodzinę...

– Proszę nie zwracać na nią uwagi, to ten wiek.

– ...po pełnych przygód poszukiwaniach, które w końcu nadadzą mojemu życiu jakiś sens.

– Proszę siadać, napijemy się, Janka prowadzi. – Mąż Chorko, jak się zaskakująco okazało, uśmiechnął się szeroko i zrobił miejsce Szackiemu na drewnianej ławce.

Ale prokurator Teodor Szacki stał w miejscu, nawet nie starając się ukryć zdumienia. To niemożliwe, przepracował z tą kobietą dwanaście lat, mając ją zawsze za zgorzkniałą starą pannę, która na dodatek czyni mu dyskretne, wprawiające w zakłopotanie awanse. Przez dwanaście lat było mu przykro, że je odrzuca, przez dwanaście lat regularnie pił jej zdrowie, myśląc, że świat jest niesprawiedliwy, że musi gdzieś być ktoś, może nie z pierwszej ligi, ale przynajmniej z obiema rękami i nogami, kto pochyli się nad nią z litości, obdarzy nawet jeśli nie miłością, to odrobiną sympatii i wniesie choć maciupinkę światła w jej szarobure życie.

Jak widać, martwił się niepotrzebnie. Jak widać, są legendy, w których nie ma ziarna prawdy. W których wszystko od początku do końca jest kłamstwem.

Wszyscy kłamią, powiedział umierający ojciec Basi Sobieraj.

– O kurwa – powiedział na głos.

Nie widział reakcji biesiadników na to nieoczekiwane zagajenie, ponieważ nagle, w końcu, jedna prosta myśl sprawiła, że runął mur, w który walił głową od początku tego śledztwa. Legendy, w których nie ma ziarna prawdy, w których wszystko jest kłamstwem. Wszystko! Zaczął przesuwać w myślach sceny śledztwa, od pierwszego zamglonego poranka pod synagogą, zakładając, że wszystko jest kłamstwem. I poderżnięte gardło, i brzytwa, i misterium krwi, i miejsce znalezienia ciała, i cała żydowska mitologia, i cała polska antysemicka mitologia, i dworek, i beczka, i malowidło w katedrze, i napis, i wszystkie te obrazy, które tak skwapliwie podsuwano mu pod nos.

– O kurwa – powtórzył, tym razem głośniej, i rzucił się biegiem przez rynek.

– Chyba nie chcę być prawnikiem – usłyszał jeszcze z tyłu komentarz syna Chorko.

Jeszcze nigdy żaden proces myślowy w jego głowie nie przebiegł tak szybko, jeszcze nigdy tyle faktów w tak krótkim błysku nie połączyło się w jeden nierozerwalny logiczny ciąg, który miał tylko jeden możliwy wynik. To było doświadczenie z pogranicza choroby, myśli przeskakiwały po neuronach w epileptycznym tempie, szara materia świeciła się platynowo od nadmiaru informacji, bał się, że coś mu się stanie, że jego mózg tego nie przerobi, że się zadławi. Ale było też w tym coś z narkotycznej euforii albo religijnej ekstazy, niedające się powstrzymać podniecenie, niepozwalające się opanować emocje. Kłamstwo, kłamstwo, wszystko kłamstwo, iluzja, ściema. W tym natłoku lunaparkowych atrakcji, w dekoracjach zbrodni, w nadmiarze faktów i ich interpretacji przeoczył najważniejsze szczegóły, a przede wszystkim najważniejszą rozmowę.

Kiedy wpadł do Ratuszowej, musiał mieć obłęd w oczach, bo mroczny kelner porzucił swoją flegmę i bojaźliwie schował się za bar. W środku prawie nikogo nie było, pod ścianą siedziały dwie rodziny zabłąkanych turystów, musiały być naprawdę bardzo głodne, skoro zdecydowały się tu zostać na posiłek.

– Gdzie są te meneliki, co tu zwykle siedzą? – wrzasnął do kelnera, ale zanim tamtemu słowa przecisnęły się przez gardło, napakowany hormonami system nerwowy Szackiego udzielił mu odpowiedzi i prokurator wybiegł, pozostawiając za sobą kolejne zdumione osoby, które tak samo jak towarzystwo w Trzydziestce spojrzały po sobie i nakreśliły kółko na skroni.

Najważniejszą rozmowę odbył z człowiekiem z zewnątrz, mądrym człowiekiem, który oceniał fakty nie na tle sandomierskiego piekiełka, tylko po prostu jako fakty. W czasie tej rozmowy irytował się na Jarosława Klejnockiego, zżymał na jego styl, denerwowała go fajeczka i wykształciuchowa gadka, znowu atrybuty zasłoniły prawdę. A prawda była taka, że Jarosław Klejnocki rozwiązał sandomierską zagadkę przed tygodniem, tylko on był zbyt głupi, zbyt utopiony w kłamstwie, zbyt pogrążony w detalach, żeby to dostrzec.

Szacki minął sprintem pocztę, przebiegł Opatowską, cudem nie przewracając starszej pani wychodzącej ze sklepu z rękodziełem, przeleciał przez przejazd Bramy Opatowskiej i dysząc, zatrzymał się koło małego skwerku. Mało nie zawył ze szczęścia, kiedy zobaczył na ławce tego samego menela, co wczoraj. Dopadł facecika, na niedużej trójkątnej twarzy ozdobionej odstającymi uszami pojawił się strach.

– Panie, co pan...

– Pan Gąsiorowski, tak?

– Eee, a kto pyta?

– Urząd Prokuratorski Rzeczpospolitej Polskiej, kurwa mać, pyta! Tak czy nie?

– Darek Gąsiorowski, bardzo mi przyjemnie.

– Panie Darku, pan może nie pamięta, ale kilka dni temu widzieliśmy się pod Ratuszową. Wychodziłem razem z inspektorem Leonem Wilczurem, pan nas zaczepił.

– No tak, pamiętam.

– O co chodziło? Co pan od niego chciał?

– Żeby Leo nam pomógł, bo znamy się kopę lat, a jak poszliśmy normalnie na policję, to nas wyśmiali.

– Żeby w jakiej sprawie pomógł?

Gąsiorowski westchnął, potarł nos nerwowym gestem, wyraźnie nie miał ochoty na ponowne kpiny.

– To bardzo ważne.

– Jest taki jeden gość, fajny gość, który wędruje po okolicy. Przyjaciel mój.

– Włóczęga?

– Nie właśnie, podobno nawet gdzieś ma dom, on tylko lubi wędrować.

– I?

– I on, ja w ogóle myślę, że to jakaś choroba, nie ten teges do końca, rozumie pan, bo on jak wędruje, to można zegarek regulować. Wiadomo, kiedy w jakim miejscu o której będzie. To znaczy, ja wiem na przykład, kiedy będzie tutaj, to się wtedy spotykamy na winko i pogadać.

– I?

– I ostatnio nie przyszedł. Dwa razy nie przyszedł. A to mu się nigdy nie zdarzyło. Poszłem na policję, żeby może się dowiedzieli, bo on bywał i w Tarnobrzegu, i w Zawichoście, i Dwikozach, i chyba Opatowie też. Żeby sprawdzili, bo jak mówię, on nie do końca ten teges, mógł na przykład dostać tej choroby, co się nic nie pamięta. Albo przecież on chodził po drogach, to wypadek czy coś, wtedy chciałby, żeby ktoś go odwiedził w szpitalu, prawda? – Zawiesił wzrok na opatrunku Szackiego.

– Prawda. Wie pan, jak on się nazywa?

– Tolo.

– Anatol?

– Tak, chyba tak. A może Antoni, też tak czasem mówią.

– A dalej?

– Fijewski.

– Poważnie?

– No.

– Pan Anatol ma nazwisko Fijewski?

– A co w tym dziwnego?

– Nieważne. Dziękuję.

Szacki zostawił Gąsiorowskiego, wyjął komórkę.

– A nie powinienem go opisać czy coś? – krzyknął facecik, podnosząc się z ławki.

– Nie trzeba! – odkrzyknął Szacki.

Spojrzał na stojący po drugiej stronie ulicy Nazaret, wzrok ześlizgnął mu się na kościół Świętego Michała, przylepiony do barokowego gmachu seminarium.

Święty Archaniele Michale, pogromco zła, patronie wszystkich walczących o sprawiedliwość, opiekunie policjantów i prokuratorów, wysłuchaj swojego wiernego sługi i spraw, żeby nie było za późno. I żeby raz w tym pieprzonym kraju dało się coś załatwić w urzędach po godzinach pracy.

Rozdział trzynasty

poniedziałek, 27 kwietnia 2009

Światowy Dzień Grafika, w Sierra Leone i Togo – Dzień Niepodległości. Kardynał Stanisław Dziwisz kończy siedemdziesiąt lat. W serwisach kryzys ekonomiczny zostaje wyparty przez świńską grypę, w Izraelu ze względu na koszerność nazwanej „meksykańską". Stan Iowa legalizuje śluby homoseksualne, General Motors ogłasza koniec pontiaca, a Bayern Monachium koniec Jürgena Klinsmanna na posadzie trenera klubu. W Polsce Jadwiga Staniszkis twierdzi, że Lech Kaczyński nie wystartuje w przyszłorocznych wyborach prezydenckich, Czesław Kiszczak, że wprowadzenie stanu wojennego było legalne, a 26 procent katolików, że zna księży, którzy żyją w konkubinacie. W świętokrzyskim grasuje puma. W Sandomierzu zapada decyzja o budowie nowoczesnego boiska przy II LO, a obok innego istniejącego boiska łupem zuchwałych złodziei pada kolejna komórka – tym razem pozostawiona w reklamówce na ziemi. Piękna wiosna, słonecznie, temperatura powyżej 20 stopni. Sucho, w lasach zagrożenie pożarowe.

1

Przyjście tutaj było niezmiernie, niesłychanie głupie, czuje strach, ale przede wszystkim złość. Złość, że teraz głupi przypadek może zakończyć sprawę. Co prawda, w urzędzie jest jak zwykle tłum ludzi, tłoczący się interesanci z całego województwa, zbiór przypadkowych osób, które nigdy wcześniej się nie widziały i nigdy więcej nie zobaczą. Taki tłum to z jednej strony bezpieczeństwo, z drugiej zagrożenie, wielkie zagrożenie. Czuje przepływające przez ciało fale paniki, kurczowo trzymany w zaciśniętej dłoni kwitek z numerkiem zamienia się w wilgotny strzęp, zauważa to i wsadza go do portfela.

Ping, przed nim jeszcze dwie osoby. Dwie osoby! Panika walczy z uczuciem euforii. Dwie osoby, krótka wizyta przy okienku, wyjście i... koniec, nareszcie koniec!

Panika wygrywa. Próbuje zająć czymś myśli, żeby zabić czas, czyta po raz kolejny wiszące na ścianie regulaminy i urzędowe obwieszczenia, czyta instrukcję obsługi gaśnicy, ale to tylko pogarsza sprawę, nie potrafi zrozumieć najprostszego słowa, uniemożliwia to gonitwa myśli, narastająca histeria. Czuje mdłości i mrowienie w dłoniach, przed oczami zaczynają latać czarne płatki. Jeśli zemdleje to koniec, koniec! Ta myśl dudni w głowie coraz głośniej i coraz szybciej, im bardziej nie chce się jej poddać, tym bardziej dudni, tym większe przerażenie, tym większy rozmiar czarnego śniegu, który coraz gęściej sypie przed oczami. Powietrze z trudem wciska się do płuc, boi się, że nie wydusi słowa, że zrobi się zamieszanie, że to zamieszanie to będzie koniec! Koniec! Koniec! Wszystko na marne, reszta życia w więzieniu, ból, zamknięcie, samotność. Koniec!!!

Ping, jeszcze jedna osoba.

Nie, nie da rady, po prostu pomału wyjdzie i zapomni o tym głupim pomyśle. Odwraca się i robi dwa kroki w stronę drzwi, ciało za bardzo nie słucha i przelewa się przez nie nowa fala paniki, mdłości wracają ze wzmożoną siłą, strach wpycha żółć do gardła. Pomału, pomalutku, bardzo powoli, uspokaja się w myślach, stawiając małe kroczki.

Ping, od razu, niemożliwe, ktoś zrezygnował! To znak! Podchodzi do okienka na miękkich nogach, ma wrażenie, że świeci na różne kolory, że panika wyskakuje na czerwono na monitorach ochrony. Trudno, teraz nie ma już odwrotu. Podaje dowód osobisty, odpowiada na kilka obojętnie zadanych pytań, czeka, aż urzędniczka skończy. Podpisuje się na formularzu odbioru, urzędniczka podaje świeżutki paszport, bordowe okładki połyskują w słońcu, przeciskającym się między wertykalami. Dziękuje grzecznie i odchodzi.

Po chwili stoi już przed wielkim, przypominającym szpital Świętokrzyskim Urzędem Wojewódzkim w Kielcach. I myśli, że zbrodnia doskonała jednak istnieje, wystarczy odrobina pracy i pomyślunku. Kto wie, może kiedyś komuś o tym opowie, może napisze książkę, zobaczymy. Teraz chce się nacieszyć wolnością. Chowa paszport do kieszeni, wyciera spocone ręce o polarową bluzę, uśmiecha się szeroko i wolnym krokiem idzie w stronę Warszawskiej. Jest piękny, słoneczny dzień, w taki dzień nawet Kielce wydają się ładne. Uspokaja się, wyluzowuje, uśmiecha do ludzi zmierzających szybkim krokiem do wejścia do urzędu, krokiem właściwym dla stolicy województwa. Stojący na dole schodów policjanci nie robią wrażenia, w końcu są na właściwym miejscu, strzegąc porządku w siedzibie władzy.

Euforia rośnie, coraz szerzej uśmiecha się do mijanych ludzi i kiedy prokurator Teodor Szacki odpowiada uśmiechem, w pierwszej chwili nawet nie czuje, że coś jest nie tak, ot, sympatyczny facet w średnim wieku, chyba przedwcześnie posiwiały. To trwa ułamek sekundy. Następny ułamek sekundy trwa myśl, że to ktoś bardzo podobny, że zaszczuty umysł płata figle. A w następnym ułamku sekundy już wie, że zbrodnia doskonała jednak nie istnieje.

– Tak, słucham pana? – próbuje jeszcze w geście rozpaczy rżnąć głupa.

– To ja pana słucham, panie Anatolu – odpowiada prokurator.

2

Później, już w Sandomierzu, w czasie trwającego wiele godzin przesłuchania, kiedy morderca przyznał się do wszystkiego, prokurator Teodor Szacki musiał zmierzyć się z dziwnym uczuciem. Zdarzało mu się wobec przesłuchiwanych czuć empatię, zdarzało współczucie, ba, zdarzało mu się nawet szanować tych, którzy zgrzeszyli i mieli odwagę stawić temu czoło. Ale chyba po raz pierwszy w swojej karierze czuł dla przestępcy może nie podziw, ale uczucie mu bliskie, niepokojąco bliskie. Bardzo się starał tego nie okazać, mimo to, poznając kolejne szczegóły przestępstwa, co jakiś czas myślał, że jeszcze nigdy nie był tak blisko zbrodni doskonałej.

PROTOKÓŁ PRZESŁUCHANIA PODEJRZANEGO. Grzegorz Budnik, urodzony 4 grudnia 1950 roku, zamieszkały w Sandomierzu przy ulicy Katedralnej 27, wykształcenie wyższe chemiczne, przewodniczący Rady Miejskiej miasta Sandomierz. Stosunek do stron: mąż Elżbiety Budnik (ofiara). Niekarany, pouczony o obowiązkach i prawach podejrzanego, wyjaśnia, co następuje:

Niniejszym przyznaję się do zabójstwa mojej żony, Elżbiety Budnik, i Jerzego Szyllera oraz do uprowadzenia i zabójstwa Anatola Fijewskiego. Pierwszego zabójstwa, Elżbiety Budnik, dokonałem w Sandomierzu w Poniedziałek Wielkanocny

13 kwietnia 2009 roku, a motywem mojego postępowania była nienawiść wobec żony, o której od dawna wiedziałem, że ma romans ze znanym mi Jerzym Szyllerem, i która tego dnia zapowiedziała, że w związku z tym chce zakończyć nasze małżeństwo, trwające od 1995 roku. Tego samego dnia wprowadziłem w życie plan, który miał doprowadzić do śmierci Jerzego Szyllera i do tego, abym uniknął odpowiedzialności karnej. Plan ten miałem przygotowany od wielu tygodni, ale do pewnego momentu nie traktowałem go serio, był to pewien rodzaj rozrywki intelektualnej...

Budnik mówił, Szacki słuchał, na cyfrowym dyktafonie przeskakiwały cyferki. Przewodniczący Rady Miejskiej, a jeszcze do niedawna zimny trup, dość beznamiętnie opisywał wydarzenia, ale były momenty, kiedy nie potrafił ukryć dumy i Szacki zrozumiał, że ta intryga, ten jeden jedyny przebłysk geniuszu, który się przytrafił w jego urzędniczym życiu, to największy sukces tego człowieka. A raczej drugi największy, pierwszym było doprowadzenie do ołtarza Elżbiety Szuszkiewicz. Budnik wyczerpująco i ze szczegółami relacjonował swoje działania, a Szacki myślał o ich poprzedniej rozmowie, kiedy – jak się okazało, słusznie – był przekonany o winie Budnika. I jak przypomniał mu się Gollum z *Władcy Pierścieni*, postać owładnięta obsesją posiadania „skarbu", dla której nie liczy się nic innego, nie liczy się nawet skarb jako taki – jedynie jego posiadanie. Bez posiadania skarbu Budnik był nikim i niczym, stał się pustą skorupą, pozbawioną wszelkich naturalnych i kulturalnych hamulców, zdolną do planowania i dokonywania zabójstw z zimną krwią. Skala zbrodni była straszna, ale bardziej przerażająca była skala obsesji Budnika na punkcie swojej żony. Szacki słuchał o podziemiach, słuchał o przygotowaniach, o głodzonych psach, o upodabnianiu się tygodniami do biednego włóczęgi, aby ukraść mu tożsamość, słuchał wytłumaczeń mniejszych i większych zagadek, których rozwiązanie i tak było jasne, odkąd wpadł na to, że Budnik musi być mordercą. Ale gdzieś tam w głębi zastanawiał się bez przerwy: czy to jest prawdziwa miłość? Tak obsesyjna, tak wyniszczająca, zdolna do największych poświęceń i największych zbrodni? Czy w ogóle można mówić o miłości, dopóki nie dozna się emocji tak silnych? Dopóki nie zrozumie się, że w porównaniu z nią cała reszta jest nieważna?

Prokurator Teodor Szacki nie był w stanie wyrzucić tych rozważań z głowy. I bał się, ponieważ było w nich coś profetycznego, coś, co sprawiało, że nie mógł traktować ich tylko teoretycznie. Jakby opatrzność szykowała dla niego największą próbę, a on szóstym zmysłem odczuł, że przyjdzie mu zważyć na jednej ręce miłość, a na drugiej czyjeś życie.

Budnik mówił monotonnie, kolejne elementy wskakiwały na swoje miejsce, układanka wyglądała jak gotowy do oprawienia obraz. Zwykle w takich chwilach prokurator Teodor Szacki czuł spokój, teraz wypełniał go dziwny, irracjonalny lęk. Grzegorz Budnik nie planował, że zostanie zabójcą. Nie urodził się z tą myślą i nigdy mu ona nie towarzyszyła. Po prostu pewnego dnia uznał, że to jedyne wyjście.

Dlaczego on był dziwnie przekonany, że dla niego taki dzień także nadejdzie?

3

Zatrzymanie Grzegorza Budnika to była bomba, w serwisach informacyjnych nawet świńska grypa zeszła na drugi plan, sandomierzanie nie mówili o niczym innym – a Basi Sobieraj ogólne zamieszanie pozwoliło ściemnić mężowi, że nie wiadomo, do kiedy będą pracowali w prokuraturze, i tak oto wylądowali w mieszkaniu u Szackiego, żeby chora na serce mężatka z piętnastoletnim stażem mogła z zaangażowaniem prymuski odkrywać swoje strefy erogenne.

Bawili się świetnie i Szacki w pewnej chwili znów zakochał się w Basi Sobieraj. Tak szczerze i po prostu. I to było bardzo miłe uczucie.

– Misia mówiła, że zachowywałeś się jak wariat.

– Tak to mogło wyglądać, przyznaję.

– Wtedy na to wpadłeś?

– Aha.

– Wiesz, że to mnie podnieca?

– Co znowu?

– Że jesteś geniuszem kryminalistyki.

– Cha, cha.

– Nie śmiej się, naprawdę. Przecież to już była rozwiązana sprawa, jak ci to przyszło do głowy?

– Przez ziarno prawdy.

– Nie rozumiem.

– Mówi się, że w każdej legendzie jest ziarno prawdy.

– Jest.

– Ale są takie legendy, jak ta cholerna antysemicka legenda o krwi, w której nie ma prawdy ani kropli, która w stu procentach jest kłamstwem i zabobonem. Myślałem o tym wtedy na rynku, nieważne dlaczego. I przypomniało mi się, co mówił twój ojciec. Że wszyscy kłamią, że nie wolno zapominać, że wszyscy kłamią. I nagle pomyślałem o tej sprawie jak o jednym wielkim kłamstwie. Co by to oznaczało, gdyby założyć, że nie ma w niej nic prawdziwego, że wszystko to kreacja. Co zostanie, jeśli odrzucić sprawy sprzed siedemdziesięciu lat, mordy rytualne, rytualne uboje, hebrajskie napisy, cytaty biblijne, wściekłe psy, mroczne podziemia i beczki najeżone gwoździami. Co się stanie, jeśli uznam, że wszystkie dowody i poszlaki, które od początku napędzały nasze śledztwo, to kłamstwo. Co zostanie?

– Trzy trupy.

– Właśnie że nie. Trzy trupy to kreacja, kłamstwo, trzy trupy są po to, żebyśmy się zastanawiali nad trzema trupami.

– No to trzy razy jeden trup.

– Dokładnie. Czułem, że to właściwe myślenie. Ale to jeszcze nie był ten moment. Wiedziałem już, że nie trzy trupy, tylko trzy razy jeden trup. Wiedziałem, że aby coś zobaczyć, muszę te trupy obedrzeć ze scenografii. Wiedziałem, że muszę uczepić się tego, co przyszło z zewnątrz, co było obiektywne, co nie zostało nam narzucone, nie zostało spreparowane, jak na przykład znaczek rodła w dłoni denatki.

– Elżbiety – cicho mruknęła Basia.

– No wiem, dobrze, Elżbiety, przepraszam – powiedział Szacki w zaskakująco dla siebie czuły sposób, przytulił do siebie szczupłe ciało kochanki i pocałował w pachnące migdałowym szamponem włosy.

– No i co przyszło z zewnątrz?

– Raczej kto.

– Klejnocki?

– Brawo! Pamiętasz, jak siedzieliśmy w czwórkę? My, Klejnocki i Wilczur. Pod wielkim zdjęciem trupa twojej koleżanki wyświetlonym na ścianie. Znowu przytłoczyła nas scenografia. To zdjęcie, irytujący sposób bycia Klejnockiego, jego fajeczka, jego rozważania lingwistyczne. Sporo się wtedy działo, chcieliśmy dużo i szybko, a on mówił rzeczy, zdawałoby się, oczywiste, jego rozważania wydawały się ubogie, bo nie wiedział tyle, co na przykład ty o Sandomierzu, o Budnikach, o relacjach między ludźmi. Ale on powiedział najważniejszą dla naszego śledztwa rzecz: że kluczem do zagadki jest pierwsze zabójstwo i stojące za nim motywy. Że pierwsze zabójstwo zostało dokonane pod wpływem największych emocji, a następne to już realizacja jakiegoś planu. Na pierwszej ofierze została wyładowana złość, nienawiść, żółć, druga natomiast została po prostu, jeśli można tak powiedzieć, zamordowana. I zacząłem myśleć. Jeśli nie potraktujemy trzech zabójstw jako całości, jeśli skupimy się na pierwszym, najważniejszym i zapomnimy na chwilę o dekoracjach, to sprawa jest oczywista. Mordercą musi być Budnik. Miał motyw w postaci zdrady żony, miał sposobność, kompletnie zerowe alibi, kręcił w zeznaniach, okłamywał nas.

– Tylko kto by podejrzewał trupa? – Basia Sobieraj wstała, założyła na siebie koszulę Szackiego i wyjęła z torebki babskie papierosy.

– Ty palisz?

– Paczkę na dwa tygodnie. Bardziej hobby niż nałóg. Mogę tutaj czy mam iść do kuchni?

Szacki machnął ręką, sam zwlókł się z wyra i sięgnął po własne fajki. Zapalił, gorący dym wypełnił płuca, a na skórze pojawiła się gęsia skórka; wiosna może i przyszła, ale noce ciągle były zimne. Owinął się kocem i zaczął dla rozgrzewki chodzić po mieszkaniu.

– Nikt nie podejrzewa trupa, proste – kontynuował prokurator. – Niemniej gdyby nie trup Budnika, to sprawa byłaby jasna, bo w przypadku Szyllera też on był najbardziej naturalnym podejrzanym. Pozostawało zastosować się do starej zasady Sherlocka Holmesa, że jak wyeliminujemy wszystkie możliwości, to ta, która pozostaje, choćby najbardziej nieprawdopodobna, musi być prawdziwa.

Sobieraj zaciągnęła się papierosem, chłód sprawił, że jej widoczne w niedopiętej koszuli piersi zrobiły się wyjątkowo ponętne.

– Dlaczego tego nie zauważyliśmy? Ty, ja, Wilczur.

– Iluzja – wzruszył ramionami Szacki. – Chyba najgenialniejszy z pomysłów Budnika. Wiesz, na czym zazwyczaj polegają sztuczki prestidigitatorskie? Na odwróceniu uwagi, prawda? Kiedy jedna ręka tasuje w powietrzu dwie talie kart albo zamienia płonącą bibułę w gołębia, nie masz ani czasu, ani ochoty na patrzenie, co robi druga. Rozumiesz? My byliśmy idealnymi widzami pokazu z różnych powodów. Ty i Wilczur na tyle tutejsi, że wszystko miało dla was zbyt duże znaczenie. Ja na tyle obcy, że nie potrafiłem oddzielić spraw ważnych od nieważnych. Cały czas patrzyliśmy na cylinder i królika. Na obrazy w kościołach, na cytaty z Ewangelii, na beczki, na gołe zwłoki w miejscu starego kirkutu. Mniej spektakularne rzeczy umykały naszej uwadze.

– Na przykład?

– Na przykład lessowy piasek za paznokciami Budnikowej. Jak komuś wyjmujesz z dłoni tajemniczy symbol, to paznokcie cię nie interesują. A gdyby zainteresowały, wcześniej byśmy zaczęli myśleć o podziemiach. Na przykład pokryte krwawą politurą nogi drugiej ofiary. Widzisz coś takiego, jeszcze ta beczka na dodatek, i nie myślisz, dlaczego urzędnik magistratu ma pokiereszowane, posiniaczone, nieforemne stopy.

– Stopy włóczęgi...

– Właśnie. Ale to cały czas we mnie siedziało, takie małe szczegóły, cały czas przypominające o swoim istnieniu. Słowa Klejnockiego, to raz. Słowa twojego ojca, to dwa.

– Że wszyscy kłamią?

– Te też, ale były inne, które swędziały. Najpierw myślałem, że chodzi o przechodzenie nienawiści z pokolenia na pokolenie, w kontekście Wilczura to było oczywiste. Ale on mówił o życiu w małym miasteczku, jak każdy każdemu w okno zagląda, że jak się żona puści, to potem trzeba obok kochanka stać w kościele. Cholera, gdzieś tam cały czas miałem tego Budnika w tyle głowy, cały czas wychodził, ale spychałem takie rozwiązanie, bo było zbyt fantastyczne. Dopiero kiedy zacząłem rozważać tę opcję, to się poukładało. Weź odwróconą literę na obrazie, rabin w Lublinie mówił, że żaden Żyd nie zrobi takiego błędu, tak samo jak my byśmy nigdy nie napisali B z brzuszkami po lewej stronie. To nie wskazuje na Wilczura. Wskazuje na kogoś, kto tak w ogóle się orientował, ale musiał co chwila zaglądać do wikipedii, żeby dograć szczegóły. A Budnik orientował się „w miarę", interesował się przecież obrazem, walczył o prawdę o nim, na tyle był otrzaskany z antysemickimi obsesjami, że dokładnie wiedział, którymi strunami szarpnąć.

To nie jedyny jego błąd zresztą. Wcisnął w martwą dłoń swojej żony rodło, bo w tym zalewie żółci – znowu Klejnocki – chciał za wszelką cenę zaszkodzić Szyllerowi, pogrążyć go. Nie pomyślał, że jak tylko trafimy do Szyllera, to od romansowej historii jak piłka kauczukowa odbijemy się prosto na jego próg. A może pomyślał, tylko sądził, że Szyller się nie wygada w trosce o dobre imię kochanki? Cholera wie. Tak czy owak, gdyby Szyller nie pojechał do stolicy, gdybym przesłuchał go dzień wcześniej – on by żył, a Budnik by siedział od tygodnia.

Sobieraj skończyła papierosa, myślał, że wróci pod kołdrę, ona jednak wróciła do grzebania w torebce, wyjęła telefon.

– Dzwonisz do męża?

– Po pizzę do Modeny. Dwie romantiki? – zatrzepotała komediowo rzęsami.

Zgodził się chętnie i zaczekał, aż Basia złoży zamówienie, po czym zaciągnął ją z powrotem pod kołdrę. Nie na seks, tak po prostu chciał się przytulić, wygadać.

– A ta sprawa z Wilczurem? – spytała. – To jakaś ściema? O co chodzi? Wypuścili go w ogóle?

– Wypuścili, wypuścili. Powiedział mi, że ma nieskończenie dobre serce, dlatego nie zgłosi swojego zatrzymania do Ligi Przeciwko Zniesławieniu i nie zrobi ze mnie naczelnego antysemity Rzeczpospolitej. Jedynie dlatego, że „Fakt" zrobi to za niego.

Parsknęła śmiechem.

– Uroczy starszy pan. A to w ogóle Żyd tak naprawdę?

– Naprawdę, naprawdę. Zresztą cała ta historia jest prawdziwa, tyle tylko, że Wilczur nie wiedział o niej aż tyle, ile nam się zdawało, na przykład nie miał pojęcia, że Elżbieta była wnuczką tej nieszczęsnej położnej, której córka przestraszyła się beczki. Budnik wiedział najwięcej. Sprawa doktora Wajsbrota i tego, co się wydarzyło zimą czterdziestego siódmego, była pilnie strzeżoną rodzinną tajemnicą. Którą Budnik poznał dopiero wtedy, kiedy zakochał się w pannie Szuszkiewiczównie. Jego ojciec, jak pamiętasz, naczelnik ubeckiego aresztu, który nie pozwolił Wajsbrotowi odebrać porodu żony, przerażony tym zbiegiem okoliczności, wyjawił wszystko synowi na łożu śmierci. Staruszek bał się klątwy, bał się, że to wszystko nie dzieje się przez przypadek, że to doktor Wajsbrot zza grobu upomina się o sprawiedliwość.

– Coś w tym jest – szepnęła Sobieraj. – Jakkolwiek patrzeć, coś w tym upiornego jest, że te losy połączyły się po raz kolejny. Zwłaszcza teraz, kiedy Budnik dożyje swoich dni w więzieniu.

Szacki wzdrygnął się. Nie myślał o tym w ten sposób, ale Sobieraj miała rację. Wygląda na to, że krążąca po Sandomierzu klątwa wykorzystała także jego, aby się dopełnić. Przypomniał sobie nagranie ze znikającym we mgle Żydem – to był jedyny aspekt śledztwa, którego nie udało się wyjaśnić. I który zamierzał zachować dla siebie, nie ma potrzeby, aby ślad tego nagrania pozostał w jakichkolwiek aktach.

– Tak – mruknął. – Jakby jakaś opatrzność...

– Antyopatrzność raczej...

– Masz rację, jakby jakaś antyopatrzność pomagała Budnikowi. Dziwne.

Przez chwilę milczeli, przytuleni do siebie, za oknem zegar na ratuszowej wieży wybił dwudziestą trzecią. Uśmiechnął się na myśl, jak bardzo brakowałoby mu teraz tych dźwięków. Pomyśleć, że jeszcze niedawno go irytowały.

– Szkoda tego łazika – westchnęła smutno, mocniej wtuliła się w Szackiego. – Jego, jak rozumiem, żadna klątwa nie dotyczy.

– Nie, chyba, nie mam pojęcia, na pewno nic o tym na razie nie wiemy.

– Boże, nie powinnam tego powtarzać, bo umrzesz przygnieciony własnym ego, ale jesteś takim geniuszem kryminalistyki, wiesz?

Wzruszył ramionami, choć jego ego faktycznie z przyjemnością schrupało ten komplement.

– Taa, kolejne rzeczy, na które powinienem zwrócić uwagę: laptop i zdjęcia rodzinne.

– Jaki laptop?

– Taki styropianowy, do jakiego pakują jedzenie na wynos w knajpach.

– Ty to „laptop" nazywasz?

– No, a co?

– Nieważne, opowiadaj.

– We wtorek kamera złapała Budnika, jak wychodzi z dwoma obiadami z Trzydziestki. To był totalny bezsens, Budnikowej już wtedy nie było, i nie było też żadnego wytłumaczenia, dlaczego potrzebne mu dwa obiady. Należało to dopiero połączyć z innymi faktami. Z tym, że jeśli Budnik ma być mordercą, to musiał kto inny zostać nabity na hak w dworku na Zamkowej. Z tym, że pewien sandomierski menelik uporczywie poszukiwał swojego zaginionego kolegi włóczęgi. No i ze zdjęciami rodzinnymi.

– Nie rozumiem, jakimi zdjęciami?

– Tutaj cały trik polegał na upodobnieniu się w miarę do włóczęgi, tego nieszczęsnego Fijewskiego. Z wyjaśnień wynika, że Budnik do zbrodni przygotowywał się wiele tygodni, miesięcy nawet. To oczywiście brzmi jak bezmiar szaleństwa, ale pamiętaj, że dopóki nie popłynęła żadna krew, mógł to traktować jako perwersyjną zabawę, sprawdzenie, jak daleko potrafi się posunąć. Budnik musiał się chorobliwie zapuścić, schudnąć, rozjaśnić trochę włosy z rudych na ryże, wyhodować brodę. Sztuczka z opatrunkiem była genialna: po raz kolejny odwrócenie uwagi godne iluzjonisty, ale na nic by się nie zdała, gdyby ktoś zaczął mieć wątpliwości, czy trup na Zamkowej jest trupem Budnika.

Dlaczego nie mieliśmy wątpliwości, a zwłaszcza ja? Widziałem na przesłuchaniu tego samego chudzielca z ryżą brodą i plastrem. Hak w policzku dodatkowo utrudniał sprawę. Widziałem tę samą twarz w dowodzie, który wyciągnąłem z portfela leżącego przy zwłokach. Tylko nie dało mi do myślenia, niestety, to, że nie ma tam prawa jazdy, a dowód został wydany dwa tygodnie wcześniej. Nie dało nikomu do myślenia, bo przez ostatnie godziny widzieliśmy wszyscy w telewizji twarz Budnika wziętą skąd? Ze zdjęcia zrobionego w czasie przesłuchania. A czy mogliśmy zobaczyć gdzie indziej jego twarz? Gdybyśmy poszukali, oczywiście. Ale w miejscu najbardziej oczywistym, czyli w jego domu, nie było żadnego zdjęcia gospodarza. Tylko Budnikowej. Wiedział, że dokładnie przeszukamy posesję po jego zniknięciu. Wiedział, że jeśli wszyscy napatrzymy się tam na jego prawdziwą twarz, możemy mieć wątpliwości. A tak mieliśmy pod powiekami tylko chudą gębę z opatrunkiem na czole.

Dzwonek przerwał wyjaśnienia Szackiego, chwilę później zajadali się pizzą i pieczywem czosnkowym, które – jak na ironię – zostało przywiezione właśnie w białym styropianowym laptopie, dokładnie takim, jaki ostatnio prokurator widział w dłoniach mordercy na niewyraźnym filmie nagranym przez kamerę na ratuszu. To sprawiło, że stracił ochotę na to akurat danie. Sobieraj chyba też, bo ani razu nie sięgnęła do pojemnika. Zresztą na pyszną jak zwykle pizzę też chyba nie miała ochoty. Zjadła jeden kawałek, drugi dziubnęła dwa razy i odłożyła.

– Przepraszam, nie mogę jednocześnie jeść i myśleć o tym wszystkim: te lochy, Szyller... Teraz oczywiście rozumiem więcej, sposób w jaki zginął... To potwierdza słowa Klejnockiego. Szyller został najbardziej okrutnie zamęczony, nienawiść do niego była największa. To też wskazywało na Budnika, prawda?

Potwierdził skinieniem głowy.

– Łazika też trzymał w tych lochach? I jak? Wchodził do nich z piwnicy? Ja nawet nie wiedziałam, że tu jest coś więcej niż ta pieprzona trasa turystyczna, a zaraz się okaże, że z każdej kamienicy można tam wejść.

– Nie można. Budnik wiedział trochę więcej od innych przez przypadek, interesowała go historia miasta, dzięki niemu Dybus z kumplami mógł prowadzić swoje badania. Innych polityków sprawa przestała obchodzić, kiedy się okazało, że nie zrobią z tego nowej atrakcji turystycznej, dla Budnika był to konik. Konik, który w kluczowym momencie okazał się bardzo przydatny. Oczywiście nie jest tak, że w każdym miejscu można zejść do podziemi. Jest znane ci wejście w Nazarecie i jak wyjaśnia Budnik, i co trzeba będzie sprawdzić, drugie obok zamku, przy tej łące na dole, stoi tam taka rudera. To by się zgadzało, przy odrobinie szczęścia można stamtąd niezauważenie dojść krzakami do synagogi i też krzakami do dworku na Zamkowej, a jak mykniesz przez ogród katedry, to lądujesz na tarasie domu Budników. Stąd wysadzenie chodnika, który prowadzi do tego wejścia. Wskazywałoby ono na Budnika, moglibyśmy wtedy zacząć go szukać. Co prawda, zamierzał być już daleko dzięki paszportowi Fijewskiego, ale wiadomo: strzeżonego...

– Przyznaj się, z tym paszportem strzelałeś?

– Ale celnie. Wpaść na to nie było trudno, kiedy już byłem prawie pewien, czyją tożsamość ukradł. Ale przekonać kilka urzędów, żeby w niedzielę wieczorem sprawdzili, czy to prawda, i kiedy zgłosi się po odbiór... Nie sądzę, żebym napotkał kiedykolwiek większe wyzwanie w swojej karierze. Wiesz, co jest ciekawe? Że najbardziej szkoda mu Dybusa.

– Pieprzony świr. Pomyśleć, że znałam go tyle lat. Ile za to dostanie?

– Dożywocie.

– I dlaczego? Po co? Nie rozumiem.

Szacki też nie rozumiał, nie do końca. Ale ciągle słyszał w uszach słowa Budnika: „Elę i Szyllera chciałem zabić, naprawdę chciałem, sprawiło mi to przyjemność. Po tych wszystkich miesiącach wyobrażania sobie, co robią razem, po słuchaniu tych kłamstw, opowieści o spotkaniach służbowych z artystami w Krakowie, Kielcach i Warszawie... Pan nie wie, jak to jest, jak taka nienawiść rośnie dzień po dniu, zalewa jak żółć, ja już byłem zdolny do wszystkiego, byleby nie czuć, jak ten kwas mnie zżera, w każdej minucie, w każdej sekundzie, przez cały czas. Zawsze wiedziałem, że nie jest dla mnie, ale jak mi to powiedziała w końcu prosto w oczy, to było straszne. Zdecydowałem, że skoro ja jej nie mogę mieć, to nikt jej nie będzie miał".

Może to i lepiej, że tego nie rozumiesz, Basiu, pomyślał Szacki. I że ja tego nie rozumiem, i w ogóle mało kto. I choć docierało do niego wytłumaczenie Budnika, choć rozumiał jego motywy, było w tym wszystkim coś, cholera, na głos mógł to poruszyć tylko w żartach, nie wierzył przecież w klątwy, nie wierzył też, że jakaś energia musi czasami wyrównać rachunki dla porządku wszechświata. Ale jednak było w tym coś niepokojącego. Jakby stare polskie miasto napatrzyło się na zbyt wiele, jakby ta zbrodnia sprzed siedemdziesięciu lat to było za dużo dla tych murów i zamiast wsiąknąć jak zwykle w czerwone cegły, zaczęła odbijać się od nich rykoszetem, aż uderzyła w Grzegorza Budnika.

Zegar na wieży ratuszowej wybił północ.

– Godzina duchów – powiedziała Basia Sobieraj i wśliznęła się do łóżka.

Prokurator Teodor Szacki pomyślał, że duchy na pewno nie przychodzą o północy.

Rozdział czternasty

piątek, 8 maja 2009

W kalendarzu żydowskim to Pesach Szeni, czyli „druga Pascha", święto wyznaczone przez Torę na 14 dzień miesiąca ijar dla tych, którzy nie mogli jej świętować we właściwym terminie i symbol danej przez Boga drugiej szansy. Benedykt XVI odwiedza Jordanię, gdzie na górze Nebo, z której Mojżesz zobaczył Ziemię Obiecaną, mówi o nierozerwalnej więzi łączącej Kościół i naród żydowski. W Hiszpanii jakiś szczęściarz wygrywa 126 milionów euro na loterii, w Kalifornii powstaje najmniejsza żarówka świata, a brytyjscy Sikhowie w policji chcą wynalezienia kuloodpornych turbanów. Już tylko miesiąc do wyborów europejskich, wedle sondaży PO wygrywa z PiS na procenty – 47:22. Sandomierz żyje latającym nad miastem helikopterem TVN, historią esbeka prześladującego opozycję, którego firma ochroniarska obsługuje dziś kościelne obiekty, oraz – jak cały region – odkryciem w Tarnobrzegu pierwszego przypadku świńskiej grypy w Polsce. Policja przyłapuje dwóch 16-latków na paleniu „odurzającego suszu", ale za to biskup Edward Frankowski wyświęca siedemnastu nowych diakonów, więc równowaga zostaje zachowana. Wiosna w rozkwicie, rano jeszcze padało, ale wieczór piękny, ciepły i słoneczny, znaleźć wolny stolik w rynku – niepodobna.

*

Nie było chyba w Polsce lepszego miejsca, żeby spędzić leniwy wiosenny wieczór przy kuflu piwa, niż ocieniony kasztanami taras Kordegardy, zwanej wśród bywalców Kordą. Nieco wyniesiony ponad poziom rynku i nieco przez to osobny, był idealny, żeby pogrążyć się w obserwacji opływających ratusz turystów, robiących sobie zdjęcia nowożeńców, przylepionych do komórek gimnazjalistów, przylepionych do waty cukrowej dzieciaków i przylepionych do siebie zakochanych.

Prokurator Teodor Szacki czekał na powrót Basi z toalety i bezczelnie gapił na siedzących wokół ludzi. Jak zwykle zazdrościł wszystkim ich życia, ckliwie mu jakoś było i tęsknie. Tuż obok niego przy ogrodzeniu tarasu siedziała para tubylców zakochanych w sobie jak nastolatkowie, choć musieli mieć dobrze po pięćdziesiątce. On w typie zażywno--dyrektorskim i rozchełstanej koszuli, ona w kolorowej bluzce i z zadziornym seksapilem, który bez szwanku przetrwał dekady pieczenia ciast i chowania potomstwa. Bez przerwy rozmawiali o dzieciach, których musieli mieć chyba trójkę, sądząc z obrazowo opisywanych życiowych perypetii – wszystkie w okolicach trzydziestki, wszystkie w Warszawie. O sobie nie powiedzieli ani słowa, bez przerwy snuli barwne opowieści o córkach, zięciach i wnukach, co robią, czego nie robią, co im się udaje, może się udać albo nie udać. On był raczej milcząco nastawiony pozytywnie, ona nakręcała się czasami na czarne scenariusze, wtedy on odchrząkiwał i mówił: „A co ty możesz o tym, Haniu, wiedzieć!". Ona wtedy na chwilę przestawała, żeby dać mu naciészyć się uczuciem, że Zdzich oczywiście wie lepiej, a ona – no cóż ona faktycznie może o tym wiedzieć – po czym wracała do narracji. Obserwowanie i podsłuchiwanie ich było rozkoszne, Szacki uśmiechał się i było mu jednocześnie przykro. Wielu dekad pielęgnowania miłości i czułości potrzeba, żeby stać się taką parą. On jedną swoją rodzinę zniszczył, na drugą był już za stary, nie dla niego będzie wchodzenie w starość z kimś, z kim dzieliło się całe dotychczasowe życie. Żeby chociaż był młodszy o te dziesięć lat. Po drugiej stronie ogródka migdaliła się taka właśnie para. Oboje wyglądali dość młodo, ale musieli być w okolicach trzydziestki, w pierwszej chwili pomyślał „moje pokolenie", ale szybko się poprawił. To nie jest już twoje pokolenie, prokuratorze, ty znasz na pamięć wszystkie kawałki Kaczmarskiego, a dla nich muzyka zaczyna się od Kurta Cobaina. Ty byłeś dorosły, kiedy „Wyborcza" wydała pierwszy numer, dla nich to był jakiś tam świstek, przyniesiony do domu przez rodziców. Niewiele jest na świecie pokoleń, gdzie różnica marnych dziesięciu lat znaczy tyle, co w tym przypadku.

Para była rozmigdalona, rozmaślona i totalnie samowystarczalna, musiał im naprawdę mocno spaść poziom glukozy, że postanowili wygrzebać się z łóżka. Ze strzępów rozmowy zrozumiał, że on ma dziś urodziny. Fajnie jest mieć w maju urodziny, pomyślał, robić imprezy przy grillu i spotykać się w knajpianych ogródkach, on w listopadzie nigdy nie miał takiej szansy. Przez chwilę chciał nawet złożyć życzenia.

Ale dał spokój, wyciąganie jubilata z namiotu, jaki tworzyły długie kasztanowe włosy jego towarzyszki, byłoby okrucieństwem. Kiedy sąsiad wyczuł jego spojrzenie i rozejrzał się czujnie po knajpie, prokurator odwrócił szybko wzrok. Coś połaskotało go w ucho. Tym czymś był perwersyjnie wielki kwiat kasztanowca, trzymany w ręku przez Basię. Złowił jeszcze kątem oka uśmiech mężczyzny, uśmiech mówiący, że tak, on też uważa Sandomierz w maju za idealne miejsce dla zakochanych.

– Lecimy?

Pokiwał głową, dopił piwo i razem zeszli po schodkach na kocie łby rynku. Zachodzące słońce świeciło czerwono u wylotu Oleśnickiego, pokrywając wszystko karmazynowym blaskiem, w tym mury starej synagogi.

– Nie możemy tu zostać, jeśli chcemy być razem – powiedziała.

Uśmiechnęła się, pocałowała go w policzek, pomachała szczupłą dłonią na pożegnanie i szybkim krokiem poszła w stronę Bramy Opatowskiej, spódnica wirowała wokół gołych, bladych i – co wiedział – mocno piegowatych łydek. Prokurator Teodor Szacki chwilę odprowadzał ją wzrokiem, po czym poszedł w stronę słońca, żeby złapać jego ostatnie promienie. Stanął pod synagogą i patrzył, jak na ścianie budynku pomarańczowe światło jest od dołu wypierane przez cień. Obserwacja pochłonęła go tak, że nie było w nim miejsca na żadną inną myśl. Dopiero kiedy zachód dobiegł końca, rozejrzał się wokół.

Osiemdziesiąt lat wcześniej we wszystkich mieszkaniach i wszystkich domach w okolicy już od kwadransa płonęłyby zapalone przez kobiety świece, znak, że rozpoczął się szabat, że trzeba się powstrzymać od wszelkich prac, zmówić kidusz i rozpocząć wieczerzę. Spojrzał w dół Żydowskiej, w stronę zamku, przypomniał sobie pokazane mu przez Wilczura nagranie, rozpływającą się we mgle postać.

Wzruszył ramionami i poszedł na spacer w tę samą stronę.

Od autora

Powstanie tej książki, po raz kolejny już, zawdzięczam mojemu bratu, który postanowił związać na dobre swoje losy z cudowną sandomierzanką Olą, przez co przyjechałem do miasta na wesele, zakochałem się w Sandomierzu po uszy i opuszczałem go w przekonaniu, że muszę napisać rozgrywającą się tam powieść. Że to kryminał i że fabuła dotyczy spraw polsko-żydowskich, to już zasługa Beaty Stasińskiej. Wielkie podziękowania należą się tym, którzy pomogli mi w czasie kilku miesięcy pobytu w Sandomierzu. Przede wszystkim rodzicom Oli i ich przyjaciołom oraz nieocenionym pani Renacie Targowskiej i panu Jerzemu Krzemińskiemu. Za iście detektywistyczny trud wyśledzenia w powieści wszelkiej maści błędów i potknięć dziękuję przede wszystkim pani Mariannie Sokołowskiej, a także Marcie Ogrodzińskiej, Marcinowi Mastalerzowi i Filipowi Modrzejewskiemu.

W pracy korzystałem z wielu źródeł, najważniejszym jednak pozostaje miasto Sandomierz, dokąd wysyłam z wizytą wszystkich, którzy chcieliby dowiedzieć się więcej o magicznym nadwiślańskim grodzie. Zainteresowani legendą o mordzie rytualnym powinni przeczytać monografię *Legendy o krwi. Antropologia przesądu* Joanny Tokarskiej-Bakir (W.A.B., Warszawa 2008). Z innych ważnych lektur muszę wymienić *Sławę i chwałę* Jarosława Iwaszkiewicza. Powieść czytałem w trakcie pisania, a jej echa uważny czytelnik odnajdzie w książce. Dla formalności dodaję, że wszystkie postaci (no, prawie; ślę tutaj ukłony dla Jarka Klejnockiego i Marcina Wrońskiego) i wszystkie wydarzenia są zmyślone, za pomyłki i celowe przeinaczenia w sferze faktów i topografii odpowiadam ja, a uczynienie z Sandomierza mrocznej stolicy zbrodni nie świadczy o moim stosunku do tego miasta, które uważam za najbardziej urokliwe w Polsce.

Sandomierz–Warszawa, 2009–2011

Redakcja: Marianna Sokołowska
Korekta: Małgorzata Kuśnierz, Justyna Żebrowska
Redakcja techniczna: Izabela Gołaszewska

Projekt okładki i stron tytułowych: Szymon Wójciak
na podstawie koncepcji graficznej Marka Goebla
Fotografie na okładce: © Paweł Malecki; © Katarzyna Napiórkowska
Fotografia autora: Albert Zawada / Agencja Gazeta

Skład i łamanie: Tekst – Małgorzata Krzywicka
Druk i oprawa:
Drukarnia POZKAL, Inowrocław

Grupa Wydawnicza Foksal Sp. z o.o.
00-372 Warszawa, ul. Foksal 17
tel. 22 828 98 08, 22 894 60 54
biuro@gwfoksal.pl
wab.com.pl

ISBN 978-83-7747-528-7